EXPLORING
THE UNIVERSE

American Foundation for Continuing Education

Edited by Louise B. Young

McGRAW-HILL BOOK COMPANY

New York   *San Francisco*   *Toronto*   *London*

891011-CR-987

Credits for Pictures of Authors

Dingle—Bassano, Ltd.
Galileo—Yerkes Observatory
Hall—Yerkes Observatory
Huygens—Yerkes Observatory
Jeans—Yerkes Observatory
Koestler—United Press International
Laplace—Yerkes Observatory
Leacock—William Notman & Son, Ltd.

Margenau—Alburtus, Yale News Bureau
Newman—Halsman
Newton—Yerkes Observatory
Ortega y Gassett—W. W. Norton & Company
*Poincaré—French Embassy Press & Information
   Division*
Shapley—Yerkes Observatory
Thiel—Rowohlt Verlag GmbH, Hamburg

FOREWORD

To understand the world we live in today, it is necessary to have some appreciation of what science is all about. It is not possible, of course, or even desirable, that everyone should be a scientist; but the scientific revolution is the greatest single influence of modern times, and one should be aware, at least, of the extent to which it is molding and shaping our lives.

Hopefully, as our children come along, they will be acquiring an updated knowledge of science from the elementary grades on. During the last few years the National Science Foundation has supported a number of broad programs directed toward improving science curriculums and courses and toward helping teachers to present science and mathematics effectively to their students. Many of the significant findings of modern research are quite novel, and certainly there have been spectacular technological developments stemming from science within the last two decades. These circumstances have made it imperative that we revise and improve our methods of teaching science so that the coming generation can have the benefit of modern thinking and new developments.

But what about the adult population, whose formal education was behind them before the day of nuclear physics, radio astronomy, the new chemistry of living matter, and the heightened interest in the earth sciences stimulated by the International Geophysical Year and the exploration of space? Intelligent adults who may be involved in the formulation or execution of public policy, who may be leaders in community and civic life, or who may be simply the all-important citizens whose vote determines who these leaders will be, need to know something of the nature of modern science and its impact on society.

Since 1947 the American Foundation for Continuing Education has conducted a study-discussion program for adults throughout the United States and parts of Canada. The foundation initially devoted itself to a consideration of international affairs and problems of American government and foreign policy, later extending its program to include the fine arts, anthropology, and economics. In 1960, with financial support from the National Science Foundation, the AFCE undertook the formidable task of presenting science on a similar basis. The present volume, *Exploring the Universe*, represents experimental study materials prepared for this purpose. In view of the immensity of the ground to be covered, this first volume has addressed itself to broad philosophical questions on the nature of science, the scientific method, the relationships of scientific facts and theories; but the students are also exposed to the growth and development of scientific ideas, largely in relation to broad cosmological questions that constitute the framework for the rest of the sciences. Such cosmological questions lead naturally, of course, into considerations of the space age that confronts us in so many spectacular ways.

The readings chosen to illustrate eleven major topics are selective and stimulating, including such diverse observers as Galileo, Einstein, Conant, Lewis Carroll, Hilaire Belloc, and Stephen Leacock. Obviously such a volume can be, as it purports to be, only an introduction to the nature of science and its influence on our lives; but it is a worthy beginning. Although the study-discussion groups undoubtedly afford the ideal means of coming to grips with subject matter that is admittedly difficult, the availability of these excellent readings in book form will enable many people to take advantage of these informative glimpses into science who might not have access to the discussion groups.

Alan T. Waterman
Director
National Science Foundation

PREFACE

The several years of work we at the American Foundation for Continuing Education have devoted to *Exploring the Universe* have deepened our concern about the level of citizen understanding of science. We are convinced that the low level of understanding of science among otherwise well-informed and thoughtful laymen is one of the most critical problems confronting adult education in the United States today.

The preparation of this book has been an adventure marked by strong contrasts between the brilliance of scientific achievement and the difficulty of citizens in general to comprehend these achievements or to perceive their implications. It has impressed upon us that hitherto well-informed people are becoming less able to understand and to deal with the proliferating impacts of science on every aspect of our lives. It is an interesting fact, for instance, that most well-educated men today know less about Newton's three laws of motion than their counterparts did two centuries ago; yet these principles form the foundation of our new space age. In the eighteenth century most educated men knew a good deal about the science of their day. Newtonian mechanics was discussed by poets, artists, and philosophers, as well as by scientists. Good books were written for the laymen by great masters, courses and demonstrations were offered, and interest in science ran high even among the ladies of the court. But today, discouraged by the very size and difficulty of the fare with which they are presented, many intelligent citizens have little interest in science. After struggling through a required high-school science course, they are happy to close the book and put the whole subject out of their minds.

Our concern is a concern for democracy itself because the lack of understanding of science raises in dramatic form a number of unsettling questions. It poses the issue of the proper relationship between laymen and experts; it compels us to consider the adequacy of the decision-making process in a free society; and it challenges us to justify, in terms that meet the demands of the modern world, the basic right of the people to govern themselves. In the past this right has been made operative by the conviction that well-informed and thoughtful men are competent to do so: that the citizen can in fact understand issues, evaluate conflicting opinions, and make intelligent decisions on matters of public policy. In a real sense the present has overwhelmed the past. In our time, when public policy has become increasingly intermeshed with science and hurtled forward by the accelerating rate of scientific discovery, unless the lay citizen develops an adequate understanding of the nature of science and of the limits of scientific expertise, he becomes less able to understand a growing number of the most significant public policy issues and less competent to make sound judgments about them.

Exploring the Universe is the outgrowth of three years of research and experimentation by the American Foundation for Continuing Education to develop study-discussion programs in science for adults. Work was started in 1959 on a grant from the Fund for Adult Education. In 1960 the National Science Foundation made a grant to the AFCE to support the research and testing of these readings as the first unit of a long-range program entitled *The Citizen and the New Age of Science*. Future units in this program will consider other scientific areas—the nature of matter, the evolution of man, and the issues these raise.

The purpose of *The Citizen and the New Age of Science* is to assist the thoughtful adult to develop a deeper understanding of the nature, the methods, and the limitations of science as the basis for sound judgments on public policy. In the deepest sense our effort is an attempt to ensure that the thoughtful citizen will not become an anachronism, that his thoughtfulness will be relevant to the demands of the modern world.

The readings in this first volume have been selected to provide the layman with a background of understanding of the principles on which the space age has been built, to give him a glimpse of the mystery and the majesty of the universe, which man has begun to explore with satellites, and, above all, to suggest the methods and nature of the search itself.

In several important ways this book represents an unusual approach to the problem of appreciating and understanding science. First, by showing historically how scientific ideas develop rather than by simply explaining the present state of scientific knowledge, these selections assist the reader to gain insight into how science works, and under what conditions important advances are made, and why scientific theories change from time to time. Second, from the original writings of many different scientists, the reader learns, in the scientists' own words, the ways in which they pursue their visions and the attitudes they have toward science. It is our hope that by following the scientist into his realm the reader will learn, not only something scientific, but something of science and will sense the qualities that give science its place in today's world. Third, unlike the usual textbook or exposition of science, there are many questions asked in these readings which are not answered. In each part a number of different points of view is presented with no editorial decision made about which is the right point of view. The reader is never told what to think. The aim of this book is to stimulate thought about some of the basic issues raised and to examine the different arguments about these issues. Confronted by differences of views, the reader will be encouraged to think through his own ideas and to deepen his understanding of the part science plays in his world.

Finally, this book is designed as a study-discussion program, an approach which we believe to be ideally suited to the needs of adult education. The study-discussion method gives the mature individual a chance to enlarge his interests and to develop his intellectual faculties. In a small, informal discussion group the participant has the opportunity to explore various aspects of a problem, to test his own comprehension of the materials, his concepts, reasoning, and views against those of his fellow participants, and to develop a deeper insight into his attitudes as well as those of other participants. We have prepared an Organizer's Manual and a Discussion Guide for *Exploring the Universe*. Persons interested in starting their own discussion groups should write to the AFCE for these manuals.

The readings in this program are intended to be read over a period of eleven weeks and are divided into eleven separate parts. Generally, the first articles in each part are descriptive and expository of a scientific concept. The articles toward the end of a part turn to an exploration of the human response or the religious, philosophical, and social aspects of the science material. As the articles in each part are selected to complement one another and are arranged to bring into focus a fundamental aspect of science, they should be read in the order in which they appear. Many of the selections have been excerpted. Titles have sometimes been changed to better indicate the nature of the selection's function in this book. In some cases footnotes and illustrations have been omitted because in this context they do not contribute to the central issue; editorial notes and illustrations have been added where they were deemed useful. Cross references to illustrations are enclosed either by parentheses or by brackets. Those enclosed in parentheses refer to figures based on illustrational concepts of the author of the article; those enclosed in brackets refer to illustrations that are either added by the editors for clarification or that appear in other articles but serve as well to illustrate points in the article where the bracketed reference appears. We have included an index of subjects and authors and a glossary of scientific terms appearing in the readings. This glossary contains definitions and equations, as well as a few simple derivations for those who prefer a mathematical explanation. At the end of each group of readings, questions are suggested for consideration, and a list of appropriate readings will help the layman to continue his own education in this very important field of human endeavor. You will see that a few of the books are mentioned frequently throughout the reading lists. You may wish to purchase these books, which will serve as valuable supplementary material. The titles listed are just a sample of the many fine science books available for the layman, and more are being published each month. Consult your local librarian and bookstore for other suggestions of good books on these subjects.

As with other study-discussion programs which the AFCE has prepared and published, we do not represent or support any particular viewpoint with respect to the public policy questions or the philosophical, religious, or social issues contained in these readings. The AFCE is a not-for-profit educational organization devoted to the development of study-discussion programs in the liberal disciplines for adults concerned with their own continuing education. This volume, as are our other study-discussion programs, is subject to continuing review by the foundation's board of directors and staff, and revisions will be made as experience demonstrates the need.

We are grateful to the many scientists and educators throughout the country who assisted us in developing the idea of a study-discussion program in science. Whereas final responsibility for the selections in this volume rests with the editor, we should especially like to thank Dr. Joseph Kaplan, Professor of Physics, University of California at Los Angeles; Dr. Victor F. Weisskopf, Professor of Physics, Massachusetts Institute of Technology and Director of Cern Laboratory, Geneva, Switzerland; and Dr. Paul B. Weisz, Professor of Biology, Brown University.

American Foundation for Continuing Education
19 South La Salle Street
Chicago 3, Illinois

CONTENTS

HUMAN DIMENSIONS

The achievements of science have come from thought and action by many men. The articles in Exploring the Universe are their records; of equal importance are the men who create them. These brief biographies of the principal authors are intended to help the reader see more clearly the human dimensions of scientific achievements.

Aristotle (384–322 B.C.) was born in Stagira, a Greek colonial town on the northwestern shore of the Aegean. His father was a doctor who had also been court physician to the father of Philip of Macedon. Some years later, Philip's son, Alexander, became Aristotle's pupil; perhaps, his most famous one. From the time he was seventeen until he was thirty-seven Aristotle studied with Plato at the Academy. And although the characters of the minds of the two men are very different (Plato, the mathematician, the abstractor; Aristotle, the observer of the facts of nature, the humanitarian), it must have been the most profound fact in Aristotle's life to have worked with the old teacher.

Aristotle was a psychologist, logician, moralist, biologist, political thinker, and the founder of literary criticism as well as a philosopher. At the death of Alexander the Great, Aristotle fled to his mother's home in Calcis, where he died at the age of sixty-two.

See pages 79 to 81.

Sir Francis Bacon (1561–1626) was an English philosopher and essayist whose career led him into a most difficult position in the famous dispute between Elizabeth I and Essex. Although Essex was his patron and although Elizabeth had repeatedly overlooked Bacon for political office, he served as the Queen's counsel in the trial of the rebels of 1601 and was instrumental in securing Essex's conviction for treason.

His efforts in the case brought him ill feeling on the part of the public and did not advance him in favor with the Queen. It was not until fifteen years after the coronation of James I that Bacon was appointed Lord Chancellor of England.

A year after he had completed his *Novum Organum* he was tried for taking bribes and accused of corrupt dealings in chancery suits. He was convicted, fined, and imprisoned. A general pardon was granted by the King, and Bacon was released after four days in the Tower. Although he admitted taking bribes, he denied they had ever influenced his decisions.

He did the major portion of his most important work after retirement from public life, including the *History of Henry VII* and the *History of Life and Death*.

See pages 142 to 148.

Lincoln Barnett, born in 1909, is one of our most accomplished writers in science. He was born in New York City, received his B.A.

from Princeton University in 1929 and his M.A. from Columbia University in 1932. During his university years he was also college correspondent for the *New York Herald Tribune*. When *Life* magazine began publication in 1937, Barnett became a staff correspondent and worked there in various departments until 1946. It was shortly afterwards that *Life* asked him to write an article on Einstein. Barnett was then working for himself and took the assignment on a free-lance basis.

The result of the research he did was spectacular. A book, *The Universe and Dr. Einstein*, evolved and was published in 1950. It became a best seller, was widely praised, won the National Book Award Special Citation, and turned Lincoln Barnett into a science writer.

See pages 203 and 204, 228 to 232, and 236 to 240.

Hermann Bondi was born in Vienna in 1919 of American parents. In 1937 he went to Trinity College, Cambridge, to continue his study of mathematics and was interned there in 1940 because he was an Austrian subject. He was awarded his B.A. degree at about the time he was released. He returned to Cambridge in 1945 to lecture on mathematics, but because of his close contact with Fred Hoyle during the war his interest had changed from classical mathematics to theoretical astronomy. He came to the United States in 1951 as a research associate at Cornell and in 1953 gave a series of Lowell Lectures at Harvard.

Besides his interest in cosmology—he proposed the steady-state theory of the expanding universe, together with Thomas Gold, in 1948—Bondi is interested in travel, other than space, and in the design of children's toys.

See pages 286 to 292.

Sir William Henry Bragg was awarded the Nobel Prize for physics and the Barnard Gold Medal (Columbia) in 1915. He shared both distinctions with his son, W. L. Bragg, also a physicist interested in X-ray defraction. Together they developed the X-ray spectrometer, which made possible the elucidation of the arrangements of atoms and crystals. *The Universe of Light* was the last of Sir William's major works. It was preceded by *The World of Sound* and *Concerning the Nature of Things*. He died in 1942, at the age of 80.

See pages 191 to 196.

Jacob Bronowski is well known for his work in two fields often thought incompatible: mathematics and literature. He was born in Poland in 1908 and educated as a mathematician, earning his Ph.D. from the University of Cambridge in 1933. He was senior lecturer in mathematics at University College until 1942, when he left that post to do wartime research. In 1953 he came to the United States as a visiting professor at the Massachusetts Institute of Technology. Besides this scientific career, he has made a considerable reputation as a radio dramatist and won the Italia Prize for the best dramatic work broadcast in Europe during the 1950-1951 season. His combination of scientific and literary ability has made him important to the modern movement of scientific humanism in England.

See pages 2 to 4, 206 to 208, and 428 to 434.

Herbert Butterfield   was born on October 7, 1900. He was educated in England and came to the United States in 1924 as a visiting fellow at Princeton University. He edited the *Cambridge Historical Journal* from 1938 until 1952 and was named vice-chancellor of the University of Cambridge in 1959. Butterfield has been interested in statecraft for many years, and his books include *The Peace Tactics of Napoleon,* a study of the historical novel, and a study of Christianity and history.

See pages 99 to 102.

John Christianson   was born in Mankato, Minnesota, in 1934. He graduated from Mankato State College, after which he spent a year of study at the University of Copenhagen. While there, his interest in Danish history increased, and this and his interest in the sixteenth century and the history of science converge in the life of the Danish nobleman and astronomer Tychoe Brahe.

In 1957, Christianson went to the University of Minnesota on a teaching assistantship and began work on his Ph.D.

See pages 151 to 155.

I. Bernard Cohen   was born in Far Rockaway, New York, in 1914. He was educated at Harvard University and was awarded his Bachelor of Science degree *cum laude* in 1937. He did his graduate work at the same university in physics, astronomy, and the history of science and received his Ph.D. in 1947.

Cohen has been on the Harvard faculty since his graduate-school days. He has also been a special lecturer at University College, London; the Sorbonne; Oxford University; as well as the University of Florence.

Cohen's avocations are travelling, tower climbing, photographing castles and fishing boats, and writing about science, which he does frequently and extremely well.

See pages 112 to 118, and 121 to 128.

James Bryant Conant,   born in 1893, was awarded his Ph.D. from Harvard University in 1916. During World War I, he spent a year in the research division of the chemical warfare service and then returned to Harvard to teach. He became widely recognized as a brilliant organic chemist, was advanced to the rank of professor, and in 1933 was made president of Harvard.

During World War II he was instrumental in organizing American scientists for the war effort and participated in the development of the atomic bomb. At the end of the war he became senior adviser to the National Science Foundation and to the Atomic Energy Commission. In 1953 he became the United States High Commissioner for Western Germany and in 1955 was made our ambassador there. When he returned to the United States in 1957, he again pursued his interest in education and completed a study on the comprehensive high school, which has been of considerable value both to the general public and to educators.

See pages 6 and 7, 18 to 34, and 37 to 43.

Edward Uhler Condon   was born in New Mexico in 1902. He worked as a newspaper reporter before entering the University of California, where he received his Ph.D. in 1926. He accepted a National Research Fellowship at Munich for the next year and returned in 1937 as a lecturer in physics at Columbia University. Condon has held many important positions both in private industry and in government. He has been the director of the National Bureau of Standards and scientific adviser to the United States Senate Special Committee on Atomic Energy. He was elected president of the American Association for the Advancement of Science in 1953.

Condon has published numerous research papers in *Physical Review* and written two important books: *Quantum Mechanics* (with P. Morse) and *Theory of Atomic Spectra* (with G. H. Shortley). He has been professor of physics and chairman of that department at Washington University since 1957.

See pages 187 to 191, and 196 to 199.

René Descartes (1596–1650), perhaps best known for his attempted geometrization of all nature and his contributions to pure mathematics, also made astonishingly brilliant contributions to theoretical physics, methodology, and metaphysics. He was the third child of a provincial French politician and was educated at the Jesuit college at La Flèche and at the University of Poitiers and graduated in law. When he was twenty-three a "marvellous science" was revealed to him in a dream showing him that all sciences should be connected "as by a chain", an idea which guided almost all his future work.

Descartes's analysis of reason as it is used in mathematics and application of this method to other sciences represent the end of the medieval approach to science, in which it was thought that different subject matter must be dealt with by different means.

His great, original invention, coordinate geometry, is one of man's most ingenious accomplishments.

See page 142.

Herbert Dingle was born in England in 1890. He was educated at the Imperial College of Science and Technology. At the beginning of his career he worked with Professor A. Fowler during the time that notable man was engaged in the spectroscopic work so essential to the progress of the Bohr theory of the atom. Dingle, therefore, was on hand during the development of the quantum theory itself. When the 1918 eclipse provided the chance to check Einstein's general theory of relativity, Dingle was working with Alfred North Whitehead and was also in close touch with Sir Arthur Eddington at the Royal Astronomical Society. These two men represented two different and important views of the philosophical aspects of the general theory of relativity and perhaps influenced the publication of Dingle's book, *Relativity for All,* which appeared in 1922.

Besides his contribution as an interpreter of modern physics, he has been a leading force in British astronomy and from 1951 to 1953 was president of the Royal Astronomical Society.

See pages 294 and 295.

Albert Einstein   was born in Ulm, Germany, in 1879. He was educated in Germany and in Switzerland. After receiving his Ph.D. from the University of Zurich, he tried, in vain, for a position with a university and finally took a job with the patent office in Berne. His job left him with much time for his own work, and in 1905 he published four important papers. It was the areas of physics dealt with in these papers in which he was to do most of his important work: the special theory of relativity, the establishment of the mass energy equivalence, the theory of Brownian motion, and the photon theory of light.

In 1921 he was awarded the Nobel Prize for his photoelectric law and his work in theoretical physics. He emigrated to the United States in 1933 and joined the Institute for Advanced Study at Princeton. He became a United States citizen in 1940.

Einstein's death in 1955 left the science of physics vastly changed. The general theory of relativity, which demonstrates that the laws of physics are the laws of geometry in four dimensions and that these laws are determined by the distribution of matter and energy in the universe, is one of the most beautiful and profound constructions ever conceived by the mind of man.

See pages 232 to 236, and 240 to 244.

Galileo Galilei   (1564–1642) was sent at seventeen by his father to the University of Pisa to study medicine. His family was noble but impoverished, and although his father was a competent mathematician, he had carefully kept his son away from the study of mathematics because he felt it would lead to the disruption of a medical career. Galileo, however, happened to overhear a lesson in geometry, which aroused his interest, and began, with his father's reluctant permission, to study mathematics and science.

His considerable reputation rests mainly on his discoveries with the telescope. He made his first instrument in 1609 and published his first observation in 1610. Among his discoveries were the satellites of Jupiter, the phases of Venus, the configuration of the moon, and sunspots.

He was tried by the Inquisition in 1633 for lending his support to the Copernican view of the universe, which held that the earth and planets moved around the sun. He recanted under the threat of torture. He was finally allowed to return to Florence and spent the remainder of his life in seclusion working on the principles of mechanics, his observations of the moon, and the application of the pendulum to the regulation of clockwork.

See pages 118 to 121, and 135.

George Gamow   was born in Odessa, Russia, in 1904. He studied nuclear physics at the University of Leningrad and received his Ph.D. there in 1928. In 1934 he came to the United States as a professor of physics at George Washington University, where he was for over twenty years. Since 1956 he has been at the University of Colorado. During this time his interest moved from the atomic nucleus to astrophysics, the theory of the expanding universe, and later to the fundamental problems of biology, including molecular genetics and the synthesis of proteins. He has written frequently for the British magazine *Discovery* and for *Scientific American*.

See pages 244 to 246, 258 to 267, 292 and 293, and 307 to 324.

Harold Leland Goodwin was born in 1914. During his school years he specialized in physics, chemistry, and electronics. During the early 1930s he became interested in news writing and wrote his first book during the early days of World War II on the techniques of aerial warfare. After service as a Marine combat photographer and a two-year tour of duty with the Foreign Service, Goodwin became a consultant to the National Security Resources Board and assisted in the working out of a National Civil Defense Program. He is currently the Director of Atomic Test Operations for the Federal Civil Defense Administration. He is the author of fifteen books and of over three hundred magazine pieces.

See pages 355 to 358.

A. R. Hall, born in 1920, was a lecturer in the history of science at the University of Cambridge and held a position for several years at the University of California. He is well known for his careful studies on historical themes. In 1954 he published an extraordinary and most readable book entitled *The Scientific Revolution: 1500–1800*, which deals with all those various elements which were a part of the formation of the modern scientific attitude. Perhaps it is not strange that such a fine history should come from a lecturer at Christ's College, a school whose libraries and halls were frequented by Newton and Darwin. He has been lecturer in the history and logic of science at Indiana University since 1961 and was recently appointed to the Imperial College, London.

See pages 148 to 151.

Fred Hoyle was born in Yorkshire, England, in 1914. By the time he was six he had taught himself the multiplication tables up to 12 times 12. When he was thirteen, his parents bought him a 3-inch telescope and indulged him by allowing him to stay up all night using it. In 1939 he won a prize fellowship to St. John's and the next year joined an Admiralty research group. He continued to devote much of his spare time to astronomy and after the war returned to Cambridge, where he became a lecturer in mathematics at St. John's College.

See pages 295 to 297, and 346 to 347.

Aldous Leonard Huxley was born July 26, 1894. After attending a preparatory school, he went to Eton on a scholarship in 1908. He began to study medicine until he contracted keratitis, which left him almost blind. At eighteen he wrote a novel which he was unable to read, and when his sight was partially restored, the manuscript had been lost. He did his graduate work in literature at Oxford College and in 1919 joined the staff of *Athenaeum*. His best-known works include *Chrome Yellow, Antic Hay,* and *Point Counter Point.* Died in 1963.

See pages 419 to 421.

Thomas Henry Huxley (1825–1895) was a distinguished English biologist and the head of an accomplished family. His eldest son, Leonard, became a classical scholar. One of his grandsons, Julian, became a famous biologist and philosopher; another, Aldous, became a well-known writer.

After Darwin's *Origin of the Species* was published in 1859, Huxley became an important defender of the work, and *Darwiniana* was published in 1863. The last twenty years of Huxley's life were devoted to public service more than to science, and his term on the London School Board deeply influenced the English national elementary school system. In 1890 he moved away from London because of his health and died at Eastbourne on June 29, 1895.

See pages 12 to 16.

Christian Huygens a contemporary of Newton's, was born at The Hague in 1629. When he was just twenty-six he was working with his brother on the improvement of the telescope when he discovered a new method of grinding lenses. The resulting clarification of images made possible the discovery of a satellite of Saturn and the resolution of Saturn's rings. He was elected to the Royal Society in 1663. From 1666 to 1681 he worked in France and did his major work on the pendulum. This concludes with the theorems on centrifugal force in circular motion, which were to prove so helpful to Newton. The *Treatise on Light*, from which the selection in the present work is taken, was written in Holland in 1678 and published at Leyden in 1690, where Huygens died five years later.

See pages 182 to 187.

Sir James Hopwood Jeans (1877–1946) was a classical mathematician and physicist widely known for his popular books on astronomy. He was born in London and educated at Cambridge and became university lecturer in applied mathematics at Cambridge and later professor of applied mathematics at Princeton University. He had marked success with applied mathematics in the fields of physics and astronomy especially. He wrote papers on many aspects of radiation, on the formation of binary stars, spiral nebulae, giant and dwarf stars, the source of stellar energy, and the evolution and radiation of gaseous stars. He was knighted in 1938 and awarded the Order of Merit in 1939.

See pages 199 to 202, 297–298, and 344.

Arthur Koestler was born in Budapest in 1905 and educated at the University of Vienna. From 1926 until 1931 he was a foreign correspondent in the Middle East, Paris, and Berlin. The next year he signed on as a member of the Graf Zeppelin Arctic Expedition. When he returned, he covered the Spanish Civil War for the *London News Chronicle* and was imprisoned for his pains by Franco. Upon his release, his interest in trouble spots led him to join the French Foreign Legion. It was after this experience that his most famous work, *Darkness at Noon*, was published. Among his other books are *Spanish Testament* and *Lotus and Robot*. His chief recreations are canoeing and chess.

See pages 128 to 132, and 156 to 167.

Pierre Simon de Laplace was born in Normandy in 1749. His genius was recognized early, as it is with many mathematicians, and he was sent to the University of Caen when he was sixteen. By the time he was twenty-four he was famous for a mathematical theorem (named after him) and had already begun to turn his attention to celestial mechanics. Between 1784 and 1786 he published a memoir which successfully explained the eccentricities of the movements of the planets in the solar system, particularly the behavior of Saturn and Jupiter, which had so perplexed Newton that he had been led to hypothesize divine intervention to set things right. His great work, the summary of the labors of three generations of mathematicians on gravitation, appeared in five volumes between 1799 and 1825.

When Napoleon became first consul, Laplace was made minister of the interior but was removed from the position because he brought "the spirit of infinitesimals into administration." After the restoration of the Bourbons, he was made a marquis. He died in Paris in 1827.

See page 206.

Stephen Butler Leacock was born in England in 1869 and emigrated to Canada with his parents when he was six. After taking his Ph.D. at the University of Chicago he became head of the department of economics and political science at McGill University, in Montreal. Although he wrote a great deal in the fields of history and political economy, his reputation derives mainly from his humorous lectures and literary fantasies. He published some thirty books of humor, many of which are satirical. He saw in humor the power to comfort, to draw men together, to relieve what he called "the appalling inequalities of the human lot."

In respect to his concern for man and his talent for comic invention he had very few peers. He died in 1944.

See pages 248 to 252.

Willy Ley was born in Berlin in 1906 and educated at the University of Berlin and Albertus University. Early in his career he became interested in the exploration of conditions in space and in the surface conditions of neighboring planets. He has served as the science editor of the newspaper *PM* and as professor of science at Fairleigh Dickinson College, in the United States. He is a member of the American Rocket Society and an honorary fellow of the British Interplanetary Society.

See pages 353 to 355, and 358 to 370.

Sir Alfred Charles Bernard Lovell was born on August 31, 1913. He was educated at the University of Bristol and in 1936 became assistant lecturer in physics at the University of Manchester. He was elected an honorary foreign member of the American Academy of Arts and Sciences in 1955. He has been director of Jodrell Bann Experimental Station since 1951. His published works include *Science and Civilization, Exploration of Space by Radio*, and *The Individual and the Universe*. When he is not hard at work he enjoys cricket, gardening, and music.

See pages 267 to 286, and 384 to 386.

Bruce Theodore Lundin was born in Alameda, California, in 1919. He graduated from the University of California in 1942 and became a design engineer for Standard Oil of California shortly after this. In 1944 the National Aeronautic and Space Administration employed him as a research engineer in the aircraft engine research laboratory. He went to the Lewis Flight Propulsion Laboratory as head of jet propulsion research in 1946 and became the assistant director of the entire center in 1958.

His principal interest is in direct and indirect energy conversion systems for space vehicles.

See pages 370 to 379.

Henry Margenau was born in Bielefeld, Germany, in 1901. He came to the United States early in his life and was educated at Midland College and Nebraska University. He received his Ph.D. from Yale in 1929. For a year after this he was a Sterling Fellow at the same university. In 1931 he became an assistant professor; in 1945, a full professor. Since 1949 he has been the Eugene Higgs Professor of physics and natural science at Yale. His main professional interest has been in high-frequency discharges and intermolecular and nuclear forces.

See page 90.

Forest Ray Moulton was born in 1872 in LeRoy, Michigan. He graduated from Albion College in 1894 and shortly after this went to the University of Chicago to teach. His interest in cosmology led him into work with Thomas C. Chamberlin, and together they developed the planetesimal hypothesis (sometimes called the spiral nebula hypothesis), which suggests that the planets of the solar system were torn from the sun by the action of a passing star. Moulton's scientific interests were varied, and he has written on celestial mechanics, astronomy, and periodic orbits as well as on descriptive anatomy. He died in 1952.

See pages 92 to 94.

James R. Newman was born in New York City in 1907. He attended the College of the City of New York and Columbia University and was admitted to the New York bar in 1929. He has held many governmental posts since then. He was chief intelligence officer in the United States Embassy in London from 1943 to 1944. He has also served as special assistant to the Undersecretary of War and in the same capacity to the Senate Committee on Atomic Energy. Since 1948 he has been a member of the board of editors of *Scientific American*.

See pages 208 and 209.

Sir Isaac Newton was born in 1624, the year in which Galileo Galilei died. This coincidence represents perhaps one of the most important turning points in the history of science, for although Galileo had come to rely more and more on the results of direct experiment, it was Newton who presented science with a new way of looking at the facts of observation. In Newton, the long-standing Aristotelian tradition of solving problems which dealt with natural philosophy (the study of light, motion, and sound) by speculation and meditation gave way to dealing with those problems by measurement and experiment. His celebrated work on light and optics and the laws of motion and gravity represents a transition from ancient methods to the modern manner of scientific thought.

He was knighted in 1705 at Cambridge by Queen Anne—the first time that this honor had ever been conferred for achievement in pure science. He died in 1727 and is buried in Westminster Abbey.

See pages 177 to 181, and 215.

José Ortega y Gasset (1883–1955) was born in Madrid, an heir to a cultural and intellectual Spanish tradition which was very nearly extinguished. When he died in the same city seventy-two years later, he left behind, not only the Instituto de Humanidades, which he founded, but also a cultural and literary revival which he had deeply influenced.

His early training was classical and accomplished under the tutelage of the Jesuits. In 1898 he went to Madrid University and after this to Germany to study for four years. When he became professor of metaphysics at Madrid in 1910 he began to diverge from the neo-Kantian school of philosophy, which had so influenced him earlier. He saw man's individual and present life as his basic reality, substituted historical reason for absolute reason and the individual's perspective for absolute truth.

Because of Spanish politics he exiled himself between 1936 and 1945. He then returned to Spain, where he founded his famous institute in 1948.

See page 89.

Andreas Osiander (1498–1552) was the prominent ancestor of an extensive line of theologians and scholars, none of whom, however, was either as brilliant or as erratic as he. His father was a blacksmith, and Osiander was fortunate to be educated as well as he was. He became a priest in 1520, after having left the University of Ingolstadt. He involved himself in the reform of the imperial free city of Nürnberg and won over Albert von Hohenzollern to the Lutheran movement. In 1543 he drafted a brilliant preface to Copernicus's *De Revolutionibus Orbium*, which was instrumental in keeping that controversial work off the Roman Catholic Index of Prohibited Books for over fifty years. He died in 1552 in the midst of a vigorous controversy over the justification of sinners, which it is generally thought he precipitated.

See page 111.

Michael William Ovenden was born in 1927. He was educated at London University and did his graduate work at Cambridge and London. He was elected secretary of the British Astronomical Association in 1946 and became president of the group in 1951. He is now a lecturer on the staff of the astronomy department at the University of Glasgow. His books include *Looking at the Stars, Artificial Satellites*, and *Life in the Universe*.

See pages 333 to 343.

Blaise Pascal (1623–1662) was a member of a highly gifted French family. His father was a respected mathematician, his sister, Jacqueline, was considered a literary prodigy, and Pascal himself was famous at twenty-one for the invention of an arithmetical machine he built to help his father in his calculations as well as for his *Essais pour les Coniques*, which had been published when he was seventeen. Pascal was not only a mathematician but a physicist(philosopher, and superb writer as well. His *Provinciales* is considered by many to mark the beginning of modern French prose. The large part of his last years were spent at Port-Royal in religious work. By 1658 he had put together the notes which were published as *Pensées*. His friends at the monastery at Port-Royal persuaded him to help in the composing of the *Elements de Géométrie*. In February of 1659 he became ill and returned to the ascetic and devotional life. He died in 1662, probably from carcinomatous meningitis, which followed the development of a malignant ulcer of the stomach.

See pages 34 to 37.

Plato (427?–347? B.C.) as a comparatively young man became a friend and student of the great Greek philosopher Socrates, although his own primary interest at the time was politics. It was only after the death of Socrates, and perhaps as a result of Socrates' treatment at the hands of the democratic leaders of Athens, that Plato decided there was no place for a man of sincere conscience in active politics. He turned his attention to philosophy and, when he was about forty, founded the Academy as an institute for the systematic pursuit of philosophical and scientific research. It is probable that he intended his dialogues to interest the outside world in the more serious and difficult labors of this school. The Academy survived well over 800 years until it was closed by the emperor Justinian in 529.

See pages 74 to 76.

Henri Jules Poincaré (1854–1912) was generally considered to be one of the greatest mathematicians and original thinkers of his day. He was educated at the Ecole Polytechnique and the Ecole des Mines and taught in Caen and Paris. From his first work in pure mathematics he went on to develop new mathematical techniques, and he founded the study of topological dynamics. In a paper on the dynamics of the electron published in 1906 he arrived at many of the results of the special theory of relativity independently of Einstein.

His writings in philosophy are just as interesting, original, and perhaps as important, as his work in mathematics. His mastery of French prose provided him with a wide and various audience for his work, and he produced more than thirty books and five hundred papers during his career.

See pages 90 and 91.

Eugene Rabinowitch was born in St. Petersburg, Russia, in 1901. He was educated in Berlin and in 1926 became an assistant at the Kaiser Wilhelm Institute for Physics and Chemistry. In 1933 he went to Denmark to the Royal Academy of Science and the next year to London. He is now professor of biophysics at the University of Illinois and also edits the *Bulletin of Atomic Scientists*. As a physicist his main interest has been in reaction kinetics; as a private person he is most interested in public affairs.

See pages 390 and 391.

Eric M. Rogers was appointed professor of physics at Princeton University in 1957. He was born in 1902 in England, educated at Cambridge, where he worked under Lord Rutherford, and assumed his first teaching post in 1930 at Harvard University. Since 1957 he has also been on the staff of the Physical Science Study Committee and has published a most readable and rewarding book entitled *Physics for the Inquiring Mind*.

See pages 49 to 57, 76 to 79, and 82 to 86.

Lord Bertrand Arthur William Russell was born on May 18, 1871. He was orphaned at three and raised by his grandmother from then on. He attended Trinity College, Cambridge, and graduated with distinction.

Russell has been interested in mathematics, logic (he believes that mathematics and formal logic are one), and philosophy, as well as in the problems of individual liberty. He received the English Order of Merit in 1949 and the Nobel Prize for literature in 1950.

His occupation with the liberty of the individual has brought him into conflict with prevailing authority on several occasions. During World War I he was fined £100 for writing a leaflet criticizing the punishment of conscientious objectors. His college deprived him of his lectureship, and he was offered one at Harvard but was refused a passport. In 1918 he was imprisoned for a pacifist article he had written and was imprisoned again in 1962 for having organized demonstrations against nuclear armament.

See pages 168 to 170, 344 and 345, and 422 to 428.

Giorgio Diaz de Santillana was born in Rome in 1902. He was awarded his Ph.D. in physics from the University of Rome in 1925. After this he became an instructor at the university, where he helped organize the School for History of Science. He came to the United States in 1936 and became a naturalized citizen in 1945. After lecturing at the New School for Social Research for one year and at Harvard University for three years, de Santillana joined the faculty of the Massachusetts Institute of Technology, where he became professor of the history and philosophy of science. He is the author of *Galileo's Dialogue on the Great World Systems*, *The Crime of Galileo*, *The Age of Adventure*, and *The Origins of Scientific Thought*.

See pages 65 to 73.

Cardinal Niccolò Schoenberg was a distinguished theologian who was appointed Archbishop of Capua in 1520. He unsuccessfully urged Copernicus to publish his early work on the heliocentric nature of our solar system. Cardinal Schoenberg was born on August 11, 1472 and died on August 10, 1537.

See pages 111 and 112.

Erwin Schrödinger was born in Vienna in 1887. He was educated at the university there and later became professor of physics at Stuttgart, Breslau, Zurich, and finally, in 1928, in Berlin. From there he went to Dublin to become a professor at The Institute for Advanced Studies. Most of his work is highly mathematical in character and has dealt with the physics of the atom. He extended De Broglie's theory of wave mechanics and applied it to the problem of atomic structure. In 1933 he won the Nobel Prize for physics for his contribution to the new science of wave mechanics. He died in 1961.

See pages 204 and 205.

Harlow Shapley was born in Nashville, Missouri, in 1885. He was educated at the University of Missouri and at Princeton. After having served at the Mount Wilson Observatory, he became professor of astronomy at Harvard and from 1921 until 1952 was director of the Harvard College Observatory.

Shapley's major work consists in or is the result of extensive surveying, particularly of the Milky Way and the Magelanic Clouds. He was able to formulate the hypothesis that globular star clusters form the center of the Milky Way and that our sun is located in the outer parts of that system. He was one of the first to demonstrate that galaxies occur in clusters and that the Milky Way is a member of a local cluster of galaxies.

His works include *Star Clusters, Flights from Chaos, Galaxies, Inner Metagalaxy,* and *Of Stars and Men.*

See pages 304 to 307, 324 to 326, and 345.

Su-Shu Huang was born in the Chinese province of Kiangsi in 1915. During his high school days he found that mathematics and physics were his easiest subjects and finally decided to become a physicist because he was more interested in natural phenomena than in abstract thought. After a time at the National Chekiang and Tsing Hua Universities he came to the United States. In 1947 he earned his Ph.D. in astrophysics at the University of Chicago. After this, he did research at the University of California for eight years and is now a physicist at the National Aeronautics and Space Flight Center in Washington.

See pages 326 to 333.

J. W. N. Sullivan was born in 1886, the son of an Irish sailor. Although he had considerable gifts as a musician and mathematician, his major work was not done in these fields themselves but in the interpretation of them to a large and interested audience. He had the ability to illumine the spirit as well as the facts of science, and perhaps his most brilliant insights are into science's aesthetic and moral values. He died in England in 1937.

Sullivan's works include the superb collection of monographs called *The Limitations of Science* and a classic work on Beethoven entitled *Beethoven: His Spiritual Development.*

See pages 403 to 419.

Rudolf Thiel was born in Kaiserslautern, Germany, in 1899. His family has been interested in astronomy for generations, and he owns one of the original Fraunhofer telescopes (instruments which, because of the excellent quality of lens Fraunhofer was able to produce, were largely responsible for the renewed interest in the refracting telescope in the first quarter of the nineteenth century). Thiel began to make astronomical observations as a boy and went on to study physics at Bonn and Munich. He has published a number of books on aspects of cultural history. The writing of *And There Was Light,* from which a selection was taken for the present work, occupied him for six years.

See pages 57 to 60.

Alfred North Whitehead   was born at Ramsgate, Kent, in 1861. He was educated at Cambridge, specializing in mathematics. He collaborated with Bertrand Russell in writing the *Principia Mathematica,* a monumental study of the history of mathematical and logical thought which was published in three volumes between 1910 and 1913.

In 1924 he came to Harvard University as professor of philosophy. He spent his later years trying to work out an organic philosophy which would correct our modern overemphasis on natural science and provide a guide for civilized living by correlating the data of social sciences with mathematics and the natural sciences together with data on aesthetic, moral, and religious experience. It was a prodigious task, and its worth is still debated.

The work from which the selections in the present work are taken is one of three books of a nontechnical nature which most completely express his mature philosophy. The others are *Process and Reality* and *Adventures of Ideas.* He died in 1947.

See pages 87 to 89, and 141 and 142.

William Persehouse Delisle Wightman   was born in 1899. He is a lecturer in the history and philosophy of science at Aberdeen University, Scotland. Among the books he has contributed to a better understanding of science are *Science and Monism, A Modern Introduction to Science,* and *Science in Scotland.*

See pages 60 to 64, and 215 to 228.

Abraham Wolf   was born in England in 1876 and educated at University College, London, and St. John's College, Cambridge. In 1915 he became an examiner in philosophy at the University of London and in 1922 took a similar position at Oxford.

Most of Wolf's academic career was spent at University College, London, where he was professor of logic and scientific method and later head of the department of the history and method of science. He has written much in both these fields and was the coeditor of the fourteenth edition of the *Encyclopedia Britannica.* He died in 1948.

See pages 102 to 110.

PART 1

WHAT IS THE NATURE OF SCIENCE?

Generations of writers have sought a simple definition of science that incorporates the range of qualities implicit in the term. These qualities vary from connotations of hard-mindedness like precise, factual, measurable, logical, calculable *to connotations of scope and free expression like* intuitive, creative, elegant, imaginative, exploratory. *Here are the efforts of a few well-known scientists to express in words the nature of science.*

Bronowski

Conant

Figure 1-1. "The Ancient of Days Striking the First Circle of the Earth," by William Blake.

The study of nature that is a part of man's intellectual life is a delight to all scientists. In their hands, science is not just a business of collecting facts or stating laws or directing experiments. It is above all an *art* of sensing the best choice of view or the most fruitful line of investigation for a growing understanding of nature.

Eric M. Rogers
Physics for the Inquiring Mind (1960)

THE CREATIVE ASPECTS OF SCIENCE*
by J. Bronowski (1956)

What is the insight with which the scientist tries to see into nature? Can it indeed be called either imaginative or creative? To the literary man the question may seem merely silly. He has been taught that science is a large collection of facts; and if this is true, then the only seeing which scientists need do is, he supposes, seeing the facts. He pictures them, the colorless professionals of science, going off to work in the morning into the universe in a neutral, unexposed state. They then expose themselves like a photographic plate. And then in the darkroom or laboratory they develop the image, so that suddenly and startlingly, it appears, printed in capital letters, as a new formula for atomic energy.

Men who have read Balzac and Zola are not deceived by the claims of these writers that they do no more than record the facts. The readers of Christopher Isherwood do not take him literally when he writes: "I am a camera." Yet the same readers solemnly carry

* From J. Bronowski, *Science and Human Values.* Copyright 1956 by J. Bronowski. Reprinted by permission of Julian Messner, Publishers, Inc., New York.

with them from their school days this foolish picture of the scientist fixing by some mechanical process the facts of nature. I have had, of all people, a historian tell me that science is a collection of facts, and his voice had not even the irony of one filing cabinet reproving another.

It seems impossible that this historian had ever studied the beginnings of a scientific discovery. The Scientific Revolution can be held to begin in the year 1543 when there was brought to Copernicus, perhaps on his deathbed, the first printed copy of the book he had written about a dozen years earlier. The thesis of this book is that the earth moves around the sun. When did Copernicus go out and record this fact with his camera? What appearance in nature prompted his outrageous guess? And in what odd sense is this guess to be called a neutral record of fact?

Copernicus found that the orbits of the planets would look simpler if they were looked at from the sun and not from the earth. But he did not in the first place find this by routine calculation. His first step was a leap of imagination—to lift himself from the earth, and put himself wildly, speculatively into the sun. "The earth conceives from the sun," he wrote; and "the sun rules the family of stars." We catch in his mind an image, the gesture of the virile man standing in the sun, with arms outstretched, overlooking the planets. Perhaps Copernicus took the picture from the drawings of the youth with outstretched arms which the Renaissance teachers put into their books on the proportions of the body. Perhaps he knew Leonardo's drawing of his loved pupil Salai. I do not know. To me, the gesture of Copernicus, the shining youth looking outward from the sun, is still vivid in a drawing which William Blake in 1780 based on all these: the drawing which is usually called *Glad Day* (Figure 1-2).

Kepler's mind, we know, was filled with just such fanciful analogies; and we know what they were. Kepler wanted to relate the speeds of the planets to the musical intervals. He tried to fit the five regular solids into their orbits. None of these likenesses worked, and they have been forgotten; yet they have been

and they remain the stepping stones of every creative mind. Kepler felt for his laws by way of metaphors, he searched mystically for likenesses with what he knew in every strange corner of nature. And when among these guesses he hit upon his laws, he did not think of their numbers as the balancing of a cosmic bank account, but as a revelation of the unity in all nature. To us, the analogies by which Kepler listened for the movement of the planets in the music of the spheres are far-fetched; but are they more so than the wild leap by which Rutherford and Bohr found a model for the atom in, of all places, the planetary system? . . .

The scientist looks for order in the appearances of nature by exploring such likenesses. For order does not display itself of itself; if it can be said to be there at all, it is not there for the mere looking. There is no way of pointing a finger or a camera at it; order must be discovered and, in a deep sense, it must be created. What we see, as we see it, is mere disorder.

This point has been put trenchantly in a fable by Professor Karl Popper. Suppose that someone wished to give his whole life to

Figure 1-2. "Glad Day," by William Blake.

science. Suppose that he therefore sat down, pencil in hand, and for the next twenty, thirty, forty years recorded in notebook after notebook everything that he could observe. He may be supposed to leave out nothing: today's humidity, the racing results, the level of cosmic radiation and the stock market prices and the look of Mars, all would be there.

He would have compiled the most careful record of nature that has ever been made; and, dying in the calm certainty of a life well spent, he would of course leave his notebooks to the Royal Society. Would the Royal Society thank him for the treasure of a lifetime of observation? It would not. It would refuse to open his notebooks at all, because it would know without looking that they contain only a jumble of disorderly and meaningless items. . . .

The progress of science is the discovery at each step of a new order which gives unity to what had long seemed unlike. Faraday did this when he closed the link between electricity and magnetism. Clerk Maxwell did it when he linked both with light. Einstein linked time with space, mass with energy, and the path of light past the sun with the flight of a bullet; and spent his dying years in trying to add to these likenesses another, which would find a single imaginative order between the equations of Clerk Maxwell and his own geometry of gravitation.

When Coleridge tried to define beauty, he returned always to one deep thought: beauty, he said, is "unity in variety." Science is nothing else than the search to discover unity in the wild variety of nature—or more exactly, in the variety of our experience. Poetry, painting, the arts are the same search, in Coleridge's phrase, for unity in variety. Each in its own way looks for likenesses under the variety of human experience. . . .

The creative act is alike in art and in science; but it cannot be identical in the two; there must be a difference as well as a likeness. For example, the artist in his creation surely has open to him a dimension of freedom which is closed to the scientist. I have insisted that the scientist does not merely record the facts, but he must conform to the facts. The sanction of truth is an exact boundary which encloses him, in a way in which it does not constrain the poet or the painter. . . .

Science is the creation of concepts and their exploration in the facts. It has no other test of the concept than its empirical truth to fact. Truth is the drive at the center of science; it must have the habit of truth, not as a dogma but as a process.

The theory that there is an ultimate truth, although very generally held by mankind, does not seem useful to science except in the sense of a horizon toward which we may proceed, rather than a point which may be reached.

Gilbert Lewis
The Anatomy of Science (1926)

The discoveries of science, the works of art are exploration—more, are explosions, of a hidden likeness. The discoverer or artist presents in them two aspects of nature and fuses them into one. This is the act of creation, in which an original thought is born, and it is the same act in original science and original art.

J. Bronowski
Science and Human Values (1956)

Figure 1-3. Planetary orbits embedded in the regular solids. From Kepler's "Mysterium Cosmographicum," 1596. (See "Kepler," in Glossary. Ed.)

Figure 1-4. "Portrait of a Lady with an Ermine," by Leonardo Da Vinci. "In the museum at Cracow there is a painting by Leonardo da Vinci called 'Portrait of a Lady with an Ermine': it shows a girl holding a stoat in her arms. . . . Leonardo has matched the stoat in the girl. In the skull under the long brow, in the lucid, in the stately, brutal, beautiful and stupid head of the girl, he has rediscovered the animal nature; and done so without malice, almost as a matter of fact" (J. Bronowski, "Science and Human Values," 1956).

Order must be discovered and, in a deep sense, it must be created.

J. Bronowski
Science and Human Values (1956)

Figure 1-5. "Head" (about 1935), by Julio Gonzalez.

TWO DEFINITIONS OF SCIENCE*
by James B. Conant (1951)

There is the static view of science and the dynamic. The static places in the center of the stage the present interconnected set of principles, laws, and theories, together with the vast array of systematized information: in other words, science is a way of explaining the universe in which we live. The proponent of this view exclaims "How marvelous it is that our knowledge is so great!" If we consider science solely as a fabric of knowledge, the world would still have all the cultural and practical benefits of modern science, even if all the laboratories were closed tomorrow. This fabric would be incomplete, of course, but for those who are impressed with the significance of science as "explanations" it would be remarkably satisfactory. How long it would remain so, however, is a question.

The dynamic view in contrast to the static regards science as an activity; thus, the present state of knowledge is of importance chiefly as a basis for further operations. From this point of view science would disappear completely if all the laboratories were closed; the theories, principles, and laws embalmed in the texts would be dogmas; for if all the laboratories were closed, all further investigation stopped, there could be no re-examination of any proposition. I have purposely overdrawn the picture. No one except in a highly argumentative mood would defend either the extreme static or the extreme dynamic interpretation of the natural sciences. But the presentation of elementary science in school and college and the popular accounts almost necessarily take the dogmatic form, and therefore the American citizen is apt to be unconsciously drawn much too far in the

*From James B. Conant, *Science and Common Sense*, Yale University Press, New Haven, Conn., 1951. Reprinted by permission of Yale University Press.

one direction. The worker in the laboratory, however, clearly would not be there if he were not primarily concerned with science as an exploration. To understand him and his predecessors who have advanced the sciences since the sixteenth century one can hardly overemphasize the dynamic nature of science.

At all events, this is my own prejudice and I shall make no attempt to conceal it. My definition of science is, therefore, somewhat as follows: *science is an interconnected series of concepts and conceptual schemes that have developed as a result of experimentation and observation and are fruitful of further experimentation and observations.*† In this definition the emphasis is on the word "Fruitful." Science is a speculative enterprise. The validity of a new idea and the significance of a new experimental finding are to be measured by the consequences—consequences in terms of other ideas and other experiments. Thus conceived, science is not a quest for certainty; it is rather a quest which is successful only to the degree that it is continuous.

† Italics by editor.

QUESTIONS TO CONSIDER

In these brief selections a number of statements are made about science:

Science is a creative act.

Science is a leap of the imagination.

Science is dynamic and progressive.

The scientist does not merely record facts but he must conform to the facts.

The scientist looks for unity and order in the wild variety of nature.

Truth is the drive at the center of science; but ultimate truth is useful only as a horizon toward which we may proceed.

Throughout the readings in this book there will be many illustrations of these facets of the scientific process, and we will return to more detailed discussions of them as we go along. Do any of these statements differ strongly from your own impressions of scientific activity?

Webster's *New International Dictionary*, Third Edition, 1961, defines, in part, science as ". . . accumulated and accepted knowledge that has been systematized and formulated with reference to the discovery of general truths or the operation of general laws: knowledge classified and made available in work, life, or the search for truth: comprehensive, profound, or philosophical knowledge. . . ." How would you define science?

SUGGESTIONS FOR FURTHER READING

* Bronowski, J.: *Science and Human Values,* Harper Torchbooks, Harper & Row, Publishers, New York, 1959. Chapters I and II, from which the quota-

* Paperback edition

tions used in this part are taken, describe the creative and imaginative aspects of scientific discovery. The selection in Part 11 is taken from chap. III. We strongly recommend reading the rest of this very fine little book.

Bulletin of the Atomic Scientists, February, 1959. A collection of very interesting essays on the relationship of science and art.

* Poincaré, Henri: *The Value of Science*, Dover Publications, Inc., New York.

————: *Science and Method*, Dover Publications, Inc., New York.

These two books are both beautifully written analyses of the philosophical significance and values of science.

"Innovation in Science," *Scientific American*, September, 1958. An issue devoted entirely to the creative aspects of scientific method.

* Waddington, C. H.: *The Scientific Attitude*, Penguin Books, Inc., Baltimore, 1948, chap. iv. The impact of science on art.

Whyte, Lancelot Law (ed.): *Aspects of Form*, Indiana University Press, Bloomington, Ind., 1951. An excellent collection of essays discussing the significance of form in art and science as well as in other fields.

2

IS THERE A SCIENTIFIC METHOD?

Science as an activity is a continuing search whose nature is determined by its methods. Readings in this part examine the techniques by which scientists are constantly pushing back the frontiers of knowledge. Is there any special scientific method, or is science simply the synthesis of many different common-sense methods tailored to the problem at hand?

Huxley

Pascal

Aristotle

INTRODUCTION

In Part 1 Conant described two views of science, the static and the dynamic. The static view places small importance on the method by which knowledge is accumulated. Once discovered, the body of knowledge itself is the significant feature. The dynamic view, however, being essentially an activity, a way of increasing our understanding of the physical world, places the methods of science in the center of the picture. In fact, science becomes identified with its methods. Most scientists view their work in this dynamic sense. It is this aspect which lends it its exciting, imaginative, and creative character.

Scientists who are working at the frontiers of knowledge rarely have the time or inclination to step back and analyze the methods that they are using. If asked to explain their techniques, they would probably say that they follow no conscious method. It is just something they do by intuition, by feel, by "the seat of their pants." On the other hand, there have been a number of theorists and philosophers who have postulated a method which scientists do follow although perhaps unconsciously, a method which is unique to science and constitutes the key to its success. This view of scientific method was first formulated during the nineteenth century, an era in which knowledge in all areas of thought seemed very secure and settled, so that it is not surprising that the descriptions of scientific thinking that emerged from these studies were characteristically rigid and formalized. The scientific method was described typically as follows: "(1) a problem is recognized and an objective formulated (2) all the relevant information is collected (3) a working hypothesis is formulated (4) deductions from the hypotheses are drawn (5) the deductions are tested by actual trial (6) depending on the outcome, the working hypothesis is accepted, modified, or discarded."* This process, if properly followed step by step in correct sequence with safeguards observed at every point of the way, would end in fruitful scientific results. It was almost a mechanical concept: feed in the proper ingredients at one end of the machine, turn the proper mental wheels, and scientific advances would emerge at the other end.

The modern view of science, as presented by Conant in these readings, is a much more flexible system. It recognizes that scientists, especially the most creative ones, do not always follow the method in its strict form. True, they

* Conant; see p. 22. Ed.

use various features of it at different times in their researches, but not necessarily in the prescribed sequence, often skipping steps or working backwards from hypotheses or intuitive hunches to the facts. In this sense, Conant says, there is not one scientific method but many scientific methods working together to produce "an interconnected series of concepts and conceptual schemes that have developed as a result of experimentation and observation and are fruitful of further experimentation and observations."

The cooperative nature of the scientific process is particularly important in understanding this more flexible interpretation of scientific method. By working together, the various scientists supplement one another, some contributing the careful experimental data, others using the data as the basis of a new theory, and still others recognizing ways in which the theory can be tested and used to predict new phenomena. Through scientific societies and publications the scientists cross-check one another, so that, taken together, the whole web of scientific activity does represent a method that has been enormously effective in pushing back the frontiers of knowledge.

In Part 1 the search for truth was presented as one of the principle aims of science. In these readings the question is raised about the nature of scientific truth. Some of the processes by which information is collected and conclusions drawn are examined. They are in many respects the same processes that are used to solve problems in everyday life, but they are performed with an extra degree of care and precision. The methods of deductive and inductive reasoning are analyzed from a logical standpoint, and the surprising fact is brought out that science cannot prove a theory or hypothesis to be definitely true. On the other hand, it can show that certain statements are incorrect; that is, they can be definitely disproven. This characteristic of scientific method, as we will see in later parts, is to a large extent responsible for the tentative, changing nature of scientific truth.

The examples of scientific methods presented in these readings are chosen from the seventeenth century because it was not until that time that the several different ways of studying nature came together to form modern science. As Conant says, "The 'new philosophy' or the 'experimental philosophy' was the result of the union of three main streams of thought and action. These may be designated as (1) speculative thinking (2) deductive reasoning (3) cut-and-try experimentation." Taken together, these three elements constitute the basic methods still used by scientists today.

SCIENTIFIC METHOD

In questions of science the authority of a thousand is not worth the humble reasoning of a single individual.

Galileo Galilei (1564–1642)

WE ARE ALL SCIENTISTS*
by T. H. Huxley (1863)

Scientific investigation is not, as many people seem to suppose, some kind of modern black art. You might easily gather this impression from the manner in which many persons speak of scientific inquiry, or talk about inductive and deductive philosophy, or the principles of the "Baconian philosophy." I do protest that, of the vast number of cants in this world, there are none, to my mind, so contemptible as the pseudo-scientific cant which is talked about the "Baconian philosophy."

To hear people talk about the great Chancellor—and a very great man he certainly was,—you would think that it was he who had invented science, and that there was no such thing as sound reasoning before the time of Queen Elizabeth! Of course you say, that cannot possibly be true; you perceive, on a moment's reflection, that such an idea is absurdly wrong. . . .

The method of scientific investigation is nothing but the expression of the necessary mode of working of the human mind. It is simply the mode at which all phenomena are reasoned about, rendered precise and exact. There is no more difference, but there is just the same kind of difference, between the mental operations of a man of science and those of an ordinary person, as there is between the operations and methods of a baker or of a butcher weighing out his goods in common scales, and the operations of a

* From T. H. Huxley, *Darwiniana*, D. Appleton-Century Company, Inc., New York. Reprinted by permission of Appleton-Century-Crofts, Inc.

chemist in performing a difficult and complex analysis by means of his balance and finely-graduated weights. It is not that the action of the scales in the one case, and the balance in the other, differ in the principles of their construction or manner of working; but the beam of one is set on an infinitely finer axis than the other, and of course turns by the addition of a much smaller weight.

You will understand this better, perhaps, if I give you some familiar example. You have all heard it repeated, I dare say, that men of science work by means of induction and deduction, and that by the help of these operations, they, in a sort of sense, wring from Nature certain other things, which are called natural laws, and causes, and that out of these, by some cunning skill of their own, they build up hypotheses and theories. And it is imagined by many, that the operations of the common mind can be by no means compared with these processes, and that they have to be acquired by a sort of special apprenticeship to the craft. To hear all these large words, you would think that the mind of a man of science must be constituted differently from that of his fellow men; but if you will not be frightened by terms, you will discover that you are quite wrong, and that all these terrible apparatus are being used by yourselves every day and every hour of your lives.

There is a well-known incident in one of Molière's plays, where the author makes the hero express unbounded delight on being told that he had been talking prose during the whole of his life. In the same way, I trust, that you will take comfort, and be delighted with yourselves, on the discovery that you have been acting on the principles of inductive and deductive philosophy during the same period. Probably there is not one who has not in the course of the day had occasion to set in motion a complex train of reasoning, of the very same kind, though differing of course in degree, as that which a scientific man goes through in tracing the causes of natural phenomena.

A very trivial circumstance will serve to exemplify this. Suppose you go into a fruiterer's shop, wanting an apple,—you take up one, and, on biting it, you find it is sour; you look at it, and see that it is hard and green. You take up another one, and that too is hard, green, and sour. The shopman offers you a third; but, before biting it, you examine it, and find that it is hard and green, and you immediately say that you will not have it, it must be sour, like those that you have already tried.

Nothing can be more simple than that, you think; but if you will take the trouble to analyse and trace out into its logical elements what has been done by the mind, you will be greatly surprised. In the first place, you have performed the operation of induction. You found that, in two experiences, hardness and greenness in apples went together with sourness. It was so in the first case, and it was confirmed by the second. True, it is a very small basis, but still it is enough to make an induction from; you generalise the facts, and you expect to find sourness in apples where you get hardness and greenness. You found upon that a general law, that all hard and green apples are sour; and that, so far as it goes, is a perfect induction. Well, having got your natural law in this way, when you are offered another apple which you find is hard and green, you say, "All hard and green apples are sour; this apple is hard and green, therefore this apple is sour." That train of reasoning is what logicians call a syllogism, and has all its various parts and terms—its major premise,

its minor premise, and its conclusion. And, by the help of further reasoning, which, if drawn out, would have to be exhibited in two or three other syllogisms, you arrive at your final determination, "I will not have that apple." So that, you see, you have, in the first place, established a law by induction, and upon that you founded a deduction, and reasoned out the special conclusion of the particular case. Well now, suppose, having got your law, that at some time afterwards, you are discussing the qualities of apples with a friend: you will say to him "It is a very curious thing,—but I find that all hard and green apples are sour!" Your friend says to you, "But how do you know that?" You at once reply, "Oh, because I have tried them over and over again, and have always found them to be so." Well, if we were talking science instead of common sense, we should call that an experimental verification. And, if still opposed, you go further, and say, "I have heard from the people in Somersetshire and Devonshire, where a large number of apples are grown, that they have observed the same thing. It is also found to be the case in Normandy, and in North America. In short, I find it to be the universal experience of mankind wherever attention has been directed to the subject." Whereupon, your friend, unless he is a very unreasonable man, agrees with you, and is convinced that you are quite right in the conclusion you have drawn. He believes, although perhaps he does not know he believes it, that the more extensive verifications are,—that the more frequently experiments have been made, and results of the same kind arrived at,—that the more varied conditions under which the same results are attained, the more certain is the ultimate conclusion, and he disputes the question no further. He sees that the experiment has been tried under all sorts of conditions, as to time, place, and people, with the same result; and he says with you, therefore, that the law you have laid down must be a good one, and he must believe it.

In science we do the same thing;—the philosopher exercises precisely the same faculties, though in a much more delicate manner.

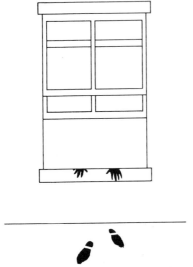

Figure 2-1. The mystery of the missing teapot and spoons.

In scientific inquiry it becomes a matter of duty to expose a supposed law to every possible kind of verification, and to take care, moreover, that this is done intentionally, and not left to a mere accident, as in the case of the apples. And in science, as in common life, our confidence in a law is in exact proportion to the absence of variation in the result of our experimental verifications. For instance, if you let go your grasp of an article you may have in your hand, it will immediately fall to the ground. That is a very common verification of one of the best established laws of nature—that of gravitation. The method by which men of science establish the existence of that law is exactly the same as that by which we have established the trivial proposition about the sourness of hard and green apples. But we believe it in such an extensive, thorough, and unhesitating manner because the universal experience of mankind verifies it, and we can verify it ourselves at any time; and that is the strongest possible foundation on which any natural law can rest.

So much, then, by way of proof that the method of establishing laws in science is exactly the same as that pursued in common life. Let us now turn to another matter (though really it is but another phase of the same question), and that is, the method by which, from the relations of certain phe-

nomena, we prove that some stand in the position of causes towards the others.

I want to put the case clearly before you, and I will therefore show you what I mean by another familiar example. I will suppose that one of you, on coming down in the morning to the parlour of your house, finds that a tea-pot and some spoons which had been left in the room on the previous evening are gone,—the window is open, and you observe the mark of a dirty hand on the window-frame, and perhaps, in addition to that, you notice the impress of a hob-nailed shoe on the gravel outside [Figure 2-1]. All these phenomena have struck your attention instantly, and before two seconds have passed you say, "Oh, somebody has broken open the window, entered the room, and run off with the spoons and the tea-pot!" That speech is out of your mouth in a moment. And you will probably add, "I know there has; I am quite sure of it!" You mean to say exactly what you know; but in reality you are giving expression to what is, in all essential particulars, an hypothesis. You do not *know* it at all; it is nothing but an hypothesis rapidly framed in your own mind. And it is an hypothesis founded on a long train of inductions and deductions.

What are those inductions and deductions, and how have you got at this hypothesis? You have observed, in the first place, that the window is open; but by a train of reasoning involving many inductions and deductions, you have probably arrived long before at the general law—and a very good one it is—that windows do not open of themselves; and you therefore conclude that something has opened the window. A second general law that you have arrived at in the same way is, that tea-pots and spoons do not go out of a window spontaneously, and you are satisfied that, as they are not now where you left them, they have been removed. In the third place, you look at the marks on the window-sill, and the shoe-marks outside, and you say that in all previous experience the former kind of mark has never been produced by anything else but the hand of a human being; and the same experience shows that no other animal but man at present wears shoes with hob-nails in them such as would produce the marks in the gravel. I do not know, even if we could discover any of those "missing links" that are talked about, that they would help us to any other conclusion! At any rate the law which states our present experience is strong enough for my present purpose. You next reach the conclusion, that as these kinds of marks have not been left by any other animals than men, or are liable to be formed in any other way than by a man's hand and shoe, the marks in question have been formed by a man in that way. You have, further, a general law, founded on observation and experience, and that, too, is, I am sorry to say, a very universal and unimpeachable one, —that some men are thieves; and you assume at once from all these premises—and that is what constitutes your hypothesis—that the man who made the marks outside and on the window-sill, opened the window, got into the room, and stole your tea-pot and spoons. You have now arrived at a *vera causa;*—you have assumed a cause which, it is plain, is competent to produce all the phenomena you have observed. You can explain all these phenomena only by the hypothesis of a thief. But that is a hypothetical conclusion, of the justice of which you have no absolute proof at all; it is only rendered highly probable by a series of inductive and deductive reasonings.

I suppose your first action, assuming that you are a man of ordinary common sense, and that you have established this hypothesis to your own satisfaction, will very likely be to go for the police, and set them on the track of the burglar, with the view to the recovery of your property. But just as you are starting with this object, some person comes in, and on learning what you are about, says, "My good friend, you are going on a great deal too fast. How do you know that the man who really made the marks took the spoons? It might have been a monkey that took them, and the man may have merely looked in afterwards." You would probably reply, "Well, that is all very well, but you see it is contrary to all experience of the way tea-pots and spoons are abstracted; so that, at any rate, your hypothesis is less probable than mine." While you are talking the thing over in this way, another friend arrives. And he might say, "Oh, my dear sir, you are certainly going on a great deal too fast. You are most presumptuous. You admit that all these occurrences took place when you were fast asleep, at a time when you could not possibly have known anything about what was taking place. How do you know that the laws of Nature are not suspended during the night? It may be that there has been some kind of supernatural interference in this case." In point of fact, he declares that your hypothesis is one of which you cannot at all demonstrate the truth and that you are by no means sure that the laws of Nature are the same when you are asleep as when you are awake.

Well, now, you cannot at the moment answer that kind of reasoning. You feel that your worthy friend has you somewhat at a disadvantage. You will feel perfectly convinced in your own mind, however, that you are quite right, and you say to him, "My good friend, I can only be guided by the natural probabilities of the case, and if you will be kind enough to stand aside and permit me to pass, I will go and fetch the police." Well, we will suppose that your journey is successful, and that by good luck you meet with a policeman; that eventually the burglar is found with your property on his person, and the marks correspond to his hand and to his boots. Probably any jury would consider those facts a very good experimental verification of your hypothesis, touching the cause of the abnormal phenomena observed in your parlour, and would act accordingly.

Now, in this suppositious case, I have taken phenomena of a very common kind, in order that you might see what are the different steps in an ordinary process of reasoning, if you will only take the trouble to analyse it carefully. All the operations I have described, you will see, are involved in the mind of any man of sense in leading him to a conclusion as to the course he should take in order to make good a robbery and punish the offender. I say that you are led, in that case, to your conclusion by exactly the same train of reasoning as that which a man of science pursues when he is endeavouring to discover the origin and laws of the most occult phenomena. The process is, and always must be, the same; and precisely the same mode of reasoning was employed by Newton and Laplace in their endeavours to discover and define the causes of the movements of the heavenly bodies, as you, with your own common sense, would employ to detect a burglar. The only difference is, that the nature of the inquiry being more abstruse, every step has to be most carefully watched, so that there may not be a single crack or flaw in your hypothesis. A flaw or crack in many of the hypotheses of daily life may be of little or no moment as affecting the general correctness of the conclusions at which we may arrive; but, in a scientific inquiry, a fallacy, great or small, is always of importance, and is sure to be in the long run constantly productive of mischievous, if not fatal results.

Do not allow yourselves to be misled by the common notion that an hypothesis is untrustworthy simply because it is an hypothesis. It is often urged, in respect to some scientific conclusion, that, after all, it is only an hypothesis. But what more have we to guide us in nine-tenths of the most important affairs of daily life than hypotheses, and often very ill-based ones? So that in science, where the evidence of an hypothesis is subjected to the most rigid examination, we may rightly pursue the same course. You may

have hypotheses and hypotheses. A man may say, if he likes, that the moon is made of green cheese; that is an hypothesis. But another man, who has devoted a great deal of time and attention to the subject, and availed himself of the most powerful telescopes and the results of the observations of others, declares that in his opinion it is probably composed of materials very similar to those of which our own earth is made up: and that is also only an hypothesis. But I need not tell you that there is an enormous difference in the value of the two hypotheses. That one which is based on sound scientific knowledge is sure to have a corresponding value; and that which is a mere hasty random guess is likely to have but little value. Every great step in our progress in discovering causes has been made in exactly the same way as that which I have detailed to you. A person observing the occurrence of certain facts and phenomena asks, naturally enough, what process, what kind of operation known to occur in Nature applied to the particular case, will unravel and explain the mystery? Hence you have the scientific hypothesis; and its value will be proportionate to the care and completeness with which its basis has been tested and verified. It is in these matters as in the commonest affairs of practical life: the guess of the fool will be folly, while the guess of the wise man will contain wisdom. In all cases, you see that the value of the result depends on the patience and faithfulness with which the investigator applies to his hypothesis every possible kind of verification.

EDITOR'S NOTE ON SCIENTIFIC REASONING AND TERMS

In describing scientific method, Huxley mentions *inductive* and *deductive* reasoning. Both of these methods of thinking contribute in different ways to the progress of science.

The first, which is the basis of all experi-

mental science, proceeds from the particular to the general. Observations and experimental evidence are collected and systemized. Then a generalization is made based on these data. For example, after watching the Moon's position for several years a scientist might "infer inductively" that the Moon travels around the Earth regularly, about 13 times a year and as long as there is no evidence to the contrary we assume that it will continue to do so. The more observations that are made which follow the rule, the more firmly established it becomes. We say that the *probability* of its being true increases but, rigorously speaking, the evidence of any number of cases is insufficient to prove it; while just one observation which goes against the rule is sufficient to disprove it. This one case may turn up at any time. However, for science a high degree of probability is good enough as a working basis. Scientists do trust and use the inductive method: Believing instinctively in the uniformity of nature, they assume that what has been found to be true up to the present time will continue to be true tomorrow.

Some rules or generalizations have been found to have such a broad application and such a high degree of probability that they have been dignified by the term, *Scientific Laws.* Many laws, especially those in physics, express a mathematical relationship between measurements of several physical quantities —as, for example, Newton's 2nd Law of Motion: force = mass × acceleration.

Deductive reasoning is the type most commonly used in mathematics and logic—the method is probably familiar to you from a study of Euclidean geometry in school. It starts with the assumption of general concepts—in science these assumptions are called postulates or hypotheses, in mathematics and logic they are called axioms or premises. From these generalizations logical conclusions are drawn. In science, the truth of the conclusion is tested by experiment or observation. For instance, Copernicus made the general assumption that all the planets revolve about the Sun. Using this assumption, he calculated what would be the observed positions of the other planets as seen from the earth at different times of the year. Finally, he compared these calculations with the observed positions of the planets and found a good correspondence between them.

This verification of the original assumption gave it the standing of a scientific *theory*.

In logic, deductive reasoning takes the form of a *syllogism*, having two premises and a conclusion following logically from them. Take the classic example:
All men are mortal. (major premise)
Socrates is a man. (minor premise)
Therefore Socrates is a mortal. (conclusion)

Now one point that is interesting to note, especially in connection with scientific work, is that a false conclusion cannot follow logically from true premises. Therefore we know that *if* the premises are true the conclusion must also be true. However, a true conclusion can also follow logically from false premises, as in the following example:
> All angels are mortal.
> Socrates is an angel.
> Therefore Socrates is mortal.

In general, if the conclusion of a deductive argument is shown to be true, it cannot be concluded that the premises are necessarily true. They may be, but they may also be false. This is an important point to remember in scientific procedures. As in the example of the Copernican Theory, an hypothesis (which is really just a good guess and whose truth is not yet established) is assumed. Then logical conclusions are drawn from it and these conclusions are tested by experiment. If they are found to check with observation, the hypothesis is accepted as a working basis or theory (although, as we now see, it has not been rigorously *proven* to be true). On the other hand, if the conclusion is shown to be false, the hypothesis is discarded. (We know that false conclusions cannot logically follow from true premises.) Again, we see that it is easier to prove something false than to prove it true.

In the last paragraph, we used the term *hypothesis* to mean a working hunch or single tentative guess, the truth of which is to be tested by experiment. This is the restricted scientific meaning of the word. However, you will find many writers using the term more loosely, and often interchangeably with the word *theory* which, strictly speaking, should refer to a broader, more definitely established conceptual scheme. The difference between theory and hypothesis is a matter of degree, both in breadth of application and extent of experimental verification. But since no sharp line can be drawn between the two terms, it is not surprising that there should be some difference of opinion about their use. Hypotheses and theories are generally arrived at by deductive reasoning methods. While scientific laws, you will remember, are more often the result of inductive processes.

Sometimes it is necessary for a scientist to make a reasoned guess about physical quantities and relationships which have not been measured. For instance, suppose an astronomer is measuring the intensity of light from a star which he has observed to be increasing in brightness from night to night. He makes a measurement on Monday, Tuesday, and Wednesday and finds that each night there has been a constant increase in brightness. On Thursday night, there are clouds obscuring that part of the sky. On Friday he continues his observations and finds that there has been twice as great an increase in the 48-hour period since Wednesday night as there had been in the 24-hour periods previously measured. He might then *interpolate* and assume that half of this increase occurred between Wednesday night and Thursday night and half between Thursday night and Friday night, following the pattern he had found to be true earlier in the week of an approximately constant increase in each 24-hour period. *Interpolation* means making a reasoned guess within a known range. It is a fairly safe procedure if used with caution, although it is obvious that the assumption is not necessarily correct. In our example, the star could have stayed the same between Wednesday and Thursday and taken a sudden jump in brightness on Friday. Experience and scientific judgment enter into making a sound interpolation.

If the scientist makes a guess that goes beyond the known range, it is called *extrapolation*. For instance, if on the basis of the observations quoted, our astronomer concluded that on Saturday there would also be the same increase in brightness, he would be extrapolating. He might even go much farther and figure that in a month, at that same rate, there would be an increase of 30 times as much. As you can see, extrapolation requires much more experience and judgment than interpolation. In the example we have given, for instance, it is known that some stars increase in brightness for a certain length of time and then start decreasing. Extrapolation is risky but when used by experienced and imaginative scientists it can lead to some of the most fruitful speculations and theories.

CONCERNING THE ALLEGED SCIENTIFIC METHOD*
by James B. Conant (1951)

Those who favor the use of the word science to embrace all the activities of the learned world are inclined to believe in the existence of *a* scientific method. Indeed, a few go further and not only claim the existence of *a* method but believe in its applicability to a wide variety of practical affairs as well. For example, a distinguished American biologist declared not long ago that "Men and women effectively trained in science *and in the scientific method*, usually ask for evidence, almost automatically." He was referring not to scientific matters but to the vexing problems which confront us in everyday life—in factories, offices, and political gatherings.

One cannot help wondering where the author of such a categorical statement obtained his evidence. But this is perhaps making a

* From James B. Conant, *Science and Common Sense*, Yale University Press, New Haven, Conn., 1951. Reprinted by permission of Yale University Press.

debater's point. The significance of the statement is that it reflects a persistent belief in the correctness of the analysis of science presented by Pearson in *The Grammar of Science*. Throughout the volume Karl Pearson refers to science as the classification of facts, and in his summary of the first chapter he writes as follows: "The scientific method is marked by the following features: (a) careful and accurate classification of facts and observation of their correlation and sequence; (b) the discovery of scientific laws by aid of the creative imagination; (c) self-criticism and the final touchstone of equal validity for all normally constituted minds." With (b) and (c) one can have little quarrel since all condensed statements of this type are by necessity incomplete, but from (a) I dissent entirely. And it is the point of view expressed in this sentence that dominates Pearson's whole discussion. It seems to me, indeed, that one who had little or no direct experience with scientific investigations might be completely misled as to the nature of the methods of science by studying this famous book.

If science were as simple as this very readable account would have us believe, why did it take so long a period of fumbling before scientists were clear on some very familiar matters? Newton's famous work was complete by the close of the seventeenth century. The cultured gentlemen of France and England in the first decade of the eighteenth century talked in terms of a solar system almost identical with that taught in school today. The laws of motion and their application to mechanics were widely understood. This being the case it might be imagined that the common phenomenon of combustion would have been formulated in terms of comparable clarity once people put their minds on scientific problems. Yet it was not until the late 1770's that the role of oxygen in combustion was discovered. Another hotly debated problem, the spontaneous generation of life, was an open question as late as the 1870's. Darwin convinced himself and later the scientific world and later still the educated public of the correctness of the general idea of evolution because of his theory as to the

mechanism by which evolution might have occurred. Today the basic idea of the evolutionary development of higher plants and animals stands almost without question, but Darwin's mechanism has been so greatly altered that we may say a modern theory has evolved. And we are no nearer a solution of the problem of how life originated on this planet than we were in Darwin's day.

The stumbling way in which even the ablest of the scientists in every generation have had to fight through thickets of erroneous observations, misleading generalizations, inadequate formulations, and unconscious prejudice is rarely appreciated by those who obtain their scientific knowledge from textbooks. It is largely neglected by those expounders of the alleged scientific method who are fascinated by the logical rather than the psychological aspects of experimental investigations. Science as I have defined the term[*] represents one segment of the much larger field of accumulative knowledge. The common characteristic of all the theoretical and practical investigations which fall within this framework—a sense of progress—gives no clue as to the *activities* of those who have advanced our knowledge. To attempt to formulate in one set of logical rules the way in which mathematicians, historians, archaeologists, philologists, biologists, and physical scientists have made progress would be to ignore all the vitality in these varied undertakings. Even within the narrow field of the development of "concepts and conceptual schemes from experiment" (experimental science) it is all too easy to be fascinated by oversimplified accounts of the methods used by the pioneers.

To be sure, it is relatively easy to deride any definition of scientific activity as being oversimplified, and it is relatively hard to find a better substitute. But on one point I believe almost all modern historians of the natural sciences would agree and be in opposition to Karl Pearson. There is no such thing as *the* scientific method. If there were, surely an examination of the history of physics, chemistry, and biology would reveal

* See p. 7. Ed.

it. For as I have already pointed out, few would deny that it is the progress in physics, chemistry, and experimental biology which gives everyone confidence in the procedures of the scientist. Yet, a careful examination of these subjects fails to reveal any *one* method by means of which the masters in these fields broke new ground.

The Birth of Experimental Science in the Seventeenth Century

As I interpret the history of science, the sudden burst of activity in the seventeenth century which contemporaries called the "new philosophy" or the "experimental philosophy" was the result of the union of three streams of thought and action. These may be designated as (1) speculative thinking (2) deductive reasoning (3) cut-and-try or empirical experimentation. The first two are well illustrated by the writings of the learned men of the middle ages. The professor of law and theology as well as the teacher of mathematics and logic from the eleventh to the seventeenth century was concerned with a rational ordering of general ideas and the development of logical processes. In so doing, they extended to some degree the philosophical and mathematical ideas of the ancient Greeks and laid the foundations for the science of mechanics, the first of the branches of physics to take on modern dress.

A simple illustration of deductive reasoning is to be found in recalling one's experience in school with plane geometry. A set of postulates or axioms is given; then by logical processes of deduction many conclusions follow. Similarly, less formal and rigid general ideas—speculative ideas—can be manipulated by logical procedures which, however, frequently lack the rigor of mathematical reasoning. The discussion of general speculative ideas and the more detailed handling of mathematics, it should be noted, involve processes of thought which are believed to be sufficient unto themselves. No one feels impelled to appeal to observation in building a purely rational system of ideas.

The sudden burst of interest in the seventeenth century in the new experimental philosophy was to a considerable extent the result of a new curiosity on the part of thoughtful men. Practical matters ranging from agriculture and medicine to the art of pumping, the working of metals, and the ballistics of cannon balls began to attract the attention of learned professors or inquiring men of leisure. The early history of science is full of examples where the observation of a practical art by a scientist suggested a problem. *But the solution of a scientific problem is something quite different from the advances which had hitherto been made by the empirical experimentation of the agriculturist or the workman.* The new element which was introduced was the use of deductive reasoning. This was coupled with one or more generalizations often derived from speculative ideas of an earlier time. The focus of attention was shifted from an immediate task of improving a machine or a process to a curiosity about the phenomena in question. New ideas or concepts began to be as important as new inventions. The experimentation of the skilled artisans or the ingenious contriver of machines and processes became joined to the mathematical mode of reasoning of the learned profession. But it took many generations before deductive reasoning and experimentation could be successfully combined and applied to many areas of inquiry.

Speculative Ideas, Working Hypotheses, and Conceptual Schemes

Science we defined . . . as "an interconnected series of concepts and conceptual schemes that have developed as a result of experimentation and observation and are fruitful of further experimentation and observations." A conceptual scheme when first formulated may be considered *a working hypothesis on a grand scale.* From it one can deduce, however, *many* consequences, each of which can be the basis of chains of reasoning yielding deductions that can be tested by experiment. *If these tests confirm the deductions in a number of instances, evidence accumulates tending to confirm the working hypothesis on a grand scale, which soon becomes accepted as a new conceptual scheme.* Its subsequent life may be short or long, for from it new deductions are constantly being made which can be verified or not by careful experimentation.

In planning the experiments to test the deductions it became necessary, as science advanced, to make more precise and accurate many vague common sense ideas, notably those connected with measurement. Old ideas were clarified or new ones introduced. These are the new concepts which are often quite as important as the broad conceptual schemes. It is often much more difficult than at first sight appears to get a clear-cut yes or no answer to a simple experimental question. And the broader hypotheses must remain only speculative ideas until one can relate them to experiment.

An understanding of the relationship between broad speculative ideas and a wide conceptual scheme is of the utmost importance to an understanding of science. A good example is furnished by the history of the atomic theory. The notion that there were fundamental units—ultimate particles—of which matter was composed goes back to ancient times. But expressed merely in general terms this is a speculative idea and can hardly be considered an integral part of the fabric of science until it becomes the basis of a working hypothesis on a grand scale from which deductions capable of experimental test can be made. This particular speculative idea or working hypothesis on a grand scale became a new conceptual scheme only after Dalton had shown, about 1800, how fruitful it was in connection with the quantitative chemical experimentation that had been initiated by the chemical revolution. Here is an instance where we can see in some detail the origins of a working hypothesis, while in other instances we are uncertain how the idea came to the proponent's mind.

The great working hypotheses in the past have often originated in the minds of the pioneers as a result of mental processes which can best be described by such words as "inspired guess," "intuitive hunch," or "brilliant flash of imagination." Rarely if ever do they seem to have been the product of a careful examination of all the facts and a logical analysis of various ways of formulating a new principle. Pearson and other nineteenth-century writers about the methods of science largely overlooked this phenomenon. They were so impressed by the classification of facts and the drawing of generalizations from facts that they tended to regard this activity as all there was to science. Nowadays the pendulum has swung to the other extreme and some writers seem to concentrate attention on the development of new ideas and their manipulation, that is on theoretical science. Both points of view minimize the significance of the experiment. To my mind this distorts the history of science and, what is worse, confuses the layman who is interested in the scientific activity which is going on all about him. For these reasons and because of the author's own predilection, the present discussion of science and common sense emphasizes and re-emphasizes the interrelation of experiments and theory.

Experimentation

The three elements in modern science already mentioned are: (1) speculative general ideas, (2) deductive reasoning, and (3) experimentation. We have discussed in a general way the manner in which new working hypotheses on a grand scale arise and how from them one may deduce certain consequences that can be tested by experiment. It has been implied that the art of experimentation long antedates the rise of science in the seventeenth century. If so, this is one way in which science and common sense are connected. A rather detailed analysis of experimentation in everyday life may serve a useful purpose at this point. For, as I hope to show, there is a continuous gradation between the simplest rational acts of an individual and the most refined scientific experiment. Not that the two extremes of this spectrum are identical. Quite the contrary: to understand science one must have an appreciation of just how common-sense trials differ from experiments in science.

Since the reader may well have been exposed at some time in his or her life to various statements about the alleged scientific method, it may be permissible to set up a few straw men and knock them down. I have read statements about the scientific method which describe fairly accurately the activity of an experimental scientist on many occasions (but not all). They run about as follows: (1) a problem is recognized and an objective formulated; (2) all the relevant information is collected (many a hidden pitfall lies in the word "relevant"!); (3) a working hypothesis is formulated; (4) deductions from the hypothesis are drawn; (5) the deductions are tested by actual trial; (6) depending on the outcome, the working hypothesis is accepted, modified, or discarded.

If this were all there was to science, one might say, in the words of a contemporary believer in *the* scientific method, that science as a method "consists of asking clear, answerable questions in order to direct one's observations which are made in a calm, unprejudiced manner, reported as accurately as possible and in such a way as to answer the questions that were asked to begin with; any assumptions that were held before the observations are now revised in the light of what has happened." But if one examines his own behavior whenever faced with a practical emergency (such as the failure of his car to start) he will recognize the preceding quotation a description of what he himself has often done. Indeed, if one attempts to present the alleged scientific method in any such way to a group of discerning young people they may well come back with the statement that they have been scientists all their lives! . . .

Testing Deductions by Experiment

Is there then no difference between science and common sense as far as method is concerned? Let us look at this question by considering in some detail first an everyday example of experimentation and then a scientific investigation. The type of activity by which the practical arts have developed over the ages is in essence a trial and error procedure. The same sort of activity is familiar in everyday life; we may call it experimentation. Let us take a very restricted and perhaps trivial example. Faced with a locked door and a bunch of keys lying on the floor, a curious man may wish to experiment with the purpose of opening the door in question. He tries first one key and then the other, each time essentially saying to himself, "If I place this key in the lock and turn it, then the result will either confirm or negate my hypothesis that this key fits the lock." This "if . . . then" type of statement is a recurring pattern in rational activity in everyday life. The hypothesis that is involved in such a specific trial is limited to the case at hand, the particular key in question. We may call it therefore a *limited working hypothesis*.

Let me turn now from an example of commonplace experimentation to a consideration of a scientific experiment. Let us examine the role of the limited working hypothesis in the testing of some scientific idea in the laboratory. For if you brought all the writers on scientific method with the most varied views together, I imagine that every one of them would agree that the testing of a deduction from a broad working hypothesis (some would say a theory) was at least a part of science . . . we are going to consider in some detail several instances of such procedures. Let us anticipate the story about atmospheric pressure only to the extent of fixing our minds on one actual experiment. It makes little difference which one we choose, for we wish to center attention on the last step, the actual experimental manipulation.

We will imagine that someone has related the broad hypothesis that we live in a sea of air that exerts pressure to a particular experiment with a particular piece of apparatus. Just before turning a certain stopcock, which we may assume to be the final step in the experiment, the investigator may formulate his ideas in some such statement as "If all my reasoning and plans are right, when I turn the stopcock, such and such will happen." He turns the stopcock and makes the observation; he can then say he has confirmed or failed to confirm his hypothesis. But, strictly speaking, let it be noted, it is only a highly limited hypothesis that has been tested by turning the stopcock and making the observation; this hypothesis may be thrown into some such form as "if I turn the stopcock, then such and such will happen." The confirmation or not of this extremely limited hypothesis is regarded as an experimental fact if repetition yields the same result. The outcome of the experiment is usually connected with the main question by a highly complex process of thought and action which brings in many other concepts and conceptual schemes. . . . The point to be emphasized here is the existence of a complicated chain of reasoning connecting the consequence deduced from a broad hypothesis and the actual experimental manipulation; furthermore, . . . many assumptions, some conscious and some unconscious, are almost always involved in this chain of reasoning.

Now perhaps I may be permitted to jump from the scientist to the everyday experiments of a householder in his garage or a housewife in her kitchen or an amateur with his radio set. If a car won't start, we certainly have a problem; we think over the various possibilities based on our knowledge of automobiles in general and the particular car in question; we construct at least one working hypothesis (the gas tank is empty!); we proceed to carry out a trial or test (an experiment) which should prove the correctness of this particular working hypothesis; if we are right then we believe we have found the trouble and proceed accordingly. (But how often have we been misled; perhaps there is more than one trouble; perhaps the tank is empty and the battery run down too!) Let us assume the simple hypothesis has led to a trial which consists of turning a particular switch or making a certain connection of wires after various other manipulations have been performed. Then one says to oneself, "Now at last if I turn the switch (or make the connection) the engine will turn over." The test is made and what is confirmed (or not) is a very limited working hypothesis hardly to be distinguished from the extremely limited working hypothesis of the scientists we have just been considering. Here science

and common sense certainly seem to have come together. But notice carefully, they are joined only in the statement of the final operation. As we trace back the line of argument the differences become apparent. These are differences as to aims, as to auxiliary hypotheses and as to assumptions.

Aims and Assumptions in Scientific Experimentation

First, as regards aims, you want the car to start (or the radio set to work, to mention another example); you wish to reach a practical objective. The scientific experimenter on the other hand wants to test a deduction from a conceptual scheme (a theory), a very different matter. But we cannot leave the distinction between science and common sense resting on that point, important as it is. The conceptual scheme is not only being tested by the experimenter but it has given rise to the experiment. And that takes us back to our definition of science and our emphasis on the significance of the fruitfulness of a new conceptual scheme. The artisans who improved the practical arts over the centuries proceeded much as you or I do today when we are confronted with a practical problem. The aim of the artisan or the agriculturist was practical, the motivation was practical, though the objective was more general than just starting a given automobile. The workmen of the Middle Ages experimented and sometimes their results left a permanent residue because their contemporaries incorporated a new procedure into an evolving art. But the artisan rarely, if ever, bothered about the testing of the consequences of any general ideas. General ideas, logical thought, were the province of learned men. Drawing deductions from conceptual schemes was the type of activity known to the mathematicians and philosophers of the Middle Ages, not to the workmen. And with rare exceptions those who understood these recondite matters paid no attention to the workmen. . . . we shall consider examples of how the two activities—those of the logicians and the artisans—came together in the sixteenth and seventeenth centuries.

There is another important difference between the artisan and the scientist. The typical procedure of the artisan is very much like that of the housewife in the kitchen. Not only are the trials of new procedures for very practical and immediate ends, but the relevant information is largely unconnected with general ideas or theories. Until as late as the nineteenth century the practical man paid very little attention to the growing body of science. By and large the practical arts and science went their own ways during the seventeenth and eighteenth centuries. We may say that experimentation in the practical arts or in the kitchen is almost wholly empirical, meaning thereby to indicate the absence of a theoretical component. However, since the transition from common sense to science is gradual and continuous, one may well question if there is ever a total absence of a theoretical background. It can be argued that the concepts and conceptual schemes we take for granted in everyday life and share in common with our ancestors are not different in principle from the "well-established" ideas of science. This I believe to be true in the sense that infrared light is not different in principle from X rays; both forms of radiant energy are parts of a spectrum, but the two forms of light are certainly not interchangeable for most practical purposes. Quite the contrary. So too, common-sense ideas are distinct in many respects from the more abstract part of the scientific fabric. During the last two hundred years more and more of the material of science has become incorporated into our common-sense assumptions. But every age and cultural group has its own way of looking at the world. The pictures of the total universe which can be collected by anthropologists and students of cultural history, while having many assumptions in common, likewise show great divergences. Therefore, if the modern man in his garage "takes for granted" many things his grandfather would have believed impossible, this in no way invalidates the differentiation between common-sense ideas and scientific theories. (Though there is a wide, fuzzy, intermediary zone.)

The Degree of Empiricism in a Science or a Practical Art

In analyzing the present relation of science to technology and medicine I have found it useful to use the term "degree of empiricism" to indicate the extent to which our knowledge can be expressed in terms of broad conceptual schemes. The same phrase is likewise useful, I am inclined to think, in connection with the history of both the sciences and the practical arts in the last three hundred years. The importance of the notion which lies back of the term, however, is that it may be of help to the layman who is confused about the relation of "pure" and "applied" science. In the last one hundred years science and technology have become so intertwined that even the practitioners in the field may be uncertain when they attempt to analyze the role of scientific theories. Yet anyone familiar with the physical sciences and modern industry would at once grant that there were wide differences in the extent to which scientists in different industries can apply scientific knowledge to the work at hand.

To illustrate what to me is a highly important point, let me contrast the business of making optical instruments with that of manufacturing rubber tires. The design of lenses and mirrors for telescopes, microscopes, and cameras is based on a theory of light which was developed 150 years ago and which can be expressed in simple mathematical terms. With the aid of this theory and a few measurements of the properties of the glasses used, it is possible to calculate with great accuracy the performance of optical equipment. Since theoretical knowledge is so complete in the field of optics, we may say that the degree of empiricism is low in this branch of physics. Because theory is so effective in the optical industry, the degree of empiricism is low. The manufacture of rubber tires is a totally different story. There is nothing comparable to the theory of light to provide a mathematical basis for calculation of what ingredients should be mixed with the rubber. The chemical change which is basic to the whole process is known as vulcanization but no one is very clear even today how to formulate it in theoretical terms. The action of the sulfur which was long thought to be an essential ingredient and of certain other chemicals known as "accelerators" is but little understood. The whole process has been built up by trial and error, by a procedure in which a vast number of experiments finally yielded knowledge in every way comparable to the knowledge of a first-rate chef. In this industry the degree of empiricism is high, and this reflects in turn the small extent to which the chemistry of rubber has been formulated in wide theoretical terms.

As in all comparative statements we must have some fixed points for standards. Therefore, without entering further into the philosophic analysis of common-sense knowledge (including the knowledge of an "art" such as cooking, or glass blowing, or metal making in the Middle Ages), we may take as an example of essentially empirical procedures those of the artisan before the advent of modern science and of the cook in a modern kitchen. Here one may arbitrarily say the degree of empiricism is practically 100 per cent. To find a case where the degree is so low that we can take it as zero on our scale, I call your attention to the work of the surveyor. The theoretical framework is here largely one branch of mathematics—geometry—and, except to a very slight extent in the building of the instruments and the efficiency of their handling, empirical procedures are conspicuous by their absence. Therefore, if the reader . . . whose acquaintance with science or technology is slight will envisage from time to time the surveyor with his transit and his measuring instruments on the one hand and the chef in the Grand Hotel on the other, he will have in mind a range of activities from zero to 100 as regards the degree of empiricism involved.

We shall return from time to time to the relation of scientific knowledge to the practical activities of the artisan, the agriculturist, and the medical man. We shall see that for an amazingly long time advances in science and progress in the practical arts ran parallel with few interconnecting ties. Thus if we take the birth of modern science as somewhere around 1600 (neglecting the long prenatal period which goes back to antiquity), one can say that it was two hundred years or more before the practical arts benefited much from science. Indeed, it would be my contention that it was not until the electrical and dyestuff industries were well started, about 1870, that science became of real significance to industry.

Let me conclude this discussion by pointing out that the degree of empiricism in a practical field today largely depends on the extent to which the corresponding scientific area can be formulated in terms of broad conceptual schemes. Therefore one may consider science as an attempt either to lower the degree of empiricism or to extend the range of theory. When scientific work is undertaken without regard for any practical application of the knowledge, it is convenient to speak of the activity as part of "pure" science. But there are certain overtones in the adjective which are unpleasant and seem to imply a hierarchy of values as between the scientists interested in theories and those interested in the practical arts. Therefore the phrase "basic science" is frequently employed. Almost all significant work of scientists today, I believe, comes under the heading of attempts to reduce the degree of empiricism; the distinction between one group and another is in the motivation. Those who are interested in the fabric of science as such are ready to follow any lead that gives promise of being fruitful in terms of extending theoretical knowledge. Others are primarily concerned with one of the ancient practical arts in modern dress; if it is some branch of industry, say metallurgy, they will be just as interested in widening the theoretical knowledge *in this field* as their colleagues in a university; they will be endeavoring to lower the degree of empiricism too, but in a limited area for a practical objective. The medical scientist is like the metallurgist except that his goal is not better metals but healthier people; both are working in applied science.

In the 1950's, therefore, we find a complex state of affairs. About three centuries ago the trial-and-error experimentation of the artisan was wedded to the deductive method of reasoning of the mathematician; the progeny of this union have returned after many generations to assist the "sooty empiric" in his labors. In so doing the applied scientist finds himself face to face with one of his distant ancestors, so to speak. For as he works in an industrial laboratory he will often find himself called on to carry out experiments for a practical purpose on nearly as empirical a basis as the artisan of the distant past. Particularly in those practical arts where the degree of empiricism is still high, men with the most advanced scientific training and using the latest equipment will often have to resort to wholly empirical procedures. On the one hand they will labor to reduce the degree of empiricism as best they can; on the other they must improve the art by using the knowledge and methods then at hand. In short, advances in science and progress in the practical arts today go hand in hand.

Science as an Organized Activity

The physical and biological sciences today consist of a closely interlocking set of principles and theories and a vast amount of classified information. They are also the product of a living organization. The theories, laws, data are to be found in libraries, herbariums, and museums; these are useful residues, deposits of the past, but essentially dead material. The activity we associate with the word "science" is the sum total of the potential findings of the workers in the laboratories; it is their plans, hopes, ambitions in the process of realization, week after week, year after year, that is the essence of modern science. Now this is a clear case, if there ever was one, of the whole being something quite different from the sum of the parts. For if the thousands of experimental scientists who are going to their laboratories tomorrow were not able to communicate with each other rapidly and easily there would be no modern science.

This is something far more complicated and far more important than the layman often realizes. Indeed, to a misunderstanding of the nature of science as an organized social activity today one can trace many a foolish statement and some practical blunders. It is amazing how much credence is given to self-deluded quacks or real charlatans, or how old wives' tales become accepted as scientific statements. The tendency to equate science with magic can be seen on almost every hand. This man tells you in all seriousness that he knows someone who knows how to stop an automobile engine at a distance of a mile by whistling the proper note; another believes that an untrained amateur has discovered a way of making real, natural rubber directly from garbage in one step; not to mention the whole host of bogus and pseudoscientific "cures" and remedies which still invade the field of medicine.

No one can be blamed for not detecting an absurd statement about alleged principles in physics, chemistry, or biology. All of us who have been engaged for many years in teaching these subjects or writing textbooks in these fields have had the experience of having to revise radically some of our basic statements to keep abreast of the advance of knowledge. But the first reaction of almost any scientist to a rumor about an alleged new step forward is one of incredulity. Maybe the step is a false one—he recalls at once the number of such instances in the field of his own experience. However, he is quite sure that in a short time the matter will be settled, unless some very revolutionary step is in the making. By the process of "publication" the new idea or new experimental finding will be made available to a host of scientists all over the world. Before long others will subject the report to critical examination if the matter is of real importance. No startling or even arresting alleged discovery will remain unnoticed.

It is not a question merely of repeating a series of calculations or checking experimental findings. There will be hundreds of implications for workers in the same or allied fields of inquiry and these will be followed up. If they fail to yield the expected result the original report may be dismissed by the scientific world as "another pipe dream." Eventually the author of the now discredited paper may discover his own error and publish a correction, or the whole matter may simply be allowed to drop. One could write a large volume on the erroneous experimental findings in physics, chemistry, and biochemistry which have found their way to print in the last hundred years; and another whole volume would be required to record the abortive ideas, self-contradictory theories and generalizations recorded in the same period.

The important fact which emerges from even a superficial study of the recent history of the experimental sciences (say, since 1850) is the existence of an organization of individuals in close communication with each other. Because of the existence of this organization new ideas spread rapidly, discoveries breed more discoveries, and erroneous observations or illogical notions are on the whole soon corrected. The deep significance of the existence of this organization is often completely missed by those who talk about science but have had no firsthand experience with it. Indeed, a failure to appreciate how scientists pool their information and by so doing start a process of cross fertilization in the realm of ideas has resulted in some strange proposals by politicians even in the United States. And in the Soviet Union we see what is apparently a deliberate attempt to alter drastically the nature of science as an organized social activity.

Science as a profession, we must remember, is a recent invention. Some of the most important advances in the early development of physics and chemistry were made by amateurs. Indeed, in the examples given in the following chapters to illustrate the methods of science we shall encounter very few men who earned their living by scientific investigation or even by teaching science. As a rough generalization one may say that modern science started in the Italian universities in the sixteenth century; it flourished in the same environment until about the middle of the seventeenth century, and then the focus of activity is to be found in Paris and in London. The role of the universities does not become significant again until the nineteenth century. The seventeenth and eighteenth centuries were the period of the learned societies, particularly the Royal Society of London and the Academie des Sciences of Paris.

The significance of the Royal Society and the French academy of science lies in the fact that these *formal* institutions are the points of origin from which have grown the informal but highly complex organizations of modern science. The Royal Society was chartered by Charles II just after the Restoration but can trace its origin to the enthusiasm of a group of amateur scientists whom the accidents of party politics placed in Oxford in the Cromwellian period (1650–60). The French academy was the creation of Louis XIV in 1666 acting on the advice of Colbert. The intellectual parent of both is generally stated to be Francis Bacon, for in his unfinished fable, "The New Atlantis," published in 1626 shortly after his death, this ardent proponent of "the new experimental philosophy" (which he only partially understood and never practiced) described a House of Salomon which was a community of investigators and philosophers. An actual society founded in Rome in 1600, the Accademia dei Lincei, seems to have been a prototype of the organization Bacon envisaged. Galileo was a member of this academy which, as early as 1612, was stated to be a "gathering . . . which directs its labors diligently and seriously to studies as yet little cultivated." A generation later a group of Galileo's disciples in Florence established the Accademia del Cimento (1657) which flourished for ten years under the patronage of the two Medici brothers, Grand Duke Ferdinand II and Leopold, who had been pupils of Galileo. This Academy of Experiment was more nearly the forerunner of a twentieth-century research institute than of the eighteenth-century learned society, for the members were engaged in cooperative experimentation, of which more will be said in another chapter.

Both these Italian scientific societies were in the tradition of the literary clubs which flourished in the centers of Renaissance culture. The history of both the Royal Society and the French academy shows a certain ambiguity as between two goals; on the one hand, the members envisioned an active cooperating group of experimenters, and on the other merely a meeting place for reporting and discussing experimental findings, quaint observations and new ideas reported on a highly individualistic basis. The fact that the Royal Society never had any more support from the government than a royal blessing prevented any serious attempt to be much more than a focal point for discussion. The French monarchy, on the other hand, made grants to some of the members of the academy, and off and on during the course of a century thus supported scientists as a royal patron might support painters and men of letters.

Some of the expeditions organized and financed by these societies are of significance in the history of science. But the prime importance of the scientific societies lies in the fact that each undertook to publish a regular journal in which members and others could record their ideas and experimental results. Of the *Transactions* of the Royal Society whose publication was started in 1665 Huxley once said, "If all the books in the world except the Philosophical Transactions were destroyed, it is safe to say that the foundations of physical science would remain unshaken, and that the vast intellectual progress of the last two centuries would be largely though incompletely, recorded." (One may doubt if those concerned today with the more descriptive sciences such as mineralogy and organic chemistry would quite agree with this remark made in the nineteenth century.)

Before the founding of the scientific societies and the establishment of regular quarterly or monthly magazines devoted to publishing the results of original work, news of scientific discoveries spread by letter.

Then, from time to time, a scientific investigator would publish a small book giving his ideas and recounting his experiments. This practice of using separate books rather than communications to journals to announce scientific findings continued late into the nineteenth century. But the scientific journals became more and more important; books are now reserved for the purpose of summing up or amplifying the results published elsewhere. Today the scientific journals, not the scientific books, are the sources of information about what is going on among those who labor on the frontiers of knowledge.

To the uninitiated it would seem impossible for anyone to find his way through the mass of articles and reports which fill tens of thousands of pages every year. Actually the task, while time consuming, is far from hopeless for an investigator who makes a practice of following what the scientist calls "the current literature." In the first place, it must be remembered that by the beginning of the twentieth century the division and subdivision of the sciences had proceeded very far. The journals of the scientific societies still accepted communications covering a wide range of subjects, but specialized journals sprang up as early as the first half of the nineteenth century. Therefore, today one can keep abreast of the advance of science in a particular field of inquiry by reading a relatively small fraction of the monthly output of learned papers. In the second place, various elaborate schemes of indexing and abstracting have been devised. In some branches of science vast encyclopedias are published which summarize the results obtained under appropriate headings. A student bent on becoming an investigator soon learns how "to use the literature." Third, the custom has been established of referring to previous publications which bear on the subject under study. Finally, a great mass of irrelevant data and poorly digested reporting is eliminated by the activities of the editors of the journals. There is some danger in this process. More than one historic instance stands as evidence of originality taking such unusual forms as to cause a too conservative group of editors to regard the communication as erroneous or so fantastic as to warrant rejection. But there are so many different journals today that at the most there is likely to be but a short delay before publication. Informed criticism would say that far too much is published which might well be refused rather than that editors were too severe. . . .

Here I wish to emphasize that the methods of communicating scientific news on a reliable basis have evolved today to a point where there is little danger that any significant new discovery will remain unnoticed.

EXAMPLES OF SCIENTIFIC METHOD
Development of a Concept

THE TORRICELLIAN EXPERIMENT*
by James B. Conant (1951)

For ages people have been aware of the fact that to drain a liquid out of a barrel there should be an opening near the bottom and one at the top; out of the lower orifice comes the wine, into the upper goes the air. Similarly, everyone knows that you can suck up liquid in a tube, close the top opening with your finger, and the liquid will not run out until the finger is removed; this is the principle of the pipette (Figure 2-2). Similar observations have been discussed since before the time of Aristotle. The standard explanation before the seventeenth century was couched in terms very similar to those which would be used by most of us today. "You have to have an opening in the top of the barrel to let the air in, otherwise the liquid won't run out." Of course, if pressed, the modern man (or woman) would have to admit to loose phraseology. He or she would probably say that the air coming in at the top was a consequence of the liquid running out. And sooner or later skillful and sympathetic cross-examination would elicit some information about the role of atmospheric pressure. Those who remembered their high-school physics might reply somewhat as follows: "The liquid in the pipette and in the barrel is prevented from running out by the pres-

sure of the atmosphere; the purpose of taking your finger off the top of the pipette or opening a hole in the top of the barrel is to let the atmospheric pressure act on the top surface of the liquid. When that is done, the amospheric pressure is essentially the same on the top and bottom of the liquid, which then runs out for the same reason a stone falls to earth."

The learned men of the Middle Ages, however, would have followed up the common-sense appraisal of the situation in very different terms. They would have taken quite literally the statement that the hole in the top of the barrel or the opening in the top of the pipette was necessary for the air to enter.

Figure 2-2. A pipette. If liquid is sucked up into a small tube and a finger pressed over the top end of the tube, the liquid will not run out.

* Conant, op. cit.

For they would have started with the assumption that the universe was full. Therefore, they maintained, there could be a movement of the liquid out of the barrel only if some place were provided for the air that had to move to make room for the liquid; the place for this air was provided by the opening in which the air could come in.

The explanation in terms of a "full universe" satisfied generations of inquirers; it was part and parcel of the view of the world which comes from the writings of Aristotle as these were interpreted by the scholars of the Middle Ages. To do justice to this world view would require many chapters. One may caricature it by picking up one of the phrases used by the Aristotelians, namely that it was a universal principle that "nature abhors a vacuum." This principle was invoked to explain why the wine would not flow out of a single opening in a barrel; it was argued that if it did and nothing entered the barrel, a vacuum would result, and this was impossible. Which is, perhaps, only a picturesque way of stating that there must be an opening to let in the air, as many a person would say in an unreflective moment in the mid-twentieth century. The common-sense view of the world even today is more Aristotelian than we sometimes like to think.

The same principle that nature abhors a vacuum could be invoked to explain why one could suck up liquid into a tube or why a lift or suction pump would raise water. Consider the action of a modern version of this very ancient device [Figure 2-3], the old-fashioned pump, not long ago a feature of every kitchen. The operation of the handle raises the plunger and if the plunger is tight the water rises, is "sucked up" we often say. Why? Because otherwise there would be a vacuum, an Aristotelian would reply, and a vacuum is impossible. Again, some such explanation seems to have satisfied philosophers for generations. The first indication of a difficulty appears in the writings of Galileo. In his *Dialogues concerning Two New Sciences*, published in 1638, he refers more or less in passing to the fact that a suction pump will not raise water more than a certain height. His explanation of this phenomenon need not detain us, for it was based on a poor analogy between the breaking of a column of water and the breaking of a long wire. But it is worth noting that this famous Florentine scientist missed the opportunity to make still another great contribution to the advance of science. Those who are inclined to think that the mere recognition of a problem by a great scientist will automatically produce the answer should ponder on this episode in the history of science.

A suction pump cannot raise water more than 34 feet. Galileo in discussing this phenomenon implies that it was first called to his attention by a workman. Suction pumps were no recent invention in Galileo's time. On the contrary, their history can be traced back for centuries; furthermore, practical men must have been long aware of the limitations on their use, for illustrations in Agricola's famous treatise on mining show suction pumps in tandem [Figure 2-4]. It is strange that no discussion of the limit in the ability of a pump to raise water has been found earlier than that in Galileo's treatment. Perhaps any who thought about the subject attributed the failure to raise water more than a certain height to mechanical imperfections; indeed, the system of plungers and valves was very crude. But I am more inclined to think that the silence is merely a striking evidence of the vast gulf that separated artisans and learned men for centuries. There were those who operated mines, smelted ores, and operated pumps; they were improving the practical arts by endless cut-and-try experimentation. Then there were the professors and the learned men at princely courts who developed mathematics, deductive reasoning, and the embryo science of mechanics. Experimental science began when these two streams of human activity converged.

What Galileo missed, his pupil Torricelli found. In 1644, six years after the publication of Galileo's fruitless interpretation and two years after the master's death, Torricelli

Figure 2-3. Cross-sectional diagram of a simple lift or suction pump. As the piston moves upward, water rises in the pipe.

Figure 2-4. An illustration from Agricola's sixteenth-century book on mining, showing the use of pumps for removing water from mines.

put down in writing some general but precise ideas about the atmosphere and atmospheric pressure. A broad hypothesis, we may call it, or a new conceptual scheme in the making. However you wish to characterize Torricelli's views, set forth in an exchange of letters with Cardinal Ricci, they represent a clean break with the Aristotelian notion of nature's abhorrence of a vacuum. In some way and at some date not recorded he saw that the limit of about 34 feet beyond which water would not rise in a suction pump might be a measure of the pressure of the atmosphere. He argued that if the earth were surrounded by a "sea of air" and if air had weight, there would be an air pressure on all objects submerged in this sea of air exactly as there is water pressure below the surface of the ocean.

Then follows a deduction from this hypothesis on a grand scale and the experimental confirmation of this deduction. If the column of water 34 feet high is sustained by the pressure of the atmosphere, the column of liquid nearly 14 times as heavy, namely liquid mercury, should be held up only 34/14 or 2⅜ feet. This is something that can be tested and it was. Again we are uncertain as to the time and place, but somewhere around 1640 and probably in Florence, Torricelli performed the classic experiment with which his name will be forever connected. . . .

This is one of the few revolutionary experiments which can be carried out with the simplest of equipment and understood with the minimum of sophistication in science or mathematics (Figure 2-5). Take a glass tube about a finger's width in diameter, 3 feet long, and sealed off at one end; fill it with liquid mercury (quicksilver); then placing the thumb or forefinger over the open end (carefully excluding any bubbles of air) invert the tube and submerge the end closed by your finger in an open vessel containing more mercury. Remove your finger and lo and behold, the mercury which had hitherto filled the tube now drops, leaving an empty space in the upper end of the tube. And the space is really empty, for you have just produced a vacuum as Torricelli did on the day when he first performed this experiment. Furthermore, you will have constructed a barometer. If you live close to sea level (and have carefully avoided air bubbles in filling the tube with the mercury) the height of the column will be approximately 30 inches. If you live at higher altitudes it will be less. Observed over a period of days, the level will fall and rise, as Torricelli soon discovered. This variation in atmospheric pressure is now a matter of daily news but it was more than a century before the relation between barometric changes and weather began to be noted.

At one stroke Galileo's disciple had invented a new instrument, tested the validity of one deduction from a working hypothesis on a grand scale, and produced a vacuum,

Figure 2-5. In the Torricellian experiment, the tube is completely filled with mercury. The open end is sealed with a finger and the tube is inverted and placed with the "open" end in a dish of mercury. When the finger is removed, the mercury drops until the column is about 30 inches high.

which the Aristotelians maintained was impossible. The significance of the experiment for those studying the methods of science lies, however, in the fact that it constitutes a simple verification of *one* consequence of a very broad hypothesis or conceptual scheme. Historically we cannot be certain that the broad hypothesis preceded the experiment, for there is no record of how Torricelli came either to his idea or his experiment. Considering the recorded discussions of the phenomenon of the water pump by his great master, however, it seems extremely probable that the idea of atmospheric pressure preceded the Torricellian experiment.

One of the most baffling features of the advance of science is the unpredictable way in which revolutionary ideas have developed. Few if any pioneers have arrived at their important discoveries by a systematic process of logical thought. Rather, brilliant flashes of imagination or "hunches" have guided their steps—often at first fumbling steps. . . .

If we may assume the usual interpretation of Torricelli's mental processes to be correct, then one deduction from his new broad hypothesis was confirmed when he constructed the first barometer. A second important deduction was soon drawn by a French mathematician and tested by experiment. Here the pioneer was that extraordinary figure in the history of science and theology, Blaise Pascal. Hearing of the Torricellian experiment through the Parisian letter writer, Father Mersenne, he at once repeated the experiment in Rouen. He also set up a water barometer by arranging a series of tubes of water so that above a column of water 34 feet high there was a vacuum. (This, however, could be hardly considered an independent check of the Torricellian hypothesis.) The new consequence to which Pascal directed attention was this: if we live in a sea of air that exerts pressure, the situation is analogous to that which exists at the bottom of the ocean. Pascal and his contemporaries understood the phenomena connected with water pressure. The laws of hydrostatics had been formulated in the preceding century and were beautifully expounded in a volume by Pascal himself.

The pressure below the surface of water in a reservoir, lake, or ocean depends on the depth. A submarine creature rising from the ocean floor toward the surface will be subjected to a regularly *diminishing* pressure. If we live in a sea of air, the same phenomenon should be observed in the atmosphere, Pascal argued. Torricelli had provided the necessary instrument to measure the pressure—his inverted tube with a column of mercury, the barometer.

Pascal, reasoning in some such fashion, arranged for his brother-in-law Perier to carry out a series of Torricellian experiments at different heights on a mountain in central France. He considered this test a crucial one. In a letter in 1647 he said that the experiment with the inverted tube of mercury gave one reason to believe that "it is not abhorrence of the vacuum that causes mercury to stand suspended, but really the pressure of the air which balances the weight of the mercury column." Nevertheless, he went on to say, the ancient principle of the abhorrence of a vacuum can also be invoked to explain the phenomenon. But he maintained that if on carrying out the Torricellian experiment at the top and at the foot of a mountain it should turn out that the height of the column were less in the first instance than in the second, then "it follows of necessity that the weight and pressure of the air are the sole cause of this suspension of the mercury, and not the abhorrence of a vacuum, for . . . one cannot well say that nature abhors a vacuum more at the foot of the mountain than at its summit."

Pascal's brother-in-law proved to be most obliging and in September, 1648, carried out his mission. The results were as expected. The height of the column in the Torricellian tube at the top of the mountain chosen (the Puy-de-Dome) was less than at the bottom by about three inches, and part way down the mountain the length of the column was a little more than at the top but definitely less than at the bottom. Perier further reported that the repetition of the experiment on the top gave the same result at five different points on the summit, some sheltered, some in the open, and one carried out when a cloud carrying rain drifted over the summit. An observer stationed at the bottom had been meanwhile watching one tube during the entire time; he had found that the level had remained unchanged (the atmospheric pressure during this period did not alter).

A second important deduction from the new hypothesis about a sea of air and atmospheric pressure had thus been verified.

THE STORY OF THE GREAT EXPERIMENT ON THE WEIGHT OF THE MASS OF AIR*
by Blaise Pascal (1648)

It is no longer open to discussion that the air has weight. It is common knowledge that a balloon is heavier when inflated than when empty, which is proof enough. For if the air were light, the more the balloon was inflated the lighter the whole would be, since there would be more air in it. But since, on the contrary, when more air is put in, the whole becomes heavier, it follows that each part has a weight of its own, and consequently that the air has weight.

Whoever wishes for more elaborate proofs can find them in the writings of those who have devoted special treatises to the subject.

If it be objected that air is light when pure, but that the air that surrounds us is not pure, being mixed with vapor and impurities which alone give it weight, my answer is brief: I am not acquainted with "pure" air, and believe that it might be very difficult to find it. But throughout this treatise I am referring solely to the air such as we breathe, regardless of its component elements. Whether it be compound or simple, that is the body which I call the air, and which I declare to have weight. This cannot be denied, and I require nothing more for my further proof. . . .

If there were collected a great bulk of wool, say twenty or thirty fathoms high, this mass would be compressed by its own weight; the bottom layers would be far more compressed than the middle or top layers, because they are pressed by a greater quantity of wool. Similarly the mass of the air, which is a com-

pressible and heavy body like wool, is compressed by its own weight, and the air at the bottom, in the lowlands, is far more compressed than the higher layers on the mountain tops, because it bears a greater load of air.

In the case of that bulk of wool, if a handful of it were taken from the bottom layer, compressed as it is, and lifted, in the same state of compression, to the middle of the mass, it would expand of its own accord; for it would then be nearer the top and subjected there to the pressure of a smaller quantity of wool. Similarly if a body of air, as found here below in its natural state of compression, were by some device transferred to a mountaintop, it would necessarily expand and come to the condition of the air around it on the mountain; for then it would bear a lesser weight of air than it did below. Hence if a balloon, only half inflated—not fully so, as they generally are—were carried up a mountain, it would necessarily be more inflated at the mountaintop, and would expand in the degree to which it was less burdened. The difference will be visible, provided the quantity of air along the mountain slope, from the pressure of which it is now relieved, has a weight great enough to cause a sensible effect.

The Story of the Great Experiment on the Equilibrium of Fluids

At the time when I published my pamphlet entitled "New Experiments touching the Vacuum, et cetera," I used the phrase "Abhorrence of the Vacuum" because it was universally accepted and because I had not then

* From Blaise Pascal, *The Physical Treatise of Pascal*, translated by I. H. B. and A. G. H. Spiers, Columbia University Press, New York, 1937. Reproduced by permission.

any convincing evidences against it; but nevertheless sensed certain difficulties which made me doubt the truth of that conception. To clarify these doubts, I conceived at that very time the experiment here described, which I hoped would yield definite knowledge as a ground for my opinion. I have called it the Great Experiment on the Equilibrium of Fluids, because it is the most conclusive of all that can be made on this subject, inasmuch as it shows the equilibrium of air and quicksilver, which are, respectively, the lightest and the heaviest of all the fluids known in nature.

But since it was impossible to carry out this experiment here, in the city of Paris, and because there are very few places in France that are suitable for this purpose and the town of Clermont in Auvergne is one of the most convenient of these, I requested my brother-in-law, Monsieur Perier, counselor in the Court of Aids in Auvergne, to be so kind as to conduct it there. . . .

Copy of the Letter Sent by Monsieur Perier to Monsieur Pascal the Younger, September 22, 1648

Monsieur,

At last I have carried out the experiment you have so long wished for. I would have given you this satisfaction before now, but have been prevented both by the duties I have had to perform in Bourbonnais, and by the fact that ever since my return the Puy-de-Dome, where the experiment is to be made, has been so wrapped in snow and fog that even in this season, which here is the finest of the year, there was hardly a day when one could see its summit, which is usually in the clouds and sometimes above them even while the weather is clear in the plains. I was unable to adjust my own convenience to a favorable state of the weather before the nineteenth of this month. But my good fortune in performing the experiment on that day has amply repaid me for the slight vexation caused by so many unavoidable delays.

I send you herewith a complete and faithful account of it, in which you will find evidence of the painstaking care I bestowed upon the undertaking, which I thought it proper to carry out in the presence of a few men who are as learned as they are irreproachably honest, so that the sincerity of their testimony should leave no doubt as to the certainty of the experiment.

Copy of the Account of the Experiment Submitted by Monsieur Perier

The weather on Saturday last, the nineteenth of this month, was very unsettled. At about five o'clock in the morning, however, it seemed sufficiently clear; and since the summit of the Puy-de-Dome was then visible, I decided to go there to make the attempt. To that end I notified several people of standing in this town of Clermont, who had asked me to let them know when I would make the ascent. Of this company some were clerics, others laymen. Among the clerics was the Very Rev. Father Bannier, one of the Minim Fathers of this city, who has on several occasions been "corrector" (that is, father superior), and Monsieur Mosnier, canon of the Cathedral Church of this city; among the laymen were Messieurs la Ville and Begon, councilors to the Court of Aids, and Monsieur la Porte, a doctor of medicine, practicing here. All these men are very able, not only in the practice of their professions, but also in every field of intellectual interest. It was a delight to have them with me in this fine work.

On that day, therefore, at eight o'clock in the morning, we started off all together for the garden of the Minim Fathers, which is almost the lowest spot in the town, and there began the experiment in this manner.

First, I poured into a vessel six pounds of quicksilver which I had rectified during the three days preceding; and having taken glass tubes of the same size, each four feet long and hermetically sealed at one end but open at the other, I place them in the same vessel and carried out with each of them the usual vacuum experiment [Figure 2-6]. Then, having set them

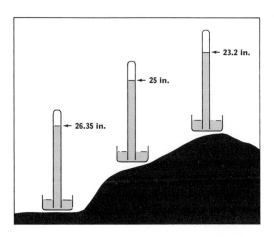

Figure 2-6. Diagram of Monsieur Perier's experimental findings.

up side by side without lifting them out of the vessel, I found that the quicksilver left in each of them stood at the same level, which was twenty-six inches and three and a half lines above the surface of the quicksilver in the vessel. I repeated this experiment twice at this same spot, in the same tubes, with the same quicksilver, and in the same vessel; and found in each case that the quicksilver in the two tubes stood at the same horizontal level, and at the same height as in the first trial.

That done, I fixed one of the tubes permanently in its vessel for continuous experiment. I marked on the glass the height of the quicksilver, and leaving that tube where it stood, I requested the Rev. Father Chastin, one of the brothers of the house, a man as pious as he is capable, and one who reasons very well upon these matters, to be so good as to observe from time to time all day any changes that might occur. With the other tube and a portion of the same quicksilver, I then proceeded with all these gentlemen to the top of the Puy-de-Dome, some five hundred fathoms above the convent. There, after I had made the same experiments in the same way that I had made them at the Minims', we found that there remained in the tube a height of only twenty-three inches and two lines of quicksilver; whereas in the same tube, at the Minims', we had found a height of twenty-six inches and three and a half lines. Thus between the heights of the quicksilver in the two experiments there proved to be a difference of three inches one line and a half. We were so carried away with wonder and delight, and our surprise was so great, that we wished, for our own satisfaction, to repeat the experiment. So I carried it out with the greatest care five times more at different points on the summit of the mountain, once in the shelter of the little chapel that stands there, once in the open, once shielded from the wind, once in the wind, once in fine weather, once in the rain and fog which visited us occasionally. Each time I most carefully rid the tube of air; and in all these experiments we invariably found the same height of quicksilver. This was twenty-three inches, and two lines, which yields the same discrepancy of three inches, one line and a half in comparison with the twenty-six inches, three lines and a half which had been found at the Minims'. This satisfied us fully.

Later, on the way down at a spot called Lafon de l'Arbre, far above the Minims' but much farther below the top of the mountain, I repeated the same experiment, still with the same tube, the same quicksilver, and the same vessel, and there found that the height of the quicksilver left in the tube was twenty-five inches. I repeated it a second time at the same spot; and Monsieur Mosnier, one of those previously mentioned, having the curiosity to perform it himself, then did so again, at the same spot. All these experiments yielded the same height of twenty-five inches, which is one inch, three lines and a half less than that which we had found at the Minims', and one inch and ten lines more than we had just found at the top of the Puy-de-Dome. It increased our satisfaction not a little to observe in this way that the height of the quicksilver diminished with the altitude of the site.

On my return to the Minims' I found that the [quicksilver in the] vessel I had left there in continuous operation was at the same height at which I had left it, that is, at twenty-six inches, three lines and a half; and the Rev. Father Chastin, who had remained there as observer, reported to us that no change had occurred during the whole day, although the weather had been very unsettled, now clear and still, now rainy, now very foggy, and now windy.

Here I repeated the experiment with the tube I had carried to the Puy-de-Dome, but in the vessel in which the tube used for the continuous experiment was standing. I found that the quicksilver was at the same level in both tubes and exactly at the height of twenty-six inches, three lines and a half, at which it had stood that morning in this same tube, and as it had stood all day in the tube used for the continuous experiment.

I repeated it again a last time, not only in the same tube I had used on the Puy-de-Dome, but also with the same quicksilver and in the same vessel that I had carried up the mountain; and again I found the quicksilver at the same height of twenty-six inches, three lines and a half which I had observed in the morning, and thus finally verified the certainty of our results. . . .

If you find any obscurities in this recital I shall be able in a few days to clear them up in conversation with you, since I am about to take a little trip to Paris, when I shall assure you that I am, Monsieur,

Your very humble and very affectionate
    servant,

                    Perier

This narrative cleared up all my difficulties and, I am free to say, afforded me great satisfaction. Seeing that a difference of twenty fathoms of altitude made a difference of two lines in the height of the quicksilver, and six or seven fathoms one of about half a line, facts which it was easy for me to verify in this city, I made the usual vacuum experiment on the top and at the base of the tower of St. Jacques de la Boucherie, which is some twenty-four or twenty-five fathoms high, and found a difference of more than two lines in the height of the quicksilver. I then repeated it in a private house ninety steps high, and found a clearly perceptible difference of half a line. These results are in perfect agreement with those given in M. Perier's narrative.

Any who care to do so, may, for themselves, confirm them at their pleasure.

Consequences

From this experiment many inferences may be drawn, such as:

A method of ascertaining whether two places are at the same altitude, that is to say, equally distant from the center of the earth, or which of the two is the higher, however far apart they may be, even at antipodes— which would be impossible by any other means.

The unreliability of the thermometer in marking degrees of heat (which is not commonly recognized), as is shown by the fact that its liquid sometimes rises when the heat increases and sometimes, on the contrary, falls when the heat decreases, even though the thermometer be kept always in the same location.

Proof of the inequality of the pressure of the air, which, at the same degree of heat, is always greater in the lowest places.

ON PASCAL, PERIER, VON GUERICKE AND BOYLE*
by James B. Conant (1951)

In Pascal's mind, at least, the results were conclusive. Indeed, we might be tempted to say that after the Puy-de-Dome experiment, Torricelli's new idea had become a new conceptual scheme! Yet with such a conclusion as well as with Pascal's confidence, one may quarrel. The history of science since his time has shown the dangers of regarding the experimental verification of any *one* deduction as conclusive evidence as to the validity of a hypothesis.

It will be worth while to examine in some detail the experiment planned by Pascal and performed by Perier. First of all, it is worth noting that the new conceptual scheme could not be directly tested by experiment, though one can easily fall into the habit of speaking as though this were possible. In general, few if any hypotheses on a grand scale or conceptual schemes can be directly tested.

A whole chain of reasoning connects a conceptual scheme with the experimental test.

This may seem a trivial point, but it is not. More than one false step has resulted at this point; hidden assumptions as prickly as thorns abound; these may puncture a line of reasoning. What was observed in an experiment may not be actually related to the conceptual scheme in the way the experimenter had believed. . . . experimental errors can lead an experimenter astray. If we were to attempt to expound the difficult subject of twentieth-century physics, we should encounter the issue in a somewhat different form. We should then find that what appeared to be obvious common-sense assumptions involved in the line of reasoning connecting experiments with conceptual schemes had to be revised when either very high speeds or very small particles were involved.

Because of their significance to an understanding of the logic of experimentation, let us examine Perier's procedures with some care. Pascal's deduction from the new conceptual scheme may be stated somewhat as

* Conant, *op. cit.*

follows: "If the earth is surrounded by a sea of air and if air has weight, the pressure of the air will be less on the top of a mountain than at the foot." To translate this deduction into a specific experiment requires a long line of argument. If the height of the Torricellian column is a measure of the atmospheric pressure, then on performing the experiment on the top of the Puy-de-Dome and at the foot, the observed height will be less in the first instance than in the second, provided no other factors have influenced the pressure in the meantime or the height of the mercury column.

The "if" and the "provided" in this argument are of extreme importance. To guard against one obvious source of error, namely variations in the atmospheric pressure, Perier, as we have seen, had someone keep watch on a tube set up at the foot of the mountain during the entire time. To assure himself that in each case the height of the column was a true measure of the pressure, he says he carefully excluded all bubbles of air (for even a small one will on ascending into the vacuum cause the mercury to fall perceptibly). He does not state how he assured himself that he had been successful in his manipulations, and the accuracy with which his repeated observations agree with each other cannot but cause a skeptic to raise his eyebrows. Indeed, I am inclined to think he allowed his enthusiasm to affect the validity of his record. But there is no need to go into this interesting historical point; suffice it to say that standards of experimentation and recording had not been established by custom in 1648.

Perier performed certain manipulations at certain spots according to a careful set of rules. What he actually observed each time was a distance between two mercury levels; he probably used a wooden measuring stick graduated in inches and in lines (a twelfth of an inch). At the time of performing the experiment Perier was reasoning very much as the artisan or the housewife who makes a test of a new approach to a practical problem, for in effect he said, "If I perform Torricelli's experiment on this spot and there have been no errors in my manipulation and

no unknown factors affecting the height of the mercury (a hypothesis limited to the case at hand), I shall observe a height of a mercury column less than is now being observed at the foot of the mountain." For all Pascal or Perier knew, a mercury column might be appreciably shorter at the top of a mountain than below for a variety of reasons: the relative densities of mercury and air might change (the ideas about gravity were then in process of formulation); the measuring stick might alter in length on being moved upward several thousand feet. Perier himself recognized that an open space and an enclosed building might make a difference, also a passing cloud. By repeating the experiment in and out of a chapel, when the air was clear and rainy, he tested the effect of certain *variables*, but the results he says were always the same.

The fact that so many variables exist in connection with testing a deduction by means of an actual experiment is the significant point. In this case, subsequent investigation has so far failed to reveal any variables that invalidate Perier's *qualitative* check on Pascal's deduction that the mercury column in a Torricellian tube is shorter on the top of a mountain than at the bottom.

Young Men and Amateurs: A Digression

At this point I propose to interrupt the story of seventeenth-century pneumatics to examine briefly an example of a recurring phenomenon in the history of science. I refer to the new waves of interest followed by important work that seem to sweep over the learned world from time to time. A new idea or new discoveries of new instruments open up a new area of inquiry: everyone rushes in and science advances in that field with astonishing speed, then progress lags and there may be a long period of marking time. The phenomenon to no small degree is connected, I believe, with the proverbial desire of young men to differ with their elders and to seek fields for new adventure. More than once the elderly scientists have said in essence, "Ah, that is a young man's game." The study of atmospheric pressure in the mid-seventeenth century was exactly that, for Torricelli was thirty-six when he wrote his famous letter to Cardinal Ricci; Pascal was twenty-four when he outlined the Puy-de-Dome experiments; Boyle, whose work we are about to consider, was thirty-two when he started his line of investigation in this field.

These men, it must be remembered, were strictly amateurs; not for many years to come was experimental science to find a home in the universities; research laboratories and institutes were a full two centuries away. . . .

The Invention of the Vacuum Pump

One more amateur must be mentioned: the inventor of the vacuum pump, Otto von Guericke. He was a man of affairs, the mayor of Magdeburg who had played an active part in the Thirty Years' War and whose own city was sacked in 1631. His interest in the new experimental philosophy was probably not unconnected with the necessity of his being concerned with matters of military engineering. The story of how he developed his ideas about the atmosphere is obscure; he may have come quite independently to the same conclusions as did Torricelli. He certainly constructed a water barometer and built the first machine for pumping air out of a container. In retrospect his invention is an obvious adaptation of the suction part of a lift water pump. (The retrospect view of all discoveries and inventions must be used with care, lest one fall into the danger of being a "Monday morning quarterback.") Instead of sucking with a piston and cylinder on a column of water, as men had done for centuries in using suction pumps for raising water, von Guericke tried to suck water out of a full wooden cask using a brass pump. There were several models of this invention, and the usual partial success and failure of the pioneer attended his efforts. He attained his results only when he started to pump air as well as water from an enclosed container and finally ended by pumping out air alone. He also found that a spherical metal receptacle was necessary to stand the resulting atmospheric pressure. By 1654 he was able

Figure 2-7. Otto von Guericke's Magdeburg hemispheres.

to carry out, before the Imperial Diet assembled at Ratisbon, the famous demonstration of the Magdeburg hemispheres [Figure 2-7]. Two hollow bronze hemispheres were fitted carefully edge to edge and the air contained in the sphere thus formed removed by a pump. After evacuation the external atmospheric pressure held the two halves together so firmly that a team of eight horses could not pull them apart. Once air was admitted through a stopcock the hemispheres fell asunder.

This striking demonstration of von Guericke's may be regarded as the verification of another deduction from Torricelli's conceptual scheme. But for our purposes the use of von Guericke's pump by Robert Boyle is more instructive.

Robert Boyle's Experiments

Boyle heard of the new pump through a book published in 1657 by a Jesuit professor at Würzburg (the communication of news of scientific discoveries was still on a most casual basis). Learning of this recent method of producing a vacuum, Boyle saw the possibility of testing still another deduction from the Torricellian conceptual scheme. His combination of logic and imagination represents a pattern repeated by many a successful investigator in the last three hundred years. More than one significant advance in science has come about because someone had the imagination to see that a new instrument made possible the testing of an important point. What Boyle proposed to do was to perform the equivalent of the Puy-de-Dome experiments in the laboratory. He had modified von Guericke's pump by providing an arrangement by which he could introduce the lower part of the Torricellian barometer into the vessel to be evacuated [Figures 2-8 to 2-10]. Then, as he worked the pump and withdrew the air from above the mercury reservoir, the mercury column fell. . . . He was able to cause the column to fall almost but not quite to the level of the mercury in the reservoir. In other words he was able to evacuate the reservoir to a pressure something less than one-thirtieth of the original pressure but, as he suspected, his apparatus was not efficient enough to proceed further with the evacuation. When air was admitted into the receiver the mercury column rose to the usual height.

One would think that by the time Boyle published the account of his experiment the whole learned world would have accepted the new ideas. But the advance of science was slow in the mid-seventeenth century, in part because of the lack of scientific societies and scientific journals. In addition to an elaborate description of his pump, . . . the author described many experiments which could be readily performed in a vacuum. . . . From these experiments . . . came quantitative measurements that resulted in the formulation of the famous Boyle's law relating to the volume and pressure of gas.*

* See "Boyle's law," in Glossary. Ed.

Figure 2-8. Boyle's first air pump.

Figure 2-9. Simplified diagram of Boyle's pump. According to Boyle, "Upon the drawing down of the sucker (the valve being shut), the cylindrical space, deserted by the sucker, is left devoid of air; and therefore, upon the turning of the key, the air contained in the receiver rusheth into the emptied cylinder. . . . Upon shutting the receiver by turning the key, if you open the valve, and force up the sucker . . . you will drive out almost a whole cylinder full of air; but at the following exsuctions you will draw less and less of air out of the receiver into the cylinder because there will remain less and less air in the receiver itself. . . ."

Figure 2-10. Diagram of Boyle's apparatus for removing the air above the reservoir of a barometer. The glass globe is the upper part of the pump. W indicates where a sealing wax was used. When the pump is operated, the mercury column decreases in height.

The Role of Accident

GALVANI'S DISCOVERIES*
by James B. Conant (1951)

Science is sometimes presented as though it were exclusively the work of high-powered mathematicians elaborating theories and sometimes as though it were all a matter of blind chance. As a consequence the reader is often confused in regard to the role of what appears to be an accidental observation. This is particularly true in connection with the development of new techniques and the evolution of new concepts from experiment. The case history which I recommend for a study of these subjects is the work of Galvani and

* Conant, *op. cit.*

Volta on the electric current. This case illustrates the fact that a chance observation may lead by a series of experiments (which must be well planned) to a new technique or a new concept or both. It also shows that in the exploration of a new phenomenon the experiments may be well planned without any "working hypothesis" as to the nature of the phenomenon but that shortly an explanation is sure to arise. A new conceptual scheme will then be evolved. This may be on a grand scale and have wide applicability or may be strictly limited to the phenomenon in question. A test of the new concept or group of concepts in either instance will probably lead to new discoveries and the eventual establishment, modification, or overthrow of the conceptual scheme in question.

The story begins with certain observations made by Luigi Galvani, an Italian physician and professor at Bologna, some time before 1786. This investigator noted the twitching of a frog's leg when the crural nerves were touched by a metallic scalpel in the neighborhood of an electrostatic machine from which sparks were drawn. *He followed up his observation:* this is the significant feature of the history of this episode. Time and time again throughout the advance of science the consequences of following up or not following up accidental discoveries have been very great. The analogy of a general's taking advantage of an enemy's error or a lucky break is clear. Pasteur once wrote that "chance favors only the prepared mind." This is excellently illustrated by the case at hand. The Dutch naturalist Swammerdam had previously discovered that if you lay bare the muscle of a frog in much the same way as Galvani did, grasp a tendon in one hand and touch the frog's nerve with a scalpel held in the other hand, a twitching will result. But Swammerdam never followed up his discovery. Galvani did. In his own words, "I had dissected and prepared a frog . . . and while I was attending to something else, I laid it on a table on which stood an electrical machine at some distance. . . . Now when one of the persons who were present touched accidentally and lightly the inner crural nerves of the frog with the point of a scalpel all the muscles of the legs seemed to contract again and again. . . . Another one who was there, who was helping us in electrical researches, thought that he had noticed that the action was excited when a spark was discharged from the conductor of the machine. Being astonished by this new phenomenon he called my attention to it, who at that time had something else in mind and was deep in thought. Whereupon I was inflamed with an incredible zeal and eagerness to test the same and to bring to light what was concealed in it."

Galvani did not succeed in bringing to light all that was concealed in the new phenomenon. But he proceeded far enough to make the subsequent discoveries inevitable. In a series of well-planned experiments he explored the obvious variables but without having a clear-cut over-all hypothesis. This is the usual situation when a new and totally unexpected phenomenon is encountered by a gifted experimenter. A series of working hypotheses spring to mind, are tested, and either discarded or incorporated into a conceptual scheme which gradually develops. For example, Galvani first determined whether or not sparks had to be drawn from the electrical machine in order to occasion twitching. He found "without fail there occurred lively contractions . . . at the same instant as that in which the spark jumped. . . ."

The nerves and muscle of the frog's leg constituted a sensitive detector of an electric charge. Galvani found that not only must a spark be passing from the electrostatic machine but the metallic blade of the scalpel must be in contact with the hand of the experimenter. In this way a small charge originating from the electrical disturbance, namely the spark, passed down the conducting human body through the scalpel to the nerve. So far the physician was on sound and fertile ground. There now occurred one of those coincidences which more than once have baffled an investigator initially but eventually have led to great advances. The frog's leg could under certain circumstances act not only as a sensitive electrical detector but as a source of electricity as well. When this happened the electricity self-generated, so to speak, actuated the detector. One can readily see that the superposition of these two effects could be most bewildering and misleading. This was particularly so since the conditions under which the frog's leg became a source of electricity were totally unconnected with any electrical phenomena then known. The variable was the nature of the metal, or rather metals, used. For Galvani discovered and duly recorded that the electrostatic machine could be dispensed with if the leg and nerve were connected by two *different* metals. Under these conditions the twitching occurred. (The experiment was usually performed as follows: a curved rod was made to touch simultaneously both a hook passing through the spinal cord of the frog and the "muscles of the leg or the feet.") "Thus, for example," wrote Galvani, "if the whole rod was iron or the hook was iron . . . the contractions either did not occur or were very small. But if one of them was iron and the other brass, or better if it was silver (silver seems to us the best of all the metals for conducting animal electricity) there occur repeated and much greater and more prolonged contractions."

Galvani had discovered the principle of the electric battery without knowing it. His two metals separated by the moist animal tissue were a battery, the frog's leg the detector. Every reader can perform the equivalent of Galvani's experiment himself. A copper coin and a silver one placed above and below the tongue when touched together produce in the tongue a peculiar "taste." A very small electric current flows, and our tongue records the fact through a series of interactions of electricity and nerves much in the same way as did Galvani's "prepared" frogs. Not having a suspicion of all this, however, Galvani developed a hypothesis on the grand scale to account for all the phenomena in terms of what was then known about electricity, which was derived entirely from experiment with electrostatic machines. Now that outside electrical disturbances had been found unnecessary (when he unwittingly used the *right* metallic combination!), the results, he says, "cause us to think that possibly the electricity was present in the animal itself." Galvani's following up of an accidental discovery by a series of controlled experiments led to a recording of the significant facts, but it was to be another Italian who developed the fruitful concept. It was Volta who in the late 1790's continuing the study of the production of electricity by the contact of two different metals, invented the electric battery as a source of what we now often call Galvanic electricity.

EXAMPLES OF UNSCIENTIFIC METHOD

The male has more teeth than the female in mankind, and sheep, and goats, and swine. This has not been observed in other animals. Those persons which have the greatest number of teeth are the longest lived; those which have them widely separated, smaller, and more scattered, are generally more short lived.

Aristotle
History of Animals (4th Century B.C.)

There are seven windows in the head, two nostrils, two eyes, two ears, and a mouth; so in the heavens there are two favorable stars, two unpropitious, two luminaries, and Mercury alone, undecided and indifferent. From which and many other similar phenomena of nature, such as the seven metals, etc., which it were tedious to enumerate, we gather that the number of planets is necessarily seven.

Francesco Sizzi

In the space of one hundred and seventy-six years the Lower Mississippi has shortened itself two hundred and forty-two miles. That is an average of a trifle over one mile and a third per year. Therefore, any calm person, who is not blind or idiotic, can see that in the old Oolitic Silurian Period, just a million years ago next November, the Lower Mississippi River was upward of one million three hundred thousand miles long, and stuck out over the Gulf of Mexico like a fishing-rod. And by the same token any person can see that seven hundred and forty-two years from now the Lower Mississippi will be only a mile and three-quarters long, and Cairo and New Orleans will have joined their streets together, and be plodding comfortably along under a single mayor and a mutual board of aldermen. There is something fascinating about science. One gets such wholesale returns of conjecture out of such trifling investment of fact.

Mark Twain
Life on the Mississippi (1875)

QUESTIONS TO CONSIDER

Bronowski said, "The scientist or the artist takes two facts or experiences which are separate, he finds in them a likeness which had not been seen before; and he creates a unity by showing the likeness." Is this the kind of reasoning that Pascal and Sizzi use in the examples on pages 34 and 43? Why does Pascal's reasoning lead to more fruitful concepts than Sizzi's?

What elements of scientific method and what processes of reasoning are used in the examples of the work of Torricelli and Pascal?

Did Perier's experiment "prove" the truth of Pascal's theory? Does scientific proof differ from logical proof?

Are there any ways in which scientific methods differ from common-sense methods of reasoning?

Taking scientific activity as a whole can we speak of the "scientific method"?

SUGGESTIONS FOR FURTHER READING

*   Beveridge, W. I. B.: *The Art of Scientific Investigation*, Vintage Books, Random House, Inc., New York, 1957. This book, which was written primarily as an aid to the young scientist, is also very interesting and instructive reading for the layman.

* Paperback edition.

* Campbell, Norman: *What Is Science?* Dover Publications, Inc., New York, 1952. A well-expressed and informative discussion of scientific method.

Cohen, I. Bernard: *Science: The Servant of Man,* Little, Brown and Company, Boston, 1948. This book elucidates scientific method by describing case histories of a number of discoveries that have improved the well-being of mankind.

* Conant, James B.: *On Understanding Science,* Mentor Books, New American of World Literature, Inc., New York, 1951.

* ———: *Science and Common Sense,* Yale University Press, New Haven, Conn., 1951.

These two books by Conant are very similar, the latter being essentially an amplification of the former. Conant uses case histories of important scientific concepts to illustrate the methods of science. In addition to the development of the concept of atmospheric pressure in the selection we use here, Conant also describes the development of a number of other fundamental concepts that the reader will find very helpful in gaining an understanding of scientific method.

* Popper, Karl: *Logic of Scientific Discovery,* Basic Books, Inc., Publishers, New York, or John Wiley & Sons, Inc., New York. This fine, authoritative book has become a classic exposition of scientific method. However, the reader will find the presentation more difficult than in the other books suggested here.

PART 3

IS THERE AN ORDER IN NATURE?

From early Greek times science has been based on the assumption that nature is orderly and that this order can be discovered and understood by man. The selections in this part examine the origin of this assumption, describe the different forms it took in ancient cosmology, and raise the question of its basic validity.

Thiel

Rogers

Wightman

De Santillana

INTRODUCTION

This part begins the historical sequence of astronomy and cosmology that will be followed throughout the remaining parts. The selections take the reader back to ancient Egyptian and Greek times to the birth of some of the most basic scientific ideas. Historians of science agree that an important start toward understanding nature was made by the Greek natural philosophers. George Sarton, in his *Introduction to the History of Science*, says, "If science is more than an accumulation of facts; if it is not simply positive knowledge, but systematized knowledge; if it is not simply unguided analysis and haphazard empiricism, but synthesis; if it is not simply recording but constructive activity; then, undoubtedly, [ancient Greece] was its cradle." John Burnet goes further and says, ". . . it is an adequate description of science to say that it is 'thinking about the world in the Greek way'. That is why science has never existed except among people who came under the influence of Greece."

What was the Greek way of thinking about the world? The authors in this session suggest that the most important feature of this world picture was the hypothesis that "nature can be understood" and that the basis for understanding it is the discovery of an order that lies beneath the variety that we observe in the external world. Whitehead puts it this way: ". . . there can be no living science unless there is a widespread instinctive conviction in the existence of an *Order of Things*, and in particular of an *Order of Nature*." In fact, this assumption has become so basic to our whole world view that it may seem trivial to question its validity and to inquire about its origin. If any justification is needed for this inquiry, we have only to remember that there have been and still are civilizations in which magic or the acts of capricious gods are held responsible for the happenings of nature, and as we will see in Part 6, some of the findings of modern physics suggest that this instinctive belief in a natural order may not be as universally valid a principle as we had at first supposed.

The readings in this part, however, are designed to present the idea of an order in nature in its historical context. Benjamin Farrington, in his book

Ortega y Gasset

Whitehead

Plato

Margenau

on Greek Science, says, ". . . there is no human knowledge which cannot lose its scientific character when men forget the conditions under which it originated, the questions which it answered, and the functions it was created to serve. A great part of the mysticism and superstition of educated men consists of knowledge which has broken loose from its historical mooring." It is important that we understand the ideas that we have inherited from Greek thought, not only to use them more effectively, but also to be free of any mystical or superstitious attachment to them.

The Greeks were the first to use effectively the ability to generalize from perceptual material to conceptual schemes. Furthermore, they believed that this process of abstraction would tell them something significant about nature. The most outstanding product of this type of thinking was mathematics and particularly the geometry that was developed by the Pythagorean school and reached its culmination in the *Elements of Euclid*. The materials throughout this book have been presented, as far as possible, in a nonmathematical fashion in order to be more understandable to a general audience. However, it would be a grave misrepresentation to underestimate the importance of mathematics as a powerful aid to physical scientists.

Mathematics helps the scientist by providing a clear shorthand language in which he can express himself without the vagueness or ambiguity of ordinary speech. For instance, the equation $a^2 + b^2 = c^2$, illustrated below, ex-

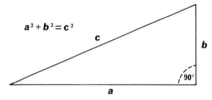

Figure 3-1. The Pythagorean theorem.

presses the Pythagorean theorem in the briefest and most concise manner. Try to put this theorem into words, and you will see how much more complicated it is. For those who are familiar with the language of mathematics the relationship is much

Poincare

Moulton

easier to visualize when it is expressed in mathematical form. Furthermore, by providing a set of rules for manipulating the relationships, mathematics can suggest new combinations and lead to broader generalizations. Descartes saw in the Pythagorean theorem a method for describing the position of bodies in three dimensional space and from this insight he invented the Cartesian coordinate system. Several centuries later, Einstein created a broader synthesis using the Cartesian coordinates as a basis for the frames of reference in his special theory of relativity. Mathematics gives the scientists a method for recognizing and revealing relationships. In so doing, it makes an important contribution to the search for an underlying form and order in nature.

The power of abstract reasoning is brilliantly demonstrated in the work of the Greek astronomers who, starting with a few simple observations of the positions of the stars and planets at different times of the year, devised vast and ingenious theoretical systems and even anticipated the heliocentric theory almost two thousand years before Copernicus. Two entirely different systems of astronomy were proposed to account for the set of known facts. Both of these systems represented a search for order in the apparent disorder of the planetary motions. Both of them accounted reasonably well for the observed facts and were able to predict the future positions within the limits of the accuracy possible at that time. In this search for order and unity in the heavens, the two schools of Greek astronomers made different simplifying assumptions. The Pythagorean school sought for harmonious numerical relationships in the spacing and the number of the planets. The school of Eudoxus and Ptolemy sought to explain the facts in terms of uniform circular motion. In retrospect, we believe today that the latter explanation was more artificial, that it represented an imposition of order on the diversity of nature, whereas the heliocentric theory, we believe, was the discovery of a real order in nature. But it could be argued that, if two different explanations account equally well for the facts, perhaps other valid explanations could also be found. Can one of these be said to be really true? In preferring the simpler explanation, have we discovered simplicity and order in nature itself or have we, as Eddington suggests, found our own footprint on the shores of the unknown?

ANCIENT COSMOLOGY

THE BEGINNING OF ASTRONOMY*
by Eric M. Rogers (1960)

For centuries very primitive man must have watched the stars, perhaps wondering a little, taking the Sun for granted, yet using it as a guide, relying on moonlight for hunting, and even reckoning simple time by moons. Then slowly gathered knowledge was built into tradition with the help of speech. The Sun offered a rough clock by day and the stars by night.[1] For simple geography, sunrise marked a general easterly region, and sunset

* From Eric M. Rogers, *Physics for the Inquiring Mind*, Princeton University Press, Princeton, N.J., 1960, and reproduced with their permission.

[1] An experienced camper can tell the time by the stars within ¼ hour.

a westerly one; and the highest Sun (noon) marked an unchanging South all the year round. At night the pole-star marked a constant North.

As the year runs through its seasons the Sun's daily path changes from a low arc in winter to a high one in summer; and the exact direction of sunrise shifts round the horizon. Thus the Sun's path provided a calendar of seasons; and so did the midnight star-pattern, which shifts from night to night through the year.

With the age of cultivation, herding and agriculture made a calendar essential. It was necessary to foretell the seasons so that the ground could be prepared and wheat planted at the right time. Sheep, among the first animals domesticated, are seasonal breeders, so the early herdsmen also needed a calendar. Crude calendar-making seems easy enough to us today, but to simple men with no written records it was a difficult art to be practised by skilled priests. The priest calendar-makers were practical astronomers. They were so important that they were exempt from work with herds or crops and were paid a good share of food, just as in many savage tribes today.

When urban civilizations developed, clear knowledge of the apparent motions of Sun, Moon, and stars was gathered with growing accuracy and recorded. These regular changes were worth codifying for the purpose of making predictions. In the great Nile valley, where one of the early civilizations grew, the river floods at definite seasons, and it was important for agriculture and for safety to predict these floods. And fishermen and other sailors at the mercy of ocean tides took careful note of tide regularities: a shifting schedule of two tides a day, with a cycle of big and little tides that follows the Moon's month. In cities, too, time was important: clocks and calendars were needed for commerce and travel.

Timekeeping promoted an intellectual development:[2] "In counting the shadow hours

and learning to use the star clock, man had begun to use geometry. He had begun to find his bearings in cosmic and terrestrial space."

Astronomy and Religion

Apart from practical uses, why did early man attach such importance to astronomy and build myths and superstitions round the Sun, Moon, and planets?

The blazing Sun assumed an obvious importance as soon as man began to think about his surroundings. It gave light and warmth for man and crops. The Moon, too, gave light for hunters, lovers, travellers, warriors. These great lamps in the sky seemed closely tied to the life of man, so it is not surprising to find them watched and worshipped. The stars were a myriad lesser lights, also a source of wonder. Men imagined that gods or demons moved these lamps, and endowed them with powers of good and evil. We should not condemn such magic as stupid superstition. The Sun *does* bring welcome summer and the Moon *does* give useful light. The simple mind might well reason that Sun and Moon could be persuaded to bring other benefits. The very bright star, Sirius, rose just at dawn at the season of the Nile floods. If the Egyptians reasoned that Sirius caused the floods, it was a forgivable mistake—the confusion of *post hoc* and *proper hoc* that is often made today.

When a few bright stars were found to wander strangely among the rest, these "planets" (literally "wanderers") were watched with anxious interest. At a later time, early civilized man evolved a great neurotic superstition that man's fate and character are controlled by the Sun, Moon, and wandering planets. This superstition of astrology, built on earlier belief in magic, added drive—and profit—to astronomical observation.

Thus the growth of astronomy was interwoven with that of religion—and they still lie very close, since modern astronomy is bounded by the ultimate questions of the beginning of the world in the past and its fate in the future. The next two sections contain speculations on the early stages of that development.

[2] Lancelot Hogben, *Science for the Citizen*, George Allen & Unwin, Ltd., London, 1938.

Science, Magic, and Religion

Science began in magic. Early man lived at the mercy of uncontrolled nature. Simple reasoning made him try to persuade and control nature as one would a powerful human neighbor. He tried simple imitative magic, such as jumping and croaking like a frog in the rain to encourage rainfall, or drawing animals on cave walls to promote success in hunting. He buried his dead near the hearth, with logical hope of restoring their warmth; and he gave them tools and provisions for future use. In a way, he was carrying out scientific experiments, with simple reasoning behind them. It was not his fault that he guessed wrong. The modern scientist disowns magicians because they refuse to learn from their results—that is the essential defect of superstition, a continuing blind faith. Primitive man, however, had neither the information nor the clear scientific reasoning to judge his magic.

As he carried out jumping ceremonies, or squatted before magic pictures, man could form the idea of presiding spirits: kindly deities who could help, malicious demons who brought disaster, powerful gods who controlled destiny. Like a child, man tried to please these gods so that they would grant good weather, health, plentiful game, fertility. The original reasons and purposes were then forgotten and the ceremonies continued by habit.

Speech was the essential vehicle of this development. Earliest man, just beginning speech, was forging his own foundations of thought, slowly and uncertainly. Other creatures communicate—bees dance well-coded news of honey, dogs bark with meaning—but man's speech opened up greater intellectual advances. In the course of a long development, it not only gave him a rich vocabulary for communicating information but it enabled him to store information in tales for later generations; and then it blossomed into a higher intellectual level with *words for abstract ideas*. Thus speech opened up a new field of *ideas and reasoning*.

Primitive religion wove together myths of gods, magic ceremonies, and tales of nature, in attempts to codify both the natural world and man's growing social system. Astronomy played an important part in this ceremonial religion. The priests—wise men of the village or tribe—were the calendar-makers, the first professional astronomers. Their successors were the powerful priesthood of the first urban civilizations. In early Babylon, for example, the priests were bankers, physicians, scientists, and rulers—they *were* the government. In their knowledge, and that of their craftsmen, there were the foundations of many sciences. The practical *information* was there, at first unrecognized, then held secret, then published in texts. Was it *science?*

Science, the Art of Understanding Nature

Curiosity and collecting knowledge go back before earliest man. Primitive man collected knowledge and used it: a beginning of applied science. Then, as a reasoner, he began to organize knowledge for use and thought. That is a difficult step, from individual examples to generalization—watch a child trying to do it. It is difficult to grasp the idea of a common behavior or a general law or an abstract quality. Yet that is the essential step in turning a "stamp collection" of facts into a piece of science. Science, as we think of it and use it now, never was just a pile of information. Scientists themselves, beginning perhaps with the early priesthood, are not just collectors. They dig under the facts for a more general understanding: they extract general ideas from observed events.

Scientists feel driven to *know*, know what happens, know how things happen; and, for ages, they have speculated why things happen. That drive to know was essential to the survival of man—a generation of children that did not want to find out, did not want to understand, would barely survive. That drive may have begun with necessity and fear; it may have been fostered by anxiety to replace capricious demons by a trustworthy rule. Yet there was also an element of wonder: an *intellectual delight* in nature, a delight in one's own sense of understanding, a delight in creating science. These delights may go back to primitive man's tales to his children, tales about the world and its nature, tales of the gods. We can read wonder and delight in stone-age man's drawings; he watched animals with intense appreciation and delighted in his art. And we meet wonder and delight in scientists of every age who make their science *an art of understanding nature*.

As scientists, we have travelled a long way from capricious gods to orderly rules; but all the way we have been driven by strong forces: a sense of urgent curiosity and a sense of delight.

Fear and anxiety, wonder and delight— these are two aspects of *awe*, mainspring of both science and religion. Lucretius held, 2000 years ago, that "Science liberates man from the terror of the gods."

Facts

Before showing how astronomy was organized into great schemes of thought, we shall review the knowledge that you—or primitive man—could gain by watching the heavens. If you have lived in the country you will be familiar with most of this. If you have grown up in a town this will seem a confusing pile of information unless you go out and watch the sky—now is the time to observe.

The Sun as a Marker

Each day the Sun rises from the eastern horizon, sweeps up in an arc to a highest point at noon, due South,[3] and down to set on the western horizon. It is too bright for accurate watching, but it casts a clear shadow of a vertical post. At noon, mid-day between sunrise and sunset, the shadow is shortest and points in the same direction, due North, every day of the year (Figure 3-2). The positions of the noon Sun in the sky from day to day mark a vertical "meridian" (= mid-day) plane running N-S.

In winter the shadows are longer because the Sun sweeps in a low arc, rising south of East and setting south of West.[3] In summer

[3] This description applies to the northern latitudes of the early civilizations.

the arc is much higher, shadows are shorter, daylight lasts longer. Half-way between these extremes are the "equinox" seasons, when day and night are equally long and the Sun rises due East, sets due West (Figure 3-3).

On the horizon—simple man's extension of the flat land he lived on—sunrise marked a general eastern region for him and the exact place of sunrise showed the season. The length of noonday shadows also provided a calendar. The shadow of a post made a rough clock. Although it told noon correctly, its other hours changed with the seasons—until some genius thought of tilting the post at the latitude-angle (parallel to the Earth's axis) to make a true sundial.

Stars

The stars at night present a constant pattern, in which early civilizations gave fanciful names to prominent groups (constellations). The whole pattern whirls steadily across the sky each night, as if carried by a rigid frame (Figure 3-4). One star, the pole-star, stays practically still while the rest of the pattern swings round it. Watch the stars for a few hours and you will see the pole-star, due North, staying still while the others move in circles around it. Or, point a camera at the sky with open lens, and let it take a picture of those circles (Figure 3-5). Night after night, year after year, the pattern rotates without noticeable change. These are the "fixed stars."[4] The pole-star is due North, in the N-S meridian plane of the noonday Sun. The star pattern revolves round it at an absolutely uniform rate. This motion of the stars gave early man a clock, and the pole-star was a clear North-pointing guide.[5]

The simplest "explanation" or descriptive scheme for the stars is that they are shining lights embedded in a great spinning bowl, and we are inside at the center. That occurred to man long ago, and you would feel it true if you watched the sky for many

[4] However, if you could live for many centuries you would notice changes in the shape of some constellations. Stars are moving.
[5] The procession of the equinoxes carries the Earth's spin-axis-direction slowly round in a cone among the stars, so only in some ages has it pointed to a bright star as pole-star. It is near to one now, our present pole-star, and was near to another when the pyramids were built. In A.D. 1000 there was no bright pole-star—perhaps that lack delayed the growth of navigation.

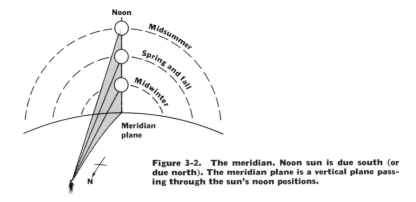

Figure 3-2. The meridian. Noon sun is due south (or due north). The meridian plane is a vertical plane passing through the sun's noon positions.

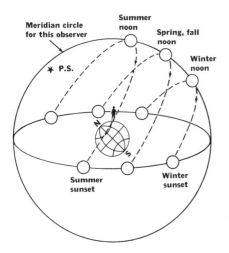

Figure 3-3. The path of the sun in the sky changes with the seasons.

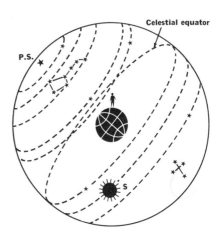

Figure 3-4. The star pattern revolves.

Lick Observatory

Figure 3-5. A photograph of the sky near the Pole Star, taken in an eight-hour exposure. The Pole Star itself made the very heavy trail near the center.

nights. It was a clever thinker who extended the bowl to a complete sphere, of which we see only half at a time. This is the celestial sphere, with its axis running through the pole-star and a celestial equator that is an extension of the Earth's equator. The celestial sphere revolves steadily, carrying all the stars, once in 24 hours. The Sun is too dazzling for us to see the stars by day, so we only see the stars that are in the celestial hemisphere above us at night, when the Sun is in the other hemisphere below. The Sun's daily path across the sky is near the celestial equator; but it wobbles above and below in the course of the year, 23½% N in summer, 23½% S in winter (Figures 3-6 to 3-8).

Though the pattern of stars has unchanging shape, we do not see it in the same position night after night. As the seasons run, the part of the pattern overhead at midnight shifts westward and a new part takes its place, a whole cycle taking a year. Stars that set an hour after sunset are 1° lower in the West next time and set a few minutes earlier; and two weeks later they are level with the Sun and set at sunset. Thus, in 24 hours the celestial sphere makes a little more than

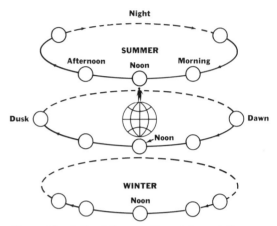

Figure 3-7. Path of the sun. Viewed from stationary earth, at various seasons. Sun positions are labeled noon, afternoon, and so on, for observers in the longitude of New York. If an observer could watch continuously, unobstructed by the earth, he would see the sun perform the "spiral of circles" sketched in Figure 3-8, during the course of six months from summer to winter; then he would see the sun spiral upwards, revolving the same way, from winter to summer.

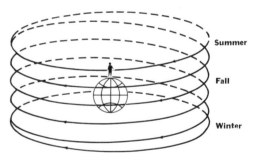

Figure 3-8. The sun's spiral of circles, in the course of half a year of seasons.

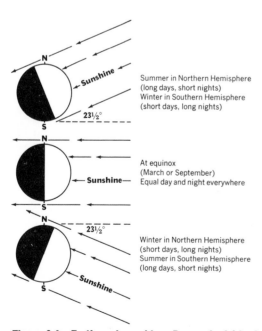

Figure 3-6. Earth and sunshine. Day and night at various seasons.

one revolution: 360° + about 1°. It is moving a little faster than the Sun, which makes one revolution, from due South to due South in the 24 hours from noon to noon. The celestial sphere of stars makes one extra complete revolution in a year.

Sun and Stars

This difference between the Sun's daily motion and that of the stars (really due to the Earth's motion in its orbit round the Sun) was obvious, and suggested that the Sun is moved by a separate agent. The Sun-god became a central figure in many primitive religions, and his travels were carefully traced by shadows and recorded by alignments of great stones in ceremonial temples.

Instead of saying the star pattern "gains" (like a clock running fast) 1° a day, we take the very constant star motion as our standard and say the Sun lags behind it 1° a day. We may stick the Sun as well as the stars on the inside of the celestial sphere; but since the Sun lags behind the stars it does not stay in a fixed place in the starry sphere; it crawls slowly *backwards* round the inside of the sphere, making a complete circuit in a year. Thus we can picture the Sun's motion compounded of a *daily motion shared with the stars* of the celestial sphere and a *yearly motion backward through the star pattern*.

Ecliptic and Zodiac

This is a sophisticated idea, a piece of scientific analysis: to separate out the Sun's yearly motion from its daily motion across the sky with the star-pattern. Once this idea was clear it was easy to map the Sun's yearly track among the stars—not directly, because the Sun outglares the nearby stars by day, but by simple reference to the pattern of stars in the sky at midnight instead of noon. The Sun's yearly track is not the celestial equator but a tilted circle making 23½° with the equator. It is this tilt that makes the Sun's *daily* path across the sky change with the seasons. At the equinoxes the Sun's yearly track crosses the equator. In summer, the tilted track has carried the daily path 23½° higher in the sky and in winter 23½° lower.

This tilted yearly track is called the *ecliptic* (Figure 3-9).

As the Sun travels round the ecliptic in the course of the year, it passes through the same constellations of stars at the same season year after year. This broad belt of constellations containing the ecliptic is called the *zodiac* (Figure 3-10). The constellations in it were given special names long ago by the astrologer priests, a named group for each month in the year.

A few bright "stars" do change their positions, and move so unevenly compared with Sun, Moon, and the rest that they are called *planets*, meaning wanderers. These planets, which look like very bright stars, with less twinkling, wander across the sky in tracks of their own *near the ecliptic* (Figure 3-11). They follow the general backward movement of the Sun and Moon through the constellations of the zodiac, but at different speeds and with occasional reverse motions. Primitive man must have observed the brighter planets but cannot have got any good use from his observations, unless like eclipses they were used to impress people.

Thus the zodiac belt includes the Sun's yearly path, the Moon's monthly path (Figure 3-12), and the wandering paths of all the planets. In modern terms, the orbits of Earth, Moon, and planets all lie near to the same plane. Astrology assigned fate and character by the places in the zodiac occupied by Sun, Moon, and planets at the time of a man's birth.

The Planets and Their Motions

Five wandering planets were known to the early civilizations, in addition to the Sun and Moon which were counted with them. These were:

Mercury and Venus, bright "stars" which never wander far from the Sun, but move to-and-fro in front of it or behind, so that they are seen only near dawn or sunset. Mercury is small and keeps very close to the Sun, so it is hard to locate. Venus is a great bright lamp in the evening or morning sky. It is called both the "evening star" and the "morning star"—the earliest astronomers did not realize that the two are the same.

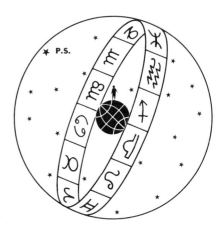

Figure 3-9. The ecliptic, the sun's track through the star pattern in the course of a year. Here the daily motion is imagined "frozen."

Figure 3-10. The zodiac was divided into twelve sections named after prominent star groups, or constellations. A belt of the celestial sphere, it is tilted 23½ degrees from the equator. The sun's yearly path (the ecliptic) runs along the middle line of this belt. The paths of moon and planets lie within this belt.

(a)

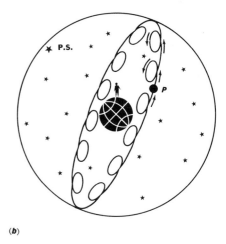

(b)

Figure 3-11. All the planets wander through the star pattern within the zodiac belt. Left, general region of a planet's path; right, in detail, a planet's path has loops —an epicycloid seen almost edge-on.

Figure 3-12. The zodiac belt with the positions of the moon, in various phases, in the course of a month. The daily motion of the celestial sphere is "frozen" here.

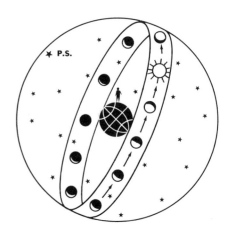

Mars, a reddish "star" wandering in a looped track round the zodiac, taking about two years for a complete trip.

Jupiter, a very bright "star" wandering slowly round the ecliptic in a dozen years.

Saturn, a bright "star" wandering slowly round the ecliptic, in about thirty years.

Jupiter and Saturn make many loops in their track, one loop in each of our years.

When one of the *outer* planets, Mars, Jupiter or Saturn makes a loop in its path it crawls slower and slower eastward among the stars, comes to a stop, crawls in reverse direction westward for a while, comes to a stop then crawls eastward again, like the Sun and Moon.

Figure 3-11 shows the looped tracks of planets through the star patterns. Once noticed, planets presented an exciting problem to early scientists: what gives them this extraordinary motion? . . . How can we explain (produce, predict) the strange motions of the planets, which excited so much wonder and superstition? We [will] study this [later] to show how scientific theory is made.

EARLY CONCEPTS OF TIME*
by Rudolph Thiel (1957)

There is good reason why the human race has been searching the skies for so long. For astronomy has given us the ideas of space and time.

It is hard for us to sense what it must have been like for human beings to live upon an unknown Earth, knowing only that endless expanses opened out in all directions. For them there were landmarks only in the immediate neighborhood. The world into which each person was born seemed limited by the horizon, "as far as the eye could reach," but the horizon always moved along from one place to the next. The ultimate boundary discovered by the boldest travelers was the ocean, but it too stretched on into infinity. Real stability seemed to exist only in the firmament. The sky appeared to revolve constantly, but its lights again and again returned along the selfsame tracks. The Sun, Moon, and stars alone enabled men to find their way about their world; these alone made possible orientation upon Earth.

"Orientation" originally meant directing oneself toward the east, toward the rising Sun. Direction, in fact, exists only in relationship to the sky; on Earth, all directions were blurred. . . .

* From Rudolf Thiel, *And There Was Light,* translated from the German by Richard and Clara Winston, Alfred A. Knopf, Inc., New York, 1957; by permission of Alfred A. Knopf, Inc., and André Deutsch, Ltd., London. Copyright, 1957 by Alfred A. Knopf, Inc.

Time Was Once Relative

Time was once relative not in a theoretical, Einsteinian sense, but perceptibly so in daily life. Each hour embraced a different span of time. At noon the hour was longer than in the evening or in the morning.

Nowadays, hours of different length are almost unimaginable. For us, time flows evenly. Yet human beings once thought otherwise. In fact, all earlier cultures had a sense of time entirely different from ours.

Men are not born with a concept of time. A child lives from moment to moment. The alteration of day and night sets up a rhythm of life to which everyone submits without thinking. In all probability the seasons, with their varying demands upon men, first produced a consciousness of regular, recurrent periods of time. The need to count days, to measure spans of time, coincides with a relatively developed form of life, such as farming. And astronomical observations were ready to hand when men, conscious of passing "time," began dividing up the day.

The first time designation was noon, the moment when the Sun's shadow is shortest. In order to determine it precisely, one of the oldest scientific instruments was invented, the vertical shadowstick. From this primitive device a logical but probably long and wearisome trail led to the sundial [Figures 3-13 to 3-15]. With the sundial, time was given concrete existence; it became, so to speak, something that human hands could make. The advance of the Sun's shadow across the graduated face of the sundial transformed an unconscious feeling more and more into a "conceptual" idea of a thing that moved, fled away, passed without man's intervention.

But to the Egyptian inventors of the sun clock, this something did not flow evenly; the speed of its passage varied. This may have come about by accident: it is noteworthy that the Egyptians marked out the dial of their sun clock in even divisions (Figure 3-13). For man does have an instinct for symmetry; when he divides any space, he tends to divide it into segments of equal size. But the Sun passes overhead in an arc, and

its shadow therefore passed across the graduations of the dial in different periods of time. The Egyptians made each of their hours a different length; moreover, they also adapted them to the season, the winter hours being one seventh shorter than the hours of summer.

It is evident that the Egyptians had no feeling for time in our sense. We cannot consider the idea of time an elementary component of our minds, or even indispensable for the ordering of our environment. "Time" is a fairly late abstraction, the end product of a long evolution in which the clock played a crucial part. And since the first clock was a sundial, in the beginning "time" moved at a varying, irregular pace.

So rooted did this idea become in the minds of the Egyptians that they arranged their water clocks to register hours of vary-

Figure 3-13. An Egyptian sundial.

Figure 3-14. A modern sundial.

Harvard College Observatory

Figure 3-15. A Chinese sundial.

ing duration. Incredible though it seems, they went to great efforts to do so. In the flow of water they had a direct image of steadily flowing time. But with extraordinary skill and ingenuity they artificially produced irregularity in a regular natural phenomenon, in order to make time flow in the only manner that seemed right to them: with the inconstancy of their sundials.

Centuries passed before they succeeded fully, as is evident from the inscription on the tomb of Prince Amenemhet, Keeper of the Seals of the New Kingdom, around 1500 B.C. Amenemhet is there praised for having at last succeeded in building a water clock that kept perfect time. His clock was able to dispense with the several jets of water formerly needed to measure the varying length of the hours. Its single stream could even be controlled to change the length of the hours with the seasons.

The probable appearance of this ingenious clock can be deduced from a late Greek water clock (Figure 3-16)—in matters of technology the Greeks were very dependent upon the Egyptians. The inflow of water in this clock was regulated by a funnel-shaped valve controlled by movable weights, and the length of the hours could be altered from month to month with the aid of a scale mounted on a rotating drum. Every hour a slave had to shift the weights, and every month he changed the position of the drum.

Egyptian time-measurement with its relative concept of time remained the model for all of antiquity. Athens, for example, was very proud of her Tower of the Winds, which in addition to a weather vane had no less than eight sundials, visible at a great distance from all directions. They told the time with an error of no more than three or four minutes, we are informed—a type of accuracy which makes us smile. Of course the duration of every hour differed; but the Greeks undoubtedly felt the same confidence in their inconstant division of time as do we in our infallible chronometers whose hands circle the dial with military precision. Human

Drum which revolves once a year, showing the hours varying in length according to the seasons. The vertical lines indicate the months

Figure which rises with float and points to the hours

Hole through which water enters

Container with float

Figure 3-16. As water pours past the weighted control valves into the container, the float rises, carrying with it the figure that points to the hours on the drum. The drum revolves once a year, showing the hours varying in length according to the seasons, which are marked by the vertical lines indicating the months. Every hour a slave had to shift the weights, and every month he changed the position of the drum.

Figure 3-17. Druidic ritual stones at Stonehenge, in southern England, were apparently used in part to mark start of the seasons. Note how time is indicated by the appearance of the rising sun through a pair of stones.

beings can grow accustomed to anything [Figure 3-17]—even to operating with two simultaneous and contradictory conceptions of time. The Babylonians and the Chinese did not fit their water clocks to their sundials; they let the water flow regularly. They there-fore had two different kinds of hours, the one changing and the other regular. As late as 1600, Father Ricci, the Jesuit who introduced pendulum clocks into China, adjusted some of them for absolute and some for relative time-measurement.

THE BIRTH OF SCIENTIFIC IDEAS*
by W. P. D. Wightman (1951)

Ideas like persons are born, have adventures, and die. But unlike most persons they do not disappear from this mortal stage; their ghosts walk, often to the confusion of new ideas. The birth of ideas, like that of persons, does not occur spontaneously, but is a culmination of travail following on, may be, centuries of gestation. Moreover their conception is often the result of a clash of cultures, if not of temperaments.

Until comparatively recent times it was be-lieved that science, like almost every strand of Western civilisation, had its origin in the

* From William P. D. Wightman, *The Growth of Scientific Ideas*, Yale University Press, New Haven, Conn., 1951. Re-printed by permission of Yale University Press and Oliver & Boyd Ltd., Edinburgh and London.

Eastern outposts of the Greek confederation. It was admitted that the Greeks had borrowed a good deal of assorted information of a practical nature from the older cultures of the East, principally Egypt and what is loosely known as Babylonia. But all this information was of a purely "rule of thumb" nature and hardly merited the name of science. Our views on this matter have recently undergone a profound change. Due in part to the enlargement of our knowledge of the quantity and quality of the eastern achievements, due perhaps equally to the enlargement of our conception of what constitutes science, we are in no doubt that science was born with infinite pains and in many places, neither by the happy inspiration of one man, nor at any clearly defined epoch. The flint knappers who learnt by observation, imagination and trial how to extend the range of the appliances obtainable from the single material at their disposal were assisting at the birth of science.

It is significant that all the early historians agreed that science had its birth at the outposts of Greece, namely where the vigorous young civilization was in intimate contact with a rich, if declining, culture. There was thus no doubt that the first speculative natural philosophers of whom we have any record were not creating something out of a cultural vacuum. To deny the title of men of science to those ingenious workers who created the technique of multiplication and division; who made an error of only one inch in the 755¾ feet base lines of the Great Pyramid: who discovered how to mark out the passing of the seasons by taking as a unit the lapse of time between two heliacal risings of the star Sirius—would be to narrow down the meaning of the term beyond what in this industrial age we should be willing to do. Yet, although the heritage of natural knowledge upon which the Greeks were able to draw is proving year by year to be far richer than was first supposed, nevertheless most contemporary historians would agree that although the Ionians did not create science they undoubtedly transformed it. The evidence for this is stated by Professor Gordon Childe, a writer who has done much to correct the former unjust estimate. In relation to arithmetic, the science in which Babylonia made the most notable progress, he says of the clay tablets which constitute the "documents": "It looks as if the research they disclose was really limited in its scope by consciously conceived possibilities of practical application. In any case no attempt was made to *generalise* the results" (italics mine). Herein lies the nature of the transformation effected by the Greeks. It was not merely that their problems were more "theoretical" in the sense of being more remote from the problems of daily activity—such a criterion for "science" would hardly be allowed in an age when the boundaries between "pure" and "applied" science are seen to be artificial and mere conveniences. What distinguishes the Greeks of the seventh century before our era from any previous thinkers of whom we have any record is that their concern is not with triangular fields but with triangles; their curiosity is not directed to the nature of the fire which is baking bricks but to the nature of fire itself. And they went further: they asked, if we can trust the testimony of Aristotle, writing three hundred years later, "What is the nature of Nature?" Lastly, with regard to mathematics, although in some respects they seem to have failed to garner the rich harvest of methods invented by their forerunners, they recognised, as the former did not, the necessity for deductive proof.

In a word, Greek thought differed from all that had gone before in respect both of generality and rigour. In general thinking, which opens up possibilities undreamed of by the severely "practical man," we pass from percepts—things to which we can point, like triangular fields—to concepts—creations of the process known as abstraction. If we ignore everything about a number of fields except the fact that they all happen to have three sides, we have arrived at the concept of triangularity. We cannot point to a triangle, because in order that triangularity may be manifested there must be something else—a hedge, a pencil line—and our abstraction has thereby become merged in the concrete instance. Moreover, since we cannot point to a triangle, we have to define it in words, that is, in the form of relations between other abstractions, such as straight lines and planes, none of which "exist" in nature. What makes this type of thought so immeasurably more powerful than thought (in so far as this is possible) about individual instances, is that we can worry out by deduction all the characteristics that must "go with" triangularity as such. Thence we return to the concrete individual, knowing that in so far as triangularity is manifested in it, so also is an infinite number of other possibilities which would never have suggested themselves by mere contemplation of a three-sided parcel of land. Science is, among other things, the generalisation of perceptual experience by means of adequate concepts; the concepts grow with the experience; history is the record of their growth; philosophy, among other things, the critique of their adequacy.

It must not be thought that the Greeks from the outset knew what they were doing; or at any rate could have expressed it in intelligible terms, because the terms themselves were created by their procedure. The conscious recognition came to birth painfully in the thought of Parmenides (ca. 500 B.C.) and especially of Plato.

In what follows we shall therefore take it as proved that so far as the existing evidence goes the birth of scientific IDEAS took place in Asia Minor in the seventh century B.C., on the ground that at that time and place the idea of nature as a whole first took shape, was explicitly stated, and systematically expounded. In our study of the growth of scientific ideas we shall therefore take as our starting point the same thinker as has traditionally been regarded as the founder of science, Thales of Miletos. . . .

Our aim therefore in Collingwood's phrase is to relive the ideas of the past in order that, by watching them grow, we may the better understand what scientific ideas really are. Incidentally we shall come to see, as President Conant has pointed out, how completely false is the belief in the triumphal march of science down the ages. Progress has resembled much more closely the infiltration of modern war,

in which tactical objectives have been seized by bold leaps, and held precariously while the main body has been slowly consolidating the ground in the rear. This explains perhaps the frequent and disconcerting inconsistencies of great thinkers.

All Nature for Their Province

There is no doubt that sometime in the seventh century before our era, probably between 630 and 620,[1] there was born at Miletos the man Thales, whom later Greeks counted as one of the Seven Sages. We can place the date of his birth fairly accurately because of the tradition reported by the historian Herodotus that he foretold an eclipse of the sun which put an end to the war between Lydians and the Medes. If this is true, it was a lucky shot; but even if it is no more than a fable, it gives us a good idea of the sort of problems people were interested in at that time. It also suggests that he was acquainted with Babylonian astronomy, in particular of the cycle of relationships between the sun and the moon as viewed from the earth, known as the Saros. Of his writings—if there were any—we know nothing; though Diogenes Laertius, a writer of the second century A.D., reports a belief that Thales wrote a book on astronomy for sailors—a significant suggestion even if unfounded. Of his reported sayings Aristotle mentions three: (a) All things are made of water on which the earth floats; (b) All things are full of "gods,"; (c) The lodestone and amber have souls.

To anyone whose knowledge of science was restricted to the standpoint of the present day these sayings would appear as childish nonsense. It is only because we are aware of the gradual development and modification of these views by his contemporaries, and of the further fact that no one before Thales seems to have put forward views of a like kind, that we revere him as the founder of natural philosophy, and through that, though at a considerable remove, of natural science. If we are to appreciate the greatness of Thales we must divest our minds at once of any idea

[1] All dates of pre-Socratic thinkers are to be regarded as approximate only.

that he was trying to found the science of chemistry on the orderly but ungeneralised observations of the copper smelters, glass-makers, and dyers of Egypt and Babylonia. Chemistry as we now know it is concerned with the composition and interaction of "pure" substance. . . . To take an example: pure salt is composed exclusively of the elements sodium and chlorine and contains no water; but *pure salt* is a product of modern laboratory technique and virtually did not exist in Thales' day. Thales on the other hand was dealing with things as they are, and not with things neatly sorted and cleaned up by chemists. His dictum then, though certainly not wholly true, was, at its face value, very far from being nonsense. The greater part of the earth's surface is water; water pervades every region of our atmosphere; life as we know it is impossible without water; water is the nearest approach to the alchemists' dream of a universal solvent; water disappears when fanned by the wind, and falls again from the clouds as rain; ice turns into water as does the snow that falls from the skies; and a whole country surrounded by a barren desert is fertile, rich, and populous because a huge mass of water sweeps through it annually. All these facts—the last particularly, for we know that he had spent much time in Egypt—gave Thales good grounds for thinking that *if there is any one thing at the basis of all nature*, that thing must be water. If there is any one thing! This supposition, that is to say, the asking as it were of this question, constitutes Thales' claim to immortality. The fact that he made a guess at the answer, and a pretty good guess at that, is of minor importance. If he had championed the cause of treacle as the sole "element" he would still have been rightly honoured as the father of speculative science. True, others before him (such as Homer and Hesiod) had sketched the origin of the world from one substance, but they were not content to deal with *verae causae*, that is with things whose existence can be verified by observation. To attempt to explain the origin and process of the world by having recourse to gods and spirits endowed with special powers, is merely to beg the question, since the existence of such beings can never be proved (nor of course disproved) by the means wherewith we know the world. In a word, it was Thales who first attempted to explain the variety of nature as the modifications of something in nature.

What of the other sayings of Thales? Here we are on more debatable ground. Most historians are agreed that they not only imply a theory as to the "go" of things, but also that the "go" is part of the stuff. . . . As usual Aristotle seems to be our safest guide, and he states that Thales "was led to this probably by the observation that the nutriment of all things was moist, and that heat itself is generated by moisture, and living beings live by it. . . ." Now if we take this in conjunction with the saying about the magnet we cannot doubt but that Thales regarded nature as a single immense organism composed of lesser organisms of which the earth was one, and also every tree and stone upon it.

At a superficial glance this attempt to explain the "go" of things is merely a bolder and yet more fantastic form of the myths in which the earlier poets, Homer and Hesiod, saw the "creation" of the earth out of the ocean, and filled every tree and brook with a god or nymph. But there is a subtle change in the emphasis; the gods and nymphs of mythology were human persons writ large— the products of the poetic fancy. The "gods" and "souls" of Thales were conceived, so it seems, as part of the nature of the natural object regarded as an organism. This is a vital step towards objectivity, that is towards the placing of man within the wider system of nature. It is not yet pure objectivity; that lies far ahead.

Why was this all-important step taken in such a way as to make the new world-view so fantastic? Here we have an example of the necessity to place ourselves as far as possible at the standpoint of the thinker we are considering. Divesting ourselves of all preoccupations with airborne microbes and the technique of sterilisation we see at once that the boundary between the living and the non-living fades out. The cattle graze upon the grass; the grass feeds upon the earth; slime feeds upon the rocks; maggots grow out of slime. Everything grows out of something else. What is man that he should draw a line between the grass and the earth, between the slime and the rock? But everywhere for growth there must be water; and for the fishes of the sea this alone seems to suffice. So the whole world grows out of water.

Seen in this light, is the picture any more perverted than that in which the soil with its teeming population is regarded merely as an anchor and a sponge for the roots of the trees we plant?

We may agree then that Thales asked one of the most important questions in human history; that the answer was framed in terms intelligible to his contemporaries, and in a form perhaps fantastic but certainly not nonsensical to us. Criticism may however be levelled at it on two quite different points. First, that the answer, even if a real answer, was barren, in that no useful consequences could be drawn from it for the improvement of man's lot. Second, that in any case it was in fact no real answer. The first criticism would never have occurred to the Greeks of his day. Speculation on the nature of things was restricted to the rich and powerful for whom an adequate slave population provided those amenities which were likely to be desired by thinkers of such temper. The second point of weakness was recognised implicity by his immediate successor, Anaximandros, namely that Thales had given no sort of clue as to *how* water could give rise to all the variety of natural beings unless it contained within itself something else with which it could react in some way or other; but in that case water as such could not be the primordial stuff. . . .

It is clear to us that a simple stuff can give rise to any form of variety only if it is either mixed with something else (in which case it would cease to be "the" material cause of nature) or capable of varying its relationships with respect to the space it occupies. The latter device was adopted by Anaximenes when he spoke of the formation of actual clouds, water, wind, earth as being formed from the ἀήρ by condensation and rarefaction. Though, as is inevitable with the pioneer, he is claiming for his principle of change more than it could achieve, yet when we think of the variation of form and texture which can be superinduced on substances held to be chemically (i.e. materially) identical (e.g. water, steam, and ice; diamond and graphite) by variation of the spatial relationships of identical units, we must concede to Anaximenes a permanent niche in the gallery of natural philosophers.

The first of the above alternatives, namely that there must be more than one primary substance (though the number may nevertheless be incomparably smaller than the huge variety of things which nature displays) was adopted by Empedokles of Akragas, who declared that four primary substances—air, fire, earth and water—are sufficient to account for all else.

Bless us, divine number, thou who generatest gods and men! O holy, holy tetraktys, thou that containest the root and the source of the eternally flowing creation! For the divine number begins with the profound, pure unity until it comes to the holy four; then it begets the mother of all, the all-comprising, the all-bounding, the first-born, the never-swerving, the never-tiring holy ten, the keyholder of all.

**Prayer of the Pythagoreans
addressed to Tetraktys (the holy fourfoldness)
(6th Century B.C.)**

THE MUSIC OF THE SPHERES*
by Giorgio de Santillana (1947)

Pythagoras

In the Island of Samos, about 590 B.C., was born the enigmatic character known to us as Pythagoras. When he was forty he removed to southern Italy, which was coming to be called Greater Greece because of the numerous Greek colonies on the coast, and there founded a brotherhood, with some monastic features, which lasted for about two hundred years and left a tradition which was still living in the early Christian centuries. Of his life we know little, and that for a significant reason. By his immediate followers, he was already recognized (like his near contemporaries, Zoroaster and Buddha) as one of those divine men who stand as mere names in history because their lives are at once transfigured into legend. He was, they said, the son of Apollo by a mortal woman. Historians recorded some of the miracles ascribed to his more than human powers. In fact, the later the story, the more wondrous. Here is one such transmission from late Antiquity; it is due to Hippolytus,† a Christian bishop.

[Pythagoras] . . . in his studies of nature, mingled astronomy and geometry and music and arithmetic. And thus he asserted that God is a monad, and examining the nature of number with especial care, he said that the universe produces melody and is put together with harmony, and he first proved the motion of the seven stars to be rhythm and melody. And in wonder at the structure of the universe, he decreed that at first his disciples should be silent, as it were mystae [adepts of the mysteries] who were coming into the order of the all; then when he thought they had sufficient education in the principles of truth, and had sought wisdom sufficiently in regard to stars and in regard to nature, he pronounced them pure and then bade them speak. He separated his disciples into two groups and called one esoteric [i.e., inner] and the other exoteric. . . . The early sect

* From *The Origins of Scientific Thought* by Giorgio de Santillana, copyright © 1961 by Giorgio de Santillana, published by arrangement with New American Library of World Literature, Inc., New York.
† Translated by Dr. Arthur Fairbanks in *The First Philosophers of Greece.* Quoted in *Selections from Early Greek Philosophy,* edited by Milton Charles Nahm, 3d ed., F. S. Crofts & Co., New York, 1947. Reprinted by permission of Appleton-Century-Crofts, Inc.

perished in a conflagration in Kroton in Italy. And it was the custom when one became a disciple for him to liquidate his property and to leave his money under a seal with Pythagoras, and he remained in silence sometimes three years sometimes five years, and studied. On being released from this, he mingled with the others and continued a disciple and made his home with them; otherwise he took his money and was sent off. . . .

Harmony and Number

Orpheus . . . had tamed animals and caused stones to rise into walls by the magic of his rhythms. Now, the myth of Orpheus contains a thought that took shape in the mind of Pythagoras. How can music possess this magical influence over the soul, and be the instrument of order already verified by the early legislators? There may be in the principle of life itself, and in the soul of man and of universal nature, chords that can answer to the touch of harmonious sound.

That is why Pythagoras taught that the soul is, or contains, a *harmonia*—the original word meaning not, as with us, a concord of several sounds, but the orderly adjustment of parts in a complex fabric, and, in particular, the tuning of a musical instrument. Now Pythagoras's one physical discovery, the original starting point of mathematical physics, was that the concordant intervals of the musical scale can be exactly expressed in terms of simple ratios. By changing the length of strings on a monochord stopped by a movable bridge, he found that the ratio of the octave is 1:2, of the fourth, 4:3, of the fifth, 3:2. These are the fixed intervals common to all Greek scales. The numbers which occur in these ratios are 1, 2, 3, 4, the sum of which is 10, the perfect number. So perfect and potent, indeed, that Pythagoras worshipped it as the Divine Ungenerated *Tetraktys,* "The source having the roots of ever-flowing nature"—a symbol of the Higher Unity wherein the One is unfolded.

Thus was the theory born: "all things are numbers"; which meant, in the old terms, "The nature of things is number." No use asking what it could mean precisely, in the moment of creative insight. There were in it centuries of thoughts and feelings unknown to us; the precise delicate twanging of the lyre bursting like stars upon the soul, turned into stars in the all-enveloping darkness of heaven; the One, the Monad of intelligent fire alone in the dark of Unlimit, populating that dark in mysterious array with units of fire like itself, as "the One begat the Two, the Two begat the Three, and the Three begat all things. . . ."

"In approaching the moment of illumination," writes Cornford, "the soul must have reached out with every power intent. . . . The final act of recognition must be overwhelming, because the truth, in such a moment of insight, is not presented as an intellectual formula, compact and comprehensible. It comes rather as an undefined mass of significance, fused in a glow of intense feeling. It may take years or generations for all the meaning and implications to be expressed in words. . . . When the feeling has passed, the thought is felt, an intellectual content distilled into the language of prose."

Of what happened in the early years of the sect little has reached us. Numbers seem to have been mainly figured as rows of monads. One such construction became fundamental. Take the row of integers as in Figure 3-18, and construct successive squares on them: the carpenter's squares or "gnomons" indicated by the lines "build" the successive squares of numbers: here is shown the virtue of the Odd, for the gnomons are the progression of odds.* The one alone is Odd-Even. The *Tetraktys* was a triangular number as in Figure 3-19, made upon the first numbers: $1 + 2$

* The series of square numbers is formed by the addition of successive odd numbers: $\boxed{1} + 3 = \boxed{4} + 5 = \boxed{9} + 7 = \boxed{16} + 9 = \boxed{25}$, etc. Ed.

$+ 3 + 4 = 10$, the perfect number, generated by the Monad and in turn conceived as generating all the other combinations of number and figure which made up what was called the *kosmos*, or "good array."

What could number come to mean in all this fermenting of ideas? There is no doubt that the Pythagoreans thought originally of physical patterns, such as are those engraved on the dice. Hence also the rather simple idea among some that shapes might be given by successive layers of gnomons or carpenter's squares, a naive kind of crystallography. And with it went a simple arithmetic of numbers made up of units, separated by gaps. But let us not forget that the "true" power of number, that which united knowledge with purification, had been discovered in the vibrating string. There it was that the *Tetraktys* rules, through the first four integers. Now, if the musical scale depends simply upon the imposition of definite proportions on the indefinite continuum of sound between high and low, might not the same principles, Limit and Unlimit, underlie the whole universe?

The System of the World

It was the Pythagoreans who invented the astronomical system of the world as we understand it. This may seem unfair to the Babylonians, who knew the planets well and computed their positions with extreme accuracy. But for them it was really a matter of special positions, like heliacal risings and settings, whose recurrence when due was supposed to confirm the stable intentions of celestial powers. What those particular stars did in between was of little concern to them; it was simply represented by columns of figures on the tables. The Pythagoreans, true to their geometrical conceptions, thought of orbits on the celestial sphere, and imagined them, like the rest of the heavenly motions, as circular. They were proper motions, from west to east against the 24-hour rotation of the stars, not simply a "lag," as before imagined. The moving stars were then called "planets," or "wanderers." The different speeds suggested different distances, and it is

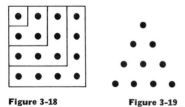

Figure 3-18   **Figure 3-19**

thus that we have, with some occasional variants, the present order of the planets, with Mercury closest to the center and Saturn farthest off. The yearly period of the Sun put it in third place, between Venus and Mars. As for the nature of the Sun, which must surely be apart, there were many theories, as we shall see.

The Earth was for the first time declared to be a sphere, for reasons of symmetry, and also because its shadow on the moon during eclipses was observed to be circular [Figure 3-29]. The author of this theory is said by some to have been Pythagoras himself; by others, more reliably, Parmenides.

As if this were not momentous enough, there follows in one or two generations another no less momentous development, for the abstract geometrical way of thinking in the School gave them a prodigious freedom of imagination. Once it had become clear that sun, moon, and planets describe orbits from west to east, it probably was felt as strange that the whole heaven should rotate so much more rapidly in the opposite direction. Would it be possible to account for this by still another motion from west to east?

Philolaus, who seems to have been the chief theoretician of the period around 450 B.C., came up with the bold idea that it was really that the Earth was moving from west to east which caused the apparent rotation of the heavens the opposite way. This was a stroke of genius: the immensity of the heavens became at once more natural in repose. But Philolaus did not imagine, as we might think, the Earth turning around its center. He imagined it on the model of the moon, revolving closely around a center while keeping always the same face outward [Figure 3-20]. And then he imagined another Earth on another circle just below it, keeping pace with us, and called it the "Counter-Earth." The only reference we have is a brief and unsympathetic account by Aristotle:

They also assume another earth, opposite to ours, which they call the "counter-earth,'" as they do not with regard to phenomena seek for

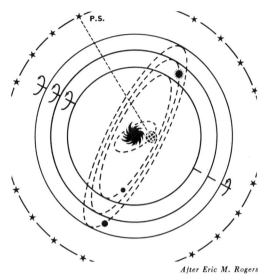

After Eric M. Rogers

Figure 3-20. Scheme of the Pythagorean Philolaus, who pictured the earth swinging around a central fire once in twenty-four hours. This accounted for the daily motion of stars, sun, moon, and planets. Then spheres spinning slowly in the same direction carried the moon, sun, and planets.

their reasons and causes, but forcibly make the phenomena fit their opinions and preconceived notions. . . . As ten is the perfect number they maintain that there must be ten bodies moving in the universe, and as only nine are visible they make the counter-earth the tenth.

This may have been for Philolaus a good reason, but certainly not the chief one. . . . there is at least one more good reason which is very evident. The sphere of the universe was conceived of as defined and bounded by the outer envelope of fire, the Olympus.[1] It stood to reason that its center might be of the same nature, as suggested by pure geometry. Philolaus postulated a Central Fire of the same Olympian nature, a "unitary harmony" around which the Earth and Counter-Earth revolve, with all the other celestial bodies, and he called it "Hearth of the all, watchtower of Zeus, altar, bond and measure of nature." In other words, the *archē* or principle must be at the strategic center. It is the only thing in the universe that does not move, while everything else does. The Central Fire

[1] This unconventional transformation of the abode of the gods may be prompted, as many other ideas of the sect, by relics of certain archaic images. A recurrent one is that of a mountain chain enclosing the course of the planets, called Elburs in Iran and Kwen Luen in China.

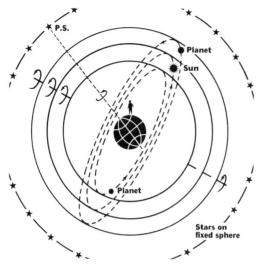

Figure 3-21. A later Pythagorean view pictured the daily motion of stars, sun, moon, and planets as accounted for by the round earth spinning. Then spheres rotating slowly in the same direction carried the moon around once in a month, the sun around once in a year, and each planet around once in that planet's "year."

After Eric M. Rogers

remains then hidden, not only from us who always face "outward," but also from the antipodes, since it is screened by the Counter-Earth. But its light, some said, is visible on the moon as "ashen light."

As the Earth goes around the Central Fire in 24 hours, all the effects are produced that we expect of the Earth rotating on herself. A question which was sharply raised was that the daily motion of the Earth on her orbit would make the distance of the moon from the Earth vary considerably in the course of a day, with a consequent change in apparent diameter. It was answered that the orbit was small with respect to that of the moon—a few times the actual radius of the Earth, which would have to be considered anyway if the Earth stayed in the center. But the objection may have moved Hiketas of Syracuse, a later Pythagorean, and Heracleides of Pontus, who was a successor of Plato, to make the Earth rotate simply on herself, with the Central Fire placed inside it [Figure 3-21] and this was the beginning of other great developments.

Another even sharper question was asked of Philolaus: if the Earth swings around the

Central Fire, should not the stars at the pole show a parallax,* i.e., an apparent counterswinging against the celestial background? The answer was that they are so distant as to make the effect unobservable. This was the correct answer and went on being so until Bessel's refined measurements in 1838.[2] With this the dimension of the heavens becomes really "astronomical" and immense. There were still at the time naturalists who made the sun be "pushed off" by the trade winds; a century or so earlier some of the "wise men" of Ionia had still thought the earth a pillar founded on the "deep," and surmounted by a brazen dome, which contained the "waters above." Now the Earth had become a "star" (a word which was still to arouse the ire of Inquisitors two thousand years later) moving like all other stars; the moon was "another Earth" and was supposed, as a matter of course, to have "trees and clouds and people on it. . . ."

* In order to understand the meaning of parallax, hold a pencil up between your eyes and a window. Now close one eye and look at a distant object, lining it up with the edge of the pencil. Holding the pencil still, close that eye and open the other one. The pencil appears to have moved in relation to the distant object. Now try observing this same effect as you move the pencil farther away from you. The amount of parallactic displacement decreases as the angle *A* decreases (Figure 3-22). If you could move your

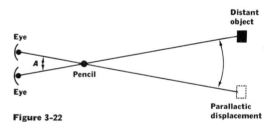

Figure 3-22

eyes farther apart the displacement would increase. Prop the pencil up on a table and move a few feet to the left, then a few feet to the right, making an observation at both positions, and you will see that this is true. You have increased the so-called base and increased the angle *A*. You have therefore increased the parallactic displacement. When the optical base is known and the parallactic displacement can be measured, it is a simple geometrical problem to calculate the distance.

If you wanted to measure the displacement of very distant objects, you would, of course, use the widest possible optical base. In Figure 4-3 the different positions of the earth in its orbit (E_1, E_2, E_3, and E_4) provide the largest optical base for observing the displacement of the stars against farther stars S_1, S_2, S_3, and S_4. However the distance between S and E is very much greater than that shown in the figure, and the displacement is too small to be observed without powerful telescopes. Ed.
[2] Galileo, once he had invented the telescope, affirmed that we would find a stellar parallax as soon as we had sufficiently precise instruments. The time came in 1838, when Bessel gave the parallax of 61 Cygni by alignment with more distant stars. In the same year Henderson measured Alpha Centauri, and Struve Alpha Lyrae. Even the nearest stars give a fraction of a second of arc. The modern unit for stellar distances is the parsec (parallax of one second).

Rhythm and Melody

The idea behind these closed circling patterns of periods-within-periods is that of the "choral dance" led by heavenly bodies, or, as Hippolytus said, "rhythm and melody." The idea occurs consistently through the early works to link astronomy with music; it accounts charmingly for the "hesitating" curves described by the planets in heaven, with their stations and retrogressions which will give so much trouble to the later mathematical astronomers. The precision of the motions, then, is that dictated by the rhythm of music.

But the over-all rotation of the sky, the obliquity of the ecliptic carrying all planetary motions in the opposite sense, seem to have suggested very soon, certainly close to the time of Parmenides (480 B.C.), the idea of separate concentric spheres as bearers of the individual motion. The "dance" is becoming geometrized, but the musical preconception remains deeply anchored. The cosmos was an ordered system which could be expressed in numerical ratios and which had partly revealed itself in the connection between the length of vibrating strings and their notes. The different radii of planetary spheres must then have harmonic ratios; they become comparable to the lengths of the string, and the angular velocities to the frequencies of vibration. Thus was born the idea of the "music of the spheres." The ones that revolve faster give a higher note than the slow ones, and all make up a harmony. "It seems to some thinkers," reports Aristotle,*

that bodies so great must inevitably produce a sound by their movements; even bodies on earth do so, although they are neither so great in bulk nor moving at so high a speed. . . . Taking this as their hypothesis, and also that the speeds of the stars, judged by their distances, are in the ratios of the musical consonances, they affirm that the sound of the stars as they revolve is concordant. To meet the difficulty that none of us is aware of this sound, they account for it by saying that the sound is with us right from

* Aristotle, *Metaphysica*, translated by W. D. Ross, in W. D. Ross (ed.), Aristotle's *Works*, Oxford University Press, Fair Lawn, N.J., 1908–1952, vol. 8.

birth and has thus no contrasting silence to show it up; for voice and silence are perceived by contrast with each other.

Two thousand years after Philolaus, Kepler tried his hand at reconstructing the "harmony of the world," but, not realizing the original meaning of the Greek word, he set up with infinite labor, out of the observed planetary velocities, a modern harmonic canon.

All this, including Kepler, may look very "archaic" compared to the achievements of the hard-headed Mesopotamian computers who had come before. It is. It turned out also to be more creative, reviving as it did vast proto-historic schemes of thought, combining precision with fantasy.

The way in which the Pythagoreans understood the cosmos corresponds to an almost lost state of consciousness—and we say lost because although we have some information we have no real representation of what ancient Greece meant by *mousikē*. It stands for an intrinsic union of *logos*, melody, and motion. Our Western poetry is preceded by great stretches of prose culture. Dante presupposes the Latin authors, the Bible and Aquinas. But in Greece philosophical thought comes of a background where technical prose was barely being born for the use of craft books and chronicles, and all serious thought still couched in the somewhat "poetic language" that Theophrastus notices in Anaximander. Even in the time of Cicero, the old laws were still chanted. The poetry of Homer or Pindar was essentially a "song," where the rhythm was dictated by the firm cadence and shape of the *logos* itself with its longs and shorts. The choruses of tragedy, like the religious hymns, were slow choral dances whose circling was marked by a subtle alternation of forward and back, a ripple and halting in the stance which brought out the free "numbers" of the song. The rhythm was not superposed, as is the metronome "beat" of modern music; the word and the act were as one body. To circle in the dance meant to experience in one's being the timelessness of first and last things, as expressed in the steady *logos* of the words. It all became, as it were, the substrate of speech, a direct ontological realization of the "divine" in immediate reality.

This is as much as to say that *mousikē* was not only an aesthetic experience as we mean it, but an activity closely tied to the poetic and the ethical side of man's being: something which affects and transforms the soul. An interchanging of tunes would make heroes out of cowards, as the story of Tyrtaeus in Sparta is meant to show, and the legend of Orpheus tells how the hidden melody of things can hold man and nature in its spell, once it is brought forth on the magic tones of the lyre. Apollo, the god of Pythagoras, is the power both of light and music, under whose strange song even stones had moved, "when Ilion like a mist rose into towers."

Towards the fourth century B.C., the old *mousikē* tends to fall apart into the more modern forms of music and poetry, and this may well be one of the causes for the eclipse of the Pythagorean school which supervenes at that time. Plato, in the *Republic* and then in the *Laws*, protests against the modern trend in the arts, which he calls a shameless mixing of styles and flouting of the laws, and advocates a system of education based on the pristine ways, right gymnastics and right music. The essence is, he adds, that harmony and rhythm should follow the "*logos* that is sung," and that the latter should be true, as the philosopher expects of the "*logos* that is not sung."

Against this background, the strict program of Pythagorean harmony stands out more clearly: silence, music, and mathematics. The soul must be kept clear to receive the true unspoken *logos*, "the secret language of the gods," in all its forms, from rhythm, number, and proportion to astronomy, and to grasp the connections between those forms which are inaccessible to discursive thought. The philosophical fragments of Philolaus and Archytas, in their fumbling, helpless style, make one think of men who would try to converse after a long sojourn in the region of silence. They lived among men, to be sure, they were versed in political counsel, they

even taught theorems, but their own creative thinking they knew not how to talk about; it belonged to their search, their inner experience, and their unformulated intuitions.

The Heliocentric Theory

. . . Heracleides [of Pontus] suggested that the center of revolution for the two lower planets ought to be the sun itself [Figure 3-23]; and as for the 24-hour revolution of the sky, he brought it back, reviving Philolaus's precedent, to a revolution of the earth itself. One perceives here the pursuit of some reasonably physical solution, and unmistakably in the Pythagorean vein, for it pointed the way to the sun's being the real Central Fire.

From the first the Pythagoreans had imagined a cosmos whose life came from the center outwards. . . .

The merit for having gone all the way belongs to Aristarchus of Samos, a great astronomer of c. 280 B.C. Like Heracleides and his own master Strato, he seems to have inclined to a corpuscular theory of reality, which remains the hallmark of the "physicalists," both Democritan and late Pythagorean [Figure 3-23]. He probably started by generalizing Heracleides' construction and placing the center of all planetary orbits in the sun, with the sun still circling around the earth, according to what we call now the Tychonian system, because Tycho Brahe proposed it in 1577 [Figure 3-23]. But he must have realized that this was only a way station towards a system making physical sense, for he came to the conclusion, as Archimedes reports, "that the fixed stars and the sun are immovable, but that the earth is carried in a circle round the sun which is in the middle of the course." The break-through had been achieved. This is what we call the Copernican system, and it was invented within fifty years of Aristotle's death.

Aristarchus was aware of the difficulties his system entailed, chief of which is the lack of an observable annual parallax of the fixed stars. Philolaus had already had to cope with that, but at least his own orbit of the earth was minuscule, and might not show up against the stars if they were kept at a reason-

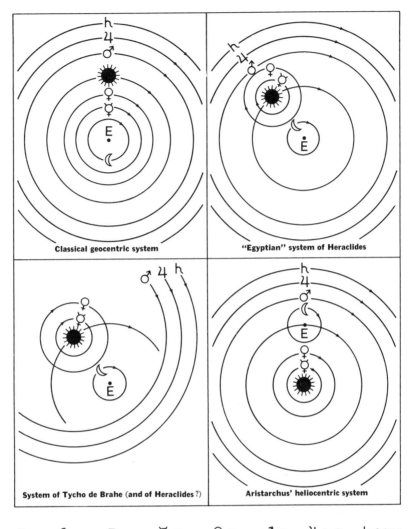

Classical geocentric system

"Egyptian" system of Heraclides

System of Tycho de Brahe (and of Heraclides?)

Aristarchus' heliocentric system

☀ Sun   ☾ Moon   E Earth   ☿ Mercury   ♀ Venus   ♂ Mars   ♃ Jupiter   ♄ Saturn

Figure 3-23. Four early schemes for describing the solar system.

able distance. But now Aristarchus had placed the earth "in the third heaven," going the Great Orb in a year in the place of the sun [Figure 3-24]. Could such a circle, too, be as nothing seen from the stars? It must be. We have for this, again, the reference of Archimedes himself in the *Sand Reckoner:*

He supposes . . . that the sphere of the fixed stars is of such a size that the circle, in which he supposes the earth to move, has the same ratio to the distance of the fixed stars as the center of the sphere has to the surface. But this is evidently impossible, for as the center of the sphere has no magnitude, it has no ratio to the surface.

The great Archimedes might have accepted this as only an image, instead of deploring his colleague's lack of precision. As an image, it can stand. It corresponds to saying there will be no parallax.

One wonders all the more, since such a passing slap at his colleague is really quite irrelevant to the subject Archimedes has undertaken to discuss, namely, is there a way to express numbers beyond the range of the ordinary Greek notation, e.g., the number of grains of sand that would be contained in the sphere of the cosmos. In fact, he has brought in Aristarchus only to have the support of his authority in supposing the cosmos

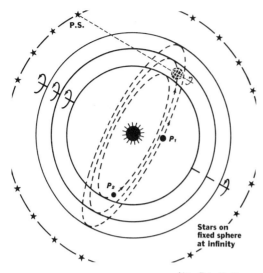

After Eric M. Rogers

Figure 3-24. Aristarchus' scheme, showing only two specimen planets. P₁ might be Mars, Jupiter, or Saturn. P₂ might be Mercury or Venus.

much larger than commonly thought. He might have considered, too, that the reasons for this poetic audacity on the part of Aristarchus did not lie only in geometrical relativism. They were mainly physical, and very novel at that. The only work of Aristarchus which has reached us is a little treatise *On the Dimensions and Distances of the Sun and Moon,* in which the first serious attempt is made at determining these quantities of observation. He observed the angle [MES] between the sun and moon at a time when the latter is half illuminated, that is, when the angle [EMS] is a right angle (Figure 3-25): a method ingenious but perforce miserably imprecise. He found 3° at most for the angle in the sun (it is actually 10′). From this he deduced that the distance of the sun must be at least eighteen times as great as the distance of the moon, and hence also the sun at least three hundred times bigger than the earth. A body of this size ought to be the center of gravity for the cosmos. It was all very well to say—as was being said—that celestial bodies move naturally and without effort in a circle, and that we should not apply our terrestrial standards of weight and lightness to matters celestial, impassible, and uncorruptible. Philolaus had applied them, when he "made of the earth a star," which

implied conversely that the stars are not without some earthiness either. Aristarchus had now lined up a massive argument in favor of that point of view. It would be reasonable, in fact, to assume that he made bold to suggest his Copernican hypothesis only after measuring the distance of the sun. He probably did no more than sketch it out (Archimedes says he "outlines certain hypotheses"); and Archimedes may have thought that this was not a serious way of dealing with a well-worked-out problem, where masses of quantitative data had to be accounted for. Still, it reveals on the part of the greatest mathematical physicist of antiquity, of the very man who had given the theory of centers of gravity, a strange insensibility to dynamic considerations. What Galileo was to feel intuitively, even before checking Copernicus's data, Archimedes did not feel at all. Was it the appalling esthetic disproportion involved in a scheme which left the solar system like a grain of sand in empty space? The fact is that he closed his mind to the new idea. This is almost the only clear fact which stands out in this strange episode of miscomprehension.

As for public opinion, it reacted almost not at all. This was too far removed from common sense to deserve comment. The philosophers reprimanded Aristarchus for speaking out of turn on a subject which they considered to be their proper domain. Cleanthes, the Stoic, scolded Aristarchus for impiety; others accused him of undermining the art of divination, which had recently been imported into Greece from the Near East. It was about the same general reaction which was to greet Copernicus. It was not strange.

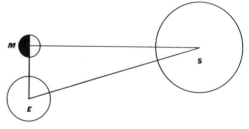

Figure 3-25. Aristarchus' method for measuring the distance to the sun from the earth, using the moon when it is half illuminated.

That was why the Pythagoreans had cloaked themselves in the magic and prophetic authority of the sect. A lone astronomer, speaking in physics only from scientific reasons, was alone indeed.

The astronomers themselves reacted coolly. They had by now become specialists, and had learned to mind their own business. They insisted that their business was to state the *how* and leave it at that. We know only of one who adopted the system a century later, Seleucus of Seleucia, an Oriental Greek from the Persian Gulf. For expert opinion, the system came probably too late to force a change of minds. Aristarchus had "saved the appearances"; he had outlined the proper symmetry of homocentric circles and velocities, but it was clear already that they could not be true sun-centered circles. They were again eccentrics with imaginary centers. Then to what profit upset the visible order of the skies and put the system of the world on its head?

THE THEORY OF PERFECT CIRCLES

EDITOR'S NOTE

The heliocentric theory of Aristarchus represents the culmination of one school of Greek cosmology, which sprang from the teaching of the Pythagorean Brotherhood. In following the logical development of this line of thought up through the third century B.C. we have passed by several important philosophers who made significant contributions to Greek astronomy (see chronological table). Now we go back about 150 years, to pick up the other school of cosmology, which also developed out of the Pythagorean concept. As we will see, this theory led to an entirely different solution to the problem of finding order in the cosmos, and it was this solution which was destined to be triumphant for almost 2,000 years.

Plato (428–348 B.C.) was deeply influenced by the Pythagorean idea of form and harmony as constituting the essential nature of things. He developed this idea into a philosophy of pure forms, which are intelligible to the mind and of which the perceptible world is just a shadow or an imperfect copy.*

* Plato's theory of pure forms, which we have not the space to present here, bears interesting analogies to the importance of form in modern atomic physics. To readers interested in understanding more about these aspects of Platonic theory we recommend Collingwood's *The Idea of Nature*, part I, chap. II, and de Santillana's *The Origins of Scientific Thought*, chap. 12. See Suggestions for Further Reading.

Plato's contribution to astronomy represented a small and relatively unimportant part of his vast philosophical system. However, the cosmological theory set forth in *Timaeus*, his principal scientific dialogue, did strongly influence the philosophers who followed him. Plato believed like Pythagoras that mathematics provided the most direct approach to an understanding of the inner harmony of nature. He reasoned that since the sphere is the perfect three-dimensional shape, the universe must be a sphere and all motion of heavenly bodies must be composed of uniform circular motions.

And he gave the universe the figure which is proper and natural. . . . Wherefore he turned it, as in a lathe, round and spherical, with its extremities equidistant in all directions from the centre, the figure of all figures most perfect and most like to itself, for he deemed the like more beautiful than the unlike. To the whole he gave, on the outside round about, a surface perfectly finished and smooth for many reasons. It had no need of eyes, for nothing visible was left outside it; nor of hearing, for there was nothing audible outside it; and there was no breath outside it requiring to be inhaled. . . . He allotted to it the motion of the seven motions which is most bound up with understanding and intelligence. Wherefore, turning it round in one and the same place upon itself, he made it move with circular rotation; all the other six motions (i.e., straight motion up and down, forward and back, right and left) he took away from it and made it exempt from their wanderings. And since for this revo-lution it had no need of feet, he created it without legs and without feet. . . . Smooth and even and everywhere equidistant from the centre, a body whole and perfect, made up of perfect bodies. . . . (*Timaeus*, Plato.)

CHRONOLOGICAL TABLE

Figure 3-26. The early philosophers.

ASTRONOMY INTO REASON*
by Plato (4th Century B.C.)

It seems to me that astronomy, as now handled by those who embark on philosophy, makes the soul look downwards.

How so?

I think you have betrayed no want of intrepidity in the conception you have formed of the true nature of that learning which deals with the things above. For probably, if a person were to throw his head back, and learn something from the contemplation of a carved ceiling, you would suppose him to be contemplating it, not with his eyes, but with his reason. Now, perhaps your notion is right, and mine foolish. For my own part, I cannot conceive that any science makes the soul look upwards, unless it has to do with the

real and invisible. It makes no difference whether a person stares stupidly at the sky, or looks with half-shut eyes upon the ground; so long as he is trying to study any sensible object, I deny that he can ever be said to have learned anything, because no objects of sense admit of scientific treatment; and I maintain that his soul is looking downwards, not upwards, though he may be lying on his back, like a swimmer, to study, either in the sea, or on dry land.

I am rightly punished, he rejoined; for I deserved your rebuke. But pray what did you mean by saying that astronomy ought to be studied on a system very different from the present one, if it is to be studied profitably for the purposes that we have in view?

I will tell you. Since this fretted sky is still

* From *The Republic*, book VII. Dialogue between Socrates and Glaucon.

a part of the visible world, we are bound to regard it, though the most beautiful and perfect of visible things, as far inferior nevertheless to those true revolutions, which real velocity, and real slowness, existing in true number, and in all true forms, accomplish relatively to each other, carrying with them all that they contain: which are verily apprehensible by reason and thought, but not by sight. Or do you think differently?

No, indeed, he replied.

Therefore we must employ that fretted sky as a pattern or plan to forward the study which aims at those higher objects, just as we might employ diagrams, which fell in our way, curiously drawn and elaborated by Daedalus or some other artist or draughtsman. For, I imagine, a person acquainted with geometry, on seeing such diagrams, would think most beautifully finished, but would hold it ridiculous to study them seriously in the hope of detecting thereby the truths of equality, or duplicity, or any other ratio.

No doubt it would be ridiculous.

And do you not think that the genuine astronomer will view with the same feelings the motions of the stars? That is to say, will he not regard the heaven itself, and the bodies, which it contains, as framed by the heavenly architect with the utmost beauty of which such works are susceptible? But as to the proportion which the day bears to the night, both to the month, the month to the year, and the other stars to the sun and moon, and to one another,—will he not, think you, look down upon the man who believes such corporeal and visible objects to be changeless and exempt from all perturbations; and will he not hold it absurd to bestow extraordinary pains on the endeavour to apprehend their true condition?

Yes, I quite think so, now that I hear you suggest it.

Hence, we shall pursue astronomy with the help of problems, just as we pursue geometry: but we shall let the heavenly bodies alone, if it is our design to become really acquainted with astronomy, and by that means to convert the natural intelligence of the soul from a useless into a useful possession.

The plan which you prescribe, said he, is, I am confident, many times more laborious than the present mode of studying astronomy.

Yes, I replied; and I imagine we shall prescribe every thing else on the same scale, if we are to be of any use as legislators. But to proceed: what other science in point can you suggest?

I cannot suggest any, on such short notice.

Well, motion, if I am not mistaken, admits of certainly more than one variety: a perfect enumeration of these varieties may perhaps be supplied by some learned philosopher. Those which are manifest to people like us are two in number.

Pray what are they?

We have already described one; the other is its counterpart.

What is that?

It would seem, I replied, that our ears were intended to detect harmonious movements, just as our eyes were intended to detect the motions of the heavenly bodies; and that these constitute in a manner two sister sciences, as the Pythagoreans assert, and as we, Glaucon, are ready to grant. If not, what other course do we take?

We take the course you mentioned first: we grant the fact.

Then, as the business promises to be a long one, we will consult the Pythagoreans upon this question, and perhaps upon some other questions too,—maintaining, meanwhile, our own principle intact.

What principle do you mean?

Never to let our pupils attempt to study any imperfect branch of these sciences, or anything that ever fails to arrive ultimately at that point which all things ought to reach, as we said just now in treating of astronomy. For you can scarcely be ignorant that harmony also is treated just like astronomy in this,—that its professors, like the astronomers, are content to measure the notes and concords distinguished by the ear, one against another and therefore toil without result.

Yes, indeed, and they make themselves quite ridiculous. They talk about "repetitions," and apply their ears closely, as if they were bent on extracting a note from their neighbours:

and then one party asserts that an intermediate sound can still be detected, which is the smallest interval, and ought to be the unit of measure; while the other party contends that now the sounds are identical,—both alike postponing their reason to their ears.

I see you are alluding to those good men who tease and torture the chords, and rack them upon the pegs. But not to make the metaphor too long by enlarging upon the blows given by the plectrum, and the peevishness, reserve and forwardness of the strings, I here abandon this style, and tell you that I do not mean these persons, but those whom

we resolved but not to consult on the subject of harmony. For they act just like the astronomer; that is, they investigate the numerical relations subsisting between these audible concords, but they refuse to apply themselves to problems, with the object of examining what numbers are, and what numbers are not, consonant, and what is the reason of the difference.

Why the work you describe would require faculties more than human.

Call it, rather, a work useful in the search after the beautiful and the good, though useless if pursued with other ends.

THE TRIUMPH OF A THEORY*
by Eric M. Rogers (1960)

[The first successful attempt to account for the planetary motions using the principle of uniform circular motion was devised by Eudoxus about 370 B.C.] He studied geometry and philosophy under Plato, then travelled in Egypt, and returned to Greece to become a great

*Rogers, *op. cit.*

mathematician and the founder of scientific astronomy. Gathering Greek and Egyptian knowledge of astronomy and adding better observations from contemporary Babylon, he devised a scheme that would save the phenomena.

The system of a few spheres, one for each moving body, was obviously inadequate. A planet does not move steadily along a circle among the stars. It moves faster and slower, and even stops and moves backwards at intervals. The Sun and Moon move with varying speeds along their yearly and monthly paths.[1] Eudoxus elaborated that scheme into a vast family of concentric spheres, like the shells of an onion (Figure 3-27). Each *planet* was given several adjacent spheres spinning about different axes, one within the next: 3 each for Sun and Moon, 4 each for the planets: and the usual outermost sphere of all for the stars. Each sphere was carried on an axle that ran in a hole in the next sphere outside it, and the axes of spin had different directions from one sphere to the next. The combined motions, with suitably chosen spins, imitated

Figure 3-27. Eudoxus' scheme of many concentric spheres. Each body, sun, moon, or planet, had several spheres spinning steadily around different axes. The combination of these motions succeeded in imitating the actual motions of sun, moon, and even planets across the star pattern.

[1] For example, the four seasons, from spring equinox to midsummer to autumn equinox, &c., are unequal. The Babylonians in their schemes for regulating the calendar by the new Moon had, essentially, time-graphs of the uneven motions of Moon and Sun.

the observed facts. Here was a system that was simple in form (spheres) with a simple principle (uniform spins), adjustable to fit the facts—by introducing more spheres if necessary. In fact, this was a good theory.

To make a good theory, we must have basic principles or assumptions that are simple; and we must be able to derive from them a scheme that fits the facts reasonably closely. Both the usefulness of a theory and our aesthetic delight in it depend on the simplicity of the principles as well as on the close fitting to facts. We also expect fruitfulness in making predictions, but that often comes with these two virtues of simplicity and accuracy. To the Greek mind, and to many a scientific mind today, a good theory is a simple one that can save all the phenomena with precision. Questions to ask, in judging a good theory, are, "Is it as simple as possible?" and "Does it save the phenomena as closely as possible?" If we also ask, "Is it *true?*", that is not quite the right requirement. We could give a remarkably *true* story of a planet's motion by just reciting its locations from day to day through the last 100 years; our account would be true, but so far from simple, so spineless, that we should call it just a list, not a theory. The earlier Greek pictures with real crystal spheres had been like myths or tales for children—simple teaching from wise men for simple people. But Eudoxus tried to devise a successful machine that would express the actual motions and predict their future. He probably considered his spheres geometrical constructions, not real globes, so he had no difficulty in imagining several dozen of them spinning smoothly within each other. He gave no mechanism for maintaining the spins—one might picture them as driven by gods or merely imagined by mathematicians.

Here is how Eudoxus accounted for the motion of a planet, with four spheres (Figure 3-28). The planet itself is carried by the innermost, embedded at some place on the equator. The outermost of the four spins round a North-South axle once in 24 hours, to account for the planet's daily motion in common with the stars. The next inner sphere spins with its axle pivoted in the

Figure 3-28. Part of Eudoxus' scheme used four spheres to imitate the motion of a planet. The sketch shows the machinery for one planet. The outermost sphere spins once in twenty-four hours. The next inner sphere rotates once in the planet's "year." The two innermost spheres spin with equal and opposite motions, once in our year, to produce the planet's epicycloid loops.

outermost sphere and tilted $23\frac{1}{2}°$ from the N-S direction, so that *its* equator is the ecliptic path of the Sun and planets. This sphere revolves in the planet's own "year" (the time the planet takes to travel round the zodiac), so its motion accounts for the planet's general motion through the star pattern.[2] These two spheres are equivalent to two spheres of the simple system, the outermost sphere of stars that carried all the inner ones with it, and the planet's own sphere. The third and fourth spheres have equal and opposite spins about axes inclined at a small angle to each other. The third sphere has its axle pivoted in the zodiac of the second, and the fourth carries the planet itself embedded in the equator. Their motions combine to add the irregular motion of stopping and backing to make the planet follow a looped path. The complete picture of this three dimensional motion is difficult to visualize.

With 27 spheres in all, Eudoxus had a system that imitated the observed motions quite well: he could save the phenomena. The basis of his scheme was simple: perfect spheres, all with the same center at the Earth, spinning with unchanging speeds. The mathematical work was far from simple: a master-

[2] In terms of our view today, the spin of the outermost sphere corresponds to the Earth's daily rotation; the spin of the next sphere corresponds to the planet's own motion along its orbit round the Sun; the spins of the other two spheres combine to show the effect of viewing from the Earth which moves yearly around the Sun.

piece of geometry to work out the effect of four spinning motions for each planet and choose the speeds and axes so that the resultant motion fitted the facts. In a sense, Eudoxus used harmonic analysis—in a three-dimensional form!—two thousand years before Fourier. It was a good theory.

But not very good: Eudoxus knew there were discrepancies, and more accurate observations revealed further troubles. The obvious cure—add more spheres—was applied by his successors. One of his pupils, after consulting Aristotle, added 7 more spheres, greatly improving the agreement. For example, the changes in the Sun's motion that make the four seasons unequal were now predicted properly. Aristotle himself was worried because the complex motion made by one planet's quartet of spheres would be handed on, unwanted, to the next planet's quartet. So he inserted extra spheres to "unroll" the motion between one planet and the next, making 55 spheres in all. The system seems to have

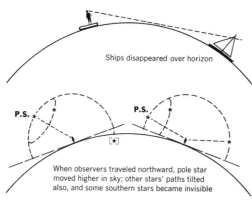

Ships disappeared over horizon

When observers traveled northward, pole star moved higher in sky; other stars' paths tilted also, and some southern stars became invisible

The Earth's shadow on the moon in an eclipse looked circular, not elliptical

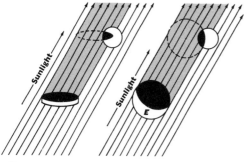

Figure 3-29. Evidences for a round earth.

stayed in use for a century or more till a simpler geometrical scheme was devised. (An Italian enthusiast attempted to revive it 2000 years later, with 77 spheres.)

Aristotle (340 B.C.), the great teacher, philosopher, and encyclopedic scientist was the "last great speculative philosopher in ancient astronomy." He had a strong sense of religion and placed much of his belief in the existence of God on the glorious sight of the starry heavens. He delighted in astronomy and gave much thought to it. In supporting the scheme of concentric spinning spheres, he gave . . . [the same reason as Plato] *the sphere is the perfect solid shape. . . .* By the same token, the Sun, Moon, planets, stars must be spherical in form. The heavens, then, are the region of perfection, of unchangeable order and circular motions. The space between Earth and Moon is unsettled and changeable, with vertical fall the natural motion.

For ages Aristotle's writings were the only attempt to systematize the whole of nature. They were translated from language to language, carried from Greece to Rome to Arabia, and back to Europe centuries later, to be copied and printed and studied and quoted as the authority. Long after the crystal spheres were discredited and replaced by eccentrics, those circles were spoken of as spheres; and the medieval schoolmen returned to crystal spheres in their short-sighted arguments, and believed them real. The distinction between the perfect heavens and the corruptible Earth remained so strong that Galileo, 2000 years later, caused great annoyance by showing mountains on the Moon and claiming the Moon was earthy; and even he, with his understanding of motion, found it hard to extend the mechanics of downward earthly fall to the circular motion of the heavenly bodies.

Aristotle made a strong case for the Earth itself being round. He gave theoretical and experimental reasons [Figure 3-29]:

(i) *Symmetry:* a sphere is symmetrical, perfect

(ii) *Pressure:* the Earth's component

pieces, falling *naturally* towards the center, would press into a round form.

(iii) *Shadow:* in an eclipse of the Moon, the Earth's shadow is always circular: a flat disc could cast an oval shadow.

(iv) *Star heights:* even in short travels Northward or Southward, one sees a change in the position of the star pattern.

This mixture of dogmatic "reasons" and experimental common sense is typical of him, and he did much to set science on its feet. His whole teaching was a remarkable life work of vast range and enormous influence. At one extreme he catalogued scientific information and listed stimulating questions; at the other extreme he emphasized the basic problems of scientific philosophy, distinguishing between the *true physical causes* of things and *imaginary schemes to save the phenomena.*

THE SHAPE OF HEAVEN AND EARTH*
by Aristotle (4th Century B.C.)

The shape of the heaven must be spherical. That is most suitable to its substance, and is the primary shape in nature. But let us discuss the question of what is the primary shape, both in plane surfaces and in solids. Every plane figure is bounded either by straight lines or by a circumference; the rectilinear is bounded by several lines, the circular by one only. Thus since in every genus the one is by nature prior to the many, and the simple to the composite, the circle must be the primary plane figure. Also, if the term "perfect" is applied, according to our previous definition, to that outside which no part of itself can be found, and addition to a straight line is always possible, to a circle never, the circumference of the circle must be a perfect line: granted therefore that the perfect is prior to the imperfect, this argument too demonstrates the priority of the circle to other figures. By the same reasoning the sphere is the primary solid, for it alone is bounded by a single surface, rectilinear solids by several. The place of the sphere among solids is the same as that of the circle among plane figures. . . .

Again, since it is an observed fact, and assumed in these arguments, that the whole revolves in a circle, and it has been shown that beyond the outermost circumference there is neither void nor place, this provides another reason why the heaven must be spherical. For if it is bounded by straight lines, that will involve the existence of place, body, and void. A rectilinear body revolving in a circle will never occupy the same space, but owing to the change in position of the corners there will at one time be no body where there was body before, and there will be body again where now there is none. It would be the same if it were of some other shape whose radii were unequal, that of a lentil or an egg for example. All will involve the existence of place and void outside the revolution, because the whole does not occupy the same space throughout. . . .

For ourselves, let us first state whether the earth is in motion or at rest. Some, as we have said, make it one of the stars, whereas others put it at the centre but describe it as winding and moving about the pole as its axis. But the impossibility of these explanations is clear if we start from this, that if the earth moves, whether at the centre or at a distance from it, its movement must be enforced: it is not the motion of the earth itself, for otherwise each of its parts would have the same motion, but as it is their motion is in-

* From Milton K. Munitz (ed.), *Theories of the Universe*, The Macmillan Company, New York, 1957. Reprinted with permission of The Macmillan Company.

variably in a straight line towards the centre. The motion therefore, being enforced and unnatural, could not be eternal; but the order of the world is eternal.

Secondly, all the bodies which move with the circular movement are observed to lag behind and to move with more than one motion, with the exception of the primary sphere: the earth therefore must have a similar double motion, whether it move around the centre or as situated at it. But if this were so, there would have to be passings and turnings of the fixed stars. Yet these are not observed to take place: the same stars always rise and set at the same places on the earth[1]

Thirdly, the natural motion of the earth as a whole, like that of its parts, is towards the centre of the Universe: that is the reason why it is now lying at the centre. It might be asked, since the centre of both is the same point, in which capacity the natural motion of heavy bodies, or parts of the earth, is directed towards it; whether as centre of the Universe or of the earth. But it must be towards the centre of the Universe that they move, seeing that light bodies like fire, whose motion is contrary to that of the heavy, move to the extremity of the region which surrounds the centre. It so happens that the earth and the Universe have the same centre, for the heavy bodies do move also towards the centre of the earth, yet only incidentally, because it has its centre at the centre of the Universe. As evidence that they move also towards the centre of the earth, we see that weights moving towards the earth do not move in parallel lines but always at the same angles to it:[2] therefore they are moving towards the same centre, namely that of the earth. It is now clear that the earth must be at the centre and immobile. To our previous

reasons we may add that heavy objects, if thrown forcibly upwards in a straight line, come back to their starting-place, even if the force hurls them to an unlimited distance.

From these considerations it is clear that the earth does not move, neither does it lie anywhere but at the centre. In addition the reason for its immobility is clear from our discussions. If it is inherent in the nature of earth to move from all sides to the centre (as observation shows), and of fire to move away from the centre towards the extremity, it is impossible for any portion of earth to move from the centre except under constraint; for one body has one motion and a simple body a simple motion, not two opposite motions, and motion from the centre is the opposite of motion towards it. If then any particular portion is incapable of moving from the centre, it is clear that the earth itself as a whole is still more incapable, since it is natural for the whole to be in the place towards which the part has a natural motion. If then it cannot move except by the agency of a stronger force, it must remain at the centre. This belief finds further support in the assertions of mathematicians about astronomy: that is, the observed phenomena—the shifting of the figures by which the arrangement of the stars is defined—are consistent with the hypothesis that the earth lies at the centre. This may conclude our account of the situation and the rest or motion of the earth.

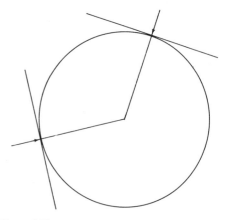

[1] The criticism depends on the analogy with the planets, following which A. assumes that if the earth moved with a motion of its own, as well as being carried round in the motion of the first heaven, its proper motion would be in the plane of the ecliptic and not of the equator. Were this so, the fixed stars would exhibit to our eyes the irregularities which he describes by the words παρόδους καὶ τροπάς; the pole-star would appear to describe a circle in the sky, and the stars would not rise and set as they do.
[2] I.e. at right angles to a tangent. Stocks explains the Greek as meaning that the angles at each side of the line of fall of any one body are equal. But does it not more naturally mean that the angles made by one falling body with the earth are similar to these made by another [Figure 3-30].

Figure 3-30

Its shape must be spherical. For every one of its parts has weight until it reaches the centre, and thus when a smaller part is pressed on by a larger, it cannot surge round it, but each is packed close to, and combines with, the other until they reach the centre. To grasp what is meant we must imagine the earth as in the process of generation in the manner which some of the natural philosophers describe (except that they make external compulsion responsible for the downward movement: let us rather substitute the true statement that this takes place because it is the nature of whatever has weight to move towards the centre). In these systems, when the mixture existed in a state of potentiality, the particles in process of separation were moving from every side alike towards the centre. Whether or not the portions were evenly distributed at the extremities, from which they converged towards the centre, the same result will be produced. It is plain, first, that if particles are moving from all sides alike towards one point, the centre, the resulting mass must be similar on all sides; for if an equal quantity is added all round, the extremity must be at a constant distance from the centre. Such a shape is a sphere. But it will make no difference to the argument even if the portions of the earth did not travel uniformly from all sides towards the centre. A greater mass must always drive on a smaller mass in front of it, if the inclination of both is to go as far as the centre, and the impulsion of the less heavy by the heavier persists to that point. . . .

If then the earth has come into being, this must have been the manner of its generation, and it must have grown in the form of a sphere: if on the other hand it is ungenerated and everlasting, it must be the same as it would have been had it developed as the result of a process. Besides this argument for the spherical shape of the earth, there is also the point that all heavy bodies fall at similar angles, not parallel to each other; this naturally means that their fall is towards a body whose nature is spherical. Either then it *is* spherical, or at least it is natural for it to be so, and we must describe each thing by that which is its natural goal or its permanent state, not by any enforced or unnatural characteristics.

Further proof is obtained from the evidence of the senses. (i) If the earth were not spherical, eclipses of the moon would not exhibit segments of the shape which they do. As it is, in its monthly phases the moon takes on all varieties of shape—straight-edged, gibbous and concave—but in eclipses the boundary is always convex. Thus if the eclipses are due to the interposition of the earth, the shape must be caused by its circumference, and the earth must be spherical. (ii) Observation of the stars also shows not only that the earth is spherical but that it is of no great size, since a small change of position on our part southward or northward visibly alters the circle of the horizon, so that the stars above our heads change their position considerably, and we do not see the same stars as we move to the North or South. Certain stars are seen in Egypt and the neighbourhood of Cyprus, which are invisible in more northerly lands, and stars which are continuously visible in the northern countries are observed to set in the others. This proves both that the earth is spherical and that its periphery is not large, for otherwise such a small change of position could not have had such an immediate effect. For this reason those who imagine that the region around the Pillars of Heracles joins on to the regions of India, and that in this way the ocean is one, are not, it would seem, suggesting anything utterly incredible. They produce also in support of their contention the fact that elephants are a species found at the extremities of both lands, arguing that this phenomenon at the extremes is due to communication between the two. Mathematicians who try to calculate the circumference put it at 400,000 stades.[3]

From these arguments we must conclude not only that the earth's mass is spherical but also that it is not large in comparison with the size of the other stars.

[3] I.e. 9987 geographical miles. Prantl remarks that this is the oldest recorded calculation of the earth's circumference. . . . (The present-day figure in English miles is 24,902.)

THE TRIUMPH OF A THEORY* (Continued)
by Eric M. Rogers (1960)

New Theories: Eccentrics; Epicycles

In the school at Alexandria, the bold suggestion [of Aristarchus] of making the Earth spin and move round a central Sun did not find favor. A stationary central Earth remained the popular basis, but spinning concentric spheres made the model too difficult. Instead, the slightly uneven motion of the Sun around its "orbit" could be accounted for by a single eccentric circle: the Sun was made to move steadily round a circle, with the Earth fixed a short distance off center. Then, as seen from the Earth, the Sun would seem to move faster at some seasons (about December, at A) and slower 6 months later (at B) (Figure 3-31). This was still good theory. For good theory, the scheme should have an appealing simplicity and be based on simple assumptions. These needs were met: a perfect circle of constant radius, and motion with *constant* speed round it. Such constancies were necessary to the Greek mind— in fact to any orderly scientific mind. Without them theory would degenerate into a pack of demons. Placing the Earth off-center was a regrettable lapse from symmetry, but then the Sun's speed *does* behave unsymmetrically

* Rogers, *op. cit.*

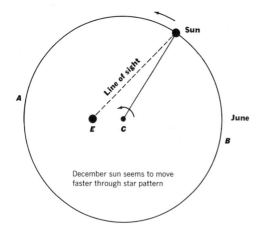

Figure 3-31. The eccentric scheme for the sun pictures the sun carried around in a circular path by a radius that rotates at constant speed, as in the simplest system of spheres. The observer, on the earth, is off-center, so that he sees the sun move unevenly—as it does—faster in December, slower in June.

—our summer is longer than our winter. A similar scheme served for the Moon, but the planets needed more machinery (Figures 3-32 and 3-33). Each planet was made to move steadily around a circle, once around in its own "year," with the Earth fixed off center; but then the whole circle, *planet's orbit and center* was made to revolve around the Earth once in 365 days. This added a small circular motion (radius EC) to the large main one, producing the planet's epicycloid track. The daily motion with the whole star pattern was superimposed on this.

Another scheme to produce the same effect used a fixed main circle (the deferent) with a radius arm rotating at constant rate (Figure 3-34). The end of that arm carried a small sub-circle (the epicycle) (Figure 3-35). A radius of that small circle carried the planet round at a steady rate, once in 365 days. Though these schemes operated with circles, they were described more grandly in terms of spinning spheres and sub-spheres. For many centuries, astronomers thought in terms of such "motions of the heavenly spheres"—the spheres themselves growing more and more real as Greek delight in pure theory gave place to childish insistence on authoritarian truth.

Hipparchus (∼ 140 B.C.), "one of the greatest mathematicians and astronomers of all time,"[1] made great advances. He was a careful observer, made new instruments and used them to measure star positions. A new star that blazed into prominence for a short time is said to have inspired him to make his great star catalogue, classifying stars by brightness and recording the positions of nearly a thousand by celestial latitude and longitude. He made the first recorded celestial globe. There were no telescopes,[2] nothing but human eyes looking through sighting holes or along wooden sticks. Simple instruments like dividers measured angles between one star (or planet) and another, or between star

[1] Sarton, *History of Science.*
[2] That invention was seventeen centuries in the future. By magnifying a patch of sky it enables much finer measurements to be made.

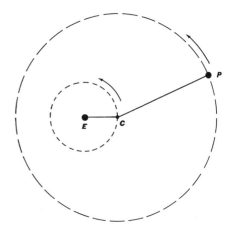

Figure 3-32. The eccentric scheme for a planet pictures each planet being carried at the end of a radius that rotates at constant speed; but this whole circle—center, radius, and planet—revolves once a year round the eccentric earth. (To picture the motion, imagine the radius CP continued out to be the handle of a frying pan. Then imagine the frying pan given a circular motion (of small radius EC) around E, as center, by a housewife who wants to melt a piece of butter in it quickly. Then make the handle CP revolve too—very slowly, for an outer planet like Jupiter.

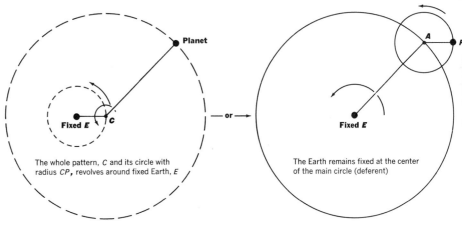

Figure 3-33. Sketch showing the machinery for motions of the sun and one planet.

Figure 3-34. The eccentric scheme and the epicycle scheme compared.

The whole pattern, C and its circle with radius CP, revolves around fixed Earth, E

— or →

The Earth remains fixed at the center of the main circle (deferent)

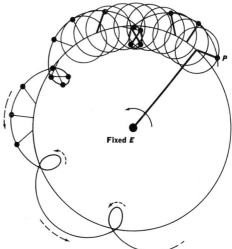

Figure 3-35. The path of a planet as pictured by the epicycle scheme, showing how the two circular motions combine to produce the epicycloid pattern that is observed for a planet.

and plumb line. Yet Hipparchus tried to measure within $\frac{1}{6}°$.

He practically invented spherical trigonometry for use in his studies of the Sun and Moon. He showed that eccentrics and epicycles are equivalent for representing heavenly motions. Adding his own observations to earlier Greek ones and Babylonian records, he worked out epicyclic systems for the Sun and Moon. The planets proved difficult for want of accurate data, so he embarked on new measurements.

From Greek observations dating back 150 years Hipparchus discovered a very small but very important astronomical creep: the "precession of the equinoxes" (Figure 3-36). At the spring equinox, midway between winter and summer, the Sun is at a definite place in the zodiac, and it returns there each year. But Hipparchus discovered that the Sun is not quite in the same patch of stars at the next equinox. In fact it gets around to the old patch of stars about 20 minutes too late, so that at the exact instant of equinox it is a little earlier on its zodiac path, about $\frac{1}{70}°$ after one year, nearly $1\frac{1}{2}°$ after a century. Hipparchus found this from changes in star longitudes between old records and new.

Longitudes are reckoned along the zodiac, from the spring equinox where the equator cuts the ecliptic. Since all longitudes seemed to be changing by one or two degrees a century, Hipparchus saw that the zodiac girdle must be slipping round the celestial sphere at this rate, carrying all the stars with it, leaving the celestial equator fixed with the fixed Earth.[3] This motion seems small—a whole cycle takes 26,000 years—yet it matters in astronomical measurements, and has always been allowed for since Hipparchus discovered it. The discovery itself was a masterpiece of careful observing and clever thinking.

Precession remained difficult to visualize until Copernicus, sixteen centuries later,

[3] The Sun's ecliptic path cuts the celestial equator in two points. When the Sun reaches either of these it is symmetrical with respect to the Earth's axis. Day and night are equal for all parts of the Earth: that is an equinox. Precession is a slow rotation of the whole celestial sphere, including the zodiac and the Sun, around the *axis of the ecliptic*, perpendicular to the ecliptic plane. From one century to the next, the creeping of precession brings a slightly different part of the zodiac belt to the equinox-points (*where ecliptic cuts equator*)—hence the name. The whole celestial sphere joins in this slow rotation round the ecliptic axis. This applies, for example, to the stars near the N-S axis, which is fixed with the Earth and $23\frac{1}{2}°$ from the ecliptic axis; so the motion carries the current pole-star away from the N-S axis and brings a new one in the course of time. Thus, in some centuries there is a bright star in the right position for pole-star, and in others there is no real star, only a blank in the pattern. In the 40-odd centuries between the building of the pyramids and the present, this motion has accumulated a considerable effect. In fact, by examining the pyramid tunnels that were built to face the dog-star Sirius at midnight at the Spring equinox, we can guess roughly how long ago they were built.

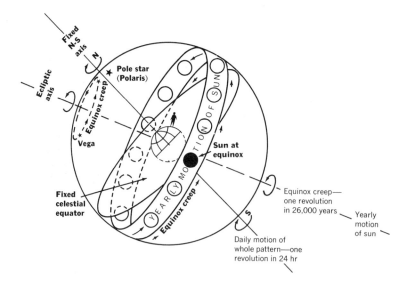

Figure 3-36. Precession of the equinoxes. In addition to the daily motion of the whole heavens around the N-S axis fixed in the fixed earth and the yearly motion of the sun around its ecliptic path in the zodiac band of stars, Hipparchus discovered a slow rotation of the whole pattern of stars around a different axis, the ecliptic axis, perpendicular to the zodiac belt.

simplified the story with a complete change of view. Even then it remained unexplained—unconnected with other celestial phenomena—until Newton gave a simple explanation. Discovered as a mysterious creep, precession is now a magnificent witness to gravitation.

Hipparchus left a fine catalogue of stars, epicycle schemes, and good planetary observations—a magnificent memorial to a great astronomer. These had to wait two and a half centuries for the great mathematician Ptolemy to organize them into a successful theory.

Ptolemy (∼A.D. 120) made a "critical reappraisal of the planetary records." He collected the work of Hipparchus and his predecessors, adding his own observations, evolving a first-class theory and left a masterly exposition that dominated astronomy for the next fourteen centuries. The positions of the Sun, Moon, and planets, relative to the fixed stars, had been mapped with angles measured to a fraction of a degree. He could therefore elaborate the system of eccentric crystal spheres and epicycles and refine its machinery, so that it carried out past motions accurately and could grind out future predictions with success. He devised a brilliant *mathematical machine*, with simple rules but complex details, that could "save the phenomena" with century-long accuracy. In this, he neglected the crystal spheres as moving agents; he concentrated on the rotating spoke or radius that carried the planet around, and he provided sub-spokes and arranged eccentric distances. He expounded his whole system for Sun, Moon, and planets in a great book, the *Almagest*.

Ptolemy set forth this general picture: the heaven of the stars is a sphere turning steadily round a fixed axis in 24 hours; the Earth must remain at the center of the heavens—otherwise the star pattern would show parallax changes; the Earth is a sphere, and it must be at rest, for various reasons—e.g., objects thrown into the air would be left behind a moving Earth. The Sun moves round the Earth with the simple epicycle arrangement of Hipparchus, and the Moon has a more complicated epicyclic scheme.

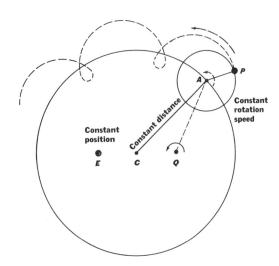

Figure 3-37. The Ptolemaic scheme imitated the motions of sun, moon, and planets very accurately.

In his study of the "five wandering stars," as he called the planets, Ptolemy found he could not "save the phenomena" with a simple epicyclic scheme. There were residual inequalities or discrepancies between theory and observation. He tried an epicycle scheme with the Earth eccentric, moved out from the center of the main circle. That was not sufficient, so he not only moved the Earth off center but also moved the center of uniform rotation out on the other side. He evolved the successful scheme shown in Figure 3-37. C is the center of the main circle; E is the eccentric Earth; Q is a point called the "equant," an equal distance the other side of C (QC = CE). An arm QA rotates with constant speed around Q, swinging through equal angles in equal times, carrying the center of the small epicycle, A, round the main circle. Then a radius, AP, of the epicycle rotates steadily, carrying the planet P. It was a desperate and successful attempt to maintain a scheme of circle, with constant rotations. The arm of the little circle carrying the planet rotated at constant rate. Ptolemy felt compelled to have an arm of the main circle also rotating at constant rate. To fit the facts, that arm could not be a radius from the center of the main circle, as in the simplest epicycle scheme. Nor could it be the arm from an eccentric Earth E. But he could save the phenomena with an arm from the equant point Q that did rotate at constant speed. Thus for each planet's main circle, there were three points, all quite close together, each with a characteristic constancy.

E	C	Q
the Earth in *fixed position*	the center of the main circle with arm CA of *constant length*	the equant point with arm QA rotating at *constant speed*

By choosing suitable radii, speeds of rotation, and eccentric distance EC (= CQ), Ptolemy could save the phenomena for all planets (though Mercury required a small additional circle). The main circle was given a different tilt for each planet, and the epicycle itself was tilted from the main circle.

Here was a gorgeously complicated system of main circles and sub-circles, with different radii, speeds, tilts, and different amounts and directions of eccentricity. The system worked: like a set of mechanical gears, it ground out accurate predictions of planetary positions

for year after year into the future, or back into the past. And, like a good set of gears, it was based on essentially simple principles: circles with *constant radii*, rotations with *constant speeds, symmetry* of equant (QC = CE), *constant* tilts of circles, and the Earth fixed in a constant position.[4]

In the *Almagest*, Ptolemy described a detailed scheme for each planet and gave tables from which the motion of each heavenly body could be read off (Figure 3-38). The book was copied (by hand, of course), translated from Greek to Latin to Arabic and back to Latin as culture moved eastward and then back to Europe. There are modern printed versions with translations. It served for centuries as a guide to astronomers, and a handbook for navigators. It also provided basic information for that extraordinary elaboration of man's fears, hopes, and greed—astrology—which needed detailed records of planetary positions.

The Ptolemaic scheme was efficient and intellectually satisfying. We can say the same of our modern atomic and nuclear theory. If you asked whether it is true, both Greeks and moderns would question your word "true"; but if you offered an alternative that is simpler and more fruitful, they would welcome it.

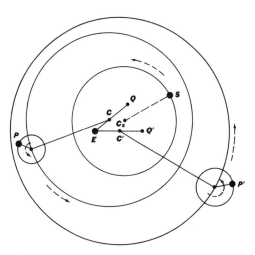

Figure 3-38. The Ptolemaic scheme for the sun, S₁ and two planets, P and P′.

[4] If this insistence on circles seems artificial—a silly way of dealing with planetary orbits—remember:
(i) that you have modern knowledge built into your own folklore,
(ii) that though this now seems to you an unreal model, it is still fashionable as a method of analysis. Adding circle on circle in Greek astronomy corresponds to our use of a series of sines (projected circular motions) to analyze complex motions. Physicists today use such "Fourier analysis" in studying any repeating motion: analyzing musical sounds, predicting tides in a port, expressing atomic behavior. *Any* repeating motion however complex can be expressed as the resultant of simple harmonic components. Each circular motion in a Ptolemaic scheme provides two such components, one up-and-down, one to-and-fro. The concentric spheres of Eudoxus could be regarded as a similar analysis, but in a more complex form. Either scheme can succeed in expressing planetary motion to any accuracy desired, if it is allowed to use enough components.

IS ORDER INHERENT IN NATURE OR IMPOSED BY MAN?

THE INSTINCTIVE CONVICTION OF ORDER*
by Alfred North Whitehead (1925)

There can be no living science unless there is a widespread instinctive conviction in the existence of an *Order of Things*, and, in particular, of an *Order of Nature*. I have used the word *instinctive* advisedly. It does not matter what men say in words, so long as their activities are controlled by settled instincts. The words may ultimately destroy the instincts. But until this has occurred, words do not count. This remark is important in respect to the history of scientific thought. . . .

Of course we all share in this faith, and we therefore believe that the reason for the faith is our apprehension of its truth. But the formation of a general idea—such as the idea of the Order of Nature—and the grasp of its importance, and the observation of its exemplification in a variety of occasions are by no means the necessary consequences of the truth of the idea in question. Familiar things happen, and mankind does not bother about them. It requires a very unusual mind to undertake the analysis of the obvious. . . .

Obviously, the main recurrences of life are too insistent to escape the notice of the least rational of humans; and even before the dawn of rationality, they have impressed themselves upon the instincts of animals. It is unnecessary to labour the point, that in broad outline certain general states of nature recur, and that our very natures have adapted themselves to such repetitions.

But there is a complementary fact which is equally true and equally obvious:—nothing ever really recurs in exact detail. No two days are identical, no two winters. What has gone, has gone forever. Accordingly the practical philosophy of mankind has been to expect the broad recurrences, and to accept the details as emanating from the inscrutable womb of things beyond the ken of rationality.

Men expected the sun to rise, but the wind bloweth where it listeth. . . .

There have been great civilisations in which the peculiar balance of mind required for science has only fitfully appeared and has produced the feeblest result. For example, the more we know of Chinese art, of Chinese literature, and of the Chinese philosophy of life, the more we admire the heights to which that civilisation attained. For thousands of years, there have been in China acute and learned men patiently devoting their lives to study. Having regard to the span of time, and to the population concerned, China forms the largest volume of civilisation which the world has seen. There is no reason to doubt the intrinsic capacity of individual Chinamen for the pursuit of science. And yet Chinese science is practically negligible. There is no reason to believe that China if left to itself would have ever produced any progress in science. The same may be said of India. Furthermore, if the Persians had enslaved the Greeks, there is no definite ground for belief that science would have flourished in Europe. . . .

Faith in reason is the trust that the ultimate natures of things lie together in a harmony which excludes mere arbitrariness. It is the faith that at the base of things we shall not find mere arbitrary mystery. The faith in the order of nature which has made possible the growth of science is a particular example of a deeper faith. This faith cannot be justified by any inductive generalisation. It springs from direct inspection of the nature of things as disclosed in our own immediate present experience. There is no parting from your shadow. To experience this faith is to know that in being ourselves we are more than ourselves: to know that our experience, dim and fragmentary as it is, yet sounds the utmost depths of reality: to know that detached details merely in order to be themselves demand that they should find themselves in a

* Reprinted with permission of the publisher from *Science and the Modern World* by Alfred North Whitehead. Copyright 1925 by The Macmillan Company. Copyright 1953 by Evelyn Whitehead.

Figure 3-39.   The search for order.

"Sculpture for the Blind" (1924) in marble by Constantin Brancusi.

"Composition in Black, White and Red" (1936) by Piet Mondrian.

Snowflakes.

Abacus, oriental calculating device.

system of things: to know that this system includes the harmony of logical rationality, and the harmony of aesthetic achievement: to know that, while the harmony of logic lies upon the universe as an iron necessity, the aesthetic harmony stands before it as a living ideal moulding the general flux in its broken progress towards finer, subtler issues.

REALITY IS A CONSTRUCTION OF MAN*
by José Ortega y Gasset

For centuries and centuries the sidereal facts of this world were set clear before the eyes of humans; yet what those facts meant, what they presented to man, what they made evident to him was by no means a reality, but quite the opposite—an enigma, a profound secret, a problem before which man trembled in terror.

Facts, then, come to be like the figures in hieroglyphic writing. Have you ever noted the paradoxical character of such figures? There they are, holding up their clean profiles to us so ostentatiously; but that very appearance of clarity is there for the purpose of presenting us with an enigma, of producing in us not clarity, but confusion. The hieroglyphic figure says to us, "You see me clearly? Good—now what you see of me is not my true being. I am here to warn you that I am not my own essential reality. My reality, my meaning, lies behind me and is hidden by me. In order to arrive at it, you must not fix your attention on me, nor take me for reality; on the contrary, you will have to interpret me, and this means that in order to arrive at the true and inward meaning of this hieroglyph, you must search for something very different from the aspect which its figures offer."

Science is the interpretation of facts. By themselves, facts do not give us reality; on the contrary, they hide it, which is to say that they present us with the problem of reality. If there were no facts, there would be no problem, there would be no enigma, there would be nothing hidden which it is necessary to de-hide, to dis-cover. The word which the Greeks used for truth is *aletheia*, which means discovery, to take away the veil that covers and hides a thing. Facts cover up reality; while we are in the midst of their innumerable swarmings we are in chaos and confusion. In order to discover reality we must for a moment lay aside the facts that surge about us, and remain alone with our minds. Then, on our own risk and account, we imagine a reality, or to put it another way, we construct an imaginary reality, a pure invention of our own; then, following in solitude the guidance of our own personal imagining, we find what aspect, what visible shapes, in short, what facts would produce that imaginary reality. It is then that we come out of our imaginative solitude, out from our pure and isolated mental state, and compare those facts which the imagined reality would produce with the actual facts which surround us. If they mate happily one with another, this means that we have deciphered the hieroglyph, that we have discovered the reality which the facts covered and kept secret.

That labor is what science is. As you see, it consists of two different operations: one purely imaginative and creative, which man produces out of his own most free substance; the other a confronting of that which is not man, but of that which surrounds him, the facts, the data. Reality is not a datum, not something given or bestowed, but a construction which man makes out of the given material.

* From José Ortega y Gasset, *Man and Crisis*, W. W. Norton and Company, Inc., New York, 1958.

THE SCIENTIST IMPOSES ORDER ON HIS DATA*
by Henry Margenau (1961)

Every observation, every measurement, indeed every perception, introduces errors. A measurement without error is an absurdity. Let the measurement (and measurement is after all only refined perception) be of a star's position in the sky, of the length of this table, of an automobile's speed, or of an electrical current; its outcome is never to be believed exactly. This is apparent in the circumstance that the same number will not ordinarily result when the measurement is repeated, regardless of the care taken in performing it. Characteristically, only the careless experimenter and the ignorant observer believe raw nature to be unambiguous. To be sure, the different numbers found by the astronomer for the latitude (and longitude) of a star in successive observations lie within a reasonable interval, and this convinces him that he is somewhere near a "true" value of the quantity he seeks, that nature is not fooling him with hallucinations. Yet in a very fundamental sense he is witnessing a behavior not unlike the lawless emissions of the microcosmic firefly; we thus see that even the macrocosm is not wholly without its vagaries, but that it confines them sufficiently so that the observer with some credulity can

* From Henry Margenau, *Open Vistas*, Yale University Press, New Haven, Conn., 1961.

feign their absence: he can blame himself for nature's equivocality and call the departures from a true value "errors."

But what is the *true* value? Let us look into scientific practice. If ten measurements of a physical quantity yield ten slightly different values, not one of them is necessarily regarded as true. Their *arithmetic mean* is singled out for this distinction, even though it may not have occurred among the measurements. The justice of this choice is not provided by the ten measurements, nor by any finite number of observations; it comes from a belief in, or rather the postulation of, a certain uniformity of nature. Thus the very determination of a true value, and in the end the selection of whatever is believed to be true perceptory fact, involves a reference to law and order not immediately presented in the sensory structure of that fact. Here we find the clearest expression of the attitude which has led to the development of deductive science: it relies upon rational elements to straighten out erratic data. It does not ignore the latter's presence, nor does it accept them unrefined. It distills from them an essence and *calls* it *true*. But the nature of the essence is partly determined by the process of distillation.

THE HARMONY OF NATURAL LAW*
by Henri Poincaré (1913)

Is Mathematical analysis, then . . . only a vain play of the mind? It can give to the physicist only a convenient language; is this not a mediocre service, which, strictly speaking, could be done without; and even is it not to be feared that this artificial language may be a veil interposed between reality and the eye of the physicist? Far from it; without this language most of the intimate analogies

* *The Foundations of Science* by Henri Poincaré, translated by George Bruce Halstead, New York and Garrison, New York: The Science Press, 1913.

of things would have remained forever unknown to us; and we should forever have been ignorant of the internal harmony of the world, which is, we shall see, the only true objective reality.

The best expression of this harmony is law. Law is one of the most recent conquests of the human mind; there still are people who live in the presence of a perpetual miracle and are not astonished at it. On the contrary, we it is who should be astonished at nature's regularity. Men demand of their gods to prove their existence by miracles; but the eternal marvel is that there are not miracles without cease. The world is divine because it is a harmony. If it were ruled by caprice, what would prove to us it was not ruled by chance?

This conquest of law we owe to astronomy, and just this makes the grandeur of the science rather than the material grandeur of the objects it considers. It was altogether natural, then, that celestial mechanics should be the first model of mathematical physics. . . .

Some people have exaggerated the role of convention in science; they have even gone so far as to say that law, that scientific fact itself, was created by the scientist. This is going much too far in the direction of nominalism. No, scientific laws are not artificial creations; we have no reason to regard them as accidental, though it be impossible to prove they are not.

Does the harmony the human intelligence thinks it discovers in nature exist outside of this intelligence? No, beyond doubt a reality completely independent of the mind which conceives it, sees or feels it, is an impossibility. A world as exterior as that, even if it existed, would for us be forever inaccessible. But what we call objective reality is, in the last analysis, what is common to many thinking beings and could be common to all, this common part, we shall see, can only be the harmony expressed by mathematical laws. It is this harmony then which is the sole objective reality, the only truth we can attain; and when I add that the universal harmony of the world is the source of all beauty, it will be understood what price we should attach to the slow and difficult progress which little by little enables us to know it better.

What we call thought (1) is itself an orderly thing, and (2) can only be applied to material, i.e. to perceptions or experiences, which have a certain degree of orderliness. This has two consequences. First, a physical organization, to be in close correspondence with thought (as my brain is with my thought) must be a very well-ordered organization, and that means that the events that happen within it must obey strict physical laws, at least to a very high degree of accuracy. Secondly, the physical impressions made upon that physically well-organized system by other bodies from outside obviously correspond to the perception and experience of the corresponding thought, forming its material, as I have called it. Therefore, the physical interactions between our system and others must, as a rule, themselves possess a certain degree of physical orderliness, that is to say, they too must obey strict physical laws to a certain degree of accuracy.

Erwin Schrodinger
What Is Life? (1944)

The man of science will act as if this world were an absolute whole controlled by laws independent of his own thoughts or acts; but whenever he discovers a law of striking simplicity or one of sweeping universality or one which points to a perfect harmony in the cosmos, he will be wise to wonder what role his mind has played in the discovery, and whether the beautiful image he sees in the pool of eternity reveals the nature of this eternity, or is but a reflection of his own mind.

Tobias Dantzig
Number: The Language of Science (1954)

We have found a strange footprint on the shores of the unknown. We have devised profound theories, one after another, to account for its origin. At last, we have succeeded in reconstructing the creature that made the footprint. And lo! It is our own.

Arthur S. Eddington
Space, Time, and Gravitation (1920)

ORDER PREVAILS*
by Forest Ray Moulton (1935)

It is from the fulfillment of perfectly definite and impersonal predictions by mathematical formulas that scientists have made their supreme discovery, a discovery that in a broad way is the most important one in the history of the world. Fortunately this discovery can be stated in the few words, *the universe is orderly*. Since this conclusion is of very great significance, it is desirable to explain what the statement means, the grounds on which it is accepted, and to consider some of its far-reaching implications.

In approaching the question of the orderliness of the universe, let us avoid as far as possible the partiality toward formulas of those who are skilled in deriving them and the awe in which they are held by those to whom they are a foreign language. Suppose we have derived a formula that gives the population of the United States at each of the fifteen decades from 1785 to 1935, and let us ask ourselves whether we can safely use it for predicting the population of the country in the year 1985. If we have derived the formula at the cost of a large amount of labor, we are likely to value it highly. But we perhaps suspect that a quite different formula might be consistent with the population for the century and a half. So we appeal to a mathematician having a profound knowledge of mathematical principles, and he tells us promptly that other formulas besides ours can be determined that will also give the population for each decade of the 150 years. Although we are disturbed by this informa-

tion, we still hope that, after all, these various formulas in some fundamental way may be equivalent, and that they will all lead to the same value for the population in 1985. Then the mathematician tells us that they may, and in all likelihood will, give wholly different results for all decade dates except those from 1785 to 1935. Consequently, we realize that our formula is not so fundamental as we thought it was, and that its agreement with considerable experience is by no means a guarantee that it will agree with experience in the future. The mathematician tells us, in fact, that he could construct a formula giving correctly the population of the United States for each decade from 1785 to 1935 and predicting any specified population whatever for 1985. Upon second thought, we see for ourselves that if we can develop a formula giving the specified population on sixteen dates, we should be able to derive one holding for one more date. Since there is nothing logically exceptional in the population problem, we conclude that formulas in general are not necessarily trustworthy guides beyond the experience they are designed to represent. They are, in fact, only precise and very convenient means of representing experience.

Now we find ourselves in what appears to be a very unhappy position. We have seen that not only can we construct our scientific theories, our models of experience, out of various materials . . . but we can represent the fundamental framework of a set of phenomena by various mathematical formulas. Just at this moment in our thought nothing seems to be perfectly determined and fixed.

We find ourselves suspended in uncertainties and longing for the restfulness of the absolute.

Before giving way to despair we note that many phenomena recur cyclically, and we inquire whether this fact may not be of profound significance. Day and night have followed one another in endless succession, not repeating exactly but nearly. The seasons—winter, spring, summer, autumn—have run their nearly similar cycles year after year, century after century across the periods of recorded history and interminably back into the geological ages. In longer cycles, perhaps 30,000 to 100,000 years in length, great sheets of ice have pushed their leisurely way down from the north to the latitude of the Ohio and Missouri rivers and have retreated again. At least five or six times in recent geological history these continental glaciers have ridden irresistibly over hills and valleys and lakes and rivers and have deposited their burdens of soil and rock on a million square miles of area. Even these great waves are comparative ripples on a larger tide, for the continent itself rises and falls as the ocean pulsates under the attraction of the sun and the moon. The huge heavings of the continents do not repeat themselves in centuries or thousands of years, but in millions of years. Time after time during the last 600,000,000 years the salty waters of the ocean have rolled over what is now prairies and mountains, as we know from the fossils of the marine life of those faraway days that are preserved in countless numbers in the rocks formed from the sediments which were deposited on the floors of ancient seas. Perhaps the earth itself is only one of a succession of planets which in the course of vastly greater periods of time revolve around our sun. However that may be, rhythmic succession of phenomena appears to be a fundamental property of the universe. This property is by no means limited to the astronomical and geological phenomena enumerated. It is illustrated in the succession of waves that determine the pitch of sound and those that determine the color of light. It is illustrated in the countless examples of similar objects ranging from atoms to stars [Figure 3-39]. It is illustrated by the beating of our hearts, our inhaling and exhaling, our periods of rest and activity, the repetitions of our physiological processes, the cycles of our lives from birth to the birth of our successors.

When we consider the matter, we find that the only general property of the universe that we know is that it continually changes and that nearly all of its changes with which we are familiar are at least approximately cyclical. If there is for us any pathway we may pursue to an understanding of nature, this is the one. Consequently let us follow it. We note first that our scientific theories, our models of experience, must provide for repetitions. Now it is evident that so far as the materials out of which we construct these models are concerned, we may use a different material for each model. . . . this property of a model is irrelevant. But when we come to the fundamental framework of it, to the properties represented by the mathematical formulas, the situation is entirely different. To simplify the problem to the extreme, let us suppose that the phenomena under consideration are strictly periodic; that is, that they are exactly repeated at equal intervals of time. Let us impose this condition and then ask the mathematician whether there are now many essentially distinct formulas which will exactly represent past experience. In this case he gives the expected answer and informs us that the formula is unique.[1] Under the hypotheses that have been adopted, the universe is orderly in the sense that its phenomena occur in regular and determinate sequences expressible by essentially unique mathematical formulas.

The ideal conditions assumed are not found, for, in general, phenomena do not appear to be strictly periodic. Even if they were, we should not be certain of it because all our observations are subject to possible errors. Hence our conclusion that the universe is orderly does not rest upon absolutely unquestionable observational evidence and reasoning. But the evidence in support of it

[1] Mathematicians will, of course, note that the variable quantity must be given for every value of the independent variable for a period.

is enormously greater and more varied than the evidence in support of any particular thing which we believe. All of science is a confirmation of it, except possibly in the domain of protons and electrons and photons, a field in which has arisen the Principle of Indeterminacy to which we shall later return. Not only are similar initial conditions always followed by similar consequences and nearly similar initial conditions by nearly similar consequences, but widely varied phenomena are unified under the principle that nature is orderly in the sense which has been defined. For example, the oscillations of a pendulum, the oblateness of the earth, the ebb and flow of the tides of the sea, the eclipses of the sun, the apparent motions of the planets, and a thousand other phenomena are completely unified by the law of gravitation.

Although the discovery of the fact that the universe is orderly depended upon the cyclical character of many phenomena, when the underlying formulas in any domain have been once established their consequences may be used for making predictions in hitherto unexplored fields. In a thousand instances mathematicians have anticipated astronomical observations. Newton calculated the oblateness of the earth before it was measured. Seventy years in advance of its reappearance, Halley predicted the return of the great comet of 1682. Adams and Leverrier reached out with the long arms of their analysis across hundreds of millions of miles and found the unknown planet Neptune from the slight effects it produced upon the motion of Uranus. The existence of the faint companion of Sirius was predicted, before its discovery, from periodic oscillations in the motions of Sirius. The formulas that describe the orderliness of the universe are our guide when we enter unknown regions. Those pertaining to astronomy are an intellectual telescope which enables us to look back in certain respects beyond human and geological history, and similarly forward to a time when the earth may cease to exist as a separate planet. By extending our knowledge backward and forward our scientific formulas in a sense make us immortal.

It was the cyclical character of astronomical phenomena that first suggested to men in ancient times that the universe is orderly. Now we find that the orderliness of the universe can be proved only from cyclical phenomena. If there were not repetitions in nature, it might indeed be true that such evidences of order as we think we find are, as Bergson and some other philosophers have suggested, only selective choices and creations of our minds. But invariable similar sequences from similar initial conditions are a complete answer to such a question. It is very unlikely that we are deceiving ourselves in this conclusion, for by reducing the laws of nature to mathematical formulas we largely remove our predictions and their verifications from the distorting influences of our prejudices and predilections.

From several points of view the orderliness of the universe is the supreme discovery of mankind. It is a partial understanding of this orderliness that aids us in adjusting ourselves to our environment and enables us to exercise a considerable degree of control over the world about us. . . . we throw aside the terrifying superstition which darkened the lives of our predecessors and stand serene and unafraid in the presence of and as a part of the Universal Order.

QUESTIONS TO CONSIDER

Is the assumption of an order in nature necessary to the pursuit of science?

Do you agree with Bronowski that "science is nothing else than a search for unity [and order] in the wild variety of nature"?

Could there be an order that man could not understand?

Are all scientific theories the imposition of an order of nature?

Can you think of examples in which nature clearly demonstrates an order that is not dependent on the mind that perceives it?

SUGGESTIONS FOR FURTHER READING

* Collingwood, P. G.: *The Idea of Nature*, Galaxy Books, Oxford University Press, Fair Lawn, N.J., 1960, part I. A philosophical analysis of the concepts of the Greek philosophers from Thales through Aristotle.

* De Santillana, Giorgio: *Origins of Scientific Thought*, Mentor Books, New American Library of World Literature, Inc., New York, 1961. In addition to the selection we have used, we recommend the rest of the book very highly for an authoritative treatment of various phases of scientific thought from 600 B.C. to A.D. 500.

* Farrington, Benjamin: *Greek Science*, Penguin Books, Inc., Baltimore, 1944. This account especially brings out "the connections of Greek science with practical life, with techniques, with the economic basis and productive activity of Greek society."

* Whitehead, Alfred North: *Science and the Modern World*, Lowell Lectures, Mentor Books, New American Library of World Literature, Inc., New York, 1948, chaps. I and II. An examination of the philosophical significance of the Greek contributions to science and mathematics.

* Paperback edition.

PART 4   IS TRUTH SCIENTIFIC?

Truth has many shades of meaning, and confusion among them has led to bitter conflicts between science and society. In this part we find the questing, questioning spirit of science, as exemplified by Galileo, clashing with the prevailing conviction that organized religion and society need a firm and absolute truth as the basis for belief and security.

INTRODUCTION

Scientific theories never stand entirely alone on their intrinsic merits; their acceptance or rejection is often closely related to the climate of thought at the time of their conception. It has happened frequently in the history of science that an idea has been proposed simultaneously by different scientists working independently. The time was ripe for that particular idea. Conversely, we saw, in our study of Greek astronomy, that Aristarchus proposed the heliocentric theory in the third century B.C. but that other scientists did not follow it up for nearly 1,800 years. It is worthwhile to consider the social and human factors that enter into the acceptance of a scientific theory and to what extent it is justified to base religious or philosophical concepts on changing scientific theories.

The readings in Part 4 describe the revolution in thought that occurred in the Renaissance when the heliocentric theory began to challenge the geocentric theory, which had dominated natural philosophy since the time of Aristotle. The new idea was more than a scientific theory; it involved a whole new world view, embracing religious, metaphysical, and even moral aspects. Scientific thought as represented by Aristotle had molded and dominated the entire view of the universe for so many years that it was unquestioningly accepted as representing an absolute form of truth. The independent, questioning spirit of the Renaissance was needed to break this hardened ground and prepare it for the beginning of a scientific revolution. The need to doubt, to question, and to disrupt all absolutes is an essential ingredient of the scientific spirit. As Gilbert Lewis said, "The theory that there is an ultimate truth, although very generally held by mankind, does not seem useful to science except in the sense of a horizon toward which we may proceed."

Some scientific theories affect basic beliefs much more directly than do other theories. The central and really revolutionary idea embodied in the Copernican theory was that the earth moved. This idea was hard to accept from many different points of view. Rationally, it appeared to contradict common sense. If the earth moved, why were not men conscious of this motion? Scientifically, it posed problems of velocity that required the introduction of a whole new physics. As Cohen points out in his article, even today we have not fully

ander

om Hofen Teuffel.

NNO M·D·LV·

Cohen

Koestler

assimilated the "new" ideas into our everyday thinking. Egocentrically, it was hard to accept because it displaced man from the center of the universe. Koestler suggests that it was not so much the representatives of the Roman Catholic Church itself as the ranks of entrenched professionals who opposed the new idea: "The inertia of the human mind and its resistance to innovation are most clearly demonstrated not, as one might expect, by the ignorant mass—which is easily swayed once its imagination is caught—but by professionals with a vested interest in tradition and in the monopoly of learning . . . they stretch, a solid and hostile phalanx of pedantic mediocrities, across the centuries."

Certainly, the men whom Galileo was fighting, both the representatives of the church and the Aristotelians at the universities, were educated men, many of them interested themselves in advancing the progress of science. But both religiously and philosophically, the Copernican theory called for major changes in accepted doctrine, and these changes seemed hardly justified on the slim evidence in favor of the theory. Cardinal Bellarmine asked for proof that the earth moved. He said that, in the absence of such proof, the heliocentric theory could be allowed as an hypothesis but not accepted as absolute truth. If there were such proof, then the church would ". . . reinterpret the Scriptures rather than declare an opinion to be false which is proved to be true." Galileo believed that he had such proof but he failed to convince many of his contemporaries. Actually, as we see in Part 2, science cannot provide the kind of proof that Bellarmine was demanding. Science can disprove a theory, and Galileo went very far toward disproving Aristotle's model of the universe. It can also increase the probability that a certain conceptual scheme does represent a true picture of reality, but still it cannot prove it to be true in a positive and absolute sense. An understanding of this limitation of science could perhaps have helped to prevent the persecution and intolerance that were to follow, not only in this argument, but in later conflicts between science and society.

Shaw points up the basic dilemma when he says we must build a society ". . . that provides a large liberty to shock conventional people" and yet ". . . we must face the fact that society is founded on intolerance." Can the need for a certain degree of stability in society be reconciled with the freedom required for creative science?

THE MEDIEVAL UNIVERSE

All things whatsoever observe a mutual order; and this the form that maketh
    the universe like unto God.
Herein the exalted creatures trace the impress of the Eternal Worth, which is
    the goal whereto was made the norm now spoken of.
In the order of which I speak all things incline, by diverse lots, more near and
    less unto their principle;
Wherefore they move to diverse ports o'er the great sea of being, and each one
    with instinct given it to bear it on.
This beareth the fire toward the moon; this is the mover in the hearts of things
    that die; this doth draw the earth together and unite it.

Dante
Divine Comedy (c. 1307–1321)

A VIEW OF THE MEDIEVAL COSMOS*
by Herbert Butterfield (1957)

An introductory sketch of the medieval view of the cosmos must be qualified first of all with the reservation that in this particular realm of thought there were variations, uncertainties, controversies and developments which it would obviously be impossible to describe in detail. On the whole, therefore, it would be well, perhaps, if we were to take Dante's view of the universe as a pattern, because it will be easy to note in parentheses some of the important variations that occurred, and at the same time this policy will enable us to see in a single survey the range of the multiple objections which it took the Copernican theory something like a hundred and fifty years to surmount.

According to Dante, what one must have in mind is a series of spheres, one inside another, and at the heart of the whole system lies the motionless earth. The realm of what we should call ordinary matter is confined to the earth and its neighbourhood—the region below the moon; and this matter, the stuff that we can hold between our fingers and which our modern physical sciences set

out to study, is humble and unstable, being subject to change and decay for reasons which we shall examine later. The skies and the heavenly bodies—the rotating spheres and the stars and planets that are attached to them—are made of a very tangible kind of matter too, though it is more subtle in quality and it is not subject to change and corruption. It is not subject to the physical laws that govern the more earthy kind of material which we have below the moon. From the point of view of what we should call purely physical science, the earth and the skies therefore were cut off from one another and were separate organisations for a medieval student, though in a wider system of thought they dovetailed together to form one coherent cosmos.

As to the ordinary matter of which the earth is composed, it is formed of four elements, and these are graded according to their virtue, their nobility. There is earth, which is the meanest stuff of all, then water, then air and, finally, fire, and this last comes highest in the hierarchy. We do not see these elements in their pure and undiluted form, however—the earthy stuff that we handle when we pick up a little soil is a base com-

* From Herbert Butterfield, *The Origins of Modern Science*, The Macmillan Company, New York, 1957, and used with permission of The Macmillan Company and G. Bell & Sons, Ltd., London.

pound and the fire that we actually see is mixed with earthiness. Of the four elements, earth and water possess gravity; they have a tendency to fall; they can only be at rest at the centre of the universe. Fire and air do not have gravity, but possess the very reverse; they are characterised by levity, an actual tendency to rise, though the atmosphere clings down to the earth because it is loaded with base mundane impurities. For all the elements have their spheres, and aspire to reach their proper sphere, where they find stability and rest; and when even flame has soared to its own upper region it will be happy and contented, for here it can be still and can most endure. If the elements did not mix—if they were all at home in their proper spheres—we should have a solid sphere of earth at the heart of everything and every particle of it would be still. We should then have an ocean covering that whole globe, like a cap that fitted all round, then a sphere of air, which far above mountain-tops was supposed to swirl round from east to west in sympathy with the movement of the skies. Finally, there would come the region of enduring fire, fitting like a sphere over all the rest.

That, however, would be a dead universe. In fact, it was a corollary of this whole view of the world that ordinary motion up or down or in a straight line could only take place if there was something wrong—something displaced from its proper sphere. It mattered very much, therefore, that the various elements were not all in order but were mixed and out of place—for instance, some of the land had been drawn out above the waters, raised out of its proper sphere at the bottom, to provide habitable ground. On this land natural objects existed and, since they were mixtures, they might, for example, contain water, which as soon as it was released would tend to seek its way down to the sea. On the other hand, they might contain the element of fire, which would come out of them when they burned and would flutter and push its way upwards, aspiring to reach its true home. But the elements are not always able to follow their nature in this pure fashion—occasion-

ally the fire may strike downwards, as in lightning, or the water may rise in the form of vapour to prepare a store of rain. On one point, however, the law was fixed: while the elements are out of their proper spheres they are bound to be unstable—there cannot possibly be restfulness and peace. Woven, as we find them, on the surface of the globe, they make a mixed and chancy world, a world that is subject to constant mutation, liable to dissolution and decay.

It is only in the northern hemisphere that land emerges, protruding above the waters that cover the rest of the globe. This land has been pulled up, out of its proper sphere, says Dante—drawn not by the moon or the planets or the ninth sky, but by an influence from the fixed stars, in his opinion. The land stretches from the Pillars of Hercules in the west to the Ganges in the east, from the Equator in the south to the Arctic Circle in the north. And in the centre of this whole habitable world is Jerusalem, the Holy City. Dante had heard stories of travellers who had found a great deal more of the continent of Africa, found actual land much farther south than he had been taught to consider possible. As a true rationalist he seems to have rejected "fables" that contradicted the natural science of his time, remembering that travellers were apt to be liars. The disproportionate amount of water in the world and the unbalanced distribution of the land led to some discussion of the whereabouts of the earth's real centre. The great discoveries, however, culminating in the unmistakable discovery of America, provoked certain changes in ideas, as well as a debate concerning the possibility of the existence of inhabited countries at the antipodes. There was a growing view that earth and water, instead of coming in two separate circles, the one above the other, really dovetailed into one another to form a single sphere.

All this concerns the sublunary region; but there is another realm of matter to be considered, and this, as we have already seen, comes under a different polity. The skies are not liable to change and decay, for they—with the sun, the stars and the planets—are formed of a fifth element, an incorruptible kind of matter, which is subject to a different set of what we should call physical laws. If earth tends to fall to the centre of the universe, and fire tends to rise to its proper sphere above the air itself, the incorruptible stuff that forms the heavens has no reason for discontent—it is fixed in its congenial place already. Only one motion is possible for it— namely, circular motion—it must turn while remaining in the same place. According to Dante there are ten skies, only the last of them, the Empyrean Heaven, the abode of God, being at rest. Each of the skies is a sphere that surrounds the globe of the earth, and though all these spheres are transparent they are sufficiently tangible and real to carry one or more of the heavenly bodies round on their backs as they rotate about the earth —the whole system forming a set of transparent spheres, one around the other, with the hard earth at the centre of all. The sphere nearest to the earth has the moon attached to it, the others carry the planets or the sun, until we reach the eighth, to which all the fixed stars are fastened. A ninth sphere has no planet or star attached to it, nothing to give visible signs of its existence; but it must be there, for it is the *primum mobile*—it turns not only itself but all the other spheres or skies as well, from east to west, so that once in twenty-four hours the whole celestial system wheels round the motionless earth. This ninth sphere moves more quickly than any of the others, for the spirits which move it have every reason to be ardent. They are next to the Empyrean Heaven.

In the system of Aristotle the spheres were supposed to be formed of a very subtle aethereal substance, moving more softly than liquids and without any friction; but with the passage of time the idea seems to have become coarsened and vulgarised. The successive heavens turned into glassy or crystalline globes, solid but still transparent, so that it became harder for men to keep in mind the fact that they were frictionless and free from weight, though the Aristotelian theory in regard to these points was still formally held. The original beauty of this essentially Aris-

totelian system had been gravely compromised, however, by the improvements which had been made in astronomical observation since the time when it had been given its original shape; for even in the ancient world astronomy afforded a remarkable example of the progress which could be achieved in science by the sheer passage of time—the accumulating store of observations and the increasing precision in the recordings. Early in the Christian era, in the age of Ptolemy, the complications had become serious, and in the middle ages both the Arabs and the Christians produced additions to the intricacies of the system. The whole of the celestial machinery needed further elaboration to account for planets which, as viewed by the observer, now stopped in the sky, now turned back on their courses, now changed their distance from the earth, now altered their speed. However irregular the motion of the planets might seem to be, however curious the path that they traced, their behaviour must somehow or other be reduced to circular, even uniform circular motion—if necessary to a complicated series of circular motions each corrective of the other. Dante explains how Venus goes round with the sphere which forms the third of the skies, but as this does not quite correspond to the phenomena, another sphere which revolves independently is fixed to the sphere of the third sky, and the planet rides on the back of the smaller sphere (sitting like a jewel there, says Dante), reflecting the light of the sun. But writers varied on this point, and we meet the view that the planet was rather like a knot in a piece of wood, or represented a mere thickening of the material that formed the whole celestial sphere—a sort of swelling that caught the sunlight and shone with special brilliance as a result.

Writers differed also on the question whether the whole of the more elaborate machinery—the eccentrics or epicycles—as devised by Ptolemy and his successors, really existed in the actual architecture of the skies, though the theory of the crystalline spheres persisted until the seventeenth century. Since the whole complicated system demanded eighty spheres, some of which must apparently intersect one another as they turned round, some writers regarded the circles and epicycles as mere geometrical devices that formed a basis for calculation and prediction. And some men who believed that the nine skies were genuine crystalline spheres might regard the rest of the machinery as a mathematical way of representing those irregularities and anomalies which they knew they were unable properly to explain. In any case, it was realised long before the time of Copernicus that the Ptolemaic system, in spite of all its complications, did not exactly cover the phenomena as observed. In the sixteenth and seventeenth centuries we shall still find people who will admit that the Ptolemaic system is inadequate, and who will say that a new one must be discovered, though for understandable reasons they reject the solution offered by Copernicus. Copernicus himself, when he explained why his mind had turned to a possible new celestial system, mentioned amongst other things the divergent views that he found already in existence. The Ptolemaic system would be described as the Ptolemaic hypothesis, and we even find the Copernican theory described by one of its supporters as "the revision of the hypotheses." Many of us have gone too far perhaps in imagining a cast-iron Ptolemaic system, to the whole of which the predecessors of Copernicus were supposed to be blindly attached.

Finally, according to Dante, all the various spheres are moved by Intelligences or Spirits, which have their various grades corresponding to the degrees of nobility that exist in the physical world. Of these, the lowliest are the angels who move the sphere of the moon; for the moon is in the humblest of the heavens; she has dark spots that show her imperfections; she is associated with the servile and poor. (It is not the moon but the sun which affords the material for romantic poetry under this older system of ideas.) Through the various Intelligences operating by means of the celestial bodies, God has shaped the material world, only touching it, so to speak, through intermediaries. What He created was only inchoate matter, and this was later moulded into a world by celestial influences. Human souls, however, God creates with his own hands; and these, again, are of a special substance—they are incorruptible. . . .

In this whole picture of the universe there is more of Aristotle than of Christianity. It was the authority of Aristotle and his successors which was responsible even for those features of this teaching which might seem to us to carry something of an ecclesiastical flavour—the hierarchy of heavens, the revolving spheres, the Intelligences which moved the planets, the grading of the elements in the order of their nobility and the view that the celestial bodies were composed of an incorruptible fifth essence. Indeed, we may say it was Aristotle rather than Ptolemy who had to be overthrown in the sixteenth century, and it was Aristotle who provided the great obstruction to the Copernican theory.

COPERNICUS

THE COPERNICAN REVOLUTION—1543*
by A. Wolf (1950)

The Life of Copernicus

Niklas Koppernigk (whom we shall henceforward designate by the more familiar latin-

ized form of his name, Nicolaus Copernicus) was born February 19, 1473, at Thorn, on the Vistula. His father was a merchant whose nationality, whether German or Polish, is still a matter of controversy. His mother was of German extraction. The father died in

* From A. Wolf, *A History of Science, Technology and Philosophy*, The Macmillan Company, New York, 1950, and used with permission of the Macmillan Company and George Allen & Unwin, Ltd., London.

1483, and Copernicus was brought up by an uncle who destined him for a career in the Church. After attending school at Thorn, Copernicus spent three years at the University of Cracow. Here his interest in mathematics and astronomy was awakened under the teaching of Albert Brudzewski, and he became accustomed to the use of astronomical instruments and to the observation of the heavens. After spending two years with his uncle, who was now Bishop of Ermland, Copernicus set out in 1496 for Italy, where, during the following ten years, he studied successively at the Universities of Bologna, Padua, and Ferrara. Law and medicine were his professed subjects of study during these years, but, although not much is known about his activities in Italy, there is good reason for supposing that he devoted much of his time there to the pursuit of astronomy, both theoretical and practical.

While at Bologna, Copernicus came into close personal touch with Comenico di Novara, the Professor of Astronomy there, a leader in that revival of Pythagorean ideals in natural philosophy which was awakening the Italian universities about that time. The two men observed together, and discussed, with a freedom unusual in the circles which Copernicus had hitherto frequented, the errors of Ptolemy's *Almagest,* and the possibility of improving upon the Ptolemaic system. There is little doubt that it was during his residence in Italy that Copernicus received the initial impulse towards that reform of astronomy which he achieved in his later, more secluded years.

During his absence in Italy Copernicus had been appointed a Canon of Frauenburg Cathedral, in his uncle's diocese, but after his return home he continued to live with his uncle at his palace at Heilsberg until the Bishop's death in 1512. He then took up his duties at Frauenburg, where he lived, with occasional interruptions, for the remaining thirty years of his life. These thirty years were, to outward appearance, the most uneventful in the life of Copernicus. He shared in the business of his Chapter, did a little political work, and gave free medical advice to the poor of the district. But it was during these years that Copernicus thought out the details of his planetary system, marshalled the intricate array of calculations by which that system was eventually reduced from speculation to numerical precision, and slowly perfected the manuscript in which the fruits of all his labours were at last given to the world.

Copernicus from the first was well aware of the opposition, based on both learned and doctrinal grounds, which would be aroused by the publication of his novel views on the constitution of the solar system. Hence, while he kept revising his manuscript year after year, he hesitated to publish it. Some inkling of his actual opinions, however, leaked out, awakening discussion and curiosity; and about 1529 he circulated among his friends a manuscript *Commentariolus.* This little tract gives a descriptive account of his system in very nearly its final form, but with all the calculations omitted. . . . Again, about ten years later, Copernicus received a long visit from a young astronomer, Georg Joachim, better known by his Latin name Rheticus, who studied the still unpublished manuscript, and made its contents known to a wide circle by means of his printed *Narratio Prima* (1540).

It was to this Rheticus, three years later, that Copernicus, now old and ill, committed his manscript when his friends at length prevailed upon him to publish it. The book was printed at Nürnberg and published in 1543; and the story goes that the first copy was given to Copernicus a few hours before his death on May 24, 1543.

The printed book bears the title *Nicolai Copernici Torimensis de revolutionibus orbium coelestium Libri VI,* and was dedicated to the reigning Pope, Paul III, whose interest and protection Copernicus claimed. The first edition, however, differs on almost every page from the original manuscript. The title itself is an addition, and there is reason to suppose that Copernicus would have preferred to call his work *De Revolutionibus* simply. The manuscript was lost for some two hundred years, but was rediscovered in

**Figure 4-1. Views of the universe, from ancient times
to the Renaissance.**

**The Boat of the Sun traveling in the sky, an Egyptian
concept.**

The Hindu earth.

The four elements: earth, water, fire, air.

A seventeenth-century engraving portraying the Ptolemaic system of the second century.

A view of the world in the Middle Ages.

The Globus Magnus of Tycho Brahe (1598).

time to serve as the basis for the Säkular-Ausgabe (Thorn, 1873), which is the authoritative edition of the text. (There is a German translation of the book by C. L. Menzzer, Thorn, 1879.)

For some years after the publication of Copernicus' book there was uncertainty as to whether his hypothesis was intended as a description of the actual motions of the Earth and planets, or merely as a computing device to facilitate the construction of planetary tables. This question was of all the more moment, as, in the state of religious opinion at the time, the acceptance or rejection of the teachings of Copernicus depended to a considerable degree upon the sense in which they were to be understood. The uncertainty arose chiefly out of the circumstances in which the book was published. Rheticus, who at first superintended the printing, was called away before it was completed, and he entrusted the supervision of the work to Andreas Osiander, a local Lutheran clergyman, who was a mathematician and a friend of Copernicus. Osiander was afraid that the doctrine of the Earth's motion would offend philosophers and strict Lutherans, and so he inserted a little preface of his own which stated that the whole was to be regarded as a mere computing device without prejudice to scriptural or physical truth.* The imposture was recognized by several friends of Copernicus from the first, and was finally exposed by Kepler. . . . It was probably well-intentioned; Osiander had previously advised Copernicus to insert such a deprecatory preface, but Copernicus had refused to do so. The preface seemed strangely at variance with the text, but could not be finally proclaimed to be an addition until the original manuscript was recovered. To Copernicus, imbued with Pythagorean ideas, the most elegant and harmonious mathematical representation of the planetary motions doubtless appeared to be the only true planetary theory.

Copernican Astronomy

In the dedicatory preface to his *De Revolutionibus* Copernicus immediately brings his

* See p. 111 for full text of Osiander's preface. Ed.

readers face to face with the long-standing problem which it was his life's work to solve. *That problem was to ascertain what geometrical laws govern the motions of the planets in order to explain the apparent motions observed in the past, and to predict how the planets would move in the future. . . .*

Copernicus describes how, . . . casting about for fresh ideas, he turned to the classical writers to see what alternative theories they had to offer. He found that quite *a number of the early thinkers, such as Hicetas, Philolaus, and Heraclides of Pontus, had attributed some form of motion* (axial rotation or revolution in a closed orbit) *to the Earth;* and he quotes several classical writers to this effect. We cannot be certain whether Copernicus really derived his ideas, in the first instance, from the writers whom he quotes, or whether he introduces their names merely for the sake of the impression which these would produce upon the readers of his day. We shall return to the question of the originality of Copernicus' conceptions later in this chapter. In any case, *he uses these classic passages as an excuse for introducing his own system, in which the Earth rotates on its axis and revolves about the Sun as one of the planets.*

"Taking occasion thence," he writes, "I too began to reflect upon the Earth's capacity for motion. And though the idea appeared absurd, yet I knew that others before me had been allowed freedom to imagine what circles they pleased in order to represent the phenomena of the heavenly bodies. I therefore deemed that it would readily be granted to me also to try whether, by assuming the Earth to have a certain motion, demonstrations, more valid than those of others, could be found for the revolution of the heavenly spheres.

"And so, having assumed those motions which I attribute to the Earth further on in the book, I found at length, by much long-continued observation, that, if the motions of the remaining planets be referred to the revolution of the Earth, and calculated according to the period of each planet, then not only would the planetary phenomena follow as a consequence, but the order of succession and the dimensions of the planets and of all the spheres, and the heaven itself, would be so bound together that in no part could anything be transposed without the disordering of the other parts and of the entire universe" (*Preface*).

The general arrangement of the solar system as conceived by Copernicus, suppressing the refinements which he subsequently introduced, is shown in his well-known diagram, where Mercury, Venus, the Earth, Mars, Jupiter, and Saturn describe concentric orbits about the Sun in the centre (Figure 4-2).

"In the midst of all dwells the Sun. For who could set this luminary in another or better place in this most glorious temple than whence he could at one and the same time lighten the whole? . . . And so, as if seated upon a royal throne, the Sun rules the family of the planets as they circle around him. . . ." (I, 10).

Ever since the days of the Pythagoreans *objection had been made to all planetary hypotheses which involved any motion of the Earth, on the ground that any such motion would give rise to a corresponding apparent motion in the stars* (Figure 4-3). Such an apparent motion, though sought, was never observed. Copernicus anticipates this sort of criticism by supposing that the stars are at a distance from us incomparably greater than the radius of the Earth's orbit, so that our annual motion makes no difference to their apparent direction. This objection, however became ever more serious as observation improved in accuracy yet failed to reveal any annual stellar parallax. It was finally removed within the last hundred years, when stellar parallax of a minute order was observed in certain stars.*

Copernicus was doubtless won over to the new point of view by its greater symmetry and coherence. These virtues would appeal to one imbued with Neo-Pythagorean ideas. *For the essence of Pythagoreanism was its insistence that the universe is to be described in terms of mathematical relations; and that, of two geometrically equivalent planetary*

* See footnotes, p. 68. Ed.

Figure 4-2. The universe according to Copernicus.

theories, the more harmonious and symmetrical was the more correct. But Copernicus had still to justify his point of view to the scholars of northern Europe, whose master was Aristotle rather than Pythagoras. He therefore devotes several of the early chapters of Book I to proving that the new system is just as much in accordance with Aristotelian physics as was the Ptolemaic system. *His problem is to confute the arguments by which Aristotle had asserted that the Earth is at rest at the centre of the universe, while at the same time preserving Aristotle's principles intact and using them as the basis of his own arguments.*

Copernicus reasons more soundly, however, from the principle that all motion is relative motion: "Every apparent change of position is due either to a motion of the object observed, or to a motion of the observer, or to unequal changes in the positions of both. . . . If then a certain motion be assigned to the Earth, it will appear as a similar but oppositely directed motion, affecting all things exterior to the Earth, as if we were passing them by" (I, 5). Copernicus applies this principle of the reciprocity of apparent motions in the first instance to account for the apparent diurnal rotation of the heavens: "If you will allow that the heavens have no part in this motion, but that the Earth turns from

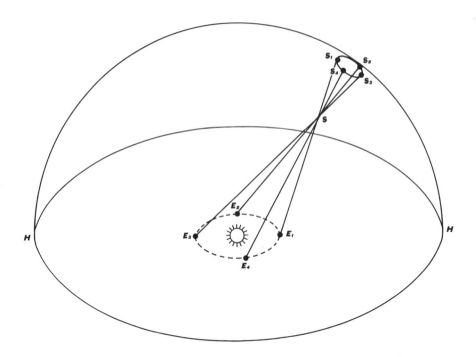

Figure 4-3. Stellar paralax. To measure the displacement of very distant objects, the widest possible optical base is used. The different positions of the earth in its orbit (E_1, E_2, E_3 and E_4) provide the largest optical base for observing the displacement of the stars against farther stars S_1, S_2, S_3, and S_4. However the distance between S and E is very much greater than that shown in the figure, and the displacement is too small to be observed without powerful telescopes.

west to east, then, so far as pertains to the apparent rising and setting of the Sun, Moon and stars, you will find, if you think carefully, that these things occur in this way" (I, 5). Later he brings this same principle to bear upon the phenomena connected with the apparent annual circuit of the Sun: "If [this circuit] be transposed from being a solar to being a terrestrial [phenomenon], and it be granted that the Sun is at rest, then the risings and settings of the constellations and the fixed stars, whereby they become morning and evening stars, will appear after the same manner [as before]" (I, 9).

The most convincing argument, however, in favour of the scientific superiority of the Copernican hypothesis was the simple explanation which it could give . of certain peculiarities in the apparent motions of the planets. If one of these bodies (say a superior planet) is observed night after night, it is found, in general, to be moving slowly across the southern sky from west to east relatively to the background of stars. From

time to time, however, this eastward motion is arrested and reversed, and the planet travels a short distance from east to west before resuming its normal eastward direction. The physical significance of these *stations* and *retrogressions* of the planets had always been an enigma to astronomers; but Copernicus was able to show that these inequalities arise as necessary consequences of the annual motion of the Earth. . . .

Ptolemy had represented this inequality in a planet's motion by supposing the planet to move upon an epicycle especially introduced for the purpose. This was equivalent to transferring the Earth's motion to the planet. But this had to be done for *each* planet, while Copernicus could explain this phenomenon in each planet by reference to a single motion of the Earth—a great gain in simplicity.

There are, however, further inequalities in the apparent paths of the planets arising, as we know now, from the ellipticity of their orbits. Moreover, the Sun's rate of apparent motion in the ecliptic is not quite uniform from day to day. In order to account for these phenomena Copernicus was obliged to refine upon the simple scheme of Figure 4-2; where the Earth and planets all describe concentric circles with the Sun in the centre. In constructing his detailed planetary orbits, a task which occupies most of the *De Revolutionibus*, Copernicus employs eccentrics and epicycles like those of the ancients, but, unlike Ptolemy, he is always careful to ensure that his circular motions are uniformly described relatively to the centres of the circles, and not merely to arbitrarily chosen points within the circles.

A whole book of the *De Revolutionibus* (the third) is devoted to the consideration of the various motions to be attributed to the Earth. Already, in the preliminary sketch of Book I, the phenomena of the seasons are shown to depend upon the Earth's revolving annually about the Sun while keeping the direction of its axis approximately invariable. In the more refined theory of Book III the Earth's orbit is assumed to be a circle having the Sun displaced a little way from its centre. Copernicus determines the direction of the apse-line of this orbit, and its eccentricity with regard to the Sun, after the manner of Hipparchus. His theory is complicated by an attempt to represent an (actual) progressive motion of the apse-line (suspected by the Arab al-Battani in the ninth century and confirmed by Copernicus), and to allow for certain (imaginary) fluctuations in this motion, and in the eccentricity of the orbit, suggested by some mediaeval observations of questionable accuracy, which he felt obliged to take into account.

An important feature of Copernicus' account of the Earth's motion is his explanation of the precession of the equinoxes. Hipparchus of Rhodes, who discovered this phenomenon about 150 B.C., attributed it to a slow rotation of the sphere of stars about the axis of the ecliptic. Copernicus introduces the modern explanation of precession as due to an alteration in the plane of the Earth's equator causing the Earth's axis to describe a cone in space. Here again he needlessly

complicates his theory in order to bring it into conformity with certain ancient and mediaeval observations. Throughout his work he adopts an entirely uncritical attitude to traditional data of this kind, and makes no allowance for the possibility of serious errors of observation, fraud, or textual corruption. This involves his theories in needless intricacies, while at the same time revealing his remarkable skill in geometry. Occasionally he relies upon twenty-seven observations of his own, which fill only one page of a modern edition, and are, on his own admission, crude. "If only I can be correct to ten minutes of arc," he once said to Rheticus, "I shall be no less elated than Pythagoras is said to have been when he discovered the law of the right-angled triangle. . . ."

Following upon this investigation of the Earth's motion, we have a book devoted to lunar theory. The Moon's relation to the Earth was unaffected by the change of outlook which Copernicus initiated, and he made no additions to the lunar inequalities in longitude known to Ptolemy. But his methods of representing these inequalities are more satisfactory than those of the *Almagest*. According to Ptolemy's theory, the angular diameter of the Moon should be twice as great at some times as it is at others; Copernicus found a means of representing the Moon's motion in longitude as correctly as Ptolemy had done, but without such a gross exaggeration of the slight fluctuations in the apparent size of its disc. Copernicus, however, adopts with only a slight alteration Ptolemy's gross underestimate of the Sun's distance from the Earth as being only about 1,200 times the Earth's radius. This error clung to astronomy until the latter half of the seventeenth century, when the use of the telescope for precise celestial measurements made an accurate determination possible.

The last two books of the *De Revolutionibus* (V and VI) treat of the motions of the planets in longitude and in latitude respectively. . . .

Copernicus' treatment of the latitudes of the inferior planets is particularly complicated, and employs methods borrowed almost wholly from the *Almagest*.

It was an ambition of Copernicus to produce numerical planetary tables as accurate as any based on the geocentric hypothesis. From the theories set forth in the *De Revolutionibus* he constructed tables enabling the positions of the Sun, Moon, and planets at any given instant to be easily calculated. These tables, which form an essential feature of the book, were in fact an improvement upon those in current use, and this circumstance helped indirectly to make the new doctrine acceptable among astronomers. But the accuracy of the tables necessarily suffered through their being based upon a bare minimum of crude and often questionable observations embodied in a theory which was strained to conform to illusory physical laws. Such little improvement as could be made by a careful reconsideration of the data was effected a few years later by Copernicus' disciple Reinhold. Before the new cosmology could bear fruit in tables worthy of itself, however, there were needed the precise and systematic observations of Tycho Brahe, and the patient but adventurous genius of Kepler.

The Originality of Copernicus

We may now face the problem of assessing the originality of Copernicus' contribution to astronomy. It cannot be denied that his debts to Ptolemy were considerable. From the *Almagest* he derived many of his observational data and geometrical devices, as well as the material for his star catalogue.

In one sense, however, Copernicus' debt to Ptolemy was insignificant, for the ideas with which he revolutionized European astronomy were entirely alien to the Alexandrians. The rudiments of these ideas are to be found, if anywhere, in the speculations of a few men who stood apart from the main current of opinion, and whose recorded teachings are scattered through classical and mediaeval literature. A study of these passages, so far as they were probably known to Copernicus, seems to make it clear that the basic ideas underlying his system did not originate with him. For instance, the complete heliocentric system had been anticipated, in its broad outlines, by Aristarchus of Samos* (c. 250 B.C.), who has been called on that account the "Copernicus of Antiquity"; though Copernicus' relation to the ideas of Aristarchus is unfortunately obscure. From whatever source he derived his fundamental ideas, however, Copernicus' great and unquestionable contribution to astronomy must be held to lie in his elaboration of those ideas into a coherent planetary theory capable of furnishing tables of an accuracy not before attained. It is true that we can no longer regard the Sun, or the centre of the Earth's orbit, or any other origin of reference, as being at rest in space except as a matter of temporary convenience in treating some special problem. Nevertheless, the scientific utility of the heliocentric point of view, and its contacts with observed fact, have increased enormously since it was formulated by Copernicus. To him it merely represented the most symmetrical arrangement of the planets, and the simplest manner of accounting for their observed motions.

* See p. 70. Ed.

Entia non sunt multiplicanda praeter necessitatem.†

William of Ockham
Commentarium in Libros IV Sententiarum Petri Lombardi (1318–1323)

† Literally, beings are not to be multiplied without necessity; or, as translated freely in the *Encyclopedia Britannica*, 1911, it is scientifically unsound to set up more than one hypothesis at once to explain a phenomenon. This principle is known as "Ockham's razor." Ed.

PREFACE TO COPERNICUS' DE REVOLUTIONIBUS
by Andreas Osiander (1543)

To the Reader Concerning the Hypotheses of This Work
Since the novelty of the hypotheses of this work has already been widely reported, I have no doubt that some learned men have taken serious offence because the book declares that the earth moves, and that the sun is at rest in the centre of the universe; these men undoubtedly believe that the liberal arts, established long ago upon a correct basis, should not be thrown into confusion. But if they are willing to examine the matter closely, they will find that the author of this work has done nothing blameworthy. For it is the duty of an astronomer to compose the history of the celestial motions through careful and skillful observation. Then turning to the causes of these motions or hypotheses about them, he must conceive and devise, since he cannot in any way attain to the true causes, such hypotheses as, being assumed, enable the motions to be calculated correctly from the principles of geometry, for the future as well as for the past. The present author has performed both these duties excellently. For these hypotheses need not be true nor even probable; if they provide a calculus consistent with the observations, that alone is sufficient. Perhaps there is someone who is so ignorant of geometry and optics that he regards the epicycle of Venus as probable, or thinks that it is the reason why Venus sometimes precedes and sometimes follows the sun by forty degrees and even more. Is there anyone who is not aware that from this assumption it necessarily follows that the diameter of the planet in perigee should appear more than four times, and the body of the planet more than sixteen times, as great as in the apogee, a result contradicted by the experience of every age? In this study there are other no less important absurdities, which there is no need to set forth at the moment. For it is quite clear that the causes of the apparent unequal motions are completely and simply unknown to this art. And if any causes are devised by the imagination, as indeed very many are, they are not put forward to convince anyone that they are true, but merely to provide a correct basis for calculation. Now when from time to time there are offered for one and the same motion different hypotheses (as eccentricity and an epicycle for the sun's motion), the astronomer will accept above all others the one which is the easiest to grasp. The philosopher will perhaps rather seek the semblance of the truth. But neither of them will understand or state anything certain, unless it has been divinely revealed to him. Let us therefore permit these new hypotheses to become known together with the ancient hypotheses, which are no more probable; let us do so especially because the new hypotheses are admirable and also simple, and bring with them a huge treasure of very skillful observations. So far as hypotheses are concerned, let no one expect anything certain from astronomy, which cannot furnish it, lest he accept as the truth ideas conceived for another purpose, and depart from this study a greater fool than when he entered it. Farewell.

LETTER TO COPERNICUS FROM CARDINAL SCHOENBERG INCLUDED BY COPERNICUS IN THE INTRODUCTION TO DE REVOLUTIONIBUS

Nicolaus Schoenberg, Cardinal of Capua, sends his greetings to Nicolaus Copernicus.

When several years ago I heard your diligence unanimously praised, I began to feel an increasing fondness for you and to deem our compatriots lucky on account of your fame. I have been informed that you not only have an exhaustive knowledge of the teachings of the ancient mathematicians, but that you have also created a new theory of the Universe according to which the Earth moves and the Sun occupies the basic and hence central position; that the eighth sphere [of the fixed stars] remains in an immobile and eternally fixed position and the Moon, together with the elements included in its sphere, placed between the spheres of Mars and Venus, revolves annually around the Sun; moreover, that you have written a treatise on this entirely new theory of astronomy, and also computed the movements of the planets and set them out in tables, to the greatest admiration of all. Therefore, learned man,

without wishing to be inopportune, I beg you most emphatically to communicate your discovery to the learned world, and to send me as soon as possible your theories about the Universe, together with the tables and whatever else you have pertaining to the subject. I have instructed Dietrich von Rheden [another Frauenburg Canon] to make a fair copy of this at my expense and send it to me. If you will do me these favours, you will find that you are dealing with a man who has your interests at heart, and wishes to do full justice to your excellence. Farewell.

Rome, November 1, 1536.

GALILEO

GALILEO'S DISCOVERIES OF 1609*
by I. Bernard Cohen (1960)

The gradual acceptance of Copernican ideas by one scholar here and another there was rudely interrupted in 1609, when a new scientific instrument changed the level and the tone of discussion of the Copernican and Ptolemaic systems to such a degree that the year overshadows 1543 in the development of modern astronomy.

It was in 1609 that man began to use the telescope to make systematic studies of the heavens. The revelations proved that Ptolemy made specific errors and important ones, that the Copernican system appeared to fit the new facts of observation, and that the moon and the planets in reality were very much like the earth in a variety of different ways and were patently unlike the stars. . . .

The scientist who was chiefly responsible for introducing the telescope as a scientific instrument, and who laid the foundations of the new physics, was Galileo Galilei. In 1609 he was a professor at the University of Padua, in the Venetian Republic, and was forty-five

* From *Birth of a New Physics* by I. B. Cohen, copyright © 1960 by Educational Services, Inc. Reprinted by permission of Doubleday & Company, Inc.

years old, which is considerably beyond the age when most men are likely to make profoundly significant scientific discoveries. The last great Italian, except for nobles and kings, to be known to posterity by his first name, Galileo was born in Pisa, Italy, in 1564, almost on the day of Michelangelo's death and within a year of Shakespeare's birth. His father sent him to the university of Pisa, where his sardonic combativeness quickly won him the nickname "wrangler." Although his first thought had been to study medicine —it was better paid than most professions— he soon found that it was not the career for him. He discovered the beauty of mathematics and thereafter devoted his life to it, physics and astronomy. We do not know exactly when or how he became a Copernican, but on his own testimony it happened earlier than 1597.

Galileo made his first contribution to astronomy before he ever used a telescope. In 1604 a "nova" or new star suddenly appeared in the constellation Serpentarius. Galileo showed this to be a "true" star, located out in the celestial spaces and not inside the sphere of the moon. That is, Galileo found that this new star had no measurable parallax and so was very far from the earth. Thus he delivered a nice blow at the Aristotelian system of physics because he proved that change could occur in the heavens despite Aristotle, who had held the heavens unchangeable and had limited the region where change may occur to the earth and its surroundings. Galileo's proof seemed to him all the more decisive in that it was the second nova to be observed and found to have no measurable parallax. . . .

Some time early in 1609 Galileo heard a report of the telescope, but without any specific information as to the way in which the instrument was constructed. He told us how:

A report reached my ears that a certain Fleming had constructed a spyglass by means of which visible objects, though very distant from the eye of the observer, were distinctly seen as if nearby. Of this truly remarkable effect several experiences were related, to which some persons gave credence while others denied them. A few days later the report was confirmed to me in a letter from a noble Frenchman at Paris, Jacques Badovere [a former pupil of Galileo], which caused me to apply myself wholeheartedly to inquire into the means by which I might arrive at the invention of a similar instrument. This I did shortly afterwards, my basis being the theory of refraction. First I prepared a tube of lead, at the ends of which I fitted two glass lenses, both plane on one side while on the other side one was spherically convex and the other concave. Then placing my eye near the concave lens I perceived objects satisfactorily large and near, for they appeared three times closer and nine times larger than when seen with the naked eye alone. Next I constructed another one, more accurate, which represented objects as enlarged more than sixty times. Finally, sparing neither labor nor expense, I succeeded in constructing for myself so excellent an instrument that objects seen by means of it appeared nearly one thousand times larger and over thirty times closer than when regarded with our natural vision.

Galileo was not the only observer to point the new instrument toward the heavens. It is even possible that two observers—Thomas Harriot in England and Simon Marius in Germany—may in some respects have been ahead of him. But there seems to be general agreement that the credit of first using the telescope for astronomical purposes may be given to Galileo because of "the persistent way in which he examined object after object, whenever there seemed any reasonable prospect of results following, by the energy and acuteness with which he followed up each clue, by the independence of mind with which he interpreted his observations, and above all by the insight with which he realized their astronomical importance," as said Arthur Berry, British historian of astronomy. . . .

To see the way in which these events occurred, let us turn to Galileo's account of his discoveries, in a book in which he called *Sidereus nuncius, The Starry Messenger* or *The Starry Message*. In its subtitle, the book is said to reveal "great, unusual, and remarkable spectacles, opening these to the consideration of every man, and especially of philosophers and astronomers." The newly observed phenomena, the title page of the book declared, were to be found "in the surface of the moon, in innumerable fixed stars, in nebulae, and above all in four planets swiftly revolving about Jupiter at differing distances and periods, and known to no one before the Author recently perceived them and decided that they should be named the Medicean Stars."

The Landscape of the Moon

Immediately after describing the construction and use of the telescope, Galileo turned to results. He would "review the observations made during the past two months, once more inviting the attention of all who are eager for true philosophy to the first steps of such important contemplations."

The first celestial body to be studied was the moon, the most prominent object in the heavens (except for the sun), and the one nearest to us. The crude woodcuts accompanying Galileo's text cannot convey the sense of wonder and delight this new picture of the moon awoke in him. The lunar landscape, seen through the telescope (Figures 4-4 and

4-5), unfolds itself to us as a dead world—a world without color, and so far as the eye can tell, one without any life upon it. But the characteristic that stands out most clearly in photographs, and that so impressed Galileo in 1609, is the fact that the moon's surface looks like a ghostly *earthly* landscape. No one who looks at these photographs, and no one who looks through a telescope, can escape the feeling that the moon is a miniature earth, however dead it may appear, and that there are on it mountains and valleys, oceans, and seas with islands in them. To this day, we refer to those oceanlike regions as "maria" even though we know, as Galileo later discovered, that there is no water on the moon, and that these are not true seas at all.

The spots on the moon, whatever may have been said about them before 1609, were seen by Galileo in a coldly new and different light [Figure 4-6]. He found "that the surface of the moon is not smooth, uniform, and precisely spherical as a great number of philosophers believe it (and the other heavenly bodies) to be, but is uneven, rough, and full

Mount Wilson and Mount Palomar Observatories

Figure 4-5. Galileo was the first to see the craters on the moon. His observations killed the ancient belief that the moon was smooth and perfectly spherical.

of cavities and prominences, being not unlike the face of the earth, relieved by chains of mountains and deep valleys." As an example of Galileo's style in describing the earthlike quality of the moon, read the following:

Again, not only are the boundaries of shadow and light in the moon seen to be uneven and wavy, but still astonishingly many bright points appear within the darkened portion of the moon, completely divided and separated from the illuminated part and at a considerable distance from it. After a time these gradually increase in size and brightness, and an hour or two later they become joined with the rest of the lighted part which has now increased in size. Meanwhile more and more peaks shoot up as if sprouting now here, now there, lighting up within the shadowed portion; these become larger, and finally they too are united with that same luminous surface which extends further. And on the earth, before the rising of the sun, are not the highest peaks of the mountains illuminated by the sun's rays while the plains remain in shadow? Does not the light go on spreading while the larger central parts of these mountains

Mount Wilson and Mount Palomar Observatories

Figure 4-4. A landscape similar to the earth's, but dead, was what impressed Galileo the first time he turned his telescope to the moon.

Figure 4-6. Galileo's own drawings of the moon.

are becoming illuminated? And when the sun has finally risen, does not the illumination of plains and hills finally become one? But on the moon the variety of elevations and depressions appears to surpass in every way the roughness of the terrestrial surface, as we shall demonstrate further on.

Not only did Galileo describe the appearance of mountains on the moon; he also measured them. It is characteristic of Galileo as a scientist of the modern school that as soon as he found any kind of phenomenon he wanted to measure it. It is all very well to be told that the telescope discloses that there are mountains on the moon, just as there are mountains on the earth. But how much more extraordinary it is, and how much more convincing, to be told that there are mountains on the moon and that they are exactly four miles high! Galileo's determination of the height of the mountains on the

moon has withstood the test of time, and today we agree with his estimate of their maximum height. . . . (For those who are interested, Galileo's method of computing the height of these mountains will be found in Figure 4-7.)

Galileo saw that the surface of the moon provided evidence that the earth is not unique. Since the moon resembles the earth, he had demonstrated that at least the nearest heavenly body does not enjoy that perfection attributed to all heavenly bodies by the classic authorities. Nor did Galileo make this a passing reference; he returned to the idea later in the book when he compared a portion of the moon to a specific region on earth: "In the center of the moon there is a cavity larger than all the rest, and perfectly round in shape. . . . As to light and shade, it offers the same appearance as would a region like Bohemia if that were enclosed on all sides by very lofty mountains arranged exactly in a circle."

Figure 4-7. Galileo's measurement of the height of mountains on the moon was simple but convincing. The point N is the terminator (boundary) between the illuminated and nonilluminated portions of moon. The point M is a bright spot observed in the shadowed region; Galileo correctly surmised that the bright spot was a mountain peak whose base remained shadowed by the curvature of the moon. He could compute the moon's radius from the moon's known distance from the earth and could estimate the distance NM through his telescope. By the Pythagorean theorem, then, $CM^2 = MN^2 + CN^2$, or, since R is the radius and X the altitude of the peak,

$$(R + X)^2 = R^2 + MN^2$$

or

$$R^2 + 2RX + X^2 = R^2 + MN^2$$

or

$$X^2 + 2RX - MN^2 = 0$$

which is easily solved for X, the altitude of the peak.

Earthshine

At this point Galileo introduces a still more startling discovery: earthshine. This phenomenon may be seen in the photograph reproduced in Figure 4-8. From the photograph it is plain, as may be seen when the moon is

Figure 4-8. "In fair and grateful exchange," as Galileo put it, the earth contributes illumination to the moon. Earthshine shows on the portion of the moon that otherwise would be in shadow.

examined through a telescope, that there is what Galileo called a "secondary" illumination of the dark surface of the moon, which can be shown geometrically to accord perfectly with light from the sun reflected by the earth into the moon's darkened regions. It cannot be the moon's own light, or a contribution of starlight, since it would then be displayed during eclipses; it is not. Nor can it come from Venus or from any other planetary source. As for the moon's being illuminated by the earth, what, asked Galileo, is there so remarkable about this? "The earth, in fair and grateful exchange, pays back to the moon an illumination similar to that which it receives from her throughout nearly all the darkest gloom of night."

Here Galileo ends his description of the moon. The subject is one which, he told his readers, he would discuss more fully in his book on the *System of the World*. "In that book," he said, "by a multitude of arguments and experiences, the solar reflection from the

earth will be shown to be quite real—against those who argue that the earth must be excluded from the dancing whirl of stars (or heavenly bodies) for the specific reason that it is devoid of motion and of light. We shall prove the earth to be a wandering body surpassing the moon in splendor, and not the sink of all dull refuse of the universe; this we shall support by an infinitude of arguments drawn from nature." This was Galileo's first announcement that he was writing a book on the system of the world, a work which was delayed for many years and which —when finally published—resulted in Galileo's trial before the Roman Inquisition.

But observe what Galileo had proved thus far. He showed that the ancients were wrong in their descriptions of the moon; the moon is not the perfect body they pictured, but resembles the earth, which therefore cannot be said to be unique and consequently different from all the heavenly objects. And if this was not enough, his studies of the moon had shown that the earth shines. No longer was it valid to say that the earth is not a shining object like the planets. And if the earth shines just as the moon does, perhaps the planets may also shine in the very same manner by reflecting light from the sun! Remember, in 1609 it was still an undecided question whether the planets shine from internal light, like the sun and the stars, or whether by reflected light, like the moon. As we shall see in a moment, it was one of Galileo's greatest discoveries to prove that the planets shine by reflected light, and that they encircle the sun in their orbits.

Stars Galore

But before turning to that subject, let us state briefly some of Galileo's other discoveries. When Galileo looked at the fixed stars, he found that they, like the planets, "appear not to be enlarged by the telescope in the same proportion as that in which it magnifies other objects, and even the moon itself." Furthermore, Galileo called attention to "the differences between the appearance of the planets and of the fixed stars" in the telescope. "The planets show their globes perfectly round and definitely bounded, looking like little moons, spherical and flooded all over with light; the fixed stars are never seen to be bounded by a circular periphery, but have rather the aspect of blazes whose rays vibrate about them and scintillate a great deal." Here was the basis of one of Galileo's great answers to the detractors of Copernicus. Plainly, the stars must be at enormous distances from the earth compared to the planets, if a telescope can magnify the planets to make them look like discs, but cannot do the same with the fixed stars.

Galileo related how he "was overwhelmed by the vast quantity of stars," so many that he found "more than five hundred new stars distributed among the old ones within limits of one or two degrees of arc." To three previously known stars in Orion's Belt and six in the Sword, he added "eighty adjacent stars." In several pictures he presented the results of his observations with a large number of newly discovered stars amongst the older ones. Although Galileo does not make the point explicitly, it is implied that one hardly needed to put one's faith in the ancients, since they had never seen most of the stars, and had spoken from woefully incomplete evidence. A weakness of naked-eye observation was exposed by Galileo in terms of "the nature and the material of the Milky Way." With the aid of the telescope, he wrote, the Milky Way has been "scrutinized so directly and with such ocular certainty that all the disputes which have vexed philosophers through so many ages have been resolved, and we are at last freed from wordy debates about it." Seen through the telescope, the Milky Way is "nothing but a congeries of innumerable stars grouped together in clusters. Upon whatever part of it the telescope is directed, a vast crowd of stars is immediately presented to view." And this was true not only of the Milky Way, but also of "the stars which have been called 'nebulous' by every astronomer up to this time," and which "turn out to be groups of very small stars arranged in a wonderful manner." . . .

Although Galileo's book ends with the description of the satellites of Jupiter, it will be wise, before we explore the implications of his research, to discuss three other astronomical discoveries made by Galileo with his telescope. The first was the discovery that Venus exhibits phases. For a number of reasons Galileo was overjoyed to discover that Venus exhibits phases. In the first place, it proved that Venus shines by reflected light, and not by a light of its own; this meant that Venus is like the moon in this regard, and also like the earth (which Galileo had previously shown to shine by reflected light of the sun). Here was another point of similarity between the planets and the earth, another weakening of the ancient philosophical barrier between earth and heavenly objects. Furthermore, as may be seen in Figure 4-9, top, if Venus moves in an orbit around the sun, not only will Venus go through a complete cycle of phases, but under constant magnification the different phases will appear to be of different sizes because of the change in the distance of Venus from the earth. . . . For instance, when Venus is at such a position as to enable us to see a complete circle or almost a complete circle, corresponding to a full moon, the planet is on the opposite side of its orbit around the sun from the earth, or is seen at its farthest distance from the earth. When Venus exhibits a half circle, corresponding to a quarter moon, the planet is not so far from the earth. Finally, when we barely see a faint crescent, Venus must be at its nearest point to the earth. Hence, we should expect that when Venus shows a faint crescent it would appear very large; when Venus shows the appearance of a quarter moon, it would be of moderate size; when we see the whole disc, Venus should be very small.

According to the Ptolemaic system, Venus (like Mercury) would never be seen far from the sun, and hence would be observed only as morning star or evening star near the place where the sun has either risen or set. The center of the orbit's epicycle would be permanently aligned between the center of the earth and the center of the sun and would move around the earth with a period of one year, just as the sun does. But it is perfectly plain, as may be seen in Figure 4-9, bottom,

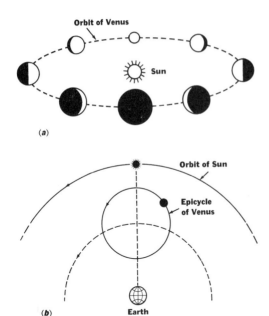

Orbit of Venus

Sun

(a)

Orbit of Sun

Epicycle of Venus

(b)   Earth

Figure 4-9. The phases of Venus, first observed by Galileo, were a powerful argument against the ancient astronomy. How the existence of phases accords with the system of Copernicus and how the change in the relative apparent diameter of Venus supports the concept of the planet having a solar orbit is shown at top. Why the phenomenon would be impossible in the Ptolemaic system is shown at bottom.

that in these circumstances we could never see the complete sequence of phases Galileo observed—and we can observe. For instance, the possibility of seeing Venus as a disc arises only if Venus is farther from the earth than the sun, and can never arise according to the principles of the Ptolemaic system. Here then was

a most decisive blow against the Ptolemaic system.

We need not say much about two further telescopic discoveries of Galileo, because they had less force than the previous ones. The first was the discovery that sometimes Saturn appeared to have a pair of "ears," and that sometimes the "ears" changed their shape and even disappeared. Galileo never could explain this strange appearance, because his telescope could not resolve the rings of Saturn. But at least he had evidence to demonstrate how erroneous it was to speak of planets as perfect celestial objects, when they could have such queer shapes. One of his most interesting observations was of the spots on the sun, described in a book that bore the title *History and Demonstrations concerning Sunspots and their Phenomena* (1613). Not only did the appearance of these spots prove that even the sun was not the perfect celestial object described by the ancients, but Galileo was able to show that from observations of these spots one could prove the rotation of the sun, and even compute the speed with which the sun rotates upon its axis. Although the fact that the sun did rotate became extremely important in Galileo's own mechanics, it did not imply, as he seems to have believed, that annual revolution of the earth around the sun must follow.

THE STARRY MESSENGER*
by Galileo Galilei (1610)

Discovery of Jupiter's Satellites, January 7, 1610

I have now finished my brief account of the observations which I have thus far made with regard to the moon, the fixed stars, and the Galaxy. There remains the matter, which seems to me to deserve to be considered the most important in this work, namely, that I should disclose and publish to the world the occasion of discovering and observing four

* From Galileo Galilei, *The Sidereal Messenger*, translated by Edward Stafford Carlos, Doubleday & Company, Inc., Garden City, N.Y. Reprinted by permission.

planets, never seen from the very beginning of the world up to our own times, their positions, and the observations made during the last two months about their movements and their changes of magnitude; and I summon all astronomers to apply themselves to examine and determine their periodic times, which it has not been permitted me to achieve up to this day, owing to the restriction of my time. I give them warning, however, again, so that they may not approach such an inquiry to no purpose, that they will want a very accurate telescope, and such as I have described in the beginning of this account.

On the seventh day of January in the present year, 1610, in the first hour of the following night, when I was viewing the constellations of the heavens through a telescope, the planet Jupiter presented itself to my view, and as I had prepared for myself a very excellent instrument, I noticed a circumstance which I had never been able to notice before, owing to want of power in my other telescope, namely, that three little stars, small but very bright, were near the planet; and although I believed them to belong to the number of the fixed stars, yet they made me somewhat wonder, because they seemed to be arranged exactly in a straight line, parallel to the ecliptic, and to be brighter than the rest of the stars equal to them in magnitude. The position of them with reference to one another and to Jupiter was as follows:

Figure 4-10

On the east [Orient] side there were two stars, and a single one toward the west [Occident]. The star which was furthest toward the east, and the western star, appeared rather larger than the third.

I scarcely troubled at all about the distance between them and Jupiter, for, as I have already said, at first I believed them to be fixed stars; but when on January 8, led by some fatality, I turned again to look at the same part of the heavens, I found a very different state of things, for there were three little stars all west of Jupiter, and nearer together than on the previous night, and they were separated from one another by equal intervals, as the accompanying figure shows.

Figure 4-11

At this point, although I had not turned my thoughts at all upon the approximation of the stars to one another, yet my surprise began to be excited, how Jupiter could one

day be found to the east of all the aforesaid fixed stars when the day before it had been west of two of them; and forthwith I became afraid lest the planet might have moved differently from the calculation of astronomers, and so had passed those stars by its own proper motion. I therefore waited for the next night with the most intense longing, but I was disappointed of my hope, for the sky was covered with clouds in every direction.

But on January 10 the stars appeared in the following position with regard to Jupiter,

Ori.   ★   ★   ●   Occ.

Figure 4-12

the third, as I thought, being hidden by the planet. They were situated just as before, exactly in the same straight line with Jupiter, and along the Zodiac.

When I had seen these phenomena, as I knew that corresponding changes of position could not by any means belong to Jupiter, and as, moreover, I perceived that the stars which I saw had always been the same, for there were no others either in front or behind, within a great distance, along the Zodiac—at length, changing from doubt into surprise, I discovered that the interchange of position which I saw belonged not to Jupiter but to the stars to which my attention had been drawn, and I thought therefore that they ought to be observed henceforward with more attention and precision.

Accordingly, on January 11 I saw an arrangement of the following kind, namely,

Ori.   ★   ★   ●   Occ.

Figure 4-13

only two stars to the east of Jupiter, the nearer of which was distant from Jupiter three times as far as from the star further to the east; and the star furthest to the east was nearly twice as large as the other one; whereas on the previous night they had appeared nearly of equal magnitude. I therefore concluded, and decided unhesitatingly, that there are three stars in the heavens moving about Jupiter, as Venus and Mercury round the sun;

which at length was established as clear as daylight by numerous other subsequent observations. These observations also established that there are not only three but four erratic sidereal bodies performing their revolutions round Jupiter, observations of whose changes of position made with more exactness on succeeding nights the following account will supply. I have measured also the intervals between them with the telescope in the manner already explained. Besides this, I have given the times of observation, especially when several were made in the same night, for the revolutions of these planets are so swift that an observer may generally get differences of position every hour.

January 12. At the first hour of the next night I saw these heavenly bodies arranged in this manner.

Ori.　　　★　＊●　★　　　　Occ.

Figure 4-14

The satellite farthest to the east was greater than the satellite farthest to the west; but both were very conspicuous and bright; the distance of each one from Jupiter was two minutes. A third satellite, certainly not in view before, began to appear at the third hour: it nearly touched Jupiter on the east side, and was exceedingly small. They were all arranged in the same straight line, along the ecliptic.

January 13. For the first time four satellites were in view in the following position with regard to Jupiter.

Ori.　　　★　●＊ ＊ ★　　　　Occ.

Figure 4-15

There were three to the west and one to the east; they made a straight line nearly, but the middle satellite of those to the west deviated a little from the straight line toward the north. The satellite farthest to the east was at a distance of 2′ from Jupiter; there were intervals of 1′ only between Jupiter and the nearest satellite, and between the satellites themselves, west of Jupiter. All the satellites appeared of the same size, and though small they were

very brilliant and far outshone the fixed stars of the same magnitude.

January 14. The weather was cloudy. . . .

These are my observations upon the four Medicean planets, recently discovered for the first time by me; and although it is not yet permitted me to deduce by calculation from these observations the orbits of these bodies, yet I may be allowed to make some statements, based upon them, well worthy of attention.

Deductions from the Previous Observations Concerning the Orbits and Periods of Jupiter's Satellites

And, in the first place, since they are sometimes behind, sometimes before Jupiter, at like distances, and withdraw from this planet toward the east and toward the west only within very narrow limits of divergence, and since they accompany this planet alike when its motion is retrograde and direct, it can be a matter of doubt to no one that they perform their revolutions about this planet, while at the same time they all accomplish together orbits of twelve years' length about the center of the world. Moreover, they revolve in unequal circles, which is evidently the conclusion to be drawn from the fact that I have never been permitted to see two satellites in conjunction when their distance from Jupiter was great, whereas near Jupiter two, three, and sometimes all four have been found closely packed together. Moreover, it may be detected that the revolutions of the satellites which describe the smallest circles round Jupiter are the most rapid, for the satellites nearest to Jupiter are often to be seen in the east, when the day before they have appeared in the west, and contrariwise. Also the satellite moving in the greatest orbits seems to me, after carefully weighing the occasions of its returning to positions previously noticed, to have a periodic time of half a month.

Besides, we have a notable and splendid argument to remove the scruples of those who can tolerate the revolution of the planets round the sun in the Copernican system, yet are so disturbed by the motion of one moon about the earth, while both accomplish an orbit of a year's length about the sun, that they consider that this theory of the universe must be upset as impossible: for now we have not one planet only revolving about another, while both traverse a vast orbit about the sun, but our sense of sight presents to us four satellites circling about Jupiter, like the moon about the earth, while the whole system travels over a mighty orbit about the sun in the space of twelve years.

THE BIRTH OF A NEW PHYSICS*
by I. Bernard Cohen (1960)

Prior to 1609 the Copernican system had seemed to men a mere mathematical speculation, a proposal made to "save the phenomenon." The basic supposition that the earth was "merely another planet" had been so contrary to all the dictates of experience and common sense that very few men had faced up to the awesome consequences of the heliostatic system. But after 1609, when men discovered through Galileo's eyes what the universe was like, they had to accept the fact that the telescope showed the world to be non-Ptolemaic and non-Aristotelian, in that the uniqueness attributed to the earth (and the physics based on that supposed uniqueness) could not fit the facts. There were only two possibilities open: One was to refuse to look through the telescope or to refuse to accept what one saw when one did; the other was to reject the physics of Aristotle and the astronomy of Ptolemy. . . .

Aristotelian physics, as we have seen, was based on two postulates which could not stand the Copernican assault: One was the immobility of the earth; the other was the distinction between the physics of the earthly four elements and the physics of the fifth celestial element. So we may understand that after 1610 it became increasingly clear that the old physics had to be abandoned, and a new physics established—a physics suitable for the moving earth required in the Copernican system.[1]

For most thinking men in the decades following Galileo's observations with the telescope the concern was not so much for the need of a new system of physics, as it was for a new system of the world. Gone forever was the concept that the earth had a fixed spot in the center of the universe, but it was now conceived to be in motion, never in the same place for any two immediately successive instants. Gone also was the comforting thought that the earth is unique, that it is an individual object without any likeness anywhere in the universe, that the uniqueness of man had given a uniqueness to his habitation. There were other problems that soon arose, of which one is the size of the universe. For the ancients the universe was finite, each of the celestial spheres, including that of the fixed stars, being a finite size and moving in its diurnal motion so that each part of it had a finite speed. If the stars were at an infinite distance, then they could not move in a daily circular motion around the earth with a finite speed, for the path of an object at an infinite distance must be infinitely long, and the time it takes to move an infinite distance is infinite. Hence in the geostatic system the fixed stars could not be infinitely far away. But in the Copernican system, when the fixed stars were not only fixed with regard to one another but were actually considered fixed in space, there was no limitation upon their distance.

Not all Copernicans considered the universe

---

* Cohen, *op. cit.*

[1] Galileo's observations of the phases and relative sizes of Venus, and of the occasional gibbous phase of Mars, proved that Venus and presumably the other planets move in orbits around the sun. There is no planetary observation by which we on earth can prove that the earth is moving in an orbit around the sun. Thus all Galileo's discoveries with the telescope can be accommodated to the system invented by Tycho Brahe just before Galileo began his observations of the heavens. In this Tychonic system, the planets Mercury, Venus, Mars, Jupiter and Saturn move in orbits around the sun, while the sun moves in an orbit around the earth in a year. Furthermore, the daily rotation of the heavens is communicated to the sun and planets, so that the earth itself neither rotates nor revolves in an orbit. The Tychonic system appealed to those who sought to save the immobility of the earth while accepting some of the Copernican innovations [Fig. 3-23].

infinite, and Copernicus himself certainly thought of the universe as finite, as did Galileo. But others saw Galileo's discoveries as indicating the presence of innumerable stars as infinite distances, and the earth itself diminished to a speck. Nowhere can one see the disruption of "this little world of man," and what has been called "the realization of how slight a part that world plays in an enlarged and enlarging universe," better than in these lines of a sensitive clergyman and poet, John Donne:

And new Philosophy calls all in doubt,
The Element of fire is quite put out;
The Sun is lost, and th' earth, and no mans wit
Can well direct him where to looke for it.
And freely men confesse that this world's spent,
When in the Planets, and the Firmament
They seeke so many new; then see that this
Is crumbled out againe to his Atomies.
'Tis all in peeces, all cohaerence gone;
All just supply, and all Relation.

The Physics of a Moving Earth

Odd as it may seem, most people's views about motion are part of a system of physics that was proposed more than 2000 years ago and was experimentally shown to be inadequate at least 1400 years ago. It is a fact that presumably well-educated men and women tend even today to think about the physical world as if the earth were at rest, rather than in motion. By this I do not mean that such people really believe the earth is at rest; if questioned, they will reply that of course they "know" that the earth rotates once a day about its axis and at the same time moves in a great yearly orbit around the sun. Yet when it comes to explaining certain common physical events, these same people are not able to tell you how it is that these everyday phenomena can happen, as we see they do, on a moving earth. In particular, these misunderstandings of physics tend to center on the problem of falling objects, on the general concept of motion. Thus we may see exemplified the precept of the Renaissance genius Leonardo da Vinci, "To understand motion is to understand nature."

Where Will It Fall?

In his inability to deal with questions of motion in relation to a moving earth, the average person is in the same position as some of the greatest scientists of the past, which may be a source of considerable comfort to him. The major difference is, however, that for the scientist of the past the inability to resolve these questions was a sign of his time, whereas for the modern man such inability is, alas, a badge of ignorance. Characteristic of these problems is a woodcut of the sixteenth century (Figure 4-16) showing a

Figure 4-16. "Will it fall back down again?" reads the legend on this old woodcut, taken from the correspondence of René Descartes. It illustrates an experiment proposed by Father Mersenne, contemporary and friend of Galileo, to test the behavior of falling bodies, by firing a cannon ball directly upward.

cannon pointing up in the air. Observe the question that is asked, *"Retombera-t-il?"* (Will it fall back down again?) If the earth is at rest, there is no doubt that the cannon ball fired straight up in the air would eventually come straight down again into the cannon. But will it on a moving earth? And if it will, why?

In a general way let us examine all the arguments. If supporters of the theory that the earth may move contended that the air must move along with the earth, and that an arrow shot up into the air would be carried along with the moving air and earth, the opponents had a ready reply: Even if the air could be supposed to move—a difficult supposition since there is no apparent cause for the air to move with the earth—would not the air move very much more slowly than the earth since it is so very different in substance and in quality? And even so would not, therefore, the arrow be left behind? And what of the high winds that a man in a tower should feel? . . .

The earth rotates upon its axis once in every 24 hours. At the equator the circumference of the earth is approximately 24,000 miles, and so the speed of rotation of any observer at the earth's equator is 1000 miles per hour. This is a linear speed of about 1500 feet per second. Conceive the following experiment. A rock is thrown straight up into the air. The time in which it rises is, let us say, two seconds, while a similar time is required for its descent. During four seconds the rotation of the earth will have moved the point from which the object was thrown a distance of some 6000 feet, a little over a mile. But the rock does not strike the earth one mile away; it lands very near the point from which it was thrown. We ask, How can this be possible? How can the earth be twirling around at this tremendous speed of 1000 miles per hour and yet we do not hear the wind whistling as the earth leaves the air behind it? Or, to take one of the other classical objections to the idea of a moving earth, consider a bird perched on the limb of a tree. The bird sees a worm on the ground and lets go of the tree. In the meanwhile the earth goes whirling by at this enormous rate, and the bird, though flapping its wings as hard as it can, will never achieve sufficient speed to find the worm—unless the worm is located to the west. But it is a fact of observation that birds do fly from trees to the earth and eat worms that lie to the east as well as to the west. Unless you can see your way clearly through these problems without a moment's thought, you do not really live modern physics to its fullest, and for you the statement that the earth rotates upon its axis once in 24 hours really has no meaning.

If the daily rotation presents a serious problem, think of the annual motion of the earth in its orbit. Let us compute the speed with which the earth moves in its orbit around the sun. There are 60 seconds in a minute and 60 minutes in an hour, or 3600 seconds in an hour. Multiply this number by 24 to get 86,400 seconds in a day. Multiply this by 365¼ days, and the result is a little more than 30 million seconds in a year. To find the speed at which the earth moves around the sun, we have to compute the size of the earth's orbit and divide it by the time it takes the earth to move through the orbit. This path is roughly a circle with a radius of about 93 million miles, and a circumference of about 580,000,000 miles (the circumference of the circle is equal to the radius multiplied by 2π). This is equivalent to saying that the earth moves through about 3,000,000,000,000 feet in every year. The speed of the earth is thus

$$\frac{3,000,000,000,000 \text{ feet}}{30,000,000 \text{ seconds}} = 100,000 \text{ ft/sec}$$

Each of the questions raised about the rotating earth can be raised again in magnified form with regard to an earth moving in an orbit. This speed of 100,000 feet per second, or about 19 miles per second, shows us the great difficulty encountered at the beginning of the chapter. Let us ask this question: Is it possible for us to move at a speed of 19 miles per second and not be aware of it? Suppose we dropped an object from a height of 16 feet; it would take about one second to strike the ground. According to our calculation, while this object was falling the earth should have been rushing away underneath, and the object would strike the ground some 19 miles from the point where it was dropped! And as for the birds on the trees, if a bird hanging on a limb for dear life were to let go for an instant, it would be lost out in space forever. Yet the fact is that birds are not lost in space but continue to inhabit the earth and to fly about it singing gaily.

These examples show us how difficult it really is to face the consequences of an earth in motion. It is plain that our ordinary ideas are inadequate to explain the observed facts of daily experience on an earth that is either rotating or moving in its orbit. There should be no doubt, therefore, that the shift from the concept of a stationary earth to a moving earth necessarily involved the birth of a new physics.

Uniform Linear Motion

Let us begin by a consideration of a limited problem: that of uniform linear motion. By this is meant motion proceeding in a straight line in such a way that if any two equal intervals of time are chosen, the distance covered in those two intervals will always be identical. This is the definition Galileo gave in his last and perhaps greatest book, *Discourses and Demonstrations Concerning Two New Sciences,* published in 1638, after his trial and condemnation by the Roman Inquisition. In this book Galileo presented his most mature views on dynamics, force in relation to motion. He emphasized particularly the fact that in defining uniform motion, it is important to make sure that the word "any" is included, for otherwise, he said, the definition would be meaningless. In this he was certainly criticizing some of his contemporaries and predecessors, and deservedly.

Suppose that there is such a motion in nature; we may ask with Galileo, what experiments could we imagine to demonstrate its nature? If we are in a ship or carriage moving uniformly in a straight line, what actually will happen to a weight allowed to fall freely? The answer, experiment will prove, is that in such circumstances the falling will be straight downward with regard to the frame of reference (say the cabin of a ship, or the interior of a carriage), and it will be so whether that frame of reference is standing still with regard to the outside environment or moving forward in a straight line at constant speed. Expressing it differently, we may state the general conclusion that no experiment can be performed within a sealed room moving in a straight line at constant speed that will tell you whether you are standing still or moving. In actual experience, we can often tell whether we are standing still or moving, because we can see from a window whether there is any relative motion between us and the earth. If the room is not closely sealed, we may feel the air rushing through and creating a wind. Or we may feel the vibration of motion or hear the wheels turning in a carriage, automobile, or railroad car. A form of relativity is involved here, and it was stated very clearly by Copernicus, because it was essential to his argument to establish that when two objects, such as the sun and earth, move relative to each other, it is impossible to tell which one is at rest and which one is in motion. Copernicus could point to the example of two ships at harbor, one pulling away from the other. A man on a ship asks which of the two, if either, is at anchor and which is moving out with the tide? The only way to tell is to observe the land, or a third ship at anchor. In present-day terms, we could use for this example two railroad trains on parallel tracks facing in opposite directions. We all have had the experience of watching a train on the adjacent track and thinking that we are in motion, only to find when the other train has left the station that we have been at rest all the time.

A Locomotive's Smokestack and a Moving Ship

But before we discuss this point further, an experiment is in order. This demonstration makes use of a toy train traveling along a straight track with what closely approximates uniform motion. The locomotive's smokestack contains a small cannon actuated by a spring, so constructed that it can fire a steel ball or marble vertically into the air. When the gun is loaded and the spring set, a release underneath the locomotive actuates a small trigger. In the first part of this experiment the train remains in place upon the track. The spring is set, the ball is placed in the small cannon, and the release mechanism triggered. In Figure 4-17, left, a scene of successive stroboscopic shots show us the position of the ball at equally separated intervals. Observe that the ball travels straight upward, reaches its maximum, then falls straight downward onto the locomotive, thus striking almost the very point from which it had been shot. In the second experiment the train is set into uniform motion, and the spring once again released. Figure 4-17, right, shows what happens. A comparison of the two pictures will convince you, incidentally, that the upward and downward part of the motion is the same in both cases, and is independent of whether the locomotive is at rest or has a forward

I. Bernard Cohen

Figure 4-17.   A ball fired with a spring gun in the smokestack of a moving toy locomotive describes a parabola (right) and lands on the locomotive instead of going straight up and down as it does when the locomotive is standing still (left). These stroboscopic pictures, with exposures at intervals of one-thirtieth of a second, vividly illustrate one of Galileo's arguments on the behavior of falling bodies and settle the ancient debate about bodies dropped from the masts of moving ships. If the speed of the locomotive were absolutely uniform and if the ball met no air resistance, it would land in the smokestack. (In fact, even under the imperfect conditions of the experiment, the ball hits the smokestack more often than not.) Note that the ball attains the same height whether the locomotive is at rest or moving. Notice, too, that in the picture where the locomotive is standing still, the distances traveled by the ball in the intervals of exposure correspond almost exactly. On the ascent, gravity slows it down; on the descent, gravity speeds it up.

motion. . . . we are primarily concerned with the fact that the ball continued to move in a forward direction with the train, and that it fell onto the locomotive just as it did when the train was at rest. Plainly then, this particular experiment, at least to the extent of determining whether the ball returns to the cannon or not, will never tell us whether the train is standing still or moving in a straight line with a constant speed.

Even those who cannot explain this experiment can draw a most important conclusion. Galileo's inability to explain how Jupiter could move without losing its satellites did not destroy the phenomenon's effectiveness as an answer to those who asked how the earth could move and not lose its moon. Just as our train experiment—even if unexplainable— would be sufficient answer to the argument that the earth must be at rest because otherwise a dropped ball would not fall vertically downward to strike the ground at a point directly below, and a cannon ball shot vertically upward would never return to the cannon. . . .

Galileo would have nodded in approval at our experiment. In his day the experiment was discussed, but not often performed. The usual reference frame was a moving ship. This was

a traditional problem, which Galileo introduced in his famous *Dialogue Concerning the Two Chief World Systems,* as a means of confuting the Aristotelian beliefs. In the course of this discussion, Galileo has Simplicio, the character in the dialogue who stands for the traditional Aristotelian, say that in his opinion an object dropped from the mast of a moving ship will strike the ship somewhere behind the mast along the deck. On first questioning, Simplicio admits that he has never performed the experiment, but he is persuaded to say that he assumes that Aristotle or one of the Aristotelians must have done this experiment or it would not have been reported. Ah no, says Galileo, this is certainly a false assumption, because it is plain that they have never performed this experiment. How can he be so sure? asks Simplicio, and he receives this reply: The proof that this experiment was never performed lies in the fact that the wrong answer was obtained. Galileo has given the right answer. The object will fall at the foot of the mast, and it will do so whether the ship is in motion or whether the ship is at rest. Incidentally, Galileo asserted elsewhere that he had performed such an experiment, although he did not say so in his treatise. Instead he said, "I, without observation, know that the result must be as I say, because it is necessary."

Why is it that an object falls to the same spot on the deck from the mast of a ship that is at rest and from the mast of a ship that is moving in a straight line with constant speed? For Galileo it was not enough that this should be so; it required some principle that would be basic to a system of dynamics that could account for the phenomena observed on a moving earth.

Galileo's Dynamics

Our toy train experiment, . . . illustrates three major aspects of Galileo's work in dynamics. In the first place, there is the principle of inertia, toward which Galileo strove but which, . . . awaited the genius of Isaac Newton for its modern definitive formulation. Secondly, the photographs of the distances of descent of the ball after successive equal intervals of time illustrate his principles of uniformly accelerated motion. Finally, in the fact that the rate of downward fall during the forward motion is the same as the rate of downward fall at rest, we may see an example of Galileo's famous principle of the composition of velocities. . . .

We shall examine these three topics by first considering Galileo's studies of accelerated motion in general, then his work dealing with inertia, and finally his analysis of complex motions.

In studying the problem of falling bodies, Galileo, we know, made experiments in which he dropped objects from heights, and— notably in the Pisan days of his youth—from a tower. Whether the tower was the famous Leaning Tower of Pisa or some other tower we cannot say; the records that he kept merely tell us that it was from some tower or other. Later on his biographer Viviani, who knew Galileo during his last years, told a fascinating story which has since taken root in the Galileo legend. According to Viviani, Galileo, desiring to confute Aristotle, ascended the Leaning Tower of Pisa, "in the presence of all other teachers and philosophers and of all students," and "by repeated experiments"

proved "that the velocity of moving bodies of the same composition, unequal in weight, moving through the same medium, do not attain the proportion of their weight, as Aristotle assigned it to them, but rather that they move with equal velocity. . . ." Since there is no record of this public demonstration in any other source, scholars have tended to doubt that it happened, especially since in its usual telling and retelling it becomes fancier each time. Whether Viviani made it up, or whether Galileo told it to him in his old age, not really remembering what had happened many decades earlier, we do not know. . . .

Such an experiment, if performed, could only have the result of proving Aristotle wrong. In Galileo's day, it was hardly a great achievement to prove that Aristotle was wrong in only one respect. Pierre de la Ramée (or Ramus) had some decades earlier made it known that everything in Aristotle's physics was unscientific. The inadequacies of the Aristotelian law of motion had been evident for at least four centuries, and during that time a considerable body of criticism had piled up. Although they struck another blow at Aristotle, experiments from the tower, whether the Tower of Pisa or any other, certainly did not disclose to Galileo a new and correct law of falling bodies. Yet formulation of the law was one of his greatest achievements.

To appreciate the full nature of Galileo's discoveries, we must understand the importance of abstract thinking, of its use by Galileo as a tool that in its ultimate polish was a much more revolutionary instrument than even the telescope. Galileo showed how abstraction may be related to the world of experience, how from thinking about "the nature of things," one may derive laws related to direct observation. . . .

Galileo demonstrated mathematically that a motion starting from rest in which the speed undergoes the same change in every equal interval of time (called *uniformly accelerated motion*) corresponds to traversing distances which are proportional to the squares of the elapsed times. Then Galileo showed by experiment that this ideal law is—within certain limits, we must interject—exemplified by motion on an inclined plane. From these two results, Galileo reasoned that in the absence of any air resistance, the motion of a freely falling body will always be accelerated according to this law. . . . When Robert Boyle, some thirty years later, was able to evacuate a cylinder, he showed that in such a vacuum all bodies fall with identical speeds no matter what their shapes. Thus proof was given of Galileo's assertion—an extrapolation from experience—that but for air resistance, all bodies fall at the same rate, with the same acceleration. Today we know the correct value of this acceleration (g) to be about 32 feet per second change of speed in each second. Hence, the speed of a falling body except for the almost negligible factor of air resistance, depends on the length of time during which it falls and not on its weight as Aristotle had supposed. . . .

In the *Discourses and Demonstrations Concerning Two New Sciences*, Galileo approached the problem of inertia chiefly in relation to his study of the path of a projectile, which he wanted to show was a parabola (Figure 4-18). Galileo considers a body sent out in a horizontal direction. It will then have two separate and independent motions. In the horizontal direction it will move with uniform velocity, except for the small slowing effect of air resistance. At the same time, its downward motion will be accelerated, just as a freely falling body is accelerated. It is the combination of these two motions that causes the trajectory to be parabolic. For his postulate that the downward component of the motion is the same as that of a freely falling body Galileo did not give an experimental proof, although he indicated the possibility of having one. He devised a little machine in which on an inclined plane a ball was projected horizontally, to move in a parabolic path.

Today we can easily demonstrate this conclusion by shooting one of a pair of balls horizontally, while the other is simultaneously allowed to fall freely from the same height. The result of such an experiment is shown in Figure 4-19, where a series of photographs

Figure 4-18. To see how Galileo analyzed projectile motion, consider a shell fired horizontally from a cannon at the edge of a cliff at a speed of 50 feet per second. The points A, B, C, D show where the shell would be at the ends of successive seconds if there were no air resistance and no downward component; in this case there being a uniform horizontal motion, the shell going 50 feet in each second. In the downward direction, there is an accelerated motion. The points a, b, c, d show where the shell would be if it were to fall with no air resistance and no forward motion. Since the distance is computed by the law D = ½AT² and the acceleration A is 32 feet per second, the distances corresponding to these times are:

T	T²	½AT²	D
1 sec	1 sec²	16 ft/sec² × 1 sec²	16 ft
2 sec	4 sec²	16 ft/sec² × 4 sec²	64 ft
3 sec	9 sec²	16 ft/sec² × 9 sec²	144 ft
4 sec	16 sec²	16 ft/sec² × 16 sec²	256 ft

Since the shell actually has the two motions simultaneously, the net path is as shown by the curve.

For those who like a bit of algebra, let v be the constant horizontal speed and x the horizontal distance, so that x = vt. In the vertical direction let the distance be y, so that y = ½AT².

Then, $x^2 = v^2t^2$, or $x^2/v^2 = t^2$, $2y/A = t^2$, and $x^2/v^2 = 2y/A$, or $y = (A/2v^2)x^2$, which is of the form $y = kx^2$, where k is a constant, and this is the classic equation of the parabola.

taken stroboscopically at successive instants shows that although one of the balls is moving forward while the other is dropping vertically, the distances fallen in successive seconds are the same for both. This is the situation of a ball falling on a train moving at constant speed along a linear track. It falls *vertically* second after second just as it would if the train were at rest. Since it also moves horizontally at the same uniform speed as the train, its true path with respect to the earth is a parabola. Yet another modern example is that of an airplane flying horizontally at constant speed and releasing a bomb or torpedo. The downward fall is the same as if the

Berenice Abbott

Figure 4-19. The independence of the vertical and horizontal components of projectile motion is illustrated in this stroboscopic photograph. In intervals of one-thirtieth of a second the projected ball falling along a parabolic path drops exactly the same distance as the ball allowed to fall vertically.

bomb or torpedo had been dropped from the same height from an object at rest, say a captive balloon on a calm day. As the bomb or torpedo falls from the airplane, it will continue to move forward with the horizontal uniform speed of the airplane and will, except for the effects of the air, remain directly

under the plane. But to an observer at rest on the earth, the trajectory will be a parabola.

Finally consider a stone dropped from a tower. With respect to the earth (and for such a short fall the movement of the earth can be considered linear and uniform), falls straight downward. But with respect to the space determined by the fixed stars, it retains the motion shared with the earth at the moment of release, and its trajectory is therefore a parabola.

These analyses of parabolic trajectories are all based on the Galilean principle of separating a complex motion into two motions (or components) at right angles to each other. It is certainly a measure of his genius that he saw that a body could simultaneously have a uniform or nonaccelerated horizontal component of velocity and an accelerated vertical component—neither one in any way affecting the other. In every such case, the horizontal component exemplifies the tendency of a body that is moving at constant speed in a straight line to continue to do so, even though it loses physical contact with the original source of that uniform motion. This may also be described as a tendency of any body to resist any change in its state of motion, a property generally known since Newton's day as a body's *inertia*.

THE BATTLE WITH AUTHORITY*
by Arthur Koestler (1959)

I shall take up the thread of Galileo's life at the point where his name suddenly burst into world fame through his discovery of the Jupiter planets. The *Star Messenger* was published in March 1610; in September, he took up his new post as "Chief Mathematician and Philosopher" to the Medicis in Florence; the following spring he spent in Rome.

The visit was a triumph. Cardinal del Monte wrote in a letter: "If we were still living under the ancient Republic of Rome, I

* From Arthur Koestler, *The Sleepwalkers*. Copyright 1959 by Arthur Koestler and used with permission of The Macmillan Company.

verily believe that there would have been a column on the Capitol erected in Galileo's honor." The select Accademia dei Lincei (the lynx-eyed), presided by Prince Federico Cesi, elected him a member and gave him a banquet; it was at this banquet that the word "telescope" was for the first time applied to the new invention. Pope Paul V received him in friendly audience, and the Jesuit Roman College honoured him with various ceremonies which lasted a whole day. The chief mathematician and astronomer of the College, the venerable Father Clavius, principal author of the Gregorian Calendar reform, who at first had laughed at the *Star Messenger*, was now entirely converted; so were the other astronomers at the College, Fathers Grienberger, van Maelcote and Lembo. They not only accepted Galileo's discoveries, but improved on his observations, particularly of Saturn and the phases of Venus. When the head of the College, the Lord Cardinal Bellarmine, asked for their official opinion on the new discoveries, they unanimously confirmed them.

This was of utmost importance. The phases of Venus, confirmed by the dozen of Jesuit astronomers, were incontrovertible proof that at least that planet revolved round the sun, that the Ptolemaic system had become untenable, and that the choice now lay between Copernicus and Brahe.† The Jesuit Order was the intellectual spearhead of the Catholic Church. Jesuit astronomers everywhere in Europe—particularly Scheiner in Ingoldstadt, Lanz in Munich, Kepler's friend Guldin in Vienna, and the Roman College in a body—began to support the Tychonic system as a half-way house to the Copernican. The Copernican system itself could be freely discussed and advocated as a working hypothesis, but it was unfavourably viewed to present it as established truth, because it seemed contrary to current interpretation of scripture—unless and until definite proof could be adduced in its favour. . . .

Within a brief period, Jesuit astronomers also confirmed the "earthly" nature of the moon, the existence of sunspots, and the fact that comets moved in outer space, beyond the moon. This meant the abandonment of the Aristotelian doctrine of the perfect and unchangeable nature of the celestial spheres. Thus the intellectually most influential order within the Catholic Church was at that time in full retreat from Aristotle and Ptolemy, and had taken up an intermediary position regarding Copernicus. They praised and feted Galileo, whom they knew to be a Copernican, and they kept Kepler, the foremost exponent of Copernicanism, under their protection throughout his life.

But there existed a powerful body of men whose hostility to Galileo never abated: the Aristotelians at the universities. The inertia of the human mind and its resistance to innovation are most clearly demonstrated not, as one might expect, by the ignorant mass—which is easily swayed once its imagination is caught—but by professionals with a vested interest in tradition and in the monopoly of learning. Innovation is a twofold threat to academic mediocrities: it endangers their oracular authority, and it evokes the deeper fear that their whole, laboriously constructed intellectual edifice might collapse. The academic backwoodsmen have been the curse of genius from Aristarchus to Darwin and Freud; they stretch, a solid and hostile phalanx of Pedantic mediocrities, across the centuries. It was this threat—not Bishop Dantiscus or Pope Paul III—which had cowed Canon Koppernigk into lifelong silence. In Galileo's case, the phalanx resembled more a rearguard still firmly entrenched in academic chairs and preachers' pulpits.

[During the next few years, Galileo's friends in Rome kept him informed about the attitude of the Church toward his work.

Letter to Galileo from Monsignor Ciampoli, 1615:]

Cardinal Barberini [the future Pope Urban VIII], who as you know from experience, has always admired your worth, told me only yesterday evening that with respect to these opinions he would like greater caution in *not going beyond the arguments used by Ptolemy and Copernicus*,[1] and finally in not exceeding the limitations of physics and mathematics. For to explain the Scriptures is claimed by theologians as their field, and if new things are brought in, even by an admirable mind, not everyone has the dispassionate faculty of taking them just as they are said. . . .

[Letter from Cardinal Piero Dini to Galileo a few days later:]

With Bellarmine I spoke at length of the things you had written. . . . And he said that as to Copernicus, there is no question of his book being prohibited; the worst that might happen, according to him, would be the addition of

† See footnote, p. 121, and Fig. 3-23. Ed.

[1] I.e., that they are to be regarded as mathematical hypotheses only, in the sense of Osiander's preface.

some material in the margins of that book to the effect that Copernicus had introduced his theory in order to save the appearances, or some such thing—just as others had introduced epicycles without thereafter believing in their existence. And *with a similar precaution you may at any time deal with these matters.* If things are fixed according to the Copernican system, [he said], it does not appear presently that they would have any greater obstacle in the Bible than the passage "(the sun) exults as a strong man to run his course," etc., which all expositors up to now have understood by attributing motion to the sun. And although I replied that this also could be explained as a concession to our ordinary forms of expression, I was told in answer that this was not a thing to be done in haste, just as the condemnation of any of these opinions was not to be passionately hurried. . . . I can only rejoice for you. . . .

The next utterance came from Bellarmine himself. It was a precise and authoritative statement of his attitude, and in view of his position as Consultor of the Holy Office, Master of Controversial Questions, etc., it amounted to an unofficial definition of the Church's attitude to Copernicus. The statement was occasioned by Father Foscarini's book advocating the Copernican system, and couched in the form of a letter of acknowledgement; but it was clearly addressed to Galileo as well, whose name is expressly mentioned. The letter is dated 4 April, 1615:*

My Very Reverend Father,

It has been a pleasure to me to read the Italian letter and the Latin paper you sent me. I thank you for both the one and the other, and I may tell you that I found them replete with skill and learning. As you ask for my opinion, I will give it as briefly as possible because, at the moment I have very little time for writing.

First, I say it seems to me that your Reverence and Signor Galileo act prudently when you content yourselves with speaking hypothetically and not absolutely, as I have always understood that Copernicus spoke. *For to say that the assumption that the Earth moves and the Sun stands still saves all the celestial appearances better than do eccentrics and epicycles, is to speak with excellent good sense and to run no*

risk whatever. *Such a manner of speaking suffices for a mathematician.* But to want to affirm that the Sun, in very truth, is at the centre of the universe and only rotates on its axis without travelling from east to west, and that the Earth is situated in the third sphere and revolves very swiftly around the Sun, is a very dangerous attitude and one calculated not only to arouse all Scholastic philosophers and theologians but also to injure our holy faith by contradicting the Scriptures. . . .

Second, I say that, as you know, the council of Trent forbids the interpretation of the Scriptures in a way contrary to the common agreement of the holy Fathers. Now if your Reverence will read, not merely the Fathers, but modern commentators on Genesis, the Psalms, Ecclesiastes, and Joshua, you will discover that all agree in interpreting them literally as teaching that the Sun is in the heavens and revolves round the Earth with immense speed and that the Earth is very distant from the heavens, at the centre of the universe, and motionless. Consider, then, in your prudence, whether the Church can support that the Scriptures should be interpreted in a manner contrary to that of the holy Fathers and of all modern commentators, both Latin and Greek. . . .

Third, I say that, *if there were a real proof* that the Sun is the centre of the universe, that the Earth is in the third sphere, and that the Sun does not go round the Earth but the Earth round the Sun, then we should have to proceed with great circumspection in explaining passages of Scripture which appear to teach the contrary, and we should rather have to say that we did not understand them than declare an opinion to be false which is proven to be true. But I do not think there is any such proof *since none has been shown to me.* To demonstrate that the appearances are saved by assuming the sun at the centre and the earth in the heavens is not the same thing as to demonstrate that *in fact* the sun is in the centre and the earth in the heavens. I believe that the *first demonstration may exist, but I have very grave doubts about the second;* and in case of doubt one may not abandon the Holy Scriptures as expounded by the holy Fathers. . . .

[Galileo's] answer to Bellarmine was contained in a letter written at some date in May to Cardinal Dini:†

---

* Italics added by Koestler. Ed.

† Italics added by Koestler. Ed.

To me, the surest and swiftest way to prove that the position of Copernicus is not contrary to Scripture would be to give a host of proofs that it is true and that the contrary cannot be maintained at all; thus, since no truths can contradict one another, this and the Bible must be perfectly harmonious. *But how can I do this, and not be merely wasting my time, when those Peripatetics who must be convinced show themselves incapable of following even the simplest and easiest of arguments? . . .*

Yet I should not despair of overcoming even this difficulty if I were in a place where I could use my tongue instead of my pen; and if I ever get well again so that I can come to Rome, I shall do so, in the hope of at least showing my affection for the holy Church. My urgent desire on this point is that no decision be made which is not entirely good. Such it would be to declare, under the prodding of an army of malign men who understand nothing of the subject, that Copernicus did not hold the motion of the earth to be a fact of nature, but as an astronomer merely took it to be a convenient hypothesis for explaining the appearances. . . .

Early in December [1615] Galileo arrived in Rome. . . . A Roman witness, Monsignor Querengo, describing Galileo in action:

We have here Signor Galileo who, in gatherings of men of curious mind, often bemuses many concerning the opinion of Copernicus, which he holds for true. . . . He discourses often amid fifteen or twenty guests who make hot assaults upon him, now in one house, now in another. But he is so well buttressed that he laughs them off; and although the novelty of his opinion leaves people unpersuaded, yet he convicts of vanity the greater part of the arguments with which his opponents try to overthrow him. Monday in particular, in the house of Federico Ghisileri, he achieved wonderful feats; and what I liked most was that, before answering the opposing reasons, he amplified them and fortified them himself with new grounds which appeared invincible, so that, in demolishing them subsequently, he made his opponents look all the more ridiculous. . . .

He is passionately involved in this quarrel, as if it were his own business, and he does not see and sense what it would comport; so that he will be snared in it, and will get himself into danger, together with anyone who seconds him.

. . . For he is vehement and is all fixed and impassioned in this affair, so that it is impossible, if you have him around, to escape from his hands. And this is a business which is not a joke but may become of great consequence, and this man is here under our protection and responsibility. . . .

On March 5, 1616 the General Congregation of the Index issued . . . a decree:

And whereas it has also come to the knowledge of the said Congregation that the Pythagorean doctrine—which is false and altogether opposed to the Holy Scripture—of the motion of the Earth, and the immobility of the Sun, which is also taught by Nicolaus Copernicus in *De revolutionibus orbium coelestium,* and by Diego de Zuniga [in his book] on Job, is now being spread abroad and accepted by many—as may be seen from a certain letter of a Carmelite Father, entitled *Letter of the Rev. Father Paolo Antonio Foscarini, Carmelite, on the Opinion of the Pythagoreans and of Copernicus concerning the Motion of the Earth, and the Stability of the Sun, and the New Pythagorean System of the World, at Naples, Printed by Lazzaro Scoriggio, 1615:* wherein the said Father attempts to show that the aforesaid doctrine of the immobility of the sun in the centre of the world, and of the Earth's motion, is consonant with truth and is not opposed to Holy Scripture. Therefore, in order that this opinion may not insinuate itself any further to the prejudice of Catholic truth, the Holy Congregation has decreed that the said Nicolaus Copernicus, *De revolutionibus orbium,* and Diego de Zuniga, *On Job,* be suspended until they be corrected; but that the book of the Carmelite Father, Paolo Antonio Foscarini, be altogether prohibited and condemned, and that all other works likewise, in which the same is taught, be prohibited, as by this present decree it prohibits, condemns, and suspends them all respectively. In witness whereof the present decree has been signed and sealed with the hands and with the seal of the most eminent and Reverend Lord Cardinal of St. Cecilia, Bishop of Albano, on the fifth day of March, 1616.

Six days after the decree, Galileo was received by the Pope, in an audience which lasted three quarters of an hour. But while everything was done to spare him public humiliation, he had been confidentially but firmly enjoined to keep within the prescribed limits. This had happened between the session of the Qualifiers on 23 February, and the publication of the decree. On Thursday, 25 February, there is the following entry in the Inquisition file:*

Thursday, 25 February 1616. The Lord Cardinal Mellini notified the Reverend Fathers, the Assessor, and the Commissary of the Holy Office that the censure passed by the theologians upon the propositions of Galileo—to the effect that the Sun is the centre of the world and immovable from its place, and that the Earth moves, and also with a diurnal motion—had been reported; and His Holiness has directed the Lord Cardinal Bellarmine to summon before him the said Galileo and admonish him to abandon the said opinion; and, *in case of his refusal to obey*, that the Commissary is to enjoin on him, before a notary and witnesses, a command to abstain altogether from teaching or defending this opinion and doctrine and even from discussing it: and, if he do not acquiesce therein, that he is to be imprisoned.

* Italics added by Koestler. Ed.

After the issue had been formally decided by the decree of 5 March . . . the Duke ordered Galileo back to Florence. For the next seven years he published nothing. . . .

Maffeo Barberini was elected to the papacy in 1623. . . . Barberini had opposed the decree of Congregation and intervened in favour of Galileo. . . . The [new] Pope showered favours on him—a pension for Galileo's son, a precious painting, a gold and silver medal. He also provided him with a glowing testimonial, addressed to the new Grand Duke, extolling the virtues and piety "of this great man, whose fame shines in the heavens, and goes on earth far and wide. . . ."

Thus encouraged, and in the full sunshine of papal favour, Galileo, who was now past sixty, felt the road at last free to embark on his great apologia of Copernicus. . . . In February 1632, the first printed copies of the *Dialogue [on the Great World Systems]* came from the press. . . . By August, the book was confiscated, and in October Galileo was summoned to appear before the Inquisition in Rome.

THE SENTENCE OF THE INQUISITION
(1633)

Whereas you, Galileo, son of the late Vincenzio Galilei, of Florence, aged 70 years, were denounced in 1615, to this Holy Office, for holding as true a false doctrine taught by many, namely, that the sun is immovable in the centre of the world, and that the earth moves, and also with a diurnal motion; also, for having pupils whom you instructed in the same opinions; also, for maintaining a correspondence on the same with some German mathematicians; also for publishing certain letters on the sunspots, in which you developed the same doctrine as true; also for answering the objections which were continually produced from the Holy Scriptures, by glozing the said Scriptures according to your own meaning; and whereas thereupon was produced the copy of a writing, in form of a letter, professedly written by you to a person formerly your pupil, in which, following the hypothesis of Copernicus, you include several propositions contrary to the true sense and authority of the Holy Scriptures; therefore (this Holy Tribunal being desirous of providing against the disorder and mischief which were thence proceeding and increasing to the detriment of the Holy Faith) by the desire of his Holiness and of the Most Eminent Lords, Cardinals of this supreme and universal Inquisition, the two propositions of the stability of the sun, and the motion of the earth, were qualified by the Theological Qualifiers as follows:

1. The proposition that the sun is in the centre of the world and immovable from its place is absurd, philosophically false, and for-

mally heretical; because it is expressly contrary to the Holy Scriptures.

2. The proposition that the earth is not the centre of the world, nor immovable, but that it moves, and also with a diurnal action, is also absurd, philosophically false, and, theologically considered, at least erroneous in faith.

But whereas, being pleased at that time to deal mildly with you, it was decreed in the Holy Congregation, held before his Holiness on the twenty-fifth day of February, 1616, that his Eminence the Lord Cardinal Bellarmine should enjoin you to give up altogether the said false doctrine; and if you should refuse, that you should be ordered by the Commissary of the Holy Office to relinquish it, not to teach it to others, nor to defend it; and in default of acquiescence, that you should be imprisoned; and whereas in execution of this decree, on the following day, at the Palace, in the presence of his Eminence the said Lord Cardinal Bellarmine, after you had been mildly admonished by the said Lord Cardinal, you were commanded by the Commissary of the Holy Office, before a notary and witnesses, to relinquish altogether the said false opinion, and, in future, neither to defend nor teach it in any manner, neither verbally nor in writing, and upon your promising obedience you were dismissed.

And, in order that so pernicious a doctrine might be altogether rooted out, not insinuate itself further to the heavy detriment of the Catholic truth, a decree emanated from the Holy Congregation of the Index prohibiting the books which treat of this doctrine, declaring it false, and altogether contrary to the Holy and Divine Scripture.

And whereas a book has since appeared published at Florence last year, the title of which showed that you were the author, which title is *The Dialogue of Galileo Galilei*, on the two principal Systems of the World—the Ptolemaic and Copernican; and whereas the Holy Congregation has heard that, in consequence of printing the said book, the false opinion of the earth's motion and stability of the sun is daily gaining ground, the said book has been taken into careful consideration, and in it has been detected a glaring violation of the said order, which had been intimated to you; inasmuch as in this book you have defended the said opinion, already, and in your presence, condemned; although, in the same book, you labour with many circumlocutions to induce the belief that it is left undecided and merely probable; which is equally a very grave error, since an opinion can in no way be probable which has been already declared and finally determined contrary to the Divine Scripture.

Therefore, by Our order, you have been cited to this Holy Office, where, on your examination upon oath, you have acknowledged the said book as written and printed by you. You also confessed that you began to write the said book ten or twelve years ago, after the order aforesaid had been given. Also, that you had demanded licence to publish it, without signifying to those who granted you this permission that you had been commanded not to hold, defend, or teach, the said doctrine in any manner. You also confessed that the reader might think the arguments adduced on the false side to be so worked as more effectually to compel conviction than to be easily refutable, alleging, in excuse, that you had thus run into an error, foreign (as you say) to your intention, from writing in the form of a dialogue, and in consequence of the natural complacency which everyone feels with regard to his own subtleties, and in showing himself more skilful than the generality of mankind in contriving, even in favour of false propositions, ingenious and plausible arguments.

And, upon a convenient time being given you for making your defence, you produced a certificate in the handwriting of his Eminence the Lord Cardinal Bellarmine, procured, as you said, by yourself, that you might defend yourself against the calumnies of your enemies, who reported that you had adjured your opinions, and had been punished by the Holy Office; in which certificate it is declared that you had not abjured nor had been punished, but merely that the declaration made by his Holiness, and promulgated by the Holy Congregation of the Index, had been announced to you, which declares that the opinion of the motion of the earth and stability of the sun is contrary to the Holy Scriptures, and, therefore, cannot be held or defended. Wherefore, since no mention is there made of two articles of the order, to wit, the order "not to teach" and "in any manner," you argued that we ought to believe that, in the lapse of fourteen or sixteen years, they had escaped your memory, and that this was also the reason why you were silent as to the order when you sought permission to publish your book, and that this is said by you, not to excuse your error, but that it may be attributed to vain-glorious ambition rather than to malice. But this very certificate, produced on your behalf, has greatly aggravated your offence, since it is therein declared that the said opinion is contrary to the Holy Scriptures, and yet you have dared to treat of it, and to argue that it is probable. Nor is there any extenuation in the licence artfully and cunningly extorted by you, since you did not intimate the command imposed upon you. But whereas it appeared to Us that you had not disclosed the whole truth with regard to your intention, We thought it necessary to proceed to the rigorous examination of you, in which (without any prejudice to what you had confessed, and which is above detailed against you, with regard to your said intention) you answered like a good Catholic.

Therefore, having seen and maturely considered the merits of your cause, with your said confessions and excuses, and everything else which ought to be seen and considered, we have come to the underwritten final sentence against you:

Invoking, therefore, the most holy name of our Lord Jesus Christ, and of His Most Glorious Virgin Mother, Mary, We pronounce this Our final sentence, which, sitting in council and judgment with the Reverend Masters of Sacred Theology and Doctors of both Laws, Our Assessors, We put forth in this writing in regard to the matters and controversies between the Magnificent Carlo Sincereo, Doctor of both Laws, Fiscal Proctor of the Holy Office, of the one part, and you, Galileo Galilei, defendant, tried and confessed as above, of the other part, We pronounce, judge, and declare, that you, the said Galileo, by reason of these things which have been detailed in the course of this writing, and which, as above, you have confessed, have rendered yourself vehemently suspected by this Holy Office of heresy, that is of having believed and held the doctrine (which is false and contrary to the Holy and Divine Scriptures), that the sun is the centre of the world, and that it does not move from east to west, and that the earth does move, and is not the centre of the world; also, that an opinion can be held and supported and probable, after it has been declared and finally decreed contrary to the Holy Scripture, and, consequently, that you have incurred all the censures and penalties enjoined and promulgated in the sacred canons and other general and particular constitutions against delinquents of this description. From which it is Our pleasure that you be absolved, provided that with a sincere heart and unfeigned faith, in Our presence, you abjure, curse, and detest, the said errors and heresies, and every other error and heresy, contrary to the Catholic and Apostolic Church of Rome, in the form now shown to you.

But that your grievous and pernicious error and transgression may not go altogether unpunished, and that you may be made more cautious in future, and may be a warning to others to abstain from delinquencies of this sort, We decree that the book *Dialogues of Galileo Galilei* be prohibited by a public edict, and We condemn you to the formal prison of this Holy Office for a period determinable at Our pleasure; and by way of salutary penance, We order you during the next three years to recite, once a week, the seven penitential psalms, reserving to Ourselves the power of moderating, commuting, or taking off, the whole or part of the said punishment or penance.

THE FORMULA OF ABJURATION
Galileo Galilei (1633)

I, Galileo Galilei, son of the late Vincenzio Galilei of Florence, aged seventy years, being brought personally to judgment, and kneeling before you, Most Eminent and Most Reverend Lords Cardinals, General Inquisitors of the Universal Christian Republic against heretical depravity, having before my eyes the Holy Gospels which I touch with my own hands, swear that I have always believed, and, with the help of God, will in future believe, every article which the Holy Catholic and Apostolic Church of Rome holds, teaches, and preaches. But because I have been enjoined, by this Holy Office, altogether to abandon the false opinion which maintains that the sun is the centre and immovable, and forbidden to hold, defend, or teach, the said false doctrine in any manner; and because, after it had been signified to me that the said doctrine is repugnant to the Holy Scripture, I have written and printed a book, in which I treat of the same condemned doctrine, and adduce reasons with great force in support of the same, without giving any solution, and therefore have been judged grievously suspected of heresy; that is to say, that I held and believed that the sun is the centre of the world and immovable, and that the earth is not the centre and movable, I am willing to remove from the minds of your Eminences, and of every Catholic Christian, his vehement suspicion rightly entertained towards me, therefore, with a sincere heart and unfeigned faith, I abjure, curse, and detest the said errors and heresies, and generally every other error and sect contrary to the said Holy Church; and I swear that I will never more in future say, or assert anything, verbally or in writing, which may give rise to a similar suspicion of me; but that if I shall know any heretic, or anyone suspected of heresy, I will denounce him to this Holy Office, or to the Inquisitor and Ordinary of the place in which I may be. I swear, moreover, and promise that I will fulfil and observe fully all the penances which have been or shall be laid on me by this Holy Office. But if it shall happen that I violate any of my said promises, oaths, and protestations (which God avert!), I subject myself to all the pains and punishments which have been decreed and promulgated by the sacred canons and other general and particular constitutions against delinquents of this description. So, may God help me, and His Holy Gospels, which I touch with my own hands, I, the above-named Galileo Galilei, have abjured, sworn, promised, and bound myself as above; and, in witness thereof, with my own hand have subscribed this present writing of my abjuration, which I have recited word for word.

At Rome, in the Convent of Minerva, June 22, 1633, I, Galileo Galilei, have abjured as above with my own hand.

It is not true that after reciting this abjuration, he muttered: *"Eppur si muove."* It was the world that said this—not Galileo.

Bertrand Russell
The Scientific Outlook (1931)

We must face the fact that society is founded on intolerance. There are glaring cases of the abuse of intolerance; but they are quite as characteristic of our own age as of the Middle Ages. The typical modern example and contrast is compulsory inoculation replacing what was virtually compulsory baptism. But compulsion to inoculate is objected to as a crudely unscientific and mischievous anti-sanitary quackery, not in the least because we think it wrong to compel people to protect their children from disease. Its opponents would make it a crime, and will probably succeed in doing so; and that will be just as intolerant as making it compulsory. Neither the Pasteurians nor their opponents the Sanitarians would leave parents free to bring up their children naked, though that course also has some plausible advocates. We prate of toleration as we will; but society must always draw a line somewhere between allowable conduct and insanity or crime, in spite of the risk of mistaking sages for lunatics and saviors for blasphemers. We must persecute, even to the death; and all we can do to mitigate the danger of persecution is, first, to be very careful what we persecute, and second, to bear in mind that unless there is a large liberty to shock conventional people, and a well informed sense of the value of originality, individuality, and eccentricity, the result will be apparent stagnation covering a repression of evolutionary forces which will eventually explode with extravagant and probably destructive violence.

George Bernard Shaw
Preface to St. Joan (1924)

QUESTIONS TO CONSIDER

How did Galileo's work help to establish the truth of the Copernican theory?

Why do we believe today that the earth moves? Does the discovery of a small stellar parallax (see page 107) prove that the earth moves?

Does "Ockham's razor" give an adequate reason for the acceptance of the Copernican theory?

Copernicus and Galileo assumed quite different attitudes toward the acceptance of the heliocentric theory. Copernicus was reluctant to publish his work and did nothing to further its acceptance. Galileo, on the other hand, was described by a contemporary as being passionately in favor of the theory that he held to be true. Does Copernicus' attitude seem to you to be better suited to the nature of scientific investigation than Galileo's?

Is there a significant difference between the kinds of truth that science and religion are seeking?

SUGGESTIONS FOR FURTHER READING

Bronowski, J., and Bruce Mazlish: *The Western Intellectual Tradition*, Harper & Row, Publishers, New York, 1960, chaps. 1–8. An excellent description of the intellectual and cultural history of the Renaissance from Leonardo through Galileo.

* Burtt, E. A.: *The Metaphysical Foundations of Modern Science*, Anchor Books, Doubleday & Company, Inc., Garden City, N.Y., 1954, chaps I, II, and III. An analysis of the metaphysical and philosophical implications of the shift from the medieval to the modern view of man's place in the universe.

* Butterfield, Herbert: *The Origins of Modern Science*, The Macmillan Company, New York, 1959, chaps. I, II, and IV. A penetrating and interesting account of the scientific revolution.

* Cohen, I. Bernard: *The Birth of a New Physics*, Anchor Books, Doubleday & Company, Inc., Garden City, N.Y., 1960. A Science Study Series book that explores the emergence and development of new concepts in physics from Copernicus to Galileo. The Cohen selection in this part is taken from this book.

* De Santillana, Giorgio: *The Crime of Galileo*, Phoenix Books, The University of Chicago Press, Chicago, 1955. A scholarly and fascinating account of the conflicts of Galileo and the Roman Catholic Church.

* Hall, A. R.: *The Scientific Revolution*, Beacon Press, Boston, 1954, chaps. 1–5. A clear, well-written scientific history of this period.

Koestler, Arthur: *The Sleepwalkers*, The Macmillan Company, New York, 1959, chaps. II–IV. An interesting account of the circumstances that led up to Galileo's trial by the Inquisition. Koestler comes to quite different conclusions concerning the treatment of Galileo than de Santillana does in his book (see above). The reader will find it very interesting to compare these two accounts of the conflict.

* Lodge, Oliver: *Pioneers of Science*, Dover Publications, Inc., New York, 1960, lectures I, IV, and V. Another historical account of the Copernican theory, Galileo's discoveries with the telescope, and his argument with the church.

* Russell, Bertrand: *A History of Western Philosophy*, Simon and Schuster, Inc., New York, 1945, book 3, part I, chap. VI. A fine analysis of the philosophical implication of the Copernican theory in its historical context.

* Paperback edition.

PART 5

WHAT IS A SCIENTIFIC FACT?

Science starts with facts and returns to them to prove itself right or wrong. This part describes the dawning recognition in the seventeenth century of the importance of facts as the touchstone of science and illustrates in the discovery of Kepler's laws how increasing precision of measurement aids the advance of science. What are scientific facts, and what are the limitations involved in finding them?

Descartes

Bacon

INTRODUCTION

Science, as we know it today, was born in the Renaissance, the result of the union of logical thought with a new appreciation of the importance of experiment and observation. In the last two parts we followed the early history of abstract reasoning and saw how it laid the groundwork for scientific thinking. Now in this part we see how the inductive method became recognized as an essential part of science. The craftsmen and artisans of the Middle Ages had long used the cut-and-try empirical approach and had developed a store of practical knowledge, but, by and large, this information did not come to the attention of the scholastics who were theorizing about the physical world. Once the significance of empirical knowledge was recognized, many of the methods that had been developed by the artisans were taken over to help build scientific tools and perfect experimental techniques.

The importance of observation was mentioned as early as the thirteenth century in the writings of Roger Bacon, but these writings were not widely read at that time and did not have much influence until several hundred years later. The first modern formulation of a philosophy of science was made by Sir Frances Bacon. His precepts became the prototype of experimental or inductive method and still form the background for many of our beliefs about science today. The term *Baconian method* is sometimes loosely used as a synonym for *pure empiricism*. But Bacon believed that a proper balance should be struck between "empirics" and "dogmatics." He said, "The former, like ants, only heap up and use their store, the latter, like spiders, spin out their own webs. The bee, a mean between both, extracts matter from the flowers of the garden and the field; but works and fashions it by its own efforts."

Fortunately, the recoil from rationality was not so violent that the power of abstract thought was entirely discredited. In Descartes, we have an example of one of the great men of the time who championed the power of reason. The recognition that these two methods must be combined was the idea of major importance for science that emerged from the Renaissance. Together they have forged a tool of unparalleled flexibility and power. As Whitehead puts it, "The union of passionate interest in detailed facts with the equal devotion to abstract generalization forms the novelty of our present society."

The belief in the validity of the experimental method rests on the assumption that significant information about the physical world is revealed through sensory experience. Bacon recognized the difficulty of this when he said ". . . by far the greatest impediment and aberration of the human understanding pro-

Hall

Christianson

Russell

ceeds from the dullness, incompetence, and errors of the senses." Locke, Berkeley, and Hume, a century later, cast even graver doubts upon the validity of sensory data and the inductive process in general. Some of these doubts are vividly presented by Russell in the selection from *The Scientific Outlook*.

As scientists became more critical of their own methods and as better instruments became available to supplement the senses, the degree of accuracy used in scientific experiments grew increasingly important. The significance of this trend is illustrated by the work of Brahe and Kepler. Scientists began to discriminate between vague observations and scientific measurements, in which the accuracy was itself criticized and the range of error specified.

At first sight, it may seem paradoxical to talk about the range of error involved in facts. The confusion arises from a difference in the use of the word *fact* in everyday language and in scientific work. C. P. Snow makes the following comment* on "scientific facts":

Science starts with facts chosen from the external world. The relation between the choice, the chooser, the external world and the fact produced is a complicated one and brings us before questions of relativity and epistemology: but one gets through in the end, unless one is spinning a metaphysical veil for the sake of the craftsmanship, to an agreement upon "scientific facts." You can call them "pointer readings" as Eddington does, if you like. They are lines on a photographic plate, marks on a screen, all the "pointer readings" which are the end of the skill, precautions, inventions, of the laboratory. They are the end of the manual process, the beginning of the scientific. For from these "pointer readings," these scientific facts, the process of scientific reasoning begins: and it comes back to them to prove itself right or wrong. For the scientific process is nothing more nor less than a hiatus between "pointer readings"; one takes some pointer readings, makes a mental construction from them in order to predict some more.

Fact in this sense does not have the same degree of certainty that it has in common usage. "Pointer readings" are true within the limits and conditions set by the experiment and may be proved false under better-controlled or more refined experimental conditions. Yet scientific facts do represent the closest approach to certain knowledge about some particular aspect of the physical world, and, as we will see in the story of *Kepler—Eight Minutes of Arc*, the knowledge of the degrees of accuracy of these facts is a significant factor in the advance of science.

* Reprinted with the permission of Charles Scribner's Sons, New York, and Macmillan & Co., Ltd., London. From *The Search* by C. P. Snow. Copyright 1934 Charles Percy Snow; renewal copyright © 1962. © 1958 Charles Percy Snow.

THE NEW MENTALITY

Without experience nothing can be sufficiently known. For there are two modes of acquiring knowledge, namely, by reasoning and experience. Reasoning draws a conclusion and makes us grant the conclusion, but does not make the conclusion certain, nor does it remove doubt so that the mind may rest on the intuition of truth, unless the mind discovers it by the path of experience; since many have the arguments relating to what can be known, but because they lack experience they neglect the arguments, and neither avoid what is harmful nor follow what is good. For if a man who has never seen a fire should prove by adequate reasoning that fire burns and injures things and destroys them, his mind would not be satisfied thereby, nor would he avoid fire, until he placed his hand or some combustible substance in the fire, so that he might prove by experience that which reasoning taught. But when he has had actual experience of combustion his mind is made certain and rests in the full light of truth. Therefore reasoning does not suffice, but experience does. . . .

He therefore who wishes to rejoice without doubt in regard to the truths underlying phenomena must know how to devote himself to experiment. For authors write many statements, and believe them through reasoning which they formulate without experience. Their reasoning is wholly false. For it is generally believed that the diamond cannot be broken except by goat's blood, and philosophers and theologians misuse this idea. But fracture by means of blood of this kind has never been verified, although the effort has been made and without that blood it can be broken easily. For I have seen this with my own eyes, and this is necessary, because gems cannot be carved except by fragments of this stone. . . .

Moreover, it is generally believed that hot water freezes more quickly than cold water in vessels, and the argument in support of this is advanced that contrary is excited by contrary, just like enemies meeting each other. But it is certain that cold water freezes more quickly for anyone who makes the experiment. . . . If hot water and cold are placed in two vessels, the cold will freeze more quickly. Therefore all things must be verified by experiment.

Roger Bacon
Opus Majus (1267)*

* From Roger Bacon, *Opus Majus*, translated by Robert B. Burke, University of Pennsylvania Press, Philadelphia, 1928. Reprinted by permission.

THE SCIENTIFIC REVOLUTION†
by Alfred North Whitehead (1925)

The new mentality is more important than the new science and the new technology. It has altered the metaphysical presuppositions and the imaginative contents of our minds; so that now the old stimuli provoke a new response.

† From Alfred North Whitehead, *Science and the Modern World*, The Macmillan Company, New York, 1925, and used with permission of The Macmillan Company.

Perhaps my metaphor of a new colour is too strong. What I mean is just that slightest change of tone which yet makes all the difference. This is exactly illustrated by a sentence from a published letter of that adorable genius, William James. When he was finishing his great treatise on the *Principles of Psychol-*

ogy, he wrote to his brother Henry James, 'I have to forge every sentence in the teeth of irreducible and stubborn facts.'

This new tinge to modern minds is a vehement and passionate interest in the relation of general principles to irreducible and stubborn facts. All the world over and at all times there have been practical men, absorbed in 'irreducible and stubborn facts': all the world over and at all times there have been men of philosophic temperament who have been absorbed in the weaving of general principles. It is this union of passionate interest in the detailed facts with equal devotion of abstract generalisation which forms the novelty in our present society. Previously it had appeared sporadically and as if by chance. This balance of mind has now become part of the tradition which infects cultivated thought.

It is the salt which keeps life sweet. The main business of universities is to transmit this tradition as a widespread inheritance from generation to generation.

Galileo keeps harping on how things happen, whereas his adversaries had a complete theory as to why things happen. Unfortunately the two theories did not bring out the same results. Galileo insists upon 'irreducible and stubborn facts,' and Simplicius, his opponent, brings forward reasons, completely satisfactory, at least to himself. It is a great mistake to conceive this historical revolt as an appeal to reason. On the contrary, it was through and through an antiintellectualist movement. It was the return to the contemplation of brute fact; and it was based on a recoil from the inflexible rationality of medieval thought.

RULES FOR RIGHTLY CONDUCTING THE REASON*
by Rene Descartes (1637)

The *first* was never to accept anything for true which I did not clearly know to be such; that is to say, carefully to avoid precipitancy and prejudice, and to comprise nothing more in my judgment than what was presented to my mind so clearly and distinctly as to exclude all ground of doubt.

The *second*, to divide each of the difficulties under examination into as many parts as possible, and as might be necessary for its adequate solution.

* From René Descartes, *Discourse on Method*, translated by Veitch, The Open Court Publishing Company, La Salle, Ill. Reprinted with permission.

The *third*, to conduct my thoughts in such order that, by commencing with objects the simplest and easiest to know, I might ascend by little and little, and, as it were, step by step, to the knowledge of the more complex; assigning in thought a certain order even to those objects which in their own nature do not stand in a relation of antecedence and sequence.

And the *last*, in every case to make enumerations so complete, and reviews so general, that I might be assured that nothing was omitted.

THE IMPORTANCE OF EXPERIMENT†
by Francis Bacon (1620)

Preface

Those who have taken upon them to lay down the law of nature as a thing already searched out and understood, whether they have spoken

† From Francis Bacon, *Novum Organum*, translated and edited by James Spedding et al., Houghton Mifflin Company, Boston, 1869–1872.

in simple assurance or professional affectation, have therein done philosophy and the sciences great injury. For as they have been successful in inducing belief, so they have been effective in quenching and stopping inquiry; and have done more harm by spoiling and putting an end to other men's efforts than good by their own. Those on the other hand who have taken a contrary course, and asserted that absolutely nothing can be known,—whether it were from hatred of the ancient sophists, or from uncertainty and fluctuation of mind, or even from a kind of fulness of learning, that they fell upon this opinion,—have certainly advanced reasons for it that are not to be despised; but yet they have neither started from true principles nor rested in the just conclusion, zeal and affectation having carried them much too far. The more ancient of the Greeks (whose writings are lost) took up with better judgment a position between these two extremes,—between the presumption of pronouncing on everything, and the despair of comprehending anything; and though frequently and bitterly complaining of the difficulty of inquiry and the obscurity of things, and like impatient horses champing the bit, they did not the less follow up their object and engage with Nature; thinking (it seems) that this very question,—viz. whether or no anything can be known,—was to be settled not by arguing, but by trying. And yet they too, trusting entirely to the force of their understanding, applied no rule, but made everything turn upon hard thinking and perpetual working and exercise of the mind. . . .

Let there be therefore (and may it be for the benefit of both) two streams and two dispensations of knowledge; and in like manner two tribes or kindreds of students in philosophy—tribes not hostile or alien to each other, but bound together by mutual services;—let there in short be one method for the cultivation, another for the invention, of knowledge. . . .

And to make my meaning clearer and to familiarise the thing by giving it a name, I have chosen to call one of these methods or ways *Anticipation of the Mind*, the other *Interpretation of Nature*.

Aphorisms Concerning the Interpretation of Nature and the Kingdom of Man

1. Man, being the servant and interpreter of Nature, can do and understand so much and so much only as he has observed in fact or in thought of the course of nature: beyond this he neither knows anything nor can do anything.

2. Neither the naked hand nor the understanding left to itself can effect much. It is by instruments and helps that the work is done, which are as much wanted for the understanding as for the hand. And as the instruments of the hand either give motion or guide it so the instruments of the mind supply either suggestions for the understanding or cautions.

3. Human knowledge and human power meet in one; for where the cause is not known the effect cannot be produced. Nature to be commanded must be obeyed; and that which in contemplation is as the cause is in operation as the rule.

9. The cause and root of nearly all evils in the sciences is this—that while we falsely admire and extol the powers of the human mind we neglect to seek for its true helps.

10. The subtlety of nature is greater many times over than the subtlety of the senses and understanding; so that all those specious meditations, speculations, and glosses in which men indulge are quite from the purpose,[1] only there is no one by to observe it.

14. The syllogism consists of propositions, propositions consist of words, words are symbols of notions. Therefore if the notions themselves (which is the root of the matter) are confused and over-hastily abstracted from the facts, there can be no firmness in the superstructure. Our only hope therefore lies in a true induction.

19. There are and can be only two ways of searching into and discovering truth. The one flies from the senses and particulars to the most general axioms, and from these principles, the truth of which it takes for settled and immoveable, proceeds to judgment and to the discovery of middle axioms. And this way is now in fashion. The other derives axioms from the senses and particulars, rising by a gradual and unbroken ascent, so that it

[1] Literally, "are a thing insane." The meaning appears to be, that these speculations, being founded upon such an inadequate conception of the case, must necessarily be so wide of the truth that they would seem like mere madness if we could only compare them with it: like the aim of a man blindfolded to bystanders looking on.—J. Spedding.

arrives at the most general axioms last of all. This is the true way, but as yet untried.

20. The understanding left to itself takes the same course (namely, the former) which it takes in accordance with logical order. For the mind longs to spring up to positions of higher generality, that it may find rest there; and so after a little while wearies of experiment. But this evil is increased by logic, because of the order and solemnity of its disputations.

21. The understanding left to itself, in a sober, patient, and grave mind, especially if it be not hindered by received doctrines, tries a little that other way, which is the right one, but with little progress; since the understanding, unless directed and assisted, is a thing unequal, and quite unfit to contend with the obscurity of things.

22. Both ways set out from the senses and particulars, and rest in the highest generalities; but the difference between them is infinite. For the one just glances at experiment and particulars in passing, the other dwells duly and orderly among them. The one, again, begins at once by establishing certain abstract and useful generalities, the other rises by gradual steps to that which is prior and better known in the order of nature.

24. It cannot be that axioms established by argumentation should avail for the discovery of new works; since the subtlety of nature is greater many times over than the subtlety of argument. But axioms duly and orderly formed from particulars easily discover the way to new particulars, and thus render sciences active.

25. The axioms now in use, having been suggested by a scanty and manipular experience and a few particulars of most general occurrence, are made for the most part just large enough to fit and take these in: and therefore it is no wonder if they do not lead to new particulars. And if some opposite instance, not observed or not known before, chance to come in the way, the axiom is rescued and preserved by some frivolous distinction; whereas, the truer course would be to correct the axiom itself.

36. One method of delivery alone remains to us; which is simply this: we must lead men to the particulars themselves, and their series and order; while men on their side must force themselves for awhile to lay their notions by and begin to familiarise themselves with facts.

37. The doctrine of those who have denied that certainty could be attained at all, has some agreement with my way of proceeding at the first setting out; but they end in being infinitely separated and opposed. For the holders of that doctrine assert simply that nothing can be known; I also assert that not much can be known in nature by the way which is now in use. But then they go on to destroy the authority of the senses and understanding; whereas I proceed to devise and supply helps for the same.

38. The idols and false notions which are now in possession of the human understanding, and have taken deep root therein, not only so beset men's minds that truth can hardly find entrance, but even after entrance obtained, they will again in the very instauration of the sciences meet and trouble us, unless men being forewarned of the danger fortify themselves as far as may be against their assaults.

45. The human understanding is of its own nature prone to suppose the existence of more order and regularity in the world than it finds. And though there be many things in nature which are singular and unmatched, yet it devises for them parallels and conjugates and relatives which do not exist. Hence the fiction that all celestial bodies move in perfect circles; spirals and dragons being (except in name) utterly rejected. Hence too the element of Fire with its orb is brought in, to make up the square with the other three which the sense perceives. Hence also the ratio of density of the so-called elements is arbitrarily fixed at ten to one. And so on of other dreams. And these fancies affect not dogmas only, but simple notions also.

46. The human understanding when it has once adopted an opinion (either as being the received opinion or as being agreeable to itself) draws all things else to support and agree with it. And though there be a greater number and weight of instances to be found

on the other side, yet these it either neglects and despises, or else by some distinction sets aside and rejects; in order that by this great and pernicious predetermination[1] the authority of its former conclusions may remain inviolate. And therefore it was a good answer that was made by one who when they showed him hanging in a temple a picture of those who had paid their vows as having escaped shipwreck, and would have him say whether he did not now acknowledge the power of the gods,—"Aye," asked he again, "but where are they painted that were drowned after their vows?" And such is the way of all superstition, whether in astrology, dreams, omens, divine judgments, or the like; wherein men, having a delight in such vanities, mark the events where they are fulfilled, but where they fail, though this happen much oftener, neglect and pass them by. But with far more subtlety does this mischief insinuate itself into philosophy and the sciences; in which the first conclusion colours and brings into conformity with itself all that come after, though far sounder and better. Besides, independently of that delight and vanity which I have described, it is the peculiar and perpetual error of the human intellect to be more moved and excited by affirmatives than by negatives; whereas it ought properly to hold itself indifferently disposed towards both alike. Indeed in the establishment of any true axiom, the negative instance is the more forcible of the two.

47. The human understanding is moved by those things most which strike and enter the mind simultaneously and suddenly, and so fill the imagination; and then it feigns and supposes all other things to be somehow, though it cannot see how, similar to those few things by which it is surrounded. But for that going to and fro to remote and heterogeneous instances, by which axioms are tried as in the fire, the intellect is altogether slow and unfit, unless it be forced thereto by severe laws and overruling authority.

48. The human understanding is unquiet; it cannot stop or rest, and still presses onward, but in vain. Therefore it is that we cannot conceive of any end or limit to the world; but always as of necessity it occurs to us that there is something beyond. Neither again can it be conceived how eternity has flowed down to the present day; for that distinction which is commonly received of infinity in time past and in time to come can by no means hold; for it would thence follow that one infinity is greater than another, and that infinity is wasting away and tending to become finite. The like subtlety arises touching the infinite divisibility of lines, from the same inability of thought to stop. But this inability interferes more mischievously in the discovery of causes: for although the most general principles in nature ought to be held merely positive, as they are discovered, and cannot with truth be referred to a cause; nevertheless the human understanding being unable to rest still seeks something prior in the order of nature. And then it is that in struggling towards that which is further off it falls back upon that which is more nigh at hand; namely, on final causes: which have relation clearly to the nature of man rather than to the nature of the universe; and from this source have strangely defiled philosophy. But he is no less an unskilled and shallow philosopher who seeks causes of that which is most general, than he who in things subordinate and subaltern omits to do so.

49. The human understanding is no dry light, but receives an infusion from the will and affections; whence proceed sciences which may be called "sciences as one would." For what a man had rather were true he more readily believes. Therefore he rejects difficult things from impatience of research; sober things, because they narrow hope; the deeper things of nature, from superstition; the light of experience, from arrogance and pride, lest his mind should seem to be occupied with things mean and transitory; things not commonly believed, out of deference to the opinion of the vulgar. Numberless in short are the ways, and sometimes imperceptible, in which the affections colour and infect the understanding.

50. But by far the greatest hindrance and aberration of the human understanding pro-

[1] Rather perhaps "prejudging the matter to a great and pernicious extent, in order that," & c. (*non sine magno et pernicioso praejudicio, quo,* & c.)—J. Spedding.

ceeds from the dulness, incompetency, and deceptions of the senses; in that things which strike the sense outweigh things which do not immediately strike it, though they be more important. Hence it is that speculation commonly ceases where sight ceases; insomuch that of things invisible there is little or no observation. Hence all the working of the spirits inclosed in tangible bodies lies hid and unobserved of men. So also all the more subtle changes of form in the parts of coarser substances (which they commonly call alteration, though it is in truth local motion through exceedingly small spaces) is in like manner unobserved. And yet unless these two things just mentioned be searched out and brought to light, nothing great can be achieved in nature, as far as the production of works is concerned. So again the essential nature of our common air, and of all bodies less dense than air (which are very many), is almost unknown. For the sense by itself is a thing infirm and erring; neither can instruments for enlarging or sharpening the senses do much; but all the truer kind of interpretation of nature is effected by instances and experiments fit and apposite; wherein the sense decides touching the experiment only, and the experiment touching the point in nature and the thing itself.

51. The human understanding is of its own nature prone to abstractions and gives a substance and reality to things which are fleeting. But to resolve nature into abstractions is less to our purpose than to dissect her into parts; as did the school of Democritus, which went further into nature than the rest. Matter rather than forms should be the object of our attention, its configurations and changes of configuration, and simple action, and law of action or motion; for forms are figments of the human mind, unless you will call those laws of action forms.

59. . . . men believe that their reason governs words; but it is also true that words react on the understanding; and this it is that has rendered philosophy and the sciences sophistical and inactive. Now words, being commonly framed and applied according to the capacity of the vulgar, follow those lines

of division which are most obvious to the vulgar understanding. And whenever an understanding of greater acuteness or a more diligent observation would alter those lines to suit the true divisions of nature, words stand in the way and resist the change. Whence it comes to pass that the high and formal discussions of learned men and oftentimes in disputes about words and names; with which (according to the use and wisdom of the mathematicians) it would be more prudent to begin, and so by means of definitions reduce them to order. Yet even definitions cannnot cure this evil in dealing with natural and material things; since the definitions themselves consist of words, and those words beget others: so that it is necessary to recur to individual instances, and those in due series and order; as I shall say presently when I come to the method and scheme for the formation of notions and axioms.

95. Those who have handled sciences have been either men of experiment or men of dogmas. The men of experiment are like the ant; they only collect and use: the reasoners resemble spiders, who make cobwebs out of their own substance. But the bee takes a middle course; it gathers its material from the flowers of the garden and of the field, but transforms and digests it by a power of its own. Not unlike this is the true business of philosophy; for it neither relies solely or chiefly on the powers of the mind, nor does it take the matter which it gathers from natural history and mechanical experiments and lay it up in the memory whole, as it finds it; but lays it up in the understanding altered and digested. Therefore from a closer and purer league between these two faculties the experimental and the rational, (such as has never yet been made) much may be hoped.

98. Now for grounds of experience—since to experience we must come—we have as yet had either none or very weak ones; no search has been made to collect a store of particular observations sufficient either in number, or in kind, or in certainty, to inform the understanding, or in any way adequate. On the contrary, men of learning, but easy withal and idle, have taken for the construction or for

the confirmation of their philosophy certain rumours and vague fames or airs of experience, and allowed to these the weight of lawful evidence. And just as if some kingdom or state were to direct its counsels and affairs, not by letters and reports from ambassadors and trustworthy messengers, but by the gossip of the streets; such exactly is the system of management introduced into philosophy with relation to experience. Nothing duly investigated, nothing verified, nothing counted, weighed, or measured, is to be found in natural history: and what in observation is loose and vague, is in information deceptive and treacherous. And if any one thinks that this is a strange thing to say, and something like an unjust complaint, seeing that Aristotle, himself so great a man, and supported by the wealth of so great a king, has composed so accurate a history of animals; and that others with greater diligence, though less pretence, have made many additions; while others, again, have compiled copious histories and descriptions of metals, plants, and fossils; it seems that he does not rightly apprehend what it is that we are now about. For a natural history which is composed for its own sake is not like one that is collected to supply the understanding with information for the building up of philosophy. They differ in many ways, but especially in this; that the former contains the variety of natural species only, and not experiments of the mechanical arts. For even as in the business of life a man's disposition and the secret workings of his mind and affections are better discovered when he is in trouble than at other times; so likewise the secrets of nature reveal themselves more readily under the vexations of art than when they go their own way. Good hopes may therefore be conceived of natural philosophy, when natural history, which is the basis and foundation of it, has been drawn up on a better plan; but not till then.

99. Again, even in the great plenty of mechanical experiments, there is yet a great scarcity of those which are of most use for the information of the understanding. For the mechanic, not troubling himself with the investigation of truth, confines his attention

to those things which bear upon his particular work, and will not either raise his mind or stretch out his hand for anything else. But then only will there be good ground of hope for the further advance of knowledge, when there shall be received and gathered together into natural history a variety of experiments, which are of no use in themselves, but simply serve to discover causes and axioms; which I call "*Experimenta lucifera*," experiments of *light*, to distinguish them from those which I call "*fructifera*," experiments of *fruit*.

Now experiments of this kind have one admirable property and condition; they never miss or fail. For since they are applied, not for the purpose of producing any particular effect, but only of discovering the natural cause of some effect, they answer the end equally well whichever way they turn out; for they settle the question.

100. But not only is a greater abundance of experiments to be sought for and procured, and that too of a different kind from those hitherto tried; an entirely different method, order, and process for carrying on and advancing experience must also be introduced. For experience, when it wanders in its own track, is, as I have already remarked, mere groping in the dark, and confounds men rather than instructs them. But when it shall proceed in accordance with a fixed law, in regular order, and without interruption, then may better things be hoped of knowledge.

102. Moreover, since there is so great a number and army of particulars, and that army so scattered and dispersed as to distract and confound the understanding, little is to be hoped for from the skirmishings and slight attacks and desultory movements of the intellect, unless all the particulars which pertain to the subject of inquiry shall, by means of Tables of Discovery, apt, well arranged, and as it were animate, be drawn up and marshalled; and the mind be set to work upon the helps duly prepared and digested which these tables supply.

103. But after this store of particulars has been set out duly and in order before our eyes, we are not to pass at once to the investigation and discovery of new particulars or

works; or at any rate if we do so we must not stop there. For although I do not deny that when all the experiments of all the arts shall have been collected and digested, and brought within one man's knowledge and judgment, the mere transferring of the experiments of one art to others may lead, by means of that experience which I term *literate*, to the discovery of many new things of service to the life and state of man, yet it is no great matter that can be hoped from that; but from the new light of axioms, which having been educed from those particulars by a certain method and rule, shall in their turn point out the way again to new particulars, greater things may be looked for. For our road does not lie on a level, but ascends and descends; first ascending to axioms, then descending to works.

104. The understanding must not however be allowed to jump and fly from particulars to remote axioms and of almost the highest generality (such as the first principles, as they are called, of arts and things), and taking stand upon them as truths that cannot be shaken, proceed to prove and frame the middle axioms by reference to them; which has been the practice hitherto; the understanding being not only carried that way by a natural impulse, but also by the use of syllogistic demonstration trained and inured to it. But then, and then only, may we hope well of the sciences, when in a just scale of ascent, and by successive steps not interrupted or broken, we rise from particulars to lesser axioms; and then to middle axioms, one above the other; and last of all to the most general. For the lowest axioms differ but slightly from bare experience, while the highest and most general (which we now have) are notional and abstract and without solidity. But the middle are the true and solid and living axioms, on which depend the affairs and fortunes of men; and above them again, last of all, those which are indeed the most general; such I mean as are not abstract, but of which those intermediate axioms are really limitations.

The understanding must not therefore be supplied with wings, but rather hung with weights, to keep it from leaping and flying. Now this has never yet been done; when it is done, we may entertain better hopes of the sciences.

106. But in establishing axioms by this kind of induction, we must also examine and try whether the axiom so established be framed to the measure of those particulars only from which it is derived, or whether it be larger and wider. And if it be larger and wider, we must observe whether by indicating to us new particulars it confirm that wideness and largeness as by a collateral security; that we may not either stick fast in things already known, or loosely grasp at shadows and abstract forms; not at things solid and realised in matter. And when this process shall have come into use, then at last shall we see the dawn of a solid hope.

IRREDUCIBLE AND STUBBORN FACTS
The Search for Precision

KEPLER AND BRAHE*
by A. R. Hall (1954)

Kepler was the discoverer of the new descriptive laws of planetary motion, but he achieved

* From A. R. Hall, *The Scientific Revolution: 1500–1800*, Longmans, Green & Co., Inc., New York, 1954. Reprinted by permission of David McKay Company, Inc., and Longmans, Green & Co., Ltd., London.

more than this, for he made the first suggestions towards a physical theory of the universe adapted to the necessities of the new description. Although his life was given over to mathematical drudgery—in which he was aided by the much improved trigonometry of his day, and the invention of logarithms—Kepler was a man of vigorous and original scientific imagination. The mathematical operations he set himself could hardly have proved creative without it. In his first work* he sought for the divine canon in celestial architecture, and this pursuit ran through all his later computations. But Kepler was no empty theorist: the divine art of proportion, the harmony of the grand design of nature, was to be elucidated from the most precise mathematical observation of the universe. Hence the turning-point in his career, the necessary foundation for his work, was Kepler's encounter with the Danish astronomer, Tycho Brahe (1546–1601), who, after a quarrel with King Christian IV, had deserted his royally endowed observatory at Hveen to enter the service of the eccentric Emperor Rudolph II, patron of alchemists and astrologers, at Prague. Thither Kepler was drawn from Graz in Styria by the undigested mass of observations, of unparalleled accuracy, which Tycho had brought with him. . . .

In many ways the Danish astronomer's role in the early history of modern astronomy is [that of] . . . the first modern exponent of the art of disinterested observation and description. . . . And certainly Tycho was unique among early modern scientists in his insistence upon the crucial importance of accurate quantitative measurement; always a desideratum in astronomy, certainly, but never previously handled with the analytical and inventive powers of Tycho, who first consciously studied methods of estimating and correcting errors of observation in order to determine their limits of accuracy. The most accurate predecessors of Tycho were not Europeans, but the astronomers who worked in the observatory founded at Samarkand by Ulugh Beigh, about 1420. Their results were correct to about ten minutes of arc (i.e. roughly twice as good as Hipparchus'); Tycho's observations were about twice as good again, falling systematically within

about four minutes of modern values.[1] This result was achieved by patient attention to detail. The instruments at Hveen were fixed, of different types for the various kinds of angular measurement, and much larger than those commonly used in the past, so that their scales could be more finely divided. They were the work of the most skilful German craftsmen, whom Tycho encouraged by his patronage and direction. He devised a new form of sight, and a sort of diagonal scale† for reading fractions of a degree. In measuring either the longitude of a star, or its right ascension, it is most convenient to proceed by a way that requires an instrument measuring time accurately, and Tycho studied the improvement of clocks for this purpose: but he found that a new technique of his own by which observations were referred to the position of the sun was more trustworthy. He was the first astronomer in Europe to use the modern celestial coordinates reckoning star-positions with reference to the celestial equator,‡ not (as formerly) to the ecliptic. Another innovation in his practice was the observation of planetary positions not at a few isolated points in the orbit (especially when in opposition to the sun), but at frequent intervals so that the whole orbit could be plotted.

The techniques and standards of precision in astronomy, of which Tycho was the real founder, were evolved slowly over a period of thirty years to fulfill a very simple ambition. When he made his first observations with a home-made quadrant, he found that places given in star-catalogues were false, and that events such as eclipses occurred as much as two or three days from the predicted times. As the Copernican "Prutenic Tables" were computed from old observations they had brought in no significant improvement. The task Tycho set himself, therefore, was very simple: to plot afresh the positions of the brightest stars, and with the fundamental map of the sky established to observe the motions

---

* Kepler's first work, *Mysterium Cosmographicum*, described the five planetary orbits as the areas circumscribed in the five regular polygons. See Fig. 1-3; also "Kepler," in Glossary. Ed.

[1] As was first pointed out by Robert Hooke, the unaided human eye is incapable of resolving points whose angular separation is less than about two minutes of arc, so that Tycho's work approximately attains the minimum theoretical limits of accuracy for instruments such as he used.
† The so-called transversal points. See Fig. 5-6. Ed.
‡ See p. 54. Ed.

of sun, moon and planets so that the elements of their orbits could be recalculated without mistake. It does not seem that he undertook this with any violently partisan intent, but it is likely that he wished to show the falsity of the Copernicans' claim to have increased the accuracy of celestial mathematics, and to bolster up the geostatic doctrine by publishing unimpugnable tables and ephemerides calculated upon that assumption. To vindicate the "Tychonic" geostatic system* was the last ambition of his life, which he charged Kepler to fulfil. However, he was no slavish adherent to conventional ideas. He did not believe that apparent changes in the sky were due to meteors in the earth's atmosphere; he proved that comets were celestial bodies, and that the spheres could have no real existence as physical bodies since comets pass through them; and his description of the planetary motions is relativistically identical with that of Copernicus. As an astronomer, indeed, Tycho in no way belonged to the past: it was as a good Aristotelian natural-philosopher that he believed the earth incapable of movement.

Tycho's observations, including his catalogue of 1,000 star-places, have not proved of enduring value. The earliest observations that have an other than historical interest are those of the English astronomer, Flamsteed, early in the eighteenth century (error c. ten *seconds* of arc), for within about sixty years of Tycho's death the optically-unaided measuring instrument, still ardently defended by Hevelius of Dantzig, was beginning to pass out of use. Within a century Tycho's tables had been thoroughly revised by such astronomers as Halley, the Cassinis, Roemer and Flamsteed. In the interval, however, Kepler's discoveries based on Tycho's work had become recognized. To appreciate the relationship between Kepler and Tycho—the inventive mathematician and the patient observer—it must be realized that the balance of choice between Keplerian and Copernican astronomy is very narrow. Until measurements were available whose accuracy could be relied upon within a range of four minutes,

or even less, there was no need to suppose that the planetary orbits were anything other than circles eccentric to the sun. Kepler, in plotting the orbit of Mars, from which he discovered the ellipticity of planetary orbits in general, was able to calculate the elements of a circular orbit which differed by less than ten minutes from the observations. It was only because he knew that Tycho's work was accurate within about half this range that he was dissatisfied and impelled to go further. *Kepler's famous "First Law" was thus the first instance in the history of science of a discovery being made as the result of a search for a theory, not merely to cover a given set of observations, but to interpret a group of refined measurements whose probable accuracy was a significant factor.†* Discrimination between measurement in a somewhat casual sense, and scientific measurement, in which the quantitative result is itself criticized and its range of error determined, only developed slowly in other sciences during the course of the scientific revolution. . . .‡

The invention of numerous scientific instruments during the seventeenth century, and their fertile use in many capacities, has long been associated with the revolution in scientific thought and method. The idea of science as a product of the laboratory (in the modern sense of the word) is indeed one of the creations of the scientific revolution. In no previous period had the study of natural philosophy or medicine been particularly linked with the use of specialized techniques or tools of inquiry, and though the surgeon or the astronomer had been equipped with a limited range of instruments, little attention was paid to their fitness for use or to the possibility of extending and perfecting their uses. More variants of the astrolabe, the most

† Italics by editor.
‡ The range or margin of error has become significant as science has become more precise. Today workers in the exact sciences wherever possible specify the margin of error involved in their observations, as for instance:

Length $AB = 6.03$ in. $\pm$ 0.02 in.
or Length $AB = 6.03$ in. $\pm$ 0.33 per cent

These statements both mean that the length may be as much as 6.05 in. or as little as 6.01 in. Within that margin the exact figure is unknown, probably because of the limitations of the device used in making the measurement. The accuracy of an experimental result is limited by the least accurate element involved in the experiment. In the example above, even if the width is known much more accurately, say $BC = 4.6285$ in. $\pm$ 0.005 per cent, then a computation of the area using the measurement for length 6.03 in. $\pm$ 0.33 per cent will also have a margin of error of 0.33 per cent. Ed.

* See Fig. 3-23. Ed.

characteristic of all medieval scientific instruments, were designed during the last half-century of its use in Europe (c. 1575–1625) than in all its preceding history. The Greeks had known the magnifying power of a spherical vessel filled with water, but the lens was an invention of the eleventh century, the spectacle glass of the thirteenth, and the optical instrument of the seventeenth. Navigational instruments also were extremely crude before the later sixteenth century. It was not that ingenuity and craftsmanship were wholly lacking (for many examples of fine metal-work, for artistic and military purposes, prove the contrary); rather the will to refine and extend instrumental techniques was absent. On the other hand, it has justly been pointed out that the early strategic stages of the scientific revolution were accomplished without the aid of the new instruments. They were unknown to Copernicus, to Vesalius, to Harvey, Bacon and Gilbert. They leave no trace in the most important of Galileo's writings, in which he reveals himself driven to measure small intervals of time by a device considerably less accurate than the ancient clepsydra. It is clear that, great as was the influence of the instrumental ingenuity of the seventeenth century upon the course of modern science, such ingenuity was not at all responsible for the original deflection of science into this new course.

Thus it would seem that the first factor limiting the introduction into scientific practice of higher standards of observation and measurement, or of more complex manipulations, lay in the nature of science itself. Only when the concept of scientific research had changed, as it had by the end of the first quarter of the seventeenth century, was it possible to pay attention to the attainment of these higher standards. A number of the new instruments of the seventeenth century were not the product of scientific invention, but were adopted for scientific purposes because the new attitude enabled their usefulness to be perceived. The balance was borrowed from chemical craftsmanship. The telescope was another craft invention, initially applied to military uses. The microscope was an amusing toy before it became a serious instrument of research. The air pump in the laboratory was an improved form of the common well pump—Otto von Guericke, its original inventor, had at the beginning exhausted vessels by pumping out water with which they had been filled. And inevitably the techniques used in the construction of the new scientific instruments were those already in existence; they were not summoned out of nothing by the unprecedented scientific demand. Some instruments were only practicable because methods of lathe-turning and screw-cutting had been gradually perfected during two or three centuries, partly owing to the more ready availability of steel tools, others, because it was possible to produce larger, stronger and smoother sheets or strips of metal. The techniques of glass grinding and blowing which provided lenses and tubes might have been turned to scientific use long before they were. The established skill of the astrolabe-maker could be devoted to the fabrication of other instruments requiring divided circles and engraved lines, that of the watch-maker to various computers and models involving exact wheel-work, and so on. Common craftsmanship held a considerable reservoir of ingenuity, when scientific imagination arrived to draw upon it.

THE CELESTIAL PALACE OF TYCHO BRAHE*
by John Christianson (1961)

[Tycho Brahe's] precise observations were made entirely without the aid of a telescope.

* From John Christianson, "The Celestial Palace of Tycho Brahe," *Scientific American*, February, 1961. Reproduced by permission.

It was not until 1609, eight years after Tycho's death, that Galileo first used the telescope for astronomical purposes. Tycho's instruments consisted of ingenious improvements on ancient devices, quadrants, armillary spheres and parallactic rulers. All were aimed at celestial objects by means of simple metal sights. . . .

In a tireless quest for accuracy Tycho filled his observatory with a succession of instruments, each more ambitious than the last. He recognized that by increasing the distance between the sights of his instruments, and by increasing the size of the calibrated arcs from which he read positions, he could gain accuracy. But he also came to realize that when he made his instruments too large, they bent and twisted of their own weight, introducing a new class of errors in place of those that size was supposed to eliminate. He recorded that this great observatory at Hven cost Frederick II "more than a tun of gold," the equivalent of about $1.5 million today. . . .

It was as instrument maker that Tycho excelled all astronomers who had lived before him. Some of the devices he built were of his own invention but most were refinements of traditional types. The basic instrument of astronomy in his day was the quadrant, a quarter-circle that was normally sighted from the angle to the arc. One of the quadrant's arms was made precisely horizontal and the other precisely vertical. The whole instrument was usually pivoted so that it could be rotated 360 degrees. When the sighting arm, or alidade, was pointed at a star or planet, the altitude was read off the 90-degree arc and the azimuth off a 360-degree circle within which the quadrant revolved.

Tycho designed at least two such instruments that had a radius of more than six feet (Figures 5-1 to 5-4). One was the *quadrans magnus chalibeus*, or great steel quadrant (Figure 5-1). A still more accurate instrument, rigidly fixed in a north-south plane—hence incapable of providing azimuth—was the *quadrans muralis sive Tichonicus:* the mural, or Tychonian, quadrant (Figure 5-5). This instrument did not survive, but Tycho declared its scale could be read directly to 10 seconds of arc and that by interpolation five seconds could be "read without difficulty." Even allowing that the 10-seconds calibrations

were made by using so-called transversal points (Figure 5-6), Tycho's statement seems almost incredible.

Assuming, however, that he did indeed inscribe the arc of his mural quadrant to read to 10 seconds, he deceived himself in a way that was to become familiar in later science. He tried to extract from his observational method greater accuracy than its least accurate element permitted. In Tycho's method the fundamental source of inaccuracy was the human eye; unaided, it cannot resolve points that are separated by less than about two minutes of arc. Actually Tycho's stellar and planetary positions fall regularly within about four minutes of modern values. In other words, his mean error was less than half the distance that separates the twin stars Mizar and Alcor in the handle of the Big Dipper. (The ability to distinguish Mizar and Alcor was often used as a test of visual acuity in earlier times.)

Some indication of the way Tycho must have driven his instrument makers is revealed in the following passage: "Only this I wish to state here with regard [to these instruments], namely, that all of it has to be as nearly perfect as is possible in every respect and that, therefore, one should employ skillful craftsmen, who know how to carry out this sort of work artfully, or else can learn to do it. And even if they cannot perhaps do it all perfectly the first time, the constructor must not let himself be discouraged, but have the work repeated and improve the defects in every way until none is left."

But Tycho did more than simply put together elegant blown-up versions of old astronomical tools. He made technical innovations that greatly increased the quality of observations, particularly when these innovations were applied to his well-made giant instruments. Perhaps the most important were his instrument sights. The Tychonic sight had adjustable slits in the eyepiece in place of the customary peephole. The slits could be opened to admit the light of a faint star or closed to observe a star of greater magnitude. The front sight was a cylinder exactly as wide as the slits were far apart. The observer sighted through one slit and then the other until he saw the star just touching each side of the cylinder (Figure 5-7). Such a sighting device proved much more accurate than a simple pierced eyepiece.

In 1597 Frederick's successor, Christian IV, lost patience with Tycho's lordly ways and withdrew his fief at Hven. Tycho left his beloved Uraniborg and moved to Prague to serve the Holy Roman Emperor Rudolph II.

It was there that Tycho met the young German mathematician Johannes Kepler and took him on as an assistant.

Tycho and Kepler turned out to be the most fortunate combination in the history of astronomy. Tycho's years of patient observation combined with Kepler's mystical, almost magical, skill at mathematics founded modern astronomy.

Figure 5-1. Great steel quadrant had as large an arc radius (76.5 inches) as the mural quadrant. Tycho said he depended chiefly on these two quadrants and the Revolving azimuth quadrant.

Figure 5-2. Revolving azimuth quadrant had an arc radius only 15 inches smaller than that of quadrant at left. Tycho advised astronomers "to consider this construction as particularly commendable."

Figure 5-3. A variety of instruments illustrates Tycho Brahe's mechanical ingenuity. The equatorial armillary was a standard device for determining declination and right ascension of a celestial body.

Figure 5-4. The great equatorial armillary was a typical Tychonic enlargement; the diameter of the revolving circle was 9 feet.

Figure 5-5. Great Mural Quadrant, in which Tycho had "great faith," measured over 6 feet (76.5 inches) from the cylindrical front sight (in opening of the wall at upper left) to the rear sight, or pinnule, which could be moved along the arc. At lower right are two clocks of "the greatest possible accuracy." The quadrant was used to measure the altitude of celestial bodies as they crossed the north-south meridian. The full-size figure of Tycho was actually part of a wall painting depicting Uraniborg's multiple activities.

Figure 5-6. Tycho's calibration method employed so-called transversal points. The scale at left represents a full-size section of the arc of the mural quadrant. Tycho claimed that each minute was subdivided into six parts as shown enlarged at right. As the long sighting arm, the pinnule, moved over the face of the scale, the subdivision of each minute was indicated by the arm's position relative to the transversal points dividing the minute. Evidently Tycho did not realize that the unassisted eye limited his sighting accuracy to about 2 minutes of arc.

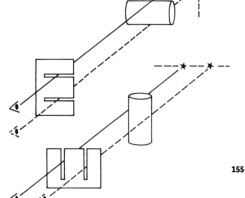

Figure 5-7. Tychonic sighting method used a cylinder as a front sight and two slits, with a spacing equal to the diameter of the cylinder, as a rear sight. In making a sighting (of altitude, at left; of azimuth, at right) the sights are aligned so that a celestial object appears equally bright on both sides of the cylinder when the eye is moved from one slit to the other.

155

The Importance of Precision

KEPLER—EIGHT MINUTES OF ARC*
by Arthur Koestler (1959)

[Kepler's] *magnum opus*, published in 1609, bears the significant title:

A NEW ASTRONOMY Based on Causation
or A PHYSICS OF THE SKY
derived from Investigations of the
MOTIONS OF THE STAR MARS
Founded on Observations of
THE NOBLE TYCHO BRAHE

Kepler worked on it, with interruptions, from his arrival at Benatek in 1600, to 1606. It contains the first two of Kepler's three planetary laws: (1) that the planets travel round the sun not in circles but in elliptical orbits, one focus of the ellipse being occupied by the sun; (2) that a planet moves in its orbit not at uniform speed but in such a manner that a line drawn from the planet to the sun always sweeps over equal areas in equal times. . . .

On the surface, Kepler's laws look as innocent as Einstein's $E = Mc^2$, which does not reveal, either, its atom-exploding potentialities. But the modern vision of the universe was shaped, more than by any other single discovery, by Newton's law of universal gravitation, which in turn was derived from Kepler's three laws. Although (owing to the peculiarities of our educational system), a person may never have heard of Kepler's laws, his thinking has been moulded by them without his knowledge; they are the invisible foundation of a whole edifice of thought.

Thus the promulgation of Kepler's laws is a landmark in history. They were the first "natural laws" in the modern sense: precise, verifiable statements about universal relations governing particular phenomena, expressed in mathematical terms. They divorced astronomy from theology, and married astronomy to physics. Lastly, they put an end to the nightmare that had haunted cosmology for the last two millennia: the obsession with

* From Arthur Koestler, *The Sleepwalkers*. Copyright 1959 by Arthur Koestler and used with permission of The Macmillan Company.

spheres turning on spheres, and substituted a vision of material bodies not unlike the earth, freely floating in space, moved by physical forces acting on them.

The manner in which Kepler arrived at his new cosmology is fascinating; I shall attempt to re-trace the zig-zag course of his reasoning. Fortunately, he did not cover up his tracks, as Copernicus, Galileo and Newton did, who confront us with the result of their labours, and keep us guessing how they arrived at it. Kepler was incapable of exposing his ideas methodically, text-book fashion; he had to describe them in the order they came to him, including all the errors, detours, and the traps into which he had fallen. The *New Astronomy* is written in an unacademic, bubbling baroque style, personal, intimate, and often exasperating. But it is a unique revelation of the ways in which the creative mind works.

"What matters to me," Kepler explained in his Preface, "is not merely to impart to the reader what I have to say, but above all to convey to him the reasons, subterfuges, and lucky hazards which led me to my discoveries. When Christopher Colombus, Magelhaen and the Portuguese relate how they went astray on their journeys, we not only forgive them, but would regret to miss their narration because without it the whole, grand entertainment would be lost. Hence I shall not be blamed if, prompted by the same affection for the reader, I follow the same method."

Before embarking on the story, it will be prudent to add my own apology to Kepler's. Prompted by the same "affection for the reader" I have tried to simplify as far as possible a difficult subject: even so, the present chapter must of necessity be slightly more technical. . . . If some passages tax his patience, even if occasionally he fails to grasp a point or loses the thread, he will, I hope, nevertheless get a general idea of Kepler's odyssey of thought, which opened up the modern universe.

[After] young Kepler's arrival at Benatek Castle, he was allotted the study of the motions of Mars which had defeated Tycho's senior assistant, Longomontanus, and Tycho himself.

"I believe it was an act of Divine Providence," he commented later on, "that I arrived just at the time when Longomontanus was occupied with Mars. For Mars alone enables us to penetrate the secrets of astronomy which otherwise would remain forever hidden from us."

The reason for this key position of Mars is that, among the outer planets, his orbit deviates more than the others' from the circle; it is the most pronouncedly elliptical. It was precisely for that reason that Mars had defied Tycho and his assistant: since they expected the planets to move in circles, it was impossible to reconcile theory with observation:

He [Mars] is the mighty victor over human inquisitiveness, who made a mockery of all the stratagems of astronomers, wrecked their tools, defeated their hosts; thus did he keep the secret of his rule safe throughout all past centuries and pursued his course in unrestrained freedom; wherefore the most famous of Latins, the priest of nature Pliny, specially indicted him: MARS IS A STAR WHO DEFIES OBSERVATION.

Thus Kepler, in his dedication of the *New Astronomy* to the Emperor Rudolph II. The dedication is written in the form of an allegory of Kepler's war against Mars, begun under "Tycho's supreme command," patiently pursued in spite of the warning example of Rheticus who went off his head over Mars, in spite of other dangers and terrible handicaps, such as a lack of supplies owing to Rudolph's failure to pay Kepler's salary—and so on to the triumphant end when the Imperial Mathematicus, riding a chariot, leads the captive enemy to the Emperor's throne.

Thus Mars held the secret of all planetary motion, and young Kepler was assigned the task of solving it. He first attacked the problem on traditional lines; when he failed, he began to throw out ballast and continued

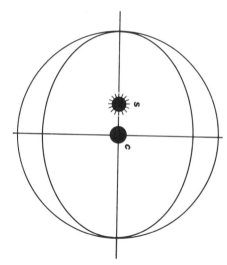

Figure 5-8

doing so until, by and by, he got rid of the whole load of ancient beliefs on the nature of the universe, and replaced it by a new science.

As a preliminary, he made three revolutionary innovations to gain elbow room, as it were, for tackling his problem. It will be remembered that the centre of Copernicus' system was not the sun, but the centre of the earth's orbit;[*] . . . already in the *Mysterium Cosmographicum* Kepler had objected to this assumption as physically absurd. Since the force which moved the planets emanated from the sun, the whole system should be centred on the body of the sun itself.

But in fact it was not. The sun occupies not the exact centre of the orbit at C; it occupies one of the two foci of the ellipse at S (Figure 5-8).

Kepler did not know as yet that the orbit was an ellipse; he still regarded it as a circle. But even so, to get approximately correct results, the centre of the circle had to be placed at C, and not in the sun. Accordingly, the question arose in his mind: if the force which moves the planets comes from S, why do they insist on turning round C? Kepler answered the question by the assumption that each planet was subject to two conflicting influences: *the force of the sun, and a second force located in the planet itself.* This tug-of-war caused it now to approach the sun, now to recede from him.

* See p. 109. Ed.

The two forces are, as we know, gravity and inertia. Kepler, as we shall see, never arrived at formulating these concepts. But he prepared the way for Newton by postulating two dynamic forces to explain the eccentricity of the orbits. Before him, the need for a physical explanation was not felt; the phenomenon of eccentricity was merely "saved" by the introduction of an epicycle or eccenter, which made C turn round S. Kepler replaced the fictitious wheels by real forces.

For the same reason, he insisted on treating the sun as the centre of his system not only in the physical but in the geometrical sense, by making the distances and positions of the planets relative to the sun (and not relative to the earth or the centre C) the basis of his computations. This shift of emphasis, which was more instinctive than logical, became a major factor in his success.

His second innovation is simpler to explain. The orbits of all planets lie very nearly, but not entirely, in the same plane; they form very small angles with each other—rather like adjacent pages of a book which is nearly, but not entirely closed. The planes of all planets pass, of course, through the sun—a fact which is self-evident to us, but not to pre-Keplerian astronomy. Copernicus, once again misled by his slavish devotion to Ptolemy, had postulated that the plane of the Martian orbit *oscillates in space;* and this oscillation he made to depend on the position of the earth—which, as Kepler remarks, "is no business of Mars." He called this Copernican idea "monstrous" (though it was merely due to Copernicus' complete indifference to physical reality) and set about to prove that the plane in which Mars moves passes through the sun, and does not oscillate, but forms a fixed angle with the plane of the earth's orbit. Here he met, for once, with immediate success. He proved, by several independent methods, all based on the Tychonic observations, that the angle between the planes of Mars and Earth remained always the same, and that it amounted to 1° 50'. He was delighted, and remarked smugly that "the observations took

the side of my preconceived ideas, as they often did before."

The third innovation was the most radical. To gain more elbow room, he had to get out of the strait-jacket of "uniform motion in perfect circles"—the basic axiom of cosmology from Plato up to Copernicus and Tycho. For the time being, he still let circular motion stand, but he threw out uniform speed. Again he was guided mainly by physical considerations: if the sun ruled the motions, then his force must act more powerfully on the planet when it is close to the source, less powerfully when away from it; hence the planet will move faster or slower, in a manner somehow related to its distance from the sun.

This idea was not only a challenge to antique tradition; it also reversed the original purpose of Copernicus. It will be remembered that Copernicus' original motive for embarking on a reform of the Ptolemaic system was his discontent with the fact that, according to Ptolemy, a planet did not move at uniform speed around the centre of its orbit, but only around a point at some distance from the centre. This point was called the *punctum equans*—the point in space, from which the planet gave the illusion of "equal motion." Canon Koppernigk regarded this arrangement as an evasion of the command of uniform motion, abolished Ptolemy's equants, and added, instead, more epicycles to his system. This did not make the planet's *real* motion either circular, or uniform, but each wheel in the imaginary clockwork which was supposed to account for it, did turn uniformly—if only in the astronomer's mind.

When Kepler renounced the dogma of uniform motion, he was able to throw out the epicycles which Copernicus had introduced to save it. Instead, he reverted to the equant as an important calculating device: (Figure 5-9).

Let the circle be the track of a toy train chugging round a room. When near the window it runs a little faster, near the door a little slower. Provided that these periodic changes of speed follow some simple, definite rule, then it is possible to find a *punctum*

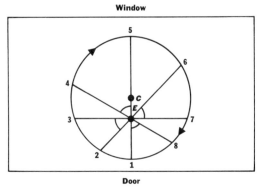

Window

Door

Figure 5-9

equans, "E," from which the train *seems* to move at uniform speed. The closer we are to a moving train, the faster it seems to move; hence the *punctum equans* will be somewhere between the centre C of the track and the door, so that the speed-surplus of the train when passing the window will be eliminated by distance, its speed-deficiency at the door compensated by closeness. The advantage gained by the introduction of this imaginary *punctum equans* is that, *seen from E,* the train seems to move uniformly, that is, it will cover equal angles at equal times—which makes it possible to compute its various positions *1, 2, 3,* etc., at any given moment.

By these three preliminary moves: (a) the shifting of the system's centre into the sun; (b) the proof that the orbital planes do not "oscillate" in space; and (c) the abolition of uniform motion, Kepler had cleared away a considerable amount of the rubbish that had obstructed progress since Ptolemy, and made the Copernican system so clumsy and unconvincing. In that system Mars ran on five circles; after the clean-up, a single eccentric circle must be sufficient—if the orbit was really a circle. He felt confident that victory was just around the corner, and before the final attack wrote a kind of obituary notice for classical cosmology:

Oh, for a supply of tears that I may weep over the pathetic diligence of Apianus [author of a very popular textbook] who, relying on Ptolemy, wasted his valuable time and ingenuity on the construction of spirals, loops, helixes,

vortices and a whole labyrinth of convolutions, in order to represent that which exists only in the mind, and which Nature entirely refuses to accept as her likeness. And yet that man has shown us that, with his penetrating intelligence, he would have been capable of mastering Nature.

The First Assault

Kepler's first attack on the problem is described in great detail in the sixteenth chapter of the *New Astronomy.*

The task before him was to define the orbit of Mars by determining the radius of the circle, the direction (relative to the fixed stars) of the axis connecting the two positions where Mars is nearest and farthest from the sun (perihelion and aphelion) (Figure 5-10), and the positions of the sun (*S*), orbital centre (*C*), and *punctum equans* (*E*), which all lie on that axis. Ptolemy had assumed that the distance between *E* and *C* was the same as between *C* and *S*, but Kepler made no such assumption, which complicated his task even more.

He chose out of Tycho's treasure four observed positions of Mars at the convenient dates when the planet was in opposition to the sun. The geometrical problem which he had to solve was, as we saw, to determine, out of these four positions, the radius of the orbit, the direction of the axis, and the position of the three central points on it. It was

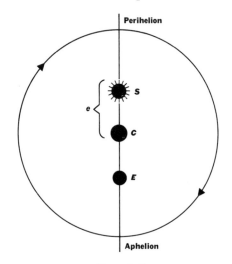

Figure 5-10

a problem which could not be solved by rigorous mathematics, only by approximation, that is, by a kind of trial-and-error procedure which has to be continued until all the pieces in the jig-saw puzzle fit together tolerably well. The incredible labour that this involved may be gathered from the fact that Kepler's draft calculations (preserved in manuscript) cover nine hundred folio pages in small handwriting.

At times he was despairing; he felt, like Rheticus, that a demon was knocking his head against the ceiling, with the shout: "These are the motions of Mars." At other times, he appealed for help to Maestlin (who turned a deaf ear), to the Italian astronomer, Magini (who did the same), and thought of sending an S.O.S. to Francois Vieta, the father of modern algebra: "Come, oh Gallic Appollonius, bring your cylinders and spheres and what other geometer's houseware you have. . . ." But in the end he had to slog it out alone, and to invent his mathematical tools as he went along.

Half-way through that dramatic sixteenth chapter, he burst out:

If thou [dear reader] art bored with this wearisome method of calculation, take pity on me who had to go through with at least seventy repetitions of it, at a very great loss of time; nor wilst thou be surprised that by now the fifth year is nearly past since I took on Mars. . . .

Now, at the very beginning of the hair-raising computations in chapter sixteen, Kepler absentmindedly put three erroneous figures for three vital longitudes of Mars, and happily went on from there, never noticing his error. The French historian of astronomy, Delambre, later repeated the whole computation, but, surprisingly, his correct results differ very little from Kepler's faulty ones. The reason is, that toward the end of the chapter Kepler committed several mistakes in simple arithmetic—errors in division which would bring bad marks to any schoolboy—and these errors happen very nearly to cancel out his earlier mistakes. We shall see, in a moment, that, at the most crucial point of the process of discovering his Second Law,

Kepler again committed mathematical sins which mutually cancelled out, and "as if by miracle" (in his own words), led to the correct result.

At the end of that breathtaking chapter, Kepler seems to have triumphantly achieved his aim. As a result of his seventy-odd trials, he arrived at values for the radius of the orbit and for the three central points which gave, with a permissible error of less than 2', the correct positions of Mars for all the ten oppositions recorded by Tycho. The unconquerable Mars seemed as last to have been conquered. He proclaimed his victory with the sober words:

Thou seest now, diligent reader, that the hypothesis based on this method not only satisfies the four positions on which it was based, but also correctly represents, within two minutes, all the other observations. . . .

There follow three pages of tables to prove the correctness of his claim; and then, without further transition, the next chapter starts with the following words:

Who would have thought it possible? This hypothesis, which so closely agrees with the observed oppositions, is nevertheless false. . . .

The Eight Minutes Arc
In the two following chapters Kepler explains, with great thoroughness and an almost masochistic delight, how he discovered that the hypothesis is false and why it must be rejected. In order to prove it by a further test, he had selected two specially rare pieces from Tycho's treasury of observations, and lo! they did not fit; and when he tried to adjust his model to them, this made things even worse, for now the observed positions of Mars differed from those which his theory demanded by magnitudes up to eight minutes of arc.

This was a catastrophe. Ptolemy, and even Copernicus, could afford to neglect a difference of eight minutes, because their observations were only accurate within a margin of ten minutes anyway. "But," the nineteenth chapter concludes, "but for us, who, by divine kindness were given an accurate observer such as Tycho Brahe, for us it is fitting that we should acknowledge this divine gift and put it to use. . . . Henceforth I shall lead the way toward that goal according to my own ideas. For, if I had believed that we could ignore these eight minutes, I would have patched up my hypothesis accordingly. But since it was not permissible to ignore them, those eight minutes* point the road to a complete reformation of astronomy: they have become the building material for a large part of this work. . . ."

It was the final capitulation of an adventurous mind before the "irreducible, obstinate facts." Earlier on, if a minor detail did not fit into a major hypothesis, it was cheated away or shrugged away. Now this time-hallowed indulgence had ceased to be permissible. A new era had begun in the history of thought: an era of austerity and rigour. As Whitehead has put it:

All the world over and at all times there have been practical men, absorbed in "irreducible and stubborn facts": all the world over and at all times there have been men of philosophic temperament who have been absorbed in the weaving of general principles. It is this union of passionate interest in the detailed facts with equal devotion to abstract generalization which forms the novelty in our present society.

This new departure determined the climate of European thought in the last three centuries, it set modern Europe apart from all other civilizations in the past and present, and enabled it to transform its natural and social environment as completely as if a new species had arisen on this planet.

The turning point is dramatically expressed in Kepler's work. In the *Mysterium Cosmographicum* the facts are coerced to fit the theory. In the *Astronomia Nova*, a theory, built on years of labour and torment, was instantly thrown away because of a discord of eight miserable minutes of arc. Instead

* In order that the reader may visualize how small an angle is represented by 8 minutes of arc, we have drawn here to scale an angle which is ten times larger, that is, 80 minutes, or 1⅓ degrees. Try dividing the angle into ten equal parts and you will see how small a measurement this is. Ed.

Figure 5-11

of cursing those eight minutes as a stumbling block, he transformed them into the cornerstone of a new science.

What caused this change of heart in him? . . . some of the general causes which contributed to the emergence of the new attitude [are] the need of navigators, and engineers, for greater precision in tools and theories; the stimulating effects on science of expanding commerce and industry. But what turned Kepler into the first law-maker of nature was something different and more specific. It was *his introduction of physical causality into the formal geometry of the skies* which made it impossible for him to ignore the eight minutes arc. So long as cosmology was guided by purely geometrical rules of the game, regardless of physical causes, discrepancies between theory and fact could be overcome by inserting another wheel into the system. In a universe moved by real, physical forces, this was no longer possible. The revolution which freed thought from the stranglehold of ancient dogma, immediately created its own, rigorous discipline.

The Second Book of the *New Astronomy* closes with the words:

And thus the edifice which we erected on the foundation of Tycho's observations, we have now again destroyed. . . . This was our punishment for having followed some plausible, but in reality false, axioms of the great men of the past.

The Wrong Law

The next act of the drama opens with Book Three. As the curtain rises, we see Kepler preparing himself to throw out more ballast. The axiom of *uniform motion* has already gone overboard; Kepler feels, and hints, that the even more sacred one of *circular* motion must follow. The impossibility of constructing a circular orbit which would satisfy all existing observations, suggests to him that the circle must be replaced by some other geometrical curve.

But before he can do that, he must make an immense detour. For if the orbit of Mars is not a circle, its true shape can only be discovered by defining a sufficient number of points on the unknown curve. A circle is defined by three points on its circumference; every other curve needs more. The task before Kepler was to construct Mars' orbit without any preconceived ideas regarding its shape; to start from scratch, as it were.

To do that, it was first of all necessary to re-examine the motion of the earth itself. For, after all, the earth is our observatory; and if there is some misconception regarding its motion, all conclusions about the motions of other bodies will be distorted. Copernicus had assumed that the earth moves at uniform speed—not, as the other planets, only "quasi-uniformly" relative to some equant or epicycle, but *really* so. And since observation contradicted the dogma, the inequality of the earth's motion was explained away by the suggestion that the orbit periodically expanded and contracted, like a kind of pulsating jellyfish. It was typical of those improvisations which astronomers could afford so long as they felt free to manipulate the universe as they pleased on their drawing boards. It was equally typical that Kepler rejected it as "fantastic," again on the grounds that no physical cause existed for such a pulsation.

Hence his next task was to determine, more precisely than Copernicus had done, the earth's motion round the sun. For that purpose he designed a highly original method of his own. It was relatively simple, but it so happened that nobody had thought of it before. It consisted, essentially, in the trick of transferring the observer's position from earth to Mars, and to compute the motions of the earth exactly as an astronomer on Mars would do it.

The result was just as he had expected: the earth, like the other planets, did not revolve with uniform speed, but faster or slower according to its distance from the sun. Moreover, at the two extreme points of the orbit, the aphelion and perihelion (Figure 5-10) the earth's velocity proved to be, simply and beautifully, inversely proportional to distance.

At this decisive point, Kepler flies off the tangent and becomes airborne, as it were. Up to here he was preparing, with painstaking patience, his second assault on the orbit of Mars. Now he turns to a quite different subject. "Ye physicists, prick your ears," he warns, "for now we are going to invade your territory." The next six chapters are a report on that invasion into celestial physics, which had been out of bounds for astronomy since Plato.

A phrase seems to have been humming in his ear like a tune one cannot get rid of; it crops up in his writings over and again: there is a force in the sun which moves the planet, there is a force in the sun, there is a force in the sun. And since there is a force in the sun, there must exist some beautifully simple relation between the planet's distance from the sun and its speed. A light shines the brighter the nearer we are to its source, and the same must apply to the force of the sun: the closer the planet to it, the quicker it will move. This is his instinctive conviction, already expressed in the *Mysterium Cosmographicum*; but now, at last, he has succeeded in proving it.

In fact he has not. He has proved the inverse ratio of speed to distance only for the *two extreme points* of the orbit; and his extension of this "Law" to the *entire* orbit was a patently incorrect generalization. Moreover, Kepler knew this, and admitted it at the end of the thirty-second chapter, before he became airborne; but immediately afterwards, he conveniently forgot it. This is the first of the critical mistakes which "as if by a miracle" cancelled out, and led Kepler to the discovery of his Second Law. It looks as if his conscious, critical faculties were anaesthetized by the creative impulse, by his impatience to get to grips with the physical forces in the solar system.

Since he had no notion of the *momentum* which makes the planet persist in its motion, and only a vague intuition of *gravity* which bends that motion into a closed orbit, he had to find, or invent, a force which, like a broom, sweeps the planet around its path. And since the sun causes all motion, he let the sun handle the broom. This required that the sun rotate round its own axis—a guess which was only confirmed much later; the force which it emitted rotated with it, like the spokes of a wheel, and swept the planets along. But if that were the only force acting on them, the planets would all have the same angular velocity, they would all complete their revolutions in the same period—which they do not. The reason, Kepler thought, was the laziness or "inertia" of the planets, who desire to remain in the same place, and resist the sweeping force. The "spokes" of that force are not rigid; they allow the planet to lag behind; it works rather like a vortex or whirlpool. The power of the whirlpool diminishes with distance, so that the farther away the planet, the less power the sun has to overcome its laziness, and the slower its motion will be.

It still remained to be explained, however, why the planets moved in eccentric orbits instead of always keeping the same distance from the centre of the vortex. Kepler first assumed that apart from being lazy, they performed an epicyclic motion in the opposite direction under their own steam, as it were, apparently out of sheer cussedness. But he was dissatisfied with this, and at a later stage assumed that the planets were "huge round magnets" whose magnetic axis pointed always in the same direction, like the axis of a top; hence the planet will periodically be drawn closer to, and be repelled by the sun, according to which of its magnetic poles faces the sun.

Thus, in Kepler's physics of the universe, the roles played by gravity and inertia are reversed. Moreover, he assumed that the sun's power diminishes in direct ratio to distance. He sensed that there was something wrong here, since he knew that the intensity of light diminishes with the *square* of distance; but he had to stick to it, to satisfy his theorem of the ratio of speed to distance, which was equally false.

The Second Law

Refreshed by this excursion into the *Himmelsphysik*, our hero returned to the more immediate task in hand. Since the earth no longer moved at uniform speed, how could one predict its position at a given time? (The method based on the *punctum equans* had

proved, after all, a disappointment.) Since he believed to have proved that its speed depended directly on its distance from the sun, the time it needed to cover a small fraction of the orbit was always proportionate to that distance. Hence he divided the orbit (which, forgetting his previous resolve, he still regarded as a circle) into 360 parts, and computed the distance of each bit of arc from the sun. The sum of all distances between, say 0° and 85°, was a measure of the time the planet needed to get there.

But this procedure was, as he remarked with unusual modesty, "mechanical and tiresome." So he searched for something simpler:

Since I was aware that there exists an infinite number of points on the orbit and accordingly an infinite number of distances [from the sun] the idea occurred to me that the sum of these distances is contained in the *area* of the orbit. For I remembered that in the same manner Archimedes too divided the area of a circle into an infinite number of triangles.

Accordingly, he concluded, the area swept over by the line connecting planet and sun AS-BS (Figure 5-12) is a measure of the time required by the planet to get from A to B; *hence the line will sweep out equal areas in equal times.* This is Kepler's immortal Second Law (which he discovered before the First)—a law of amazing simplicity at the end of a dreadfully confusing labyrinth.

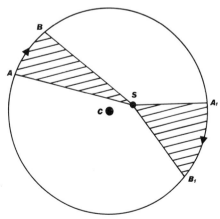

Area **ABS** = Area **A₁ B₁ S**

Figure 5-12

Yet the last step which had got him out of the labyrinth had once again been a faulty step. For it is not permissible to equate an area with the sum of an infinite number of neighbouring lines, as Kepler did. Moreover, he knew this well, and explained at length why it was not permissible. He added that he had also committed a second error, by assuming the orbit to be circular. And he concluded: "But these two errors—it is like a miracle—cancel out in the most precise manner, as I shall prove further down."

The correct result is even more miraculous than Kepler realized, for his explanation of the reasons why his errors cancel out was once again mistaken, and he got, in fact, so hopelessly confused that the argument is practically impossible to follow—as he himself admitted. And yet, by three incorrect steps and their even more incorrect defence, Kepler stumbled on the correct law. It is perhaps the most amazing sleepwalking performance in the history of science—except for the manner in which he found his First Law, to which we now turn.

The First Law

The Second Law determined the variations of the planet's speed along its orbit, but it did not determine the shape of the orbit itself.

At the end of the Second Book, Kepler had acknowledged defeat in his attempts to define the Martian orbit—a defeat caused by a discrepancy of eight minutes arc. He had then embarked on an enormous detour, starting with the revision of the earth's motion, followed by physical speculations, and terminating in the discovery of the Second Law. In the Fourth Book he resumed his investigation of the Martian orbit where he had left off. By this time, four years after his first, frustrated attempts, he had become even more sceptical of orthodox dogma, and gained an unparalleled skill in geometry by the invention of methods all his own.

The final assault took nearly two years; it occupies chapters 41 to 60 of the *New Astronomy*. In the first four (41–44), Kepler tried for the last time, with savage thoroughness, to attribute a circular orbit to Mars and failed: this section ends with the words:

The conclusion is quite simply that the planet's path is not a circle—it curves inward on both sides and outward again at opposite ends. Such a curve is called an oval. The orbit is not a circle, but an oval figure.

But now a dreadful thing happened, and the next six chapters (45–50) are a nightmare journey through another labyrinth. This oval orbit is a wild, frightening new departure for him. To be fed up with cycles and epicycles, to mock the slavish imitators of Aristotle is one thing; to assign an entirely new, lopsided, implausible path for the heavenly bodies is quite another.

Why indeed an oval? There is something in the perfect symmetry of spheres and circles which has a deep, reassuring appeal to the unconscious—otherwise it could not have survived two millennia. The oval lacks all such archetypal appeal. It has an arbitrary form. It distorts that eternal dream of the harmony of the spheres, which lay at the origin of the whole quest. Who art thou, Johann Kepler, to destroy divine symmetry? All he has to say in his own defence is, that having cleared the stable of astronomy of cycles and spirals, he left behind him "only a single cart-ful of dung": his oval.

At this point, the sleepwalker's intuition failed him, he seems to be overcome by dizziness, and clutches at the first prop that he can find. He must find a physical cause, a cosmic *raison d'être* for his oval in the sky—and he falls back on the old quack remedy which he has just abjured, the conjuring up of an epicycle! To be sure, it is an epicycle with a difference: it has a physical cause. We have heard earlier on that while the sun's force sweeps the planet round in a circle, a second, antagonistic force, "seated in the planet itself" makes it turn in a small epicycle in the opposite direction. It all seems to him "wonderfully plausible," for the result of the combined movement is indeed an oval. But a very special oval: it has the shape of an egg, with the pointed end at the perihelion, the broad end at the aphelion.

No philosopher had laid such a monstrous egg before. Or, in Kepler's own words of wistful hindsight:

What happened to me confirms the old proverb: a bitch in a hurry produces blind pups. . . . But I simply could not think of any other means of imposing an oval path on the planets. When these ideas fell upon me, I had already celebrated my new triumph over Mars without being disturbed by the question. . . . whether the figures tally or not. . . . Thus I got myself into a new labyrinth. . . . The reader must show tolerance to my gullibility.

The battle with the egg goes on for six chapters, and took a full year of Kepler's life. It was a difficult year; he had no money, and was down with "a fever from the gall." A threatening new star, the *nova* of 1604 had appeared in the sky; Frau Barbara [his wife] was also ill, and gave birth to a son—which provided Kepler with an opportunity for one of his dreadful jokes: "Just when I was busy squaring my oval, an unwelcome guest entered my house through a secret doorway to disturb me."

To find the area of his egg, he again computed a series of one hundred and eighty Sun-Mars distances and added them together; and this whole operation he repeated no less than forty times. To make the worthless hypothesis work, he temporarily repudiated his own, immortal Second Law—to no avail. Finally, a kind of snowblindness seemed to descend on him: he held the solution in his hand without seeing it. On 4 July, 1603, he wrote to a friend that he was unable to solve the geometrical problems of his egg; but "if only the shape were a perfect ellipse all the answers could be found in Archimedes' and Apollonius' work." A full eighteen months later, he again wrote to the same correspondent that the truth must lie somewhere halfway between egg-shape and circular-shape "just as if the Martian orbit were a perfect ellipse. But regarding that I have so far explored nothing." What is even more astonishing, he constantly used ellipses in his calculations—but merely as an *auxiliary* device to determine, by approximation, the area of his egg-curve—which by now had become a veritable fixation.[1] . . .

[1] Copernicus, too, stumbled on the ellipse and kicked it aside; but Copernicus, who firmly believed in circles, had much less reason to pay attention to it than Kepler, who had progressed to the oval.

And yet, these years of wandering through the wilderness were not entirely wasted. The otherwise sterile chapters in the *New Astronomy* devoted to the egg hypothesis, represent an important further step towards the invention of the infinitesimal calculus. Besides, Kepler's mind had by now become so saturated with the numerical data of the Martian orbit, that when the crucial hazard presented itself, it responded at once like a charged cloud to a spark.

The hazard is perhaps the most unlikely incident in this unlikely story. It presented itself in the shape of a number which had stuck in Kepler's brain. The number was 0.00429.

When he at last realized that his egg had "gone up in smoke" and that Mars, whom he had believed a conquered prisoner "securely chained by my equations, immured in my tables," had again broken loose, Kepler decided to start once again from scratch.

He computed very thoroughly a score of Mars-Sun distances at various points of the orbit. They showed again that the orbit was some kind of oval, looking like a circle flattened inward at two opposite sides, so that there were two narrow sickles or "lunulae" left between the circle and the Martian orbit. The width of the sickle, where it is thickest, amounted to 0.00429 of the radius: (Figure 5-13).

At this point Kepler, for no particular reason, became interested in the angle at M—

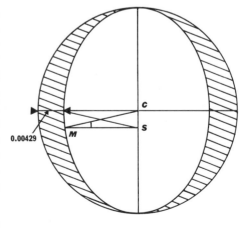

Figure 5-13

the angle formed between the sun and the centre of the orbit, as seen from Mars. This angle was called the "optical equation." It varies, of course, as Mars moves along its orbit; its maximum value is 5° 18'. This is what happened next, in Kepler's own words:

I was wondering why and how a sickle of just this thickness (0.00429) came into being. While this thought was driving me around, while I was considering again and again that . . . my apparent triumph over Mars had been in vain, I stumbled entirely by chance on the secant* of the angle 5° 18', which is the measure of the greatest optical equation. When I realized that this secant equals 0.00429, I felt as if I had been awakened from a sleep. . . .

It had been a true sleepwalker's performance. At the first moment, the reappearance of the number 0.00429 in this unexpected context must have appeared as a miracle to Kepler. But he realized in a flash that the apparent miracle must be due to a fixed relation between the angle at M and the distance to S, a relation which must hold true for any point of the orbit; only the manner in which he had stumbled on that relation was due to chance. "The roads that lead man to knowledge are as wondrous as that knowledge itself."

Now at last, at long last, after six years of incredible labour, he held the secret of the Martian orbit. He was able to express the manner in which the planet's distance from the sun varied with its position, in a simple formula, a mathematical Law of Nature. *But he still did not realize that this formula specifically defined the orbit as an ellipse.*[2] Nowadays, a student with a little knowledge of analytical geometry would real-

ize this at a glance; but analytical geometry came after Kepler. He had discovered his magic equation empirically, but he could no more identify it as the shorthand sign for an ellipse than the average reader of this book can; it was nearly as meaningless to him. He had reached his goal, but he did not realize that he had reached it.

The result was that he went off on one more, last, wild goose chase. He tried to construct the orbit which would correspond to his newly discovered equation; but he did not know how, made a mistake in geometry, and arrived at a curve which was too bulgy; the orbit was a *via buccosa*, chubby-faced, as he noted with disgust.

What next? We have reached the climax of the comedy. In his despair, Kepler threw out his formula (which denoted an elliptic orbit) because he wanted to try out an entirely new hypothesis: to wit, an elliptic orbit. It was as if the tourist had told the waiter, after studying the menu: "I don't want *côtellette d'agneau*, whatever that is; I want a lamb chop."

By now he was convinced that the orbit must be an ellipse, because countless observed positions of Mars, which he knew almost by heart, irresistibly pointed to that curve; but he still did not realize that his equation, which he had found by chance-plus-intuition, *was* an ellipse. So he discarded that equation, and constructed an ellipse by a different geometrical method. And then, at long last, he realized that the two methods produced the same result.

With his usual disarming frankness, he confessed what had happened:

Why should I mince my words? The truth of Nature, which I had rejected and chased away, returned by stealth through the backdoor, disguising itself to be accepted. That is to say, I laid [the original equation] aside, and fell back on ellipses, believing that this was a quite different hypothesis, whereas the two, as I shall prove in the next chapter, are one and the same. . . I thought and searched, until I went nearly mad, for a reason why the planet preferred an elliptical orbit [to mine]. . . . Ah, what a foolish bird I have been!

---

* Mathematically, the secant of an acute angle of a right triangle is the ratio of the hypotenuse to the side adjacent to the angle in question. In the illustration below, the secant of the angle at M is the ratio MC:MS. These letters correspond to those in Fig. 5-13. Ed.

5°18'

M   C   S

Figure 5-14

[2] In modern denotation, the formula is: $R = 1 + e \cos \beta$ where R is the distance from the sun, β the longitude referred to the centre of the orbit, and e the eccentricity. [See "*ellipse*," in Glossary. Ed.]

But in the List of Contents, in which he gives a brief outline of the whole work, Kepler sums up the matter in a single sentence:

I show [in this chapter] how I unconsciously repair my error.

The remainder of the book is in the nature of a mopping-up operation after the final victory.

The Third Law

The *Harmonice Mundi* [published in 1619] contains. . . . Kepler's Third Law of planetary motion. It says, put into modern terms, that the square of the periods of revolution of any two planets are as the cubes of their mean distances from the sun. Here is an illustration of it. Let the earth's distance from the sun be our unit measure, then Saturn's distance from the sun will be a little over nine units. The square root of 1 is 1; the square root of 9 = 3. The cube of 1 is 1, the cube of 3 is 27. Thus a Saturn year will be a little over twenty-seven earth years; in fact it is thirty years. Apologies for the coarse example—it is Kepler's own. Unlike his First and Second Laws . . . the Third Law was the fruit of nothing but patient, dogged trying. When after endless trials, he had at last hit on the square-to-cube ratio, he of course promptly found a reason why it should be just that and none other; I have said before that Kepler's *a priori* proofs were often invented *a posteriori*.

The exact circumstances of the discovery of the Third Law were again faithfully recorded by Kepler:

On March 8 of this present year 1618, if precise dates are wanted, (the solution) turned up in my head. But I had an unlucky hand and when I tested it by computations I rejected it as false. In the end it came back again to me on May 15, and in a new attack conquered the darkness of my mind; it agreed so perfectly with the data which my seventeen years of labour on Tycho's observations had yielded, that I thought at first I was dreaming. . . .

He had been searching for this Third Law, that is to say, for a correlation between a planet's period and its distance, since his youth. Without such a correlation, the universe would make no sense to him; it would be an arbitrary structure. If the sun had the power to govern the planets' motions, then that motion must somehow depend on their distance from the sun; but how? Kepler was the first who saw the problem—quite apart from the fact that he found the answer to it, after twenty-two years of labour. The reason why nobody before him had asked the question is that nobody had thought of cosmological problems in terms of actual physical forces. So long as cosmology remained divorced from physical causation in the mind, *the right question could not occur in that mind.* . . .

I have tried to re-trace the tortuous progress of his thought. Perhaps the most astonishing thing about it is the mixture of cleanness and uncleanness in his method. On the one hand, he throws away a cherished theory, the result of years of labour, because of those wretched eight minutes of arc. On the other hand he makes impermissible generalizations, knows that they are impermissible, yet does not care. . . .

We saw him plod, with infinite patience, along dreary stretches of trial-and-error procedure, then suddenly become airborne when a lucky guess or hazard presented him with an opportunity. What enabled him to recognize instantly his chance when the number 0.00429 turned up in an unexpected context was the fact that not only his waking mind, but his sleep-walking unconscious self was saturated with every conceivable aspect of his problem, not only with the numerical data and ratios, but also with an intuitive "feel" of the physical forces, and of the Gestalt-configurations which it involved. A locksmith who opens a complicated lock with a crude piece of bent wire is not guided by logic, but by the unconscious residue of countless past experiences with locks, which lend his touch a wisdom that his reason does not possess.

LIMITATIONS OF THE INDUCTIVE METHOD

LIMITATIONS OF THE SCIENTIFIC METHOD*
by Bertrand Russell (1931)

The sort of things that are demanded on a passport, such as name, date of birth, colour of grandfather's eyes, etc., are brute facts; the past existence of Caesar and Napoleon, the present existence of the earth and the sun and the other heavenly bodies, may also be regarded as brute facts. That is to say, most of us accept them as such, but strictly speaking, they involve inferences which may, or may not, be correct. If a boy learning history were to refuse to believe in the existence of Napoleon, he would probably be punished, which might, for a pragmatist, constitute sufficient proof that there was such a man; but if the boy were not a pragmatist, he might reflect that if his teacher had had any reason to believe in Napoleon, the reason might have been disclosed. Very few teachers of history, I believe, would be able to produce any good argument to show that Napoleon was not a myth. I am not saying that such arguments do not exist; I am only saying that most people do not know what they are. Clearly, if you are going to believe anything outside your own experience, you should have some reason for believing it. Usually the reason is authority. When it was first proposed to establish laboratories at Cambridge, Todhunter, the mathematician, objected that it was unnecessary for students to see experiments performed, since the results could be vouched for by their teachers, all of them men of the highest character, and many of them clergymen of the Church of England. Todhunter considered that the argument from authority should suffice, but we all know how often authority has been proved mistaken. It is true that most of us must inevitably depend upon it for most of our knowledge. I accept on authority the existence of Cape Horn, and it is clearly impossible that each of us should verify all the facts of geography; but it is important that the opportunity for verification should exist, and that its occasional necessity should be recognized.

To revert to history: as we proceed into the past there is a gradually increasing doubt. Did Pythagoras exist? Probably. Did Romulus exist? Probably not. Did Remus exist? Almost certainly not. But the difference between the evidence for Napoleon and the evidence for Romulus is only one of degree. Strictly speaking, neither the one nor the other can be accepted as mere matter of fact, since neither comes within our direct experience.

Does the sun exist? Most people would say that the sun does come within our direct experience in a sense in which Napoleon does not, but in thinking this, they would be mistaken. The sun is removed from us in space as Napoleon is removed from us in time. The sun, like Napoleon, is known to us only through its effects. People say they see the sun; but that only means that something has travelled through the intervening ninety-three million miles, and produced an effect upon the retina, the optic nerve, and the brain. This effect, which happens where we are, is certainly not identical with the sun as understood by astronomers. Indeed, the same effect might be produced by other means: in theory, a hot globe of molten metal could be hung up in such a position that, to a given observer, it would seem just like the sun. The effect upon the observer might be made indistinguishable from the effect which the sun produces. The sun, therefore, is an inference from what we see, and is not the actual patch of brightness of which we are immediately aware.

It is characteristic of the advance of science that less and less is found to be datum, and more and more is found to be inference. The inference is, of course, quite unconscious, except in those who have trained themselves

* From Bertrand Russell, *The Scientific Outlook*, W. W. Norton & Company, Inc., New York, 1931, copyright 1931 and 1959 by Bertrand Russell and reprinted by permission of the publisher and George Allen & Unwin, Ltd., London.

to philosophical scepticism; but it must not be supposed that an unconscious inference is necessarily valid. Babies think that there is another baby on the other side of the looking-glass, and although they have not arrived at this conclusion by a logical process, it is nevertheless mistaken. Many of our unconscious inferences, which are, in fact, conditioned reflexes acquired in early infancy, are highly dubious as soon as they are subjected to logical scrutiny. . . .

In science, we always argue that since the observed facts obey certain laws, therefore other facts in the same region will obey the same laws. We may verify this subsequently over a greater or smaller region, but its practical importance is always in regard to those regions where it has not yet been verified. We have verified the laws of statics, for example, in countless cases, and we employ them in building a bridge; in regard to the bridge, they are not verified until we find that the bridge stays up, but their importance lies in enabling us to predict beforehand that the bridge will stay up. It is easy to see why we *think* it will; this is merely an example of Pavlov's conditioned reflexes, which cause us to expect whatever combinations we have frequently experienced in the past. But if you have to cross a bridge in a train, it is no comfort to you to know why the engineer thought it was a good bridge: the important thing is that it should be a good bridge, and this requires that his induction from the laws of statics in observed cases to the same laws in unobserved cases should be a valid one.

Now, unfortunately, no one has hitherto shown any good reason for supposing that this sort of inference is sound. Hume, nearly two hundred years ago, threw doubt upon induction, as, indeed, upon most other things. The philosophers were indignant, and invented refutations of Hume which passed muster on account of their extreme obscurity. Indeed, for a long time philosophers took care to be unintelligible, since otherwise everybody would have perceived that they had been unsuccessful in answering Hume. It is easy to invent a metaphysic which will have as a consequence that induction is valid, and many men have done so; but they have not shown any reason to believe in their metaphysic except that it was pleasant. The metaphysic of Bergson, for example, is undoubtedly pleasant: like cocktails, it enables us to see the world as a unity without sharp distinctions, and all of it vaguely agreeable, but it has no better claim than cocktails have to be included in the technique for the pursuit of knowledge. There may be valid grounds for believing in induction, and, in fact, none of us can help believing in it, but it must be admitted that, in theory, induction remains, an unsolved problem of logic. As this doubt, however, affects practically the whole of our knowledge, we may pass it by, and assume pragmatically that inductive procedure, with proper safe-guards, is admissible. . . .

As we observed above, what is actually experienced is much less than one would naturally suppose. You may say, for example, that you see your friend, Mr. Jones, walking along the street; but this is to go far beyond what you have any right to say. You see a succession of coloured patches, traversing a stationary background. These patches, by means of a Pavlov conditioned reflex, bring into your mind the word "Jones," and so you say you see Jones; but other people, looking out of their windows from different angles, will see something different, owing to the laws of perspective: therefore, if they are all seeing Jones, there must be as many different Joneses as there are spectators, and if there is only one true Jones, the sight of him is not vouchsafed to anybody. If we assume for a moment the truth of the account which physics gives, we shall explain what you call "seeing Jones" in some such terms as the following. Little packets of light, called "light quanta," shoot out from the sun, and some of these reach a region where there are atoms of a certain kind, composing Jones's face, and hands, and clothes. . . . Some of the light quanta, when they reach Jones's atoms, upset their internal economy. This causes him to become sunburnt, and to manufacture vitamin D. Others are reflected, and of those that are reflected, some enter your eye. They there cause a complicated disturbance of the rods and cones, which, in turn, sends a current along the optic nerve. When this current reaches the brain, it produces an event. The event which it produces is that which you call "seeing Jones." As is evident from this account, the connexion of "seeing Jones" with Jones is a remote, roundabout causal connexion. Jones himself, meanwhile, remains wrapped in mystery. He may be thinking about his dinner, or about how his investments have gone to pieces, or about that umbrella he lost; these thoughts are Jones, but these are not what you see. To say that you see Jones is no more correct than it would be, if a ball bounced off a wall in your garden and hit you, to say that the wall had hit you. Indeed, the two cases are closely analogous.

We do not, therefore, ever see what we think we see. Is there any reason to think that what we think we see exists, although we do not see it? Science has always prided itself on being empirical, and believing only what could be verified. Now you can verify the occurrences in yourself which you call "seeing Jones," but you cannot verify Jones himself. You may hear sounds which you call Jones speaking to you; you may feel sensations of touch which you call Jones bumping into you. If he has not lately had a bath, you may also have olfactory sensations of which you suppose him to be the source. If you have been impressed by this argument, you may address him as if he were at the other end of the telephone, and say, "Are you there?" And you may subsequently hear the words: "Yes, you idiot, can't you see me?" But if you regard these as affording evidence that he is there, you have missed the point of the argument. The point is that Jones is a convenient hypothesis by means of which certain of your own sensations can be collected into a bundle; but what really makes them belong together is not their common hypothetical origin, but certain resemblances and causal affinities which they have to each other. These remain, even if their common origin is

mythical. When you see a man in the cinema, you know that he does not exist when he is off the stage, though you suppose that there was an original who did exist continuously. But why should you make this supposition? Why should not Jones be like the man you see at the cinema? He may get annoyed with you if you suggest such an idea, but he will be powerless to disprove it, since he cannot give you any experience of what he is doing when you do not experience him.

We are, in fact, led to the position of Berkeley, according to which only thoughts exist. Berkeley saved the universe and the permanence of bodies by regarding them as God's thoughts, but this was only a wish-fulfilment, not logical thinking. However, as he was at once a bishop and an Irishman, we ought not to be too hard on him. The fact is that science started with a large amount of what Santayana calls "animal faith," which is, in fact, thought dominated by the principle of the conditioned reflex. . . .

The problem is not essentially one for the physicist, but for the logician. It is, in essence, a simple one, namely: are circumstances ever such as to enable us, from a set of known events, to infer that some other event has occurred, is occurring, or will occur? Or, if we cannot make such an inference with certainty, can we ever make it with any high degree of probability, or at any rate with a probability greater than a half? If the answer to this question is in the affirmative, we may be justified in believing, as we all do in fact believe, in the occurrence of events which we have not personally experienced. If the answer is in the negative, we can never be justified in our belief. Logicians have hardly ever considered this question in its naked simplicity, and I do not know of any clear answer to it. Until an answer is forthcoming, one way or another, the question must remain an open one, and our faith in the external world must be merely animal faith.

As to past *Experience*, it can be allowed to give *direct* and *certain* information of those precise objects only, and that precise period of time, which fell under its cognizance: but why this experience should be extended to future times, and to other objects, which for aught we know, may be only in appearance similar; this is the main question on which I would insist. The bread, which I formerly eat, nourished me; that is, a body of such sensible qualities was, at that time, endued with such secret powers: but does it follow, that other bread must also nourish me at another time, and that like sensible qualities must always be attended with like secret powers? The consequence seems nowise necessary. At least, it must be acknowledged that there is here a consequence drawn by the mind; that there is a certain step taken; a process of thought, and an inference, which wants to be explained. These two propositions are far from being the same, *I have found that such an object has always been attended with such an effect*, and *I foresee, that other objects, which are, in appearance, similar, will be attended with similar effects*. I shall allow, if you please, that the one proposition may justly be inferred from the other: I know, in fact, that it always is inferred. But if you insist that the inference is made by a chain of reasoning, I desire you to produce that reasoning. The connexion between these propositions is not intuitive. There is required a medium, which may enable the mind to draw such an inference, if indeed it be drawn by reasoning and argument. What that medium is, I must confess, passes my comprehension; and it is incumbent on those to produce it, who assert that it really exists, and is the origin of all our conclusions concerning matter of fact.

David Hume
Concerning Human Understanding (1748)

The community of sensations is our chief and final test that experiences are true sensations such as give information about the external world; if we apply other tests, it is only because this chief test is not available, and any other tests we may apply are based on the results which we are accustomed to obtain with this chief test. . . .

Other people agree with me much more closely about sensations than they do about any other kind of thought. The fact, expressed in that manner, is extremely familiar. If I am in a room when the electric light bulb bursts, not only I, but everyone else in the room (unless some of them are blind or deaf), hears the explosion and experiences the change from light to darkness. On the other hand, apart from sensations, we may all have been thinking about different things, remembering different things, following different trains of reasoning, and experiencing different desires. This community of sensations, contrasted with the particularity of other kinds of thoughts, leads naturally to the view that the sensations are determined by something that is not me or you or anybody else in the room, but is something external to us all; while the other thoughts, which we do not share, are parts of the particular person, experiencing them. This simple experience is probably the main reason why we have come to believe so firmly that there is an external world and that our perceptions received by our senses give us information about it. . . .

Science is the study of those judgements concerning which universal agreement can be obtained.

Norman Campbell
What Is Science? (1921)

False facts are highly injurious to the progress of science, for they often endure long; but false views, if supported by some evidence, do little harm, for every one takes a salutary pleasure in proving their falseness.

Charles Darwin
The Descent of Man (1871)

A hypothesis or theory is clear, decisive, and positive, but it is believed by no one but the man who created it. Experimental findings, on the other hand, are messy, inexact things which are believed by everyone except the man who did that work.

Harlow Shapley
Harvard Crimson (1935)

The Microbe

The microbe is so very small
You cannot make him out at all,
But many sanguine people hope
To see him through a microscope,
His jointed tongue that lies beneath
A hundred curious rows of teeth;
His seven tufted tails with lots
Of lovely pink and purple spots,
On each of which a pattern stands,
Composed of forty separate bands;
His eyebrows of a tender green;
All these have never yet been seen,
But scientists, who ought to know,
Assure us that they must be so. . . .
Oh! let us never, never doubt—!
What nobody is sure about!

Hilaire Belloc
More Beasts and Worse Children (1897)

QUESTIONS TO CONSIDER

Do these readings throw new light on the statement "The scientist does not merely record the facts but he must conform to the facts"?

Hall said that Kepler's first law was ". . . the first instance in the history of science of a discovery being made as the result of a search for a theory, not merely to cover a given set of observations, but to interpret a group of refined measurements whose probable accuracy was a significant factor." What is meant by this statement?

What is the difference between measurement in the somewhat casual sense and scientific measurement?

What are the limitations of accuracy, and how do scientists attempt to overcome these limitations?

What is a scientific fact?

SUGGESTIONS FOR FURTHER READING

Bronowski, J., and Bruce Mazlish: *The Western Intellectual Tradition*, Harper & Row, Publishers, New York, 1960, chaps. 10, 11, and 12. A history of the formation of the Royal Society and a discussion of the philosophies of Hobbes, Locke, and Descartes.

* Burtt, E. A.: *The Metaphysical Foundations of Modern Science*, Anchor Books, Doubleday & Company, Inc., Garden City, N.Y., 1954, chaps. IV, V, and VI. A detailed and interesting discussion of Descartes as well as the philosophical problems of knowledge, causality, sense perception, and the reality of secondary qualities.

* Butterfield, Herbert: *The Origins of Modern Science*, The Macmillan Company, New York, 1959, chaps. V, VI, and VII. A very fine analysis of the use of the experimental method, the influence of Bacon and Descartes.

* Cohen, I. Bernard: *The Birth of a New Physics*, Anchor Books, Doubleday & Company, Inc., Garden City, N.Y., 1960, chap. VI. A good discussion of Kepler's laws.

* Conant, James B.: *Science and Common Sense*, Yale University Press, New Haven, Conn., 1951, chap. 6. An explanation of the relationship between abstract reasoning and quantitative experimentation.

* Lodge, Oliver: *Pioneers of Science*, Dover Publications, Inc., New York, 1960, lectures II and III. The story of Tycho Brahe's life and work and Kepler's discovery of the laws of planetary motion.

* Russell, Bertrand: *A History of Western Philosophy*, Simon and Schuster, Inc., New York, 1945, book 3, part I, chaps. VII, IX, XIII, XVI, and XVII. An analysis of the philosophies of Francis Bacon, Descartes, Locke, Berkeley, and Hume.

* Paperback edition.

PART **6**

IS THERE A LIMIT TO MAN'S UNDERSTANDING OF NATURE?

A study of the development of two contradictory theories of the nature of light brings into focus the philosophical crisis arising from the discoveries of modern physics. Can a model or picture of reality be formulated that fits the known facts and is consistent with the basic assumption that there is an order in nature that man can understand?

Newton

Huygens

Condon

INTRODUCTION

Light is the principal source of our knowledge of the universe. Without it, our world would be small indeed, confined to what we could touch, taste, hear, or smell. The light from the sun and stars was first used to estimate their relative sizes and distances from us. Later it was discovered that the messages we receive contain much more information about the bodies that are radiating or reflecting this light. The complicated code of these messages was gradually deciphered as scientists investigated the nature of light itself. It was found to contain data about the temperature, composition, size, and age of the stars as well as their velocity in relation to the earth. Although we still do not understand exactly why light behaves as it does, we have learned a great deal about how it behaves and have used this knowledge very effectively to build useful devices and learn more about other parts of the universe.

The readings in this part trace the search for a satisfactory theory of light from Newton and Huygens to the modern quantum theory and bring out the fact that the nature of light is still one of the greatest mysteries of science. In modern physics, theories of light merge with theories of the nature of matter and become an integral part of the broader theory known as quantum mechanics. At this point we have made an effort to include selections that bear directly on the nature of light itself, in order to keep the material within limits that can reasonably be handled in one part and have left the study of the nature of matter to another time when it can be handled in much greater detail. The modern concept of an electron is mentioned in these readings only insofar as the idea is necessary to an understanding of the uncertainty principle, which has had such important repercussions on philosophical thought.

As a result of quantum theory and the uncertainty principle, three of the most basic beliefs of science have been brought into question. The first of these is the uniformity of nature, which we discussed in Part 3. That "instinctive belief in the order of nature" that appeared to be essential to the growth of the scientific spirit has been, if not actually destroyed, at least seriously shaken. This situation is illustrated by a joke current among physicists that light behaves as waves on Mondays, Wednesdays, and Fridays and as quanta on the other days. It may seem surprising to the layman that scientists can continue to work effectively in this state of suspended judgment, when even the most basic

Bragg

Jeans

Barnett

assumption of scientific activity has been shaken. But actually, the state of mind represented here is a necessary facet of the scientific spirit. To some extent, science must always reserve final judgment, as we will see in Part 7 and must stand ready to change basic concepts in the face of new evidence.

The second tenet that has been shaken by modern physics is the ability of science to remain objective. In studying the very smallest units of mass and energy, the differentiation between subject and object becomes blurred, and this changed relationship poses the problem of how to preserve the objective scientific attitude as man attempts to probe further into the nature of light and matter.

The third fundamental concept that is questioned is the nature of causality. The causal relationship that has been extensively used in scientific reasoning was shaken by the discovery that we cannot form a continuous description of elementary particles. There are gaps in continuity due to the quantization of energy by which we perceive and measure events in space and time. Heisenberg's uncertainty principle is a mathematical statement of this difficulty. If it is theoretically impossible ever to formulate a complete description of the situation at one instant in time, then it is also impossible to predict what will happen as a result of this state. The picture presented by Laplace in 1814 that ". . . we can regard the present state of the universe as the effect of its anterior state and as the cause of the one which is to follow" becomes forever inaccessible. Some modern physicists take the position that what can never be observed is meaningless and that because no strict causal relationship can be proven, man has been given back free will. Others take the view that a more unified theory and possibly even a satisfactory model that resolves the conflicting concepts can and must be found. Selections at the end of this part illustrate these two different points of view toward one of the fundamental problems in modern physics. Whichever point of view you may believe, it is certainly true that, as Margenau says, ". . . the problem of freedom has been taken out of the wastebasket of paradoxes and placed on the shelf of challenging problems to be solved."

Taken all together, the questioning of these three basic tenets leads to an even more challenging problem. Is there a natural barrier beyond which man's understanding cannot penetrate? Have we, as Bridgeman suggests, reached the limit of vision?

Schrödinger

De Laplace

Newman

TWO THEORIES OF THE NATURE OF LIGHT

In the beginning God created the heaven and the earth. And the earth was without form, and void; and darkness *was* upon the face of the deep. And the Spirit of God moved upon the face of the waters.
And God said, Let there be light: and there was light.
And God saw the light, that it was good: and God divided the light from the darkness.
And God called the light Day, and the darkness he called night. And the evening and the morning were the first day.

Genesis, 1:1-5
King James Bible (1604–1611)

DISPERSION OF LIGHT*
by Sir Isaac Newton (1672)

In the year 1666, (at which time I applied myself to the grinding of optick glasses of other figures than spherical) I procured me a triangular glass prism to try therewith the celebrated phaenomena of colours. And in order thereto, having darkened my chamber, and made a small hole in my window-shuts, to let in a convenient quantity of the sun's light, I placed my prism at its entrance, that it might be thereby refracted to the opposite wall. It was at first a very pleasing divertisement, to view the vivid and intense colours produced thereby; but after a while applying myself to consider them more circumspectly, I became surprised, to see them in an oblong form; which, according to the received laws of refraction, I expected should have been circular. They were terminated at the sides with straight lines, but at the ends, the decay of light was so gradual that it was difficult to determine justly, what was their figure; yet they seemed semicircular.

Comparing the length of this colour'd Spectrum with its breadth, I found it about five times greater, a disproportion so extravagant, that it excited me to a more than ordinary curiosity to examining from whence it might proceed. I could scarce think, that the various

thicknesses of the glass, or the termination with shadow or darkness, could have any influence on light to produce such an effect; yet I thought it not amiss, first to examine those circumstances, and so try'd what would happen by transmitting light through parts of the glass of diverse thicknesses, or through holes in the window of diverse bignesses, or by setting the prism without, so that the light might pass through it, and be refracted, before it was terminated by the hole: But I found none of those circumstances material. The fashion of the colours was in all these cases the same.

Then I suspected, whether by any unevenness in the glass or other contingent irregularity, these colours might be thus dilated. And to try this, I took another prism like the former, and so placed it, that the light passing through them both might be refracted contrary ways, and so by the latter returned into that course from which the former had diverted it. For by this means I thought the regular effects of the first prism would be destroyed by the second prism, but the irregular ones more augmented, by the multiplicity of refractions. The event was, that the light, which by the first prism was diffused into an oblong form was by the second reduced into an orbicular one, with as much regularity as when it did not at all pass through them.

* From Sir Isaac Newton, *Principia Mathematica*, edited by Florian Cajois, from the translation by Andrew Motte, University of California Press, Berkeley, Calif., 1934. Reprinted by permission.

Then I began to suspect, whether the rays, after their trajection through the prism, did not move in curve lines, and according to their more or less curvity tend to divers parts of the wall. And it increased my suspicion, when I remembered that I had often seen a tennis ball struck with an oblique racket, describe such a curve line. For, a circular as well as a progressive motion being communicated to it by that stroke, its parts on that side where the motions conspire, must press and beat the contiguous air more violently than on the other, and there excite a reluctancy and reaction of the air proportionably greater. And for the same reason, if the rays of light should possibly be globular bodies, and by their oblique passage out of one medium into another, acquire a circulating motion, they ought to feel the greater resistance from the ambient ether, on that side, where the motions conspire, and thence be continually bowed to the other. But notwithstanding this plausible ground of suspicion, when I came to examine it, I could observe no such curvity in them. And besides (which was enough for my purpose) I observed, that the difference 'twixt the length of the image, and the diameter of the hole, through which the light was transmitted, was proportionable to their distance.

The gradual removal of these suspicions at length led me to the *Experimentum Crucis*, which was this: I took two boards, and placed one of them close behind the prism at the window, so that the light might pass through a small hole, made in it for the purpose, and fall on the other board, which I placed at about 12 feet distance, having first made a small hole in it also, for some of the incident light to pass through. Then I placed another prism behind this second board, so that the light trajected through both the boards might pass through that also, and be again refracted before it arrived at the wall. This done, I took the first prism in my hand, and turned it to and fro slowly about its axis, so much as to make the several parts of the image cast, on the second board, successively pass through the hole in it, that I might observe to what

places on the wall the second prism would refract them. And I saw by the variation of those places, that the light, tending to that end of the image, towards which the refraction of the first prism was made, did in the second prism suffer a refraction considerably greater than the light tending to the other end. And so the true cause of the length of that image was detected to be no other, than the light is not similar or homogenial, but consists of *Difform Rays, some of which are more Refrangible than others*; so that without any difference in their incidence on the same medium, some shall be more Refracted than others; and therefore that, according to their *particular Degrees of Refrangibility*, they were transmitted through the prism to divers parts of the opposite wall.

Now I shall proceed to acquaint you with another more notable *Difformity* in its rays, wherein the origin of colours is unfolded: concerning which I shall lay down the doctrine first, and then for its examination give you an instance or two of the experiments, as a specimen of the rest.

The doctrine you will find comprehended and illustrated in the following propositions:

1. As the rays of light differ in degrees of refrangibility so they also differ in their disposition to exhibit, this or that particular colour. Colours are not qualifications of light, derived from refractions, or reflections of natural bodies (as 'tis generally believed) but original and connate properties, which in divers rays are divers. Some rays are disposed to exhibit a red colour and no other; some a yellow and no other, some a green and no other, and so of the rest. Nor are there only rays proper and particular to the more eminent colours, but even to all their intermediate gradations.

2. To the same degree of refrangibility ever belongs the same colour, and to the same colour ever belongs the same degree of refrangibility. The least refrangible rays are all disposed to exhibit a red colour, and contrarily those rays which are disposed to exhibit a red colour, are all the least refrangible: so the most refrangible rays are all

disposed to exhibit a deep violet colour, and contrarily those which are apt to exhibit such a violet colour are all the most refrangible. And so to all the intermediate colours in a continued series belong intermediate degrees of refrangibility. And this Analogy 'twixt colours and refrangibility is very precise and strict; the rays always either exactly agreeing in both, or proportionally disagreeing in both [Figure 6-1].

3. The species of colour, and degree of refrangibility proper to any particular sort of rays, is not mutable by refraction, nor by reflection from natural bodies, nor by any other cause that I could yet observe. When any one sort of rays hath been well parted from those of other kinds, it hath afterwards obstinately retained its colour, notwithstanding my utmost endeavors to change it. I have refracted it with prisms, and reflected it with bodies, which in daylight were of other colours; I have intercepted it with the coloured film of air, interceeded two compressed plates of glass; transmitted it through coloured mediums, and through mediums irradiated with other sorts of rays, and diversely terminated it; and yet could never produce any new colour out of it. It would by contracting or dilating become more brisk, or faint, and by the loss of many rays, in some cases very obscure and dark; but I could never see it changed in specie.

4. Yet seeming transmutations of colours may be made, where there is any mixture of

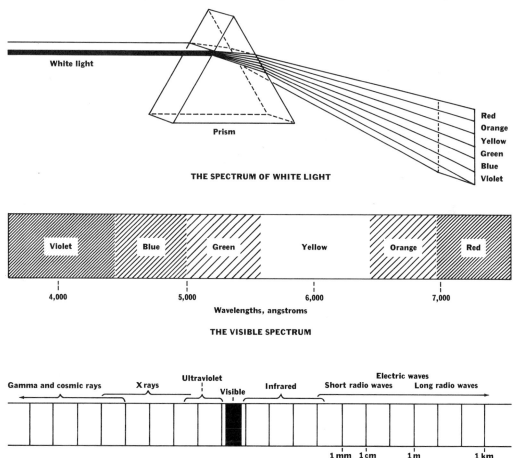

White light

Prism

Red
Orange
Yellow
Green
Blue
Violet

THE SPECTRUM OF WHITE LIGHT

| Violet | Blue | Green | Yellow | Orange | Red |

4,000   5,000   6,000   7,000

Wavelengths, angstroms

THE VISIBLE SPECTRUM

Gamma and cosmic rays   X rays   **Ultraviolet**   Infrared   **Electric waves**
Visible   Short radio waves   Long radio waves

1 mm   1 cm   1 m   1 km

Wavelengths :   Angstroms   Microns   Meters

THE COMPLETE ELECTROMAGNETIC SPECTRUM

Figure 6-1. The place of the visible spectrum in the electromagnetic spectrum.

divers sorts of rays. For in such mixtures, the component colours appear not, but, by their mutual allaying each other, constitute a midling colour. And therefore, if by refraction, or any other of the aforesaid causes, the difform rays, latent in such a mixture, be separated, there shall emerge colours different from the colour of the composition. Which colours are not new generated, but only made apparent by being parted; for if they be again entirely mixt and blended together, they will again compose that colour, which they did before separation. And for the same reason, transmutations made by the convening of divers colours are not real; for when the difform rays are again severed, they will exhibit the very same colours which they did before they entered the composition; as you see blue and yellow powders, when finely mixed, appear to the naked eye, green, and yet the colours of the component corpuscles are not thereby really transmuted, but only blended. For when viewed with a good microscope they still appear blue and yellow interspersedly.

5. There are therefore two sorts of colours. The one original and simple, and the other compounded of these. The original or primary colours are red, yellow, green, blue, and a violet-purple, together with orange, indico, and an indefinite variety of intermediate gradations.

6. The same colours in species with these primary ones, may be also produced by composition. For a mixture of yellow and blue makes green; of red and yellow makes orange; of orange and yellowish green makes yellow. And in general, if any two colours be mixed, which in the series of those generated by the prism are not too far distant one from another, they by their mutual alloy compound that colour, which in the said series appeareth in the midway between them. But those which are situated at too great a distance, do not so. Orange and indico produce not the intermediate green, nor scarlet and green the intermediate yellow.

7. But the most surprising, and wonderful composition was that of whiteness. There is no one sort of rays which alone can exhibit this. 'Tis ever compounded, and to its composition, are requisite all the aforesaid primary colours, mixed in a due proportion. I have often with admiration beheld that all the colours of the prism being made to converge, and thereby to be again mixed, as they were in the light before it was incident upon the prism, reproduced light, entirely and perfectly white, and not at all sensibly differing from a direct light of the sun, unless when the glasses, I used, were not sufficiently clear; for then they would a little incline it to their colour.

8. Hence therefore it comes to pass, that whiteness is the usual colour of light; for light is a confused aggregate of rays indued with all sorts of colours, as they were promiscuously darted from the various parts of luminous bodies. And of such a confused aggregate, as I said, is generated whiteness, if there be a due proportion of the ingredients; but if any one predominate, the light must incline to that colour; as it happens in the blue flame of brimstone; the yellow flame of a candle; and the various colours of the fixed stars.

9. These things considered, the manner how colours are produced by a prism is evident. For, of the rays, constituting the incident light, since those which differ in colour proportionally differ in refrangibility, they by their unequal refractions must be severed and dispersed into an oblong form in an orderly succession, from the least refracted scarlet, to the most refracted violet. And for the same reason it is, that objects when looked upon through a prism, appear coloured. For the difform rays, by their unequal refractions, are made to diverge towards several parts of the Retina, and these express the images of things coloured, as in the former case they did the sun's image upon a wall. And by this inequality of refractions, they become not only coloured, but also very confused and indistinct.

10. Why the colours of the rainbow appear in falling drops of rain, is also from hence evident. For those drops which refract the

rays, disposed to appear purple, in greatest quantity to the spectator's eye, refract the rays of other sorts so much less, as to make them pass beside it; and such are the drops on the inside of the primary bow, and on the outside of the secondary or exterior one. So those drops, which refract in greatest plenty the rays, apt to appear red, toward the spectator's eye, refract those of other sorts so much more, as to make them pass beside it; and such are the drops on the exterior part of the primary, and interior part of the secondary bow.

11. The odd phaenomena of an infusion of *Lignum Nephriticum*, leaf-gold, fragments of coloured glass, and some other transparently coloured bodies, appearing in one position of one colour, and of another in another, are on these grounds ṇo longer riddles. For those are substances apt to reflect one sort of light, and transmit another; as may be seen in a dark room, by illuminating them with familiar or uncompounded light. For then they appear of that colour only, with which they are illuminated, but yet in one position more vivid and luminous than in another, accordingly as they are disposed more or less to reflect or transmit the incident colour.

12. From hence also is manifest the reason of an unexpected experiment which *Mr. Hook*, somewhere in his *Micrography* relates to have made with two wedge-like transparent vessels, filled the one with a red, the other with a blue liquor: namely, that though they were severally transparent enough, yet both together became opake; for if one transmitted only red, and the other only blue, no rays could pass through both.

13. I might add more instances of this nature, but I shall conclude with this general one. That the colours of all natural bodies have no other origin than this, that they are variously qualified, to reflect one sort of light in greater plenty than another. And this I have experimented in a dark room, by illuminating those bodies with uncompounded light of divers colours. For by that means any body may be made to appear of any colour. They have there no appropriate colour, but ever appear of the colour of the light cast upon them, but yet with this difference, that they are most brisk and vivid in the light of their own daylight colour. Minimum appeareth there of any colour indifferently, with which it is illustrated, but yet most luminous in red, and so bise appeareth indifferently of any colour, but yet most luminous in blue. And therefore minimum reflecteth rays of any colour, but most copiously those endowed with red, and consequently when illustrated with daylight; that is, with all sorts of rays promiscuously blended, those qualified with red shall abound most in the reflected light, and by their prevalence cause it to appear of that colour. And for the same reason bise, reflecting blue most copiously, shall appear blue by the excess of those rays in its reflected light; and the like of other bodies. And that this is the entire and adequate cause of their colours, is manifest, because they have no power to change or alter the colours of any sort of rays incident apart, but put on all colours indifferently, with which they are enlightened.

These things being so, it can be no longer disputed, whether there be colours in the dark, or whether they be the qualities of the objects we see, no nor perhaps, whether light be a body. For, since colours are the qualities of light, having its rays for their entire and immediate subject, how can we think those rays qualities also, unless one quality may be the subject of, and sustain another; which in effect is to call it substance. We should not know bodies for substances; were it not for their sensible qualities, and the principal of those being now found due to something else, we have as good reason to believe that to be a substance also.

Besides, who ever thought any quality to be a heterogeneous aggregate, such as light is discovered to be? But to determine more absolutely what light is, after what manner refracted, and by what modes or actions it produceth in our minds the phantasms of colours, is not so easie; and I shall not mingle conjectures with certainties.

TREATISE ON LIGHT*
by Christian Huygens (1678)

It is inconceivable to doubt that light consists in the motion of some sort of matter. For whether one considers its production, one sees that here upon the Earth it is chiefly engendered by fire and flame which contain without doubt bodies that are in rapid motion, since they dissolve and melt many other bodies, even the most solid; or whether one considers its effects, one sees that when light is collected, as by concave mirrors, it has the property of burning as a fire does, that is to say it disunites the particles of bodies. This is assuredly the mark of motion, at least in the true Philosophy, in which one conceives the causes of all natural effects in terms of mechanical motions. This, in my opinion, we must necessarily do, or else renounce all hopes of ever comprehending anything in Physics.

And as, according to this Philosophy, one holds as certain that the sensation of sight is excited only by the impression of some movement of a kind of matter which acts on the nerves at the back of our eyes, there is here yet one reason more for believing that light consists in a movement of the matter which exists between us and the luminous body.

Further, when one considers the extreme speed with which light spreads on every side, and how, when it comes from different regions, even from those directly opposite, the rays traverse one another without hindrance, one may well understand that when we see a luminous object, it cannot be by any transport of matter coming to us from this object, in the way in which a shot or an arrow traverses the air; for assuredly that would too greatly impugn these two properties of light, especially the second of them. It is then in some other way that light spreads; and that which can lead us to comprehend it is the knowledge which we have of the spreading of Sound in the air.

We know that by means of the air, which is an invisible and impalpable body, Sound spreads around the spot where it has been produced, by a movement which is passed on successively from one part of the air to another; and that the spreading of this movement, taking place equally rapidly on all sides, ought to form spherical surfaces ever enlarging and which strike our ears. Now there is no doubt at all that light also comes from the luminous body to our eyes by some movement impressed on the matter which is between the two; since, as we have already seen, it cannot be by the transport of a body which passes from one to the other. If, in addition, light takes time for its passage—which we are now going to examine—it will follow that this movement, impressed on the intervening matter, is successive; and consequently it spreads, as Sound does, by spherical surfaces and waves: for I call them waves from their resemblance to those which are seen to be formed in water when a stone is thrown into it, and which present a successive spreading as circles, though these arise from another cause, and are only in a flat surface.

To see then whether the spreading of light takes time, let us consider first whether there are any facts of experience which can convince us to the contrary. As to those which can be made here on the Earth, by striking lights at great distances, although they prove that light takes no sensible time to pass over these distances, one may say with good reason that they are too small, and that the only conclusion to be drawn from them is that the passage of light is extremely rapid.

It is true that we are here supposing a strange velocity that would be a hundred thousand times greater than that of Sound. For Sound, according to what I have observed, travels about 180 Toises† in the time of one Second, or in about one beat of the pulse. But this supposition ought not to seem to be an impossibility; since it is not a question of the transport of a body with so great a speed, but of a successive movement which is passed on from some bodies to others. I have then made no difficulty, in meditating on these things, in supposing that the emanation

* From *Moments of Discovery: The Origins of Science*, Edited by George Schwartz and Philip W. Bishop, Copyright 1958, by Basic Books, Inc.

† About 1,115 feet. Ed.

of light is accomplished with time, seeing that in this way all its phenomena can be explained, and that in following the contrary opinion everything is incomprehensible. For it has always seemed to me that even Mr. Des Cartes, whose aim has been to treat all the subjects of Physics intelligibly, and who assuredly has succeeded in this better than any one before him, has said nothing that is not full of difficulties, or even inconceivable in dealing with Light and its properties.

But that which I employed only as a hypothesis, has recently received great seemingness as an established truth by the ingenious proof of Mr. Römer which I am going here to relate, expecting him himself to give all that is needed for its confirmation. It is founded as is the preceding argument upon celestial observations, and proves not only that Light takes time for its passage, but also demonstrates how much time it takes, and that its velocity is even at least six times greater than that which I have just stated.

For this he makes use of the Eclipses suffered by the little planets which revolve around Jupiter, and which often enter his shadow: and see what is his reasoning [Figure 6-2]. Let A be the Sun, BCDE the annual orbit of the Earth, F Jupiter, GN the orbit of the nearest of his Satellites, for it is this one which is more apt for this investigation than any of the other three, because of the quickness of its revolution. Let G be this Satellite entering into the shadow of Jupiter, H the same Satellite emerging from the shadow.

Let it be then supposed, the Earth being at B some time before the last quadrature, that one has seen the said Satellite emerge from the shadow; it must needs be, if the Earth remains at the same place, that, after $42\frac{1}{2}$ hours, one would again see a similar emergence, because that is the time in which it makes the round of its orbit, and when it would come again into opposition to the Sun. And if the Earth, for instance, were to remain always at B during 30 revolutions of this Satellite, one would see it again emerge from the shadow after 30 times $42\frac{1}{2}$ hours.

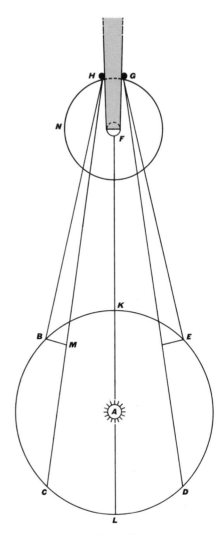

Figure 6-2

But the Earth having been carried along during this time to C, increasing thus its distance from Jupiter, it follows that if Light requires time for its passage the illumination of the little planet will be perceived later at C than it would have been at B, and that there must be added to this time of 30 times $42\frac{1}{2}$ hours that which the Light has required to traverse the space MC, the difference of the spaces CH, BH. Similarly at the other quadrature when the earth has come to E from D while approaching toward Jupiter, the immersions of the Satellite ought to be observed at E earlier than they would have been seen if the Earth had remained at D.

Now in quantities of observations of these

Eclipses, made during ten consecutive years, these differences have been found to be very considerable, such as ten minutes and more; and from them it has been concluded that in order to traverse the whole diameter of the annual orbit KL, which is double the distance from here to the sun, Light requires about 22 minutes of time.

The movement of Jupiter in his orbit while the Earth passed from B to C, or from D to E, is included in this calculation; and this makes it evident that one cannot attribute the retardation of these illuminations or the anticipation of the eclipses, either to any irregularity occurring in the movement of the little planet or to its eccentricity.

If one considers the vast size of the diameter KL, which according to me is some 24 thousand diameters of the Earth, one will acknowledge the extreme velocity of Light. For, supposing that KL is no more than 22 thousand of these diameters, it appears that being traversed in 22 minutes this makes the speed a thousand diameters in one minute, that is $16\frac{2}{3}$ diameters in one second or in one beat of the pulse, which makes more than 11 hundred times a hundred thousand Toises; since the diameter of the Earth contains 2,865 leagues, reckoned at 25 to the degree, and each league is 2,282 Toises, according to the exact measurement which Mr. Picard made by order of the King in 1669. But Sound, as I have said above, only travels 180 toises in the same time of one second: hence the velocity of Light is more than six hundred thousand times greater than that of Sound. This, however, is quite another thing from being instantaneous, since there is all the difference between a finite thing and an infinite. Now the successive movement of Light being confirmed in this way, it follows, as I have said, that it spreads by spherical waves, like the movement of Sound.

But if the one resembles the other in this respect, they differ in many other things; to wit, in the first production of the movement which causes them; in the matter in which the movement spreads; and in the manner in which it is propagated. As to that which occurs in the production of Sound, one knows that it is occasioned by the agitation undergone by an entire body, or by a considerable part of one, which shakes all the contiguous air. But the movement of the Light must originate as from each point of the luminous object, else we should not be able to perceive all the different parts of that object, as will be more evident in that which follows. And I do not believe that this movement can be better explained than by supposing that all those of the luminous bodies which are liquid, such as flames, and apparently the sun and the stars, are composed of particles which float in a much more subtle medium which agitates them with great rapidity, and makes them strike against the particles of the ether which surrounds them, and which are much smaller than they. But I hold also that in luminous solids such as charcoal or metal made red hot in the fire, this same movement is caused by the violent agitation of the particles of the metal or of the wood; those of them which are on the surface striking similarly against the ethereal matter. The agitation, moreover, of the particles which engender the light ought to be much more prompt and more rapid than is that of the bodies which cause sound, since we do not see that the tremors of a body which is giving out a sound are capable of giving rise to Light, even as the movement of the hand in the air is not capable of producing sound.

Now if one examines what this matter may be in which the movement coming from the luminous body is propagated, which I call Ethereal matter, one will see that it is not the same that serves for the propagation of Sound. For one finds that the latter is really that which we feel and which we breathe, and which being removed from any place still leaves there the other kind of matter that serves to convey Light. This may be proved by shutting up a sounding body in a glass vessel from which the air is withdrawn by the machine which Mr. Boyle has given us, and with which he has performed so many beautiful experiments [Figure 6-3]. But in doing this of which I speak, care must be taken to place the sounding body on cotton or on feathers, in such a way that it cannot

Figure 6-3. At upper right a wood engraving of Boyle's apparatus for striking a bell in a vacuum.

communicate its tremors either to the glass vessel which encloses it, or to the machine; a precaution which has hitherto been neglected. For then after having exhausted all the air one hears no Sound from the metal, though it is struck.

One sees here not only that our air, which does not penetrate through glass, is the matter by which Sound spreads; but also that it is not the same air but another kind of matter in which Light spreads; since if the air is removed from the vessel the Light does not cease to traverse it as before.

And this last point is demonstrated even more clearly by the celebrated experiment of Torricelli, in which the tube of glass from which the quicksilver has withdrawn itself, remaining void of air, transmits Light just the same as when air is in it. For this proves that a matter different from air exists in this tube, and that this matter must have penetrated the glass or the quicksilver, either one or the other, though they are both impenetrable to the air. And when, in the same experiment, one makes the vacuum after putting a little water above the quicksilver, one concludes that the said matter passes through glass or water, or through both.

As regards the different modes in which I have said the movements of Sound and of Light are communicated, one may sufficiently comprehend how this occurs in the case of Sound if one considers that the air is of such a nature that it can be compressed and reduced to a much smaller space than that which it ordinarily occupies. And in proportion as it is compressed the more does it exert an effort to regain its volume; for this property along with its penetrability, which remains notwithstanding its compression, seems to prove that it is made up of small bodies which float about and which are agitated very rapidly in the ethereal matter composed of much smaller parts. So that the cause of the spreading of Sound is the effort which these little bodies make in collisions with one another, to regain freedom when they are a little more squeezed together in the circuit of these waves than elsewhere.

But the extreme velocity of Light, and other properties which it has, cannot admit of such a propagation of motion, and I am about to show here the way in which I conceive it must occur. For this, it is needful to explain the property which hard bodies must possess to transmit movement from one to another.

When one takes a number of spheres of equal size, made of some very hard substance, and arranges them in a straight line, so that they touch one another, one finds, on striking with a similar sphere against the first of these spheres, that the motion passes as in an instant to the last of them, which separates itself from the row, without one's being able to perceive that the others have been stirred [Figure 6-4]. And even that one which was used to strike remains motionless with them. Whence one sees that the movement passes with an extreme velocity which is the greater, the greater the hardness of the substance of the spheres.

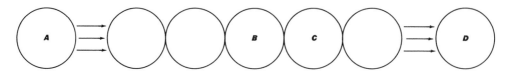

Figure 6-4

But it is still certain that this progression of motion is not instantaneous, but successive, and therefore must take time. For if the movement, or the disposition to movement, if you will have it so, did not pass successively through all these spheres, they would all acquire the movement at the same time, and hence would all advance together; which does not happen. For the last one leaves the whole row and acquires the speed of the one which was pushed. Moreover there are experiments which demonstrate that all the bodies which we reckon of the hardest kind, such as quenched steel, glass, and agate, act as springs and bend somehow, not only when extended as rods but also when they are in the form of spheres or of other shapes. That is to say they yield a little in themselves at the place where they are struck, and immediately regain their former figure. For I have found that on striking with a ball of glass or of agate against a large and quite thick piece of the same substance which had a flat surface, slightly soiled with breath or in some other way, there remained round marks, of smaller or larger size according as the blow had been weak or strong. This makes it evident that these substances yield where they meet, and spring back: and for this time must be required.

I have then shown in what manner one may conceive Light to spread successively, by spherical waves, and how it is possible that this spreading is accomplished with as great a velocity as that which experiments and celestial observations demand. Whence it may be further remarked that although the particles are supposed to be in continual movement (for there are many reasons for this) the successive propagation of the waves cannot be hindered by this; because the propagation consists nowise in the transport of those particles but merely in a small agitation which cannot help communicating to

those surrounding, notwithstanding any movement which may act on them causing them to be changing positions amongst themselves.

But we must consider still more particularly the origin of these waves, and the manner in which they spread. And first, it follows from what has been said on the production of Light, that each little region of a luminous body, such as the Sun, a candle, or a burning coal, generates its own waves of which that region is the centre. Thus in the flame of a candle, having distinguished the points A, B, C, concentric circles described about each of these points represent the waves which come from them. And one must imagine the same about every point of the surface and of the part within the flame.

But as the percussions at the centres of these waves possess no regular succession, it must not be supposed that the waves themselves follow one another at equal distance: and if the distances marked in the figure [Figure 6-5] appear to be such, it is rather to mark the progression of one and the same wave at equal intervals of time than to represent several of them issuing from one and the same centre.

After all, this prodigious quantity of waves which traverse one another without confusion and without effacing one another must not be deemed inconceivable; it being certain that one and the same particle of matter can serve for many waves coming from different sides or even from contrary directions, not only if it is struck by blows which follow one another closely but even for those which act on it at the same instant. It can do so because the spreading of the movement is successive. This may be proved by the row of equal spheres of hard matter, spoken of above. If against this row there are pushed from two opposite sides at the same time two similar spheres A and D, one will see each of them rebound with the same velocity which it had in striking, yet the whole row will remain in its place, although the movement has passed along its whole length twice over. And if these contrary movements happen to meet one another at the middle sphere, B, or at some other such as C, that sphere will yield and act as a spring at both sides, and so will serve at the same instant to transmit these two movements.

But what may at first appear full strange and even incredible is that the undulations produced by such small movements and corpuscles, should spread to such immense distances; as for example from the Sun or from the Stars to us. For the force of these waves must grow feeble in proportion as they move away from their origin, so that the action of each one in particular will without doubt become incapable of making itself felt to our sight. But one will cease to be astonished by considering how at a great distance from the luminous body an infinitude of waves, though they have issued from different points of this body, unite together in such a way that they sensibly compose one single wave only, which, consequently, ought to have enough force to make itself felt. Thus this infinite number of waves which originate at the same instant from all points of a fixed star, big it may be as the Sun, make practically only one single wave which may well have force enough to produce an impression on our eyes. More-

Figure 6-5

over from each luminous point there may come many thousands of waves in the smallest imaginable time, by the frequent percussion of the corpuscles which strike the Ether at these points: which further contributes to rendering their action more sensible.

THE TWO THEORIES OF LIGHT*
by Edward Condon (1955)

Three centuries ago, when men speculated about the nature of the influence we call light, that which proceeds from a candle to the eye, some believed that the candle projects outward a stream of minute corpuscles of light which fly through space and even through dense transparent materials such as glass. This is the corpuscular theory of light.

Others thought that the influence called

* From Edward Condon, "Physics," in James R. Newman (ed.), *What Is Science?* Simon and Schuster, Inc., New York, 1955. Reprinted by permission.

light was a wave motion. These waves were supposed to travel in a space-filling material called the luminiferous ether, which was later identified with the space-filling ether presumed to be the means of propagating electric and magnetic effects. This was the wave theory of light.

Newton favored the corpuscular theory, and Christian Huygens, a great Dutch contemporary of his, favored the wave theory.

The shadow of an object in light from a

Figure 6-6. In the corpuscular view, a shadow cast on a screen by an opaque object has a sharp edge if the light source is small or very distant.

small source is quite sharp. (Figure 6-6.) There is an abrupt break between the surrounding brightness and the cast shadow. This is the pattern to be expected if light consists of a stream of particles moving out from the source in straight lines.

How waves behave when they encounter an obstacle is familiar to us from observing the ripples on a pond. Water waves are not cut sharply by an obstacle; instead, they bend partially around it and then continue, so that the wave motion can be seen on the side of the obstacle away from the wave source. Thus if light were propagated by wave motion, we should expect the shadows cast by objects to have soft, diffused edges. The observed sharpness of shadow edges seems, therefore, to support the theory that light consists of a stream of particles. This course of reasoning was decisive in leading Newton to reject the wave theory. (Figure 6-7.)

But the problem is not so simple. Experiments performed many years after Newton revealed that the bending of waves into the region behind an obstacle is only noticeable when the obstacle is small compared with the length (distance from crest to crest measured in the direction of travel) of the waves; in

the opposite case, where the wave length is small compared to the obstacle, the wave motion is inappreciable and apt to escape detection. In other words if the wave length is small compared to the object casting the shadow—the most common occurrence—only the most delicate tests will help clarify the issue between the corpuscular and the wave theory of light.

When experimental techniques and instruments had been sufficiently refined, a higher level of understanding was attained. Physicists were able to show that light really does bend somewhat into the shadowed region. The phenomenon is called diffraction. To be sure, a person who was determined to hold onto his belief in the corpuscular theory might start speculating that the material of the opaque screen exerts attractive forces on the light corpuscles that fly past near the edge of the screen and bends their trajectories into the region that otherwise would be the dark shadow. But exact and detailed studies of how much the light is bent into the shadow when passing objects of various shapes and sizes gave results that could not be accounted for in this way. On the other hand, they could be beautifully described according to

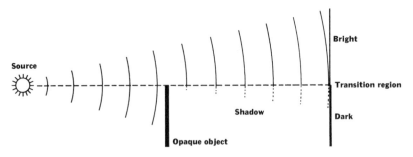

Figure 6-7. In the wave view, the shadow does not have a sharp edge, but some light penetrates into the transition region.

the theory of wave propagation on the supposition that light of a particular color consists of waves of a particular wave length. Blue light in this view has a wave length of close to 4×10^{-5} cm; red light, at the other end of the visible spectrum, moves in waves about twice as long. The invisible ultra-violet radiations have a wave length shorter than the violet and the invisible infrared radiations have wave lengths longer than the red [Figure 6-1].

It is the smallness of these wave lengths compared with the million times greater wave lengths for the ripples on a pond that made the diffraction effects more difficult to observe and resulted in their being hidden from the eyes of man so long. Nevertheless, now that these matters are more thoroughly understood, optical effects which directly exhibit the wave nature of light may be easily observed.

Look at a distant street light through a silk umbrella or a tightly stretched silk handkerchief held several feet in front of the eyes. Instead of seeing only the ordinary direct image of the street light, perhaps a little blurred by scattering in the fabric, you will see two additional series of images extending away from the central direct image in two perpendicular directions. The directions in which these images extend will be easily found to be along the directions of the threads of the fabric. (Figures 6-8 and 6-9.)

These additional images are quantitatively explainable on the wave theory of light. The essential thing here is that a wave motion

Figure 6-9. The central part of the drawing shows how a very distant and small source of light appears when viewed through a small rectangular opening held at arm's length from the eyes, the rectangular opening being the shape shown in the lower right-hand corner. Note that there is a whole series of images extending in each direction and that they are more closely spaced in the direction corresponding to the long dimension of the rectangle. If the picture were executed in color, it would be seen that the more or less overlapping images of the separate blobs of light away from the central image are colored with the rainbow colors, the red end being farthest away from the central image. Such extra images and dozens of other similar experiments with light going through openings of other shapes are interpreted as indicating that light is propagated as a wave motion.

spreads out from the distant street light and impinges on different parts of the fabric so that parts of the wave motion get through to the other side by going through the different regularly spaced openings on the fabric. The ideas involved may be more simply considered if we suppose that the light from the distant source goes through a screen having two very narrow and closely spaced slitlike openings in it as indicated in Figure 6-10. If one wants to go to the trouble he can make such an opaque screen from a densely-exposed photographic plate, using a razor blade to rule two very narrow slits on it quite close together. The razor blade cuts away a narrow strip of the darkened film and allows the light to get through. When such a plate is used to view a distant light source it will be found that the direct image is also accompanied on each side by several weaker side images in directions at right angles to the direction of the rulings on the plate. Careful observation of the side images either as seen through the silk umbrella or as seen through the two-slit plate will show that the central image is white, but that the side images are colored like the rainbow, with the red end of the spectrum at the end farthest away from the central image.

Now we can return to the consideration of

Figure 6-8. The drawing at left shows the evenly spaced threads of the weave of silk cloth. At right is the pattern of light of a distant small source, like a street light, observed through such a closely woven cloth. The central image is round and white. The others are elongated and show rainbow colors with the red end away from the central image.

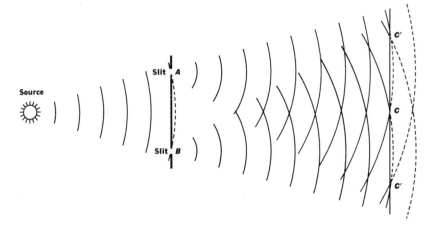

Figure 6-10. The passage of light through a screen having two slit-shaped openings.

Figure 6-10. Suppose the screen is set up in such a way that slit A and slit B are at the same distance from source S. This is not essential but simplifies the discussion. Then the crests of waves from S will reach A and B at the same time. On the other side of the screen two new sets of waves will spread out from A and B as new centers and these will be synchronized because they are the result of feeding the new sources A and B with light coming from source S. Next we have to recognize that what affects any light-detecting device such as the eye is the resultant amplitude of all the different waves which reach it. Suppose C is a point equidistant from A and B. Then crests of waves from A will arrive at C at the same time as crests from B and will reinforce each other to make bigger waves. Thus we may expect the brightest illumination at C even though it lies within the shadow of the screen between A and B and therefore on the corpuscular view should be dark. Consider now what will be observed at a point C′, a little above or below C. In moving from C to C′ the distance from B is increased and the distance from A decreased. Suppose, in particular, that C′ is so located that the difference between AC′ and BC′ is exactly half a wave length. Then at C′ the crests of waves from A will fall on troughs of waves from B, and the waves will just cancel each other; in other words, assuming light is a wave motion, C′ will be dark. Now move C′ further up so that the

difference between the distances from A and from B is equal to a whole wave length. In this case, again, the crest of each wave from A falls on the crest from B, intensifying the light. As we continue moving up C′, it will alternately be light and dark as the differences between the paths is an integral multiple and an integral-and-a-half multiple of a wave length. This special property of waves of reinforcing each other or destroying each other according as crest falls on crest or crest on trough is called interference. It accounts quantitatively for the light images seen through the silk umbrella. For example the reason the red end of the spectrum is farther out than the blue is because the red wave length is greater than the blue; so it is necessary to go farther out to get a half wave length path difference with red light than it is with blue light.

During the nineteenth century a great many special cases of the behavior of light in going through obstacles having one or several holes of different shapes were analyzed carefully, both theoretically and experimentally. The results were found to be quantitatively describable in terms of the mathematical theory of wave propagation. Thus the wave theory of light became firmly established: students were taught that light is a wave motion and received good marks on examination papers for repeating this back to their professors.

However, new phenomena began to be studied which pointed once more toward the corpuscular theory. Effects . . . pointed strongly to the conclusion that a beam of light consists of a stream of particles of definite size, possessing energy and momentum content. Physicists were thus confronted with two independent sets of evidence. One set gave convincing "proof" that light is a wave motion and the other gave equally convincing "proof" that a beam of light is a stream of corpuscles. Light is emitted and absorbed as if it were a stream of particles but it moves from place to place past obstacles as if it were a wave motion. Clearly there is truth in both models, and a synthesis of the two views into a unified picture is urgently needed. This wave-particle duality is an unsolved dilemma of modern physics.

LIGHT FROM THE SUN AND STARS

THE UNIVERSE OF LIGHT*
by Sir William Bragg (1933)

Stars appear to us as bright points which move together across the sky. Astronomers have shown us long ago that in so doing they are telling us of the rotation of the earth rather than of their own movements. Very patient and skilled observation shows that there are relative motions amongst them, yet so small that the constellations have retained their form since man was first able to describe them. In the last hundred years the power of interpreting the messages brought by light has increased greatly. We are in touch with the stars. They are no longer a mere medley of bright points irregularly spread over the sky; nor even of suns that emit light like ours and are scattered through the depths of space. They have become to us parts of an active universe of which our own solar system is also a part. We can measure their distance, their weights, their luminosities, their compositions, their movements, and even estimate their historic past and their future. Our world of knowledge and perception has suddenly increased, and we begin to have understanding of its greater laws.

The very ancient science of astronomy has in times past relied almost entirely upon observations of the positions of the heavenly bodies. Light has been used as a means of measuring angles and so of plotting the apparent motions of sun, moon and stars upon a celestial sphere. The very great extension of astronomical knowledge which has occurred in the last hundred years had its beginnings in the examination of light itself and not only of the direction from which it came. The quality of the light from the sun, and its intensity are characteristic of the nature and physical conditions of the source: their study provides new means of enquiry, and at the same time, gives new possibilities to the means that have been so long in use. . . .

The Analysis of the Light from the Stars
The first step in the acquirement of this knowledge is made when we use a prism or a grating to analyse the light.† In every case we find the same spectrum colours, running from red to violet, for our eyes perceive these alone of the complex which each star emits. But the emphasis in different parts of the spectrum is not always the same: it varies from star to star. A blue star is always hotter than a red star. The temperature of the star can in fact be determined from the

* Sir William Bragg, The Universe of Light, Dover Publications, Inc., New York, 1933. Reprinted by permission of Dover Publications, Inc., and G. Bell & Sons, Ltd., London.

† The modern instrument used for this analysis is called a spectroscope. Ed.

Figure 6-11. A few star spectra showing the shift of the maximum intensities from hot white stars of class F to cooler red stars of class M.

Yerkes Observatory

position of greatest emphasis. This would not be possible were it not for a very remarkable natural law, namely, that the quality of the light emitted by a substance depends only, except in special cases, on the temperature and not upon the nature of the substance. If, for example, we gaze into a hollow in a glowing coal fire, a red hot cave with as small an opening as possible, where everything is at the same high temperature, we do not see the outlines of the pieces of coal inside, nor of pieces of metal or china if they are well inside the hole and have acquired the fire temperature. Being at the same temperature, coal, metal and china all send out radiation of the same quality and so they cannot be distinguished from one another. In a furnace where the temperature is raised by a blast the quality of the light is not the same as that of the light from a coal fire. It is whiter because the emphasis has been shifted towards the blue end of the spectrum: more blue rays are present. If a temperature of 6000° Centigrade could be reached the light would have the quality of daylight because that is the temperature approximately of the sun. Some of the stars are hotter still and the blue rays increase still more in relative intensity. Thus the temperature of a star is told by the quality

of its spectrum, that is to say, by the relative distribution of energy among the various wave-lengths. . . .

Examples of star spectra are given in Figure 6-11.

A very simple experiment illustrates this connection between quality and temperature. We throw upon the screen the spectrum of the light from an electric arc, and then cut off the current. As the glow of the carbon fades and its temperature declines, we see that the spectrum disappears but the blue goes first and the red last.

Spectrum Analysis Applied to the Stars

By a still closer observation of the spectrum of a star we can find its nature. When the light is analysed by the prism, it is found that the spectrum is, allowing for the effects of temperature, like that of any other glowing mass, as for example, the carbon in the arc lamp, with an important exception. A number of clearly defined ranges of wave-length, generally exceedingly narrow ranges, are missing. . . . Illustrations of this peculiarity may be seen in the reproductions of spectra in Figure 6-12.

The explanation is ready to hand: We can base it on the analogies . . . [with] tuning forks, and the wireless sets. . . .

Our first point is simple enough. A single tuning fork gives out a very pure note: in other words, the sound which it emits consists of air waves of a definite frequency. This sound wave spreads out in all directions. If in one direction it passes by another tuning fork of exactly the same pitch, it will set this second fork going and of course it will spend energy in doing so. Thus the sound travelling in this special direction is weakened: there has been absorption. Nor is this loss made up by the sounding of the second fork, because the latter spreads its sound in all directions and cannot make good the loss in the particular direction. This is the basis of the absorption and production of colour. . . . It will be observed that the emitter and receiver are of the same pitch. Just so a radio station emits waves which are sharply adjusted within a certain range of frequency: if care were not taken in this respect broadcasting would be impossible. And if the receiver can be sharply tuned to the same frequency, it will absorb some of the energy distributed from the central station, which energy is diminished thereby. A wireless set can be made to radiate at least feebly, and if it does it emits waves of exactly the same pitch as that of the sending station to which it responds. Some wireless sets as we know can be tuned very sharply: if the radio station is sending out waves which adhere closely to their proper frequency such sets will only respond if the tuning is carefully done, and then the response will be strong.

In the same way an atom may be set into vibration by heating the body or gas of which it is a part. If the radiation which it emits meets a number of atoms capable of vibrating with exactly the same frequency—or it may be frequencies—its energy is absorbed in part and passes on diminished. And here again the matter of the exactness of tuning is important. An atom by itself, uninfluenced by neighbours, is like a good radio transmitter, its emitted vibrations lie within a very narrow range. We should say ranges rather than range, because an atom should be compared rather with a bell or a violin string than a tuning fork. The fork is exceedingly simple, emitting little more than one note; whereas bell and string and atom each emit a number of notes at one and the same time. Each note, however, is very sharply defined and can be tuned to with great exactness. This sharpness of tuning is characteristic of the atoms in a gas, for in this condition the atoms are independent of one another for most of the time: collisions occur, but the times during which the atoms are so close to one another as to influence each other's vibrations do not last long. Thus a multitude of atoms forming a gas will resemble a good radio station if they are emitting, and a good or "selective" wireless set if they are receiving.

If then a ray of light containing all frequencies passes through a crowd of such "selective" atoms there will be a sharp absorption or selection of particular frequencies,

Figure 6-12. The spectra of the luminous gases of various elements vaporized in the electric arc.

and the spectrum will show a number of narrow gaps, as illustrated in Figure 6-11. If the gas is emitting, it will send out light of the same frequencies as that which it absorbs. This effect is shown in Figure 6-12.

The Spectrum of the Sun

The spectrum of the sun shows an immense number of these sharply defined gaps or "lines" as they are generally called. When the temperatures of various substances, iron, calcium, hydrogen, etc., are raised by heating until they become luminous vapours, it is found that they emit, each of them, light of a certain number of sharply defined frequencies. It is also found that these correspond line by line to the lines in the spectrum of the sun. The conclusion is obvious: the light from the sun must have gone through clouds of these atoms somewhere, and in respect to such substances as iron or calcium, or most other elements, this must have happened on the sun because in no other part of the path of the light has there been enough heat to bring the substances to the state of a luminous gas. If therefore, the spectra of the sun and stars and other luminous bodies be analysed and compared with the spectra emitted in the laboratory by the various elements brought to the condition of luminous gases, it becomes possible at once to say whether or no these elements exist in the heavenly bodies as well as on the earth. These investigations were first carried out on the great scale by the enthusiasm of Huggins, Lockyer and their contemporaries. From that time to this they have increased in interest and importance because it has been found that there is far more in them than mere correspondences between the positions of definite frequencies in the two classes of spectra. The frequencies characteristic of each element depend on the condition of the element, which may be stripped of one or more of its electrons and at each such alteration may alter its notes: the condition depends on the temperature and the density of the gas, and thus the analysis of stellar spectra gives information of the state of the star as well as of its composition.

The elements that are found on the earth are found also in the stars. In one notable case the existence of an element was proved by Lockyer's observation of the sun's spectrum before it had been handled in the laboratory. Certain well marked lines were found which corresponded to nothing then known, and Lockyer deduced the presence of some new substance which he called "helium": it was not until long afterwards that it was extracted from cleveite and other minerals. It is now well known as the best gas for the inflation of dirigible balloons, since it is almost as much lighter than air as hydrogen is, and it is not inflammable. In the labora-

tory it is an object of extraordinary interest, since the atom of helium is the alpha particle which radioactive substances emit. . . .

But now there is one very important question to which some answer must be found. We have supposed that a radiation is emitted by the sun, which would have given a complete spectrum, were it not that on its way to us it has passed through an atmosphere surrounding the sun and containing the various elements in the form of gases. These gases themselves must be luminous and be emitting light of the very frequencies which we suppose them to have been absorbing and therefore causing black lines to appear in the spectrum. What is the origin of the original radiation? It must be so plentiful that its absorption in the sun's atmosphere makes a difference which the luminosity of the atmosphere itself does not make good. And its energy is distributed all over the spectrum: it is not limited to a number of definite frequencies.

We have already seen that independent atoms would issue their proper frequencies exactly. But they are not wholly independent: they spend a certain fraction of their time in each other's neighbourhood when their motions cause them to collide. During those moments they do not issue their proper frequencies so strictly. If they are so crowded together as to spend a large part of their time under each other's influence the ranges of proper frequency will spread until they meet and overlap and the whole spectrum is emitted. In a roughly analogous way, if a number of tuning forks, each on its stand, were thrown anyhow into a box which was then shaken violently, a medley of jangling sound would issue which would no longer be confined to the particular notes of the tuning forks. In the body of the sun the atoms are crowded together and violently agitated by the tremendous temperature: and it is in this way that we can account for the continuity of the spectrum. The somewhat cooler atmosphere surrounding the sun removes certain frequencies and hence the spectrum lines. . . .

When there is a total eclipse of the sun the incandescent vapours of its atmosphere can be seen to extend far beyond the obscured disc [Figure 6-13]: and their spectra consists of a series of bright lines as we should expect.

It is an interesting and important point that a luminous gas which gives a "bright line" spectrum will give a full spectrum if there is enough of the gas. There is always a certain amount of general radiation as well as that of particular frequencies of the atoms of which the gas is made. Now the latter is absorbed in going through the gas more than the former, and so it happens that it comes only from the external layers, while the latter, the general radiation, can come from greater depths. If the depth of the gas is great enough the two effects compensate so as to give equal weight to the two varieties of radiation, and the spectrum is complete. It becomes that which is characteristic of the temperature and is independent of the nature of the emitting body. Thus the completeness of the spectrum of a heavenly body does not mean that it is a solid, but merely that there is enough of it.

The Motions of the Stars to and from the Earth

By another form of careful observation it is possible to determine the rate at which a star is approaching or receding from the earth. For if, say, the star is rushing towards the earth it is crushing up the waves from the rear and all the wave-lengths are artificially shortened. . . . Just so an approaching motor-car crushes up the sound waves, and, as it

Figure 6-13. The sun's corona.

recedes, draws them out [Figure 6-14]. All day the motor-cars go by and the pitches of all the noises made by a car drop at the moment of passing. If the car is travelling at 25 miles an hour the drop is nearly a semi-tone. If the star gave a complete spectrum free from lines we should not be able to detect this shift, because the wave-lengths that gave the extreme violet would have been shortened and become invisible, while at the red end wave-lengths just too long to be visible would now be shortened and enter the red. All the wave-lengths would be shortened somewhat, both visible and invisible: but the visible colours would be supplied to our eyes just the

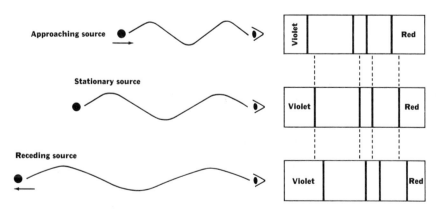

Figure 6-14. The Doppler effect. The lines in the spectrum shift toward the violet end (left) when the light source is approaching. When the source recedes, the spectral lines shift toward the red end (right).

same, and we should see no change. There is however an observable shift in the lines of the spectrum, an effect which was first described by Doppler. And as the positions of the lines can be very exactly measured, and as the shift is proportional to the speed of the star relative to the earth, it becomes possible to measure the relative motion of the two bodies along the line joining them. . . . The two spectra that are shown in this illustration are due to light received from the two edges of the sun, eastern and western. In one case, the source of light is coming towards the earth, on account of the sun's revolution, in the other it is receding. In both cases the light has passed through the earth's atmosphere, and certain lines in the spectra are due to absorption by oxygen. The two spectra are put together so that these lines fit, so that the wave-lengths in the two correspond exactly. It will then be observed that other lines are slightly out of adjustment. These lines are due to absorption by the sun's atmosphere. The lack of adjustment is due to the Doppler effect, the lines being shifted slightly towards the short wave end in the case of light coming from the approaching edge of the sun and vice versa. The presence of the oxygen lines makes it possible to register the two spectra exactly. The shifts in a star's spectrum are not so easily displayed as in this case. It is to be observed that the shift is the same for all the sun's lines.

These measurements are independent of distance and so arises the curious situation that, while most of the stars are too far away to be seen moving across the sky, motions of approach or recession can be measured with considerable accuracy. In this way for example, it is found that the distant nebulae, or at least the few that give enough light for the experiment, are receding: and apparently those that are furthest away are going the fastest, whence the modern conception of an expanding universe. Many stars approach and recede at regular intervals: and it is clear that each such star has a dark companion about which it is revolving. . . . [We] have seen how full of information are the characteristics of the light that comes to us from all parts of the universe. . . .

The Wave and the Corpuscle

A range of ether waves is at our disposal for experiment. Certain of them which lie within a narrow range are visible to our eyes: others may be detected by their action on a photographic plate. . . .

There is one particular phenomenon which is shown markedly by the radiations of the shortest wave-lengths, and to a less observable extent by the longer waves: it is known as the photo-electric effect. At this point the wave theory which has helped us so far fails to suggest an explanation. It is this fact and others associated with it that show our wave hypothesis to be incomplete, and lead to the curious position of physics at the present time. In 1905 Einstein suggested that the corpuscular theory had been set aside too hastily.

QUANTUM MECHANICS AND THE UNCERTAINTY PRINCIPLE

THE TWO THEORIES OF LIGHT (Continued)*
by Edward Condon (1955)

Before considering detailed effects, let it be observed that on the wave view the intensity of light is connected with the amplitude of swing of the waves, to be specific, it is proportional to the square of the wave amplitude. As a wave spreads out this becomes continuously smaller with consequent reduction in the intensity of the light (Figure 6-15). On the corpuscular view the energy in the light beam is

* Condon, op. cit.

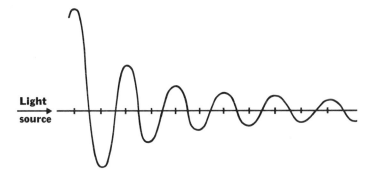

Figure 6-15. The amplitude of a wave dies off inversely to the distance from the source as the wave spreads out in all directions. The intensity or brightness of the light is proportional to the square of the amplitude and so falls off with the inverse square of the distance from the source.

the total energy of a large number of independently moving corpuscles, called light quanta in modern terminology. The energy carried by each quantum is always the same—the decrease in intensity of the beam is a consequence only of the decrease in the number of particles crossing unit area in unit time. On one view the energy is continuously spread out over all the space occupied by the light beam; on the other it is localized in small bundles occupying a part of the total space, just as the molecules of a gas at ordinary pressure occupy only about one billionth of the total space which is filled by the gas.

The photoelectric effect gave the first clue to the corpuscular nature of light emission and absorption. If a piece of metal, insulated from the ground, is charged with negative electricity, the charge will leak off through the air when light, especially violet and ultraviolet light, shines on it. In this simple version of the experiment the effects are complicated by the action of the air layers which are absorbed on the metal.[1] Consequently, physicists who wish to study the photoelectric effect enclose

the metal in a high-vacuum tube from which the gas can be removed to an extremely low pressure.

The amount of charge which is set free from a metal surface is proportional to the intensity of the light falling on it. This fact is explainable either on wave or corpuscular views. But it is found that the leakage of negative charge from the metal comes about through the ejection by the light of negatively charged electrons. Measurements of the speed of ejection of these electrons show that the energy with which they are ejected is approximately inversely proportional to the wave length of the light used. Actually the energy of motion of the liberated electrons is a little less than such a rule would imply. Einstein in 1905 pointed out that this experimental result could be most simply understood if one supposed that the light energy was absorbed in definite quanta of energy, the energy of one quantum going to the individual act of liberating one electron. The energy of one quantum was taken to be hc/λ, where h is a coefficient known as Planck's constant, c is the velocity of light and λ is the wave length of the light. The observed energy of motion of the freed electron is less than this by an approximately constant amount because a part of the energy supplied by the light quantum is used up in releasing the electron from

[1] Although qualitative effects are easily demonstrated with the experiment done in air, exact measurements of the motion of the electrons ejected by the light require that the metal be enclosed in a vacuum tube, both because of chemical actions of the gas of the air, especially moisture, on the metal which strongly change its ability to emit electrons, and also because if gas is present the electrons very quickly become scattered and attached to gas molecules, making it difficult to observe the speed with which they are thrown out.

the attractive forces which normally bind it within the metal.

Similar effects are observed when X-rays are used instead of light to cause the ejection of electrons. The quantum effects are even more pronounced because the X-ray wave lengths are approximately ten thousand times smaller than those of visible light and therefore the energy in an X-ray quantum is some ten thousand times greater than in a visible light quantum. But because the wave lengths are so much smaller, it was for a long time impossible to observe, in the case of X-rays, the diffraction and interference effects which give us our most decisive criterion for the wave nature of visible light.

It happens, however, that the wave length of X-rays is just about the same as the distance between the layers of atoms in the regular arrangements that occur in crystals such as those of quartz or rocksalt [Figure 6-16]. This means that interference effects such as those described for light going through the silk umbrella are observed when a beam of X-rays is scattered by falling on a crystal. Instead of the scattered radiations going out from the crystal more or less equally in all directions, they are scattered only in certain specific directions. These directions are determined by relations between the X-ray wave length and the spacing of atoms in the crystal. Thus the effect can be used with a known crystal to determine the wave length of X-rays

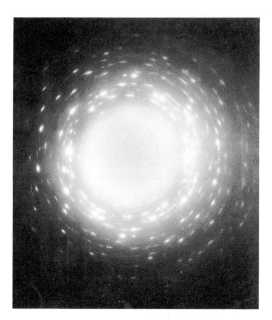

Philips Electronic Instruments
Figure 6-17. Diffraction of X rays.

from a variety of sources. Or it can be used the other way round—to discover with X-rays of known wave lengths exact information about the arrangement of atoms in crystals whose geometry is not known. This diffraction of X-rays by the orderly arrangement of atoms in crystals was discovered in 1912 by Max Von Laue [Figure 6-17]. In such work the scattering is effected by electrons that are relatively securely bound to the atoms of which the crystal is made.

In 1922 Arthur H. Compton discovered another characteristic of the scattering of X-rays by matter. He noticed, particularly when high energy X-rays are scattered by lighter elements such as carbon, that the wave length of the deflected X-ray is somewhat longer than that of the X-ray before deflection, and that the amount of this Compton-shift toward longer wave length increases steadily from zero as the angle of deflection increases. Compton showed that this behavior was exactly what is to be expected from the quantum or corpuscular theory. If the X-rays are tied up in quanta of energy, it is natural to suppose that these quanta also carry definite amounts of momentum. When they strike an

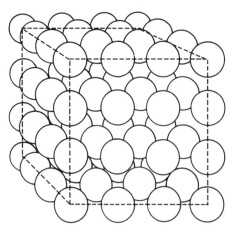

Figure 6-16. Schematic drawing of atoms in a crystal.

almost free or loosely bound electron and are scattered, they rebound from it, Compton supposed, according to the same mechanical laws as those governing the collisions of billiard balls. At a very glancing blow the X-ray is only slightly deflected in direction and gives up very little energy to the electron with which it collided. When the blow is more central it is deflected through a wider angle and gives up more energy to the struck electron, losing thereby more of its own energy and thus having its wave length increased.

This completed the duality. X-rays which—in respect of their being scattered by the tightly bound electrons in the regularly spaced atoms of a crystal—behave like a train of waves of a definite wave length, also behave—in respect of their scattering by loosely bound electrons—as if they were little bundles of energy and momentum rather than continuously spread out waves, these little bundles or quanta obeying the ordinary laws of collision mechanics when they collide with an electron. In order to describe all of the phenomena it is necessary to talk some of the time as if the X-rays are a wave motion and some of the time as if they are a stream of particles.

There used to be a joke current among physicists that X-rays were to be regarded as waves on Mondays, Wednesdays and Fridays and as quanta on the other days. In point of fact, however, the two aspects are so closely intertwined that no such neat separation of viewpoints can be effected; in Compton's experiments, for example, the scattering in carbon which is described by quantum or corpuscular language is followed by another scattering of the same X-rays by a crystal for the purpose of demonstrating that their wave length was altered in the first scattering.

PROBABILITY AND UNCERTAINTY*
by Sir James Jeans (1943)

The Particle- and Wave-pictures

We now have two distinct pictures of the nature of radiation, one depicting it as particles and the other as waves. The particle-picture is obviously the more suitable when the radiation is falling on matter, and the wave-picture when it is travelling through space. For a time there was a disposition to conclude that light must consist of two parts, a wave part and a particle part, but it is now clear that this is not so. The wave-picture and the particle-picture do not show two different things, but two aspects of the same thing. They are simply partial pictures which are appropriate to different sets of circumstances—. . .—and so are complementary but not additive. As soon as light shows the properties of particles, its wave properties disappear, and vice versa; the two sets of properties are never in evidence at the same time. Thus as we follow a beam of light, or even a single quantum, in its course, we must imagine the wave- and particle-pictures taking control of the situation alternately.

The wave-picture explains much in its own proper province, but it brings its own difficulties with it. In particular, it is not easy to pass back from the wave-picture to the particle-picture. For all waves scatter as they travel through space, and it is difficult to imagine how waves which have once scattered as the undulatory theory directs can recombine and concentrate their attack on single molecules or electrons in the way they are observed to do as soon as they encounter matter.

Waves of Probability

Let us [consider the] . . . imaginary experiment in which a single quantum of radiation is emitted from a source of light to fall on one point or another of a system of distant screens. We know that the whole energy of the quantum will concentrate on a single point of the screens, but which point will it be?

The obvious answer is that sometimes it will be one point, and sometimes another. It

* From Sir James Jeans, *Physics and Philosophy*, Cambridge University Press, New York, 1943. Reprinted by permission.

cannot always be the same point, or else when quanta were being emitted in millions, this one specially favoured point would be intensely bright and all others completely dark. Actually when quanta are being emitted in millions, there are some places on the screens at which the illumination is very bright, these indicating regions in which many photons have struck, and also places of less illumination, these indicating regions in which few photons have struck. Even the most faintly illuminated parts of the screen must have been struck by some photons.

If we now fix our attention on a single quantum of radiation of which we know nothing except that it belonged to the original beam, we may say that the extent to which either screen is illuminated at any point gives a measure of the *probability* that the quantum shall condense into a photon at this point. In this way we may interpret the waves of the undulatory theory as waves of probability; the extension of the wave system in space marks out the region within which a photon may be supposed to be travelling, while the intensity of the waves at each point within this region gives a measure of the probability that a photon will occur at that point if matter is placed there.

When half a million babies are born in England in a year, we may say that 20 per cent of them are born in London, 2 per cent in Manchester, 1 per cent in Bristol, and so on. But when we think of the one baby born in a single minute of time, we cannot say that 20 per cent of it is born in London, 2 per cent in Manchester, and so on. We can only say that there is a 20 per cent probability of its being born in London, a 2 per cent probability of its being born in Manchester, and so on. If we disregard variations of birth-rate with locality, a map exhibiting the density of population in different parts of England will also act as a chart showing the number of births per annum; but with reference to the birth occurring at any one instant, it merely shows the relative probabilities of the baby appearing in different areas. As soon as the waves of the undulatory theory fall on matter, they provide a precisely similar chart for the

probability of photons appearing in the different areas of the matter. The waves, then, are again mental constructs—not enabling us to see what *will* happen, but what *may* happen.

Waves of Knowledge

The waves may equally well be interpreted as representations of our knowledge. In the experiment with the single photon, we do not know where the photon is, but the wave-picture gives a sort of diagrammatic representation of what we do know. We know that the photon must be within a certain region of space; this being the region mapped out by the waves at each instant. We may know that it is much more likely to be in a region A than in some other region B; if so, the waves represent this knowledge by being much more intense in the region A than in the region B, and so on. . . . .

The Uniformity of Nature

Before the quantum theory appeared, the principle of the uniformity of nature—that like causes produce like effects—had been accepted as a universal and indisputable fact of science. As soon as the atomicity of radiation became established, this principle had to be discarded.

In the experiment described on p. 199, the uniformity of nature would have required that every photon should hit the screen at the same point. Actually we have seen that they hit at different points, so that if a single quantum is discharged from the source several times in succession, different experiments will be found to give different results, and this although the conditions before the experiments were, so far as we could tell, precisely identical.

In this way we find that the atomicity of radiation destroys the principle of the uniformity of nature, and the phenomena of nature are no longer governed by a causal law —or at least if they are so governed, the causes lie beyond the series of phenomena as known to us. If, then, we wish to picture the happenings of nature as still governed by causal laws, we must suppose that there is a substratum, lying beyond the phenomena and so also beyond our access, in which the happenings in the phenomenal world are somehow determined. . . .

The Principle of Uncertainty

. . . Physics sets before itself the task of co-ordinating the various sense-data which reach us from the world beyond our sense-organs. If our senses could receive and measure infinitely delicate sense-data, we should be able in principle to form a perfectly precise picture of this outer world. Our senses have limitations of their own, but these can to a large extent be obviated by instrumental aid; telescopes, microscopes, etc. exist to make good the deficiencies of our eyes. But there is a further limitation which no instrumental aid can make good; it arises from the circumstances that we can receive no message from the outer world smaller than that conveyed by the arrival of a complete photon. As these photons are finite chunks of energy, infinite refinement is denied us; we have clumsy tools at best, and these can only make a blurred picture. It is like the picture a child might make by sticking indivisible wafers of colour onto a canvas. We might think we could avoid this complication by using radiation of infinite wave-length. For the quanta of this radiation have zero energy, and so might be expected to provide infinitely sensitive probes with which to explore the outer world. And so they do, so long as we only want to measure energy, but a true picture of the outer world will depend also on the exact measurement of lengths and positions. For this, long-wave quanta are useless. To measure a length accurately to within a millionth of an inch, we must have a measure graduated to millionths of an inch; a yardstick graduated only to inches is useless. Now quanta of one inch wave-length are, in a sense, graduated only to inches, while quanta of infinite wave-length are not graduated at all. Passing from quanta of short wave-length to quanta of long wave-length only shifts, but does not remove, the difficulty.

A rough analogy is to be found in the problem of photographing a rapidly moving object. A sensitized film can record no detail on a scale which is smaller than the grain of the film, so that if we use a large-grained film, all the fine detail of our picture will be blurred. If we try to escape this difficulty by using a film of very small grain, we merely cross over from Scylla to Charybdis; the speed of the film is now reduced so much that the picture is blurred through its subject having moved appreciably during the time necessary for exposure.

Subject and Object

It used to be supposed that in making an observation on nature, as also in the more general activities of our everyday life, the universe could be supposed divided into two detached and distinct parts, a perceiving subject and a perceived object. Psychology provided an obvious exception, because the perceiver and perceived might be the same; subject and object might be identical, or might at least overlap. But in the exact sciences, and above all in physics, subject and object were supposed to be entirely distinct, so that a description of any selected part of the universe could be prepared which would be entirely independent of the observer as well as of the special circumstances surrounding him.

The theory of relativity (1905) first showed that this cannot be entirely so; the picture which each observer makes of the world is in some degree subjective. . . .*

The theory of quanta carries us further along the same road. For every observation involves the passage of a complete quantum from the observed object to the observing subject, and a complete quantum constitutes a not negligible coupling between the observer and the observed. We can no longer make a sharp division between the two; to try to do so would involve making an arbitrary decision as to the exact point at which the division should be made. Complete objectivity can only be regained by treating observer and observed as parts of a single system; these must now be supposed to constitute an indivisible whole, which we must now identify with nature, the object of our studies.

* The theory of relativity will be taken up in Part 7. Ed.

It now appears that this does not consist of something we perceive, but of our perceptions; it is not the object of the subject-object relation, but the relation itself. But it is only in the small-scale world of atoms and electrons that this new development makes any appreciable difference; our study of the man-sized world can go on as before.

For instance, when an astronomer is observing the motion of a planet in the solar system, it is emitting millions of quanta every second, some of which pass through the telescope of the astronomer and into his eye. By noting the directions from which these arrive, he can follow and describe the motion of the planet across the sky. With the departure of each quantum, the planet suffers a recoil which changes its motion, but the changes are so minute that they may properly be disregarded. But it is different when a physicist tries to follow the motion of an electron inside an atom. He can only obtain knowledge of the internal state of the atom by causing it to discharge a full quantum of radiation, and . . . the emission of a quantum of radiation is so atom-shaking an event that the whole motion of the atom is changed, and the result is practically a new atom. A succession of quanta may give scraps of information about various stages of the atom, but can give no record of continuous change. In fact there can be no continuous change to record, since every departure of a quantum breaks the continuity.

For this reason it is futile to discuss whether the motion of the atom conforms to a causal law or not. The mere formulation of the law of causality presupposes the existence of an isolated objective system which an isolated observer can observe without disturbing it. The question is whether he, noticing that such a system is in a certain state at one instant, can or cannot foretell that it will be in some other specifiable state at some future instant. But if there is no sharp distinction between observer and observed, this becomes meaningless since any observation he makes must influence the future course of the system.

In more general terms, we may say that the law of causality acquires a meaning for us only if we have infinitesimals at our disposal with which to observe the system without disturbing it. When the smallest instruments at our disposal are photons and electrons, the law of causality becomes meaningless for us, except with reference to systems containing immense numbers of photons and electrons. For such systems the classical mechanics has already told us that causality prevails; for other systems causality becomes meaningless so far as our knowledge of the system is concerned if it controls the pattern of events, we can never know it.

We have now seen that six important consequences follow from the mere fact of the atomicity of radiation, coupled with those well-established facts of the undulatory theory of light that have been mentioned. These are:

(1) So far as the phenomena are concerned, the uniformity of nature disappears.

(2) Precise knowledge of the outer world becomes impossible for us.

(3) The processes of nature cannot be adequately represented within a framework of space and time.

(4) The division between subject and object is no longer definite or precise; complete precision can only be regained by uniting subject and object into a single whole.

(5) So far as our knowledge is concerned, causality becomes meaningless.

(6) If we still wish to think of the happenings in the phenomenal world as governed by a causal law, we must suppose that these happenings are determined in some substratum of the world which lies beyond the world of phenomena, and so also beyond our access. . . .

The old physics showed us a universe which looked more like a prison than a dwelling place. The new physics shows us a universe which looks as though it might conceivably form a suitable dwelling-place for free men, and not a mere shelter for brutes— a home in which it may at least be possible for us to mould events to our desires and live lives of endeavour and achievement.

UNCERTAINTY AND FREEWILL*
by Lincoln Barnett (1957)

While quantum physics thus defines with great accuracy the mathematical relationships governing the basic units of radiation and matter, it seems to obscure our picture of the true nature of both. Most modern physicists, however, consider it rather naïve to speculate about the true nature of anything. They are "positivists"—or "logical empiricists"— who contend that a scientist can do no more than report his observations. And so if he performs two experiments with different instruments and one seems to reveal that light is made up of particles and the other that light is made up of waves, he must accept both results, regarding them not as contradictory but as complementary. By itself neither concept suffices to explain light, but together they do. Both are necessary to describe reality and it is meaningless to ask which is really true. For in the abstract lexicon of quantum physics there is no such word as "really."

It is futile, moreover, to hope that the invention of more delicate tools may enable man to penetrate much farther into the microcosm. There is an indeterminacy about all the events of the atomic universe which refinements of measurement and observation can never dispel. The element of caprice in atomic behavior cannot be blamed on man's coarse-grained implements. It stems from the very nature of things, as shown by Heisenberg in 1927 in a famous statement of physical law known as the "Principle of Uncertainty." To illustrate his thesis Heisenberg pictured an imaginary experiment in which a physicist attempts to observe the position and velocity[1] of a moving electron by using an immensely powerful supermicroscope. Now, as has already been suggested, an individual electron appears to have no definite position or velocity. A physicist can define electron behavior accurately enough so long as he is dealing with great numbers of them.

But when he tries to locate a particular electron in space the best he can say is that a certain point in the complex superimposed wave motions of the electron group represents the *probable* position of the electron in question. The individual electron is a blur—as indeterminate as the wind or a sound wave in night—and the fewer the electrons with which the physicist deals, the more indeterminate his findings. To prove that this indeterminacy is a symptom not of man's immature science but of an ultimate barrier of nature, Heisenberg presupposed that the imaginary microscope used by his imaginary physicist is optically capable of magnifying by a hundred billion diameters—i.e., enough to bring an object the size of an electron within the range of human visibility. But now a further difficulty is encountered. For inasmuch as an electron is smaller than a light wave, the physicist can "illuminate" his subject only by using radiation of shorter wave length. Even X-rays are useless. The electron can be rendered visible only by the high-frequency gamma rays of radium. But the photoelectric effect, it will be recalled, showed that photons of ordinary light exert a violent force on electrons; and X-rays knock them about even more roughly. Hence the impact of a still more potent gamma ray would prove disastrous.

The Principle of Uncertainty asserts therefore that it is impossible with any of the principles now known to science to determine the position and the velocity of an electron at the same time—to state confidently that an electron is "right here at this spot" and is moving at "such and such a speed." For by the very act of observing its position, its velocity is changed; and, conversely, the more accurately its velocity is determined, the more indefinite its position becomes. And when the physicist computes the mathematical margin of uncertainty in his measurements of an electron's position and velocity he finds it is always a function of that mysterious quantity—Planck's Constant, h.

Quantum physics thus appears to shake

[1] In physics the term "velocity" connotes direction as well as speed.

two pillars of the old science, causality and determinism. For by dealing in terms of statistics and probabilities it abandons all idea that nature exhibits an inexorable sequence of cause and effect between individual happenings. And by its admission of margins of uncertainty it yields up the ancient hope that science, given the present state and velocity of every material body in the universe, can forecast the history of the universe for all time. One by-product of this surrender is a new argument for the existence of free will. For if physical events are indeterminate and the future is unpredictable, then perhaps the unknown quantity called "mind" may yet guide man's destiny among the infinite uncertainties of a capricious universe. Another conclusion of greater scientific importance is that in the evolution of quantum physics the barrier between man, peering dimly through the clouded windows of his senses, and whatever objective reality may exist has been rendered almost impassable. For whenever he attempts to penetrate and spy on the "real" objective world, he changes and distorts its workings by the very process of his observation. And when he tries to divorce this "real" world from his sense perceptions he is left with nothing but a mathematical scheme. He is indeed somewhat in the position of a blind man trying to discern the shape and texture of a snowflake. As soon as it touches his fingers or his tongue it dissolves. A wave electron, a photon, a wave of probability, cannot be visualized; they are simply symbols useful in expressing the mathematical relationships of the microcosm.

To the question, why does modern physics employ such esoteric methods of description, the physicist answers: because the equations of quantum physics define more accurately than any mechanical model the fundamental phenomena beyond the range of vision. In short, *they work*, as the calculations which hatched the atomic bomb spectacularly proved. The aim of the practical physicist, therefore, is to enunciate the laws of nature in ever more precise mathematical terms. Where the nineteenth century physicist envisaged electricity as a fluid and, with this metaphor in mind, evolved the laws that generated our present electrical age, the twentieth century physicist tries to avoid metaphors. He knows that electricity is not a physical fluid, and he knows that such pictorial concepts as "waves" and "particles," while serving as guideposts to new discovery, must not be accepted as accurate representations of reality. In the abstract language of mathematics he can describe how things behave though he does not know—or need to know— what they are.

Yet there are present-day physicists to whom the void between science and reality presents a challenge. Einstein more than once expressed the hope that the statistical method of quantum physics would prove a temporary expedient. "I cannot believe," he wrote, "that God plays dice with the world." He repudiated the positivist doctrine that science can only report and correlate the results of observation. He believed in a universe of order and harmony. And he believed that questing man may yet attain a knowledge of physical reality.

DOES PHYSICS NEED PICTURES?*
by Erwin Schrödinger (1935 and 1947)

Discoveries in physics cannot in themselves— so I believe—have the authority of forcing

* From Edwin Schrödinger, *Science Theory and Man*, Dover Publications, Inc., New York, 1935, and *On the Peculiarity of the Scientific World-view*, Cambridge University Press, New York, 1947. Reproduced by permission.

us to put an end to the habit of picturing the physical world as a reality.

I believe the situation is this. We have taken over from previous theory the idea of a particle and all the technical language concerning it. This idea is inadequate. It constantly drives our mind to ask for information which has obviously no significance. Its imaginative structure exhibits features which are alien to the real particle. An adequate picture must not trouble us with this disquieting urge; it must be incapable of picturing more than there is; it must refuse any further addition. Most people seem to think that no such picture can be found. One may, of course, point to the circumstantial evidence (which I am sorry to say is not changed by this essay) that in fact none has been found. I can, however, think of some reasons for this, apart from the genuine intricacy of the case. The palliative, taken from positivist philosophy and purporting to be a reasonable way out, was administered early and authoritatively. It seemed to relieve us from the search for what I should call real understanding; it even rendered the endeavour suspect, as betraying an unphilosophical mind— the mind of a child who regretted the loss of its favourite toy (the picture or model) and would not realize that it was gone for ever. . . .

To-day we are told . . . that we must not expect more from our science than those ad nauseam reiterated prophecies. Away with "image worship." Let us only have differential equations or other mathematical procedures and a recipe for deriving from them and from a set of actually performed observations all statements about all future observations of which foreknowledge is in principle at all possible. The desire to visualize, so we are told, means wanting to know how Nature is really constituted, and that is metaphysics—an expression that in present-day science is mainly used as an insult.

As is well known, Heisenberg's uncertainty assertion is strongly involved in the discussion. . . . It leads to the view that even straightforward observation of and experimentation with ordinary inanimate matter all at once confronts us with the whole profound perplexity of the subject-object relationship.

If those who believe that were right, it would mean for us here that the intelligible objectified world-picture . . . fails . . . not only in some specific form under consideration, but in any one at all that we might try to give it.

Perhaps this possibility cannot be ruled out. I do not think it is likely. So far it seems to me that the only reason for the iconoclastic uproar is the following: the corpuscle concept has, it is true, become the unquestioned and inalienable possession of the physicist who continuously uses it as a mental construct in his laboratory and at his desk, but on the other hand, it leads to considerable embarrassment because we have not yet succeeded in fusing it with the wave concept which, as one knows to-day, ought to be applied not to different phenomena, but rather to exactly the same ones as the corpuscle concept, i.e., both have to be applied to simply everything. Some people believe that they have in Mach's principle* found a wonderful way out of this dilemma which frees from the obligation to search for clear conceptions of Nature by condemning the belief in them as gross superstition. . . .

Why should we here be allowed to take recourse to an epistemological principle as an excuse for our failures?

It seems to me that what we are striving for here (in physics) . . . is a comprehensive picture of the subject under investigation, a picture which becomes ever more distinct, lucid, and clearly understood in its interrelations. . . . the coherence would be utterly destroyed if we felt bound by pangs of conscience to omit all that is not directly ascertained or cannot, if so desired, be confirmed by sense perceptions; if we felt bound to formulate all propositions in such a way that their relations to sense perceptions were immediately manifest.

---

* Mach believed that the laws of physics should be formulated so that they contain only concepts which can be defined by direct observations of nature or by a short chain of reasoning from these observations. Ed.

CONCERNING PROBABILITY*
by Pierre Simon de Laplace (1814)

All events, even those which on account of their insignificance do not seem to follow the great laws of nature, are a result of it just as necessarily as the revolutions of the sun. In ignorance of the ties which unite such events to the entire system of the universe, they have been made to depend upon final causes or upon hazard, according as they occur and are repeated with regularity, or appear without regard to order; but these imaginary causes have gradually receded with the widening bounds of knowledge and disappear entirely before sound philosophy, which sees in them only the expression of our ignorance of the true causes.

Present events are connected with preceding ones by a tie based upon the evident principle that a thing cannot occur without a cause which produces it. This axiom, known by the name of *the principle of sufficient reason*, extends even to actions which are considered indifferent; the freest will is unable without a determinative motive to give them birth; if we assume two positions with exactly similar circumstances and find that the will is active in the one and inactive in the other, we say that its choice is an effect without a cause. It is then, says Leibnitz, the blind chance of the Epicureans. The contrary opinion is an illusion of the mind, which, losing sight of the evasive reasons of the

choice of the will in indifferent things, believes that choice is determined of itself and without motives.

We ought then to regard the present state of the universe as the effect of its anterior state and as the cause of the one which is to follow. Given for one instant an intelligence which could comprehend all the forces by which nature is animated and the respective situation of the beings who compose it—an intelligence sufficiently vast to submit these data to analysis—it would embrace in the same formula the movements of the greatest bodies of the universe and those of the lightest atom; for it, nothing would be uncertain and the future, as the past, would be present to its eyes. The human mind offers, in the perfection which it has been able to give to astronomy, a feeble idea of this intelligence. Its discoveries in mechanics and geometry, added to that of universal gravity, have enabled it to comprehend in the same analytical expressions the past and future states of the system of the world. Applying the same method to some other objects of its knowledge, it has succeeded in referring to general laws observed phenomena and in foreseeing those which given circumstances ought to produce. All these efforts in the search for truth tend to lead it back continually to the vast intelligence which we have just mentioned, but from which it will always remain infinitely removed.

* From P. S. de Laplace, *Philosophical Essays on Probability*, John Wiley & Sons, Inc., New York, 1956. Reprinted by permission.

THE PRINCIPLE OF UNCERTAINTY†
by J. Bronowski (1953)

The fundamental step which created quantum physics had been taken in 1900 by Max Planck, when he discovered that energy, like matter, is not continuous, but appears always in packets or quanta of definite sizes. From the beginning, the ideas of quantum physics

could not be matched with the classical mechanics of particles. Fantastic properties had to be given to an electron whenever it sent out or took up a quantum of energy. The difficulties grew until in the 1920's it began to be seen that we simply cannot make a theory to describe these minute happenings and still hope to keep it rigidly laid out in the classical pattern of causes and effects. There

† From J. Bronowski, *The Common Sense of Science*, Harvard University Press, Cambridge, Mass., 1953. Reprinted by permission of Harvard University Press and William Heinemann, Ltd., London.

is no way at all of describing the present and the future of these tiny particles and events so that they appear completely determined. This was put into a formal principle in 1927 by the German physicist Heisenberg, and given the sensible name of the principle of uncertainty.

Heisenberg showed that every description of nature contains some essential and irremovable uncertainty. For example the more accurately we try to measure the position of a fundamental particle, of an electron say, the less certain will we be of its speed. The more accurately we try to estimate its speed, the more uncertain will we be of its precise position. Therefore we can never predict the future of the particle with complete certainty; because as a matter of fact we cannot be completely certain of its present. If we want to predict its future sensibly, then we must allow it to have some uncertainty: some range of alternatives, some slack—what engineers call some tolerance. We may have what metaphysical prejudices we choose, whether the future really and truly, essentially, is determined by the present. But the physical fact about these small scale events is beyond dispute. Their future cannot be foretold with complete assurance by anyone observing them in the present. And of course, once we have any uncertainty in prediction, in however small and distant a corner of the world, then the future is essentially uncertain—although it may remain overwhelmingly probable. . . .

The principle of uncertainty . . . shook us all a good deal. After all, it said that nature could not be described as a rigid mechanism of causes and effects. And I recall again that all the successes of science, Newton's success and those of the nineteenth century, seemed to have been won hitherto by fitting nature with just this kind of machine. To say suddenly that at bottom these causal chains are not true, that the whole thing cannot be done —that seemed a strange discovery, and a disagreeable one.

It was a discovery, and it has had a profound effect. But it does not seem nearly so strange or unsettling now. On the contrary,

to my generation the principle of uncertainty seems the most natural and sensible remark in the world. It does not seem to us to have taken the order out of science. It has taken out the metaphysics and left what had long been forgotten, the scientific purpose.

The purpose of science is to describe the world in an orderly scheme or language which will help us to look ahead. We want to forecast what we can of the future behaviour of the world; particularly we want to forecast how it would behave under several alternative actions of our own between which we are usually trying to choose. This is a very limited purpose. It has nothing whatever to do with bold generalisations about the universal workings of cause and effect. It has nothing to do with cause and effect at all, or with any other special mechanism. Nothing in this purpose, which is to order the world as an aid to decision and action, implies that the order must be of one kind rather than another. The order is what we find to work, conveniently and instructively. It is not something we stipulate; it is not something we can dogmatise about. It is what we find; it is what we find useful.

In order to act, it is not necessary to have a metaphysical belief that the rules by which we are acting are universal and that all other rules are just like them. On the contrary, at bottom all general beliefs of this kind are at odds with the principles of science. Laplace believed that if we knew the present completely, we could completely determine the future. This belief had some political and religious force for Frenchmen of the Revolution. But it has no scientific meaning at all. It does not resemble a scientific statement, or for that matter a literary one, because it is not a statement about reality, either now or in the future. There simply is no sense in asserting what would happen if we knew the present completely. We do not, and plainly we never can.

This is precisely what the principle of uncertainty says to modern physics. It makes no assertions at all about whether we could or could not predict the future of an electron, supposing that we knew this or that about its present. It simply points out that we cannot completely know its present. For instance, we can know either its whereabouts or its speed with high precision; but we cannot know both. And, in consequence, we cannot predict its future.

At bottom then, the principle of uncertainty states in special terms what was always known, which is this. Science is a way of describing reality; it is therefore limited by the limits of observation; and it asserts nothing which is outside observation. Anything else is not science; it is scholastics. The nineteenth century was dominated by Laplace's belief that everything can be described by its causes. But this is no less scholastic than the medieval belief, that everything is contained in the First Cause.

At this stage those to whom causality is second nature are tempted to open a new line of retreat. Why, they say, should we not go on believing in a strictly determined nature anyway? Why must we say that some future event is not determined, simply because science says that it cannot be predicted? Even suppose, as science now insists, that this is not merely a momentary gap. Even suppose that scientists are right and that they will never discover new laws which will make them able to predict these small events. Granted all this, say the doubters: granted that there are material events which can be shown to be unpredictable by any scientific method at all now or in the future. Is that so profound a discovery? Is it indeed a discovery about anything but science itself? Is it more than

a demonstration that the methods of science have shortcomings and are limited in scope? Why must we assume that because science cannot uncover the network of cause and effect in nature, therefore this network is not there? After all, even Laplace never supposed that any human being really could calculate the future conclusively from the present, in practice. He was perfectly aware of the practical limitations to scientific prediction. Why cannot we go on holding his view then, that the future is determined in theory, whether scientists in practice can predict it or not?

Alas, these winning and ingenuous remarks quite miss the point. Of course Laplace did not believe that the future could be punched out from the present on any calculating machine which men could build in practice. But he believed that in principle it could be done, if not by a human then by a superhuman computer. He believed that the future is fully and finally determined. The future as it were already exists in the mathematics; and the world itself is precisely a machine which calculates it by strict mechanical processes.

This is quite different from our own picture of the relation between present and future. Indeed, we would not be able to begin to set up the present on any universal machine like Laplace's, for two reasons. One is that Relativity has pointed out the difficulties in defining the present instant at two points which are far apart in space. And the other is that the principle of uncertainty has made it clear that even at one point the present cannot be defined with unlimited accuracy.

COMMENTARY ON UNCERTAINTY*
by James R. Newman (1956)

What are the limits of physical knowledge? The question would have been answered more optimistically half a century ago than today. The fact is we are confronted with a paradox: despite the immense progress in physics during the past fifty years, it is now generally believed that we cannot find out certain things

*From *The World of Mathematics*. Copyright 1956 by James R. Newman. Reprinted by permission of Simon and Schuster, Inc., New York.

about a physical system which any self-respecting scientist of the eighteenth or nineteenth century would have confidently asserted could be found out. The most secure part of our present knowledge is knowing what it is that we cannot know. . . .

The distinguished contemporary mathematician and physicist, Sir Edmund Whittaker . . . gathers together a number of statements, each of which asserts "the impossibility of achieving something, even though there may be an infinite number of ways of trying to achieve it."[1] These "Postulates of Impotence" include . . . the celebrated uncertainty principle of Heisenberg—a basic postulate of quantum mechanics—that it is impossible "to measure precisely the momentum of a particle at the same time as a precise measurement of its position is made." Whittaker's postulates, it should be observed, are neither statements of experimental fact nor a logical necessity. Each one simply expresses a conviction that any attempt to do a certain thing will fail. At the very least this is a more modest stand than Laplace's. He was not a modest man.

Heisenberg's principle concerns the accuracy with which certain physical quantities can be measured, the *theoretical*, not merely the practical limits of precision. It had long been supposed that the precision of measurements was limited only by the instruments and methods used, and that as these were improved a corresponding improvement in accuracy would result—without limit. Heisenberg showed that this faith in the perfectability of measurement was unjustified as regards the observation of very small particles. The very act of observing the position and the velocity of an electron interferes with it sufficiently to produce errors of measurement. It turns out that the more sharply one specifies the position of a particle, the less sharply can its velocity or momentum be determined; and vice versa. At best, according to Heisenberg, the product of these errors cannot be less than $h/2\pi$ where h is Planck's constant, the minimum packet of energy encountered in nature. . . .

We are faced here with an essential principle of physics. It is doubtful that it is also an essential principle of philosophy, as Eddington and others have concluded. Eddington called Heisenberg's result the principle of indeterminacy.[2] By "indeterminacy" he meant not only the fact that we as observers cannot tell exactly what is happening in the world of tiny dimensions—that "every time we determine something in the present we spoil something else" (as Bragg said)—but also the fact that the particles of that world are not ruled by the law of cause and effect. If one cannot describe a causal chain—well, then there simply is none; a curious sort of reasoning. Its appeal lay in providing an escape from the inflexible determinism of the Laplacean universe. Clergymen, as Bertrand Russell and Susan Stebbing have remarked, were particularly grateful for this solace. The announcement that electrons enjoyed free will —whatever that might mean—was cheerful news; it almost offset the series of blows that formal religion suffered in the generations from Galileo to Darwin.

Russell was right that too much fuss has been made about the uncertainty principle.[3] This is not to pooh-pooh its importance to physics. But it is essential not to confuse matters, and to keep in mind that this postulate of impotence pertains to the observer and not to the observed. To say that a psychological examination disturbs the person being examined, no matter how carefully the test is conducted, is not the same as saying that his mental behavior is not determined.

[1] Sir Edmund T. Whittaker, *From Euclid to Eddington*, Cambridge University Press, New York, 1949, pp. 58–60.

[2] Sir William Dampier, *A History of Science*, 4th ed., Cambridge University Press, New York, 1949, p. 397.
[3] Bertrand Russell, *Human Knowledge: Its Scope and Limits*, New York, 1948.

In this physical world there is no real chaos; all is in fact orderly; all is ordered by the physical principles. Chaos is but unperceived order; it is a word indicating the limitations of the human mind and the paucity of observational facts. The words "chaos," "accidental," "chance," "unpredictable," are conveniences behind which we hide our ignorance.

Harlow Shapley
Of Stars and Men (1958)

Old-style physical science kept the riddle of freedom from being seriously debated by locking it in the dusty storeroom of mechanical models, where it subsided like a conundrum among weighty problems. Mechanisms obeying Newton's laws permit no freedom; if they are taken to describe exhaustively man's make-up, then his life and his actions are as narrowly determined as the path of a missile; he has a fate but not a history.

Quantum theory rescues man's destiny from the fateful web of physical determination. It injects uncertainties into the concatenation of events, and these uncertainties *may* harbor freedom. No physicist has shown how freedom results from the laws of quantum mechanics, but there is clearly room for it. Some writers, eager to make a case for freedom, have mistaken it for absence of determination, thus committing the error of supposing that to be free is to be unpredictable. For if only the probabilities of quantum mechanics determined our behavior, we should be forced to act erratically, the quality of our actions would be determined in the mean, and a case for moral responsibility could hardly be made.

To state the issue correctly, one should say that freedom is no longer a pseudo-problem or a subjective affair of introspection that has no correlate in the external world: it has been taken out of the wastebasket of paradoxes and placed on the shelf of challenging problems to be solved. To obtain the solution, the scientist can go—and has gone—a certain distance; the philosopher versed in science must do the rest.

Henry Margenau
Perspectives of Science (1959)*

Finally, I come to what it seems to me may well be from the long-range point of view the most revolutionary of the insights to be derived from our recent experiences in physics, more revolutionary than the insights afforded by the discoveries of Galileo and Newton, or of Darwin. This is the insight that it is impossible to transcend the human reference point. . . . The new insight comes from a realization that the structure of nature may eventually be such that our processes of thought do not correspond to it sufficiently to permit us to think about it all. We have already had an intimation of this in the behavior of very small things in the quantum domain . . . there can be no difference of opinion with regard to the dilemma that now confronts us in the direction of the very small. We are now approaching a bound beyond which we are forever stopped from pushing our inquiries, not by the construction of the world, but by the construction of ourselves. The world fades out and eludes us because it becomes meaningless. We cannot even express this in the way we would like. We cannot say that there exists a world beyond any knowledge possible to us because of the nature of knowledge. The very concept of existence becomes meaningless. It is literally true that the only way of reacting to this is to shut up. We are confronted with something truly ineffable. We have reached the limit of the vision of the great pioneers of science, the vision, namely that we live in a sympathetic world, in that it is comprehensible by our minds.

P. W. Bridgman
Philosophical Implications of Physics (1950)†

* From Henry Margenau, "Perspectives of Science," *The Key Reporter*, Autumn, 1959, copyright United Chapters of Phi Beta Kappa. Reprinted by permission.
† From P. W. Bridgman, "Philosophical Implications of Physics," *Bulletin of the American Academy of Arts and Sciences*, vol. 3, no. 5, February, 1950. Reprinted by permission from the publisher.

QUESTIONS TO CONSIDER

The Biblical account of the creation gives light a position of supreme importance in the universe. Have scientific investigations changed this evaluation?

Since we know so much about light, why is its nature still a mystery?

Is it necessary to have a picture or model in order to understand the physical world?

Jeans says, "The division between the subject and object is no longer definite or precise; complete precision can only be regained by uniting subject and object into a single whole." Would not this suggestion be contrary to the objective scientific attitude?

What causes the gaps in our knowledge of atomic phenomena? Does the existence of these gaps lead to the possibility of free will? Does the world of Laplace seem to you like a "prison" and the world of uncertainty "a more suitable dwelling place for free men"?

SUGGESTIONS FOR FURTHER READING

* Born, Max: *The Restless Universe*, rev. ed., Dover Publications, Inc., New York, 1951, chap. III. An excellent description of modern concepts of light. Chapters I and II should be read first as background for chap. III.

* Bragg, William: *The Universe of Light*, Dover Publications, Inc., New York, 1933. In addition to the selection that we have used in this part, we recommend this entire Bragg book for a clear and understandable account of the phenomena of reflection, refraction, polarization, and many other aspects of the nature of light that we did not have the space to include in these readings.

* Bronowski, J.: *The Common Sense of Science*, Vintage Books, Random House, Inc., New York, 1953. A very well-written discussion of the historical development and significance of the concepts of order, chance, and causality.

* Jaffe, Bernard: *Michelson and the Speed of Light*, Anchor Books, Doubleday & Company, Inc., Garden City, N.Y., 1960. A Science Study Series biography of Michelson, including descriptions of his contributions to optics, the determination of the speed of light, and the Michelson-Morley experiment.

* Lodge, Oliver: *Pioneers of Science*, Dover Publications, Inc., New York, 1960, lecture X. A description of the experiments of Roemer and Bradley measuring the speed and aberration of light.

* Paperback edition.

PART 7

ARE THEORIES TRUE?

The changing and progressive aspect of science is illustrated in these readings which trace the evolution of the theory of gravity from Newton through Einstein and bring out the reasons why a theory that was true yesterday may be only partially true today.

Leacock

Einstein

INTRODUCTION

The readings in this part describe the evolution of a scientific theory. Bronowski said in Part 1 that a theory is the product of a creative imagination, resulting from the perception of a hidden likeness between apparently diverse phenomena. In this part we see how Newton created a new synthesis from Galileo's mechanics and Kepler's three laws of planetary motions. He united these apparently isolated principles into a broad working hypothesis and drew deductions from it that were confirmed in so many instances that the conceptual scheme became known as the law of gravity, one of the most comprehensive laws discovered by science. This law had great influence for many years and served as the foundation for the mechanistic and materialist thought of the eighteenth and nineteenth centuries.

However, toward the beginning of the twentieth century there began to appear several experimental facts that did not fit the Newtonian physics. This experimental evidence was of an extremely refined order of magnitude. We remember that Kepler threw out his first idea of planetary motion because of a discrepancy of eight minutes of arc in the orbit of Mars. But it was a difference of forty-three seconds of arc per century in the orbit of Mercury that was one of the observational facts not accounted for by Newton's law of gravity. In the Michelson-Morley experiment, it was necessary to be able to measure a time difference of 5×10^{-17} second in order that the results would be significant. This was the kind of experimental evidence that called for a revision in thinking and led to Einstein's broader synthesis, the theory of relativity.

Conant, in his book *On Understanding Science*, says, "We can put it down as one of the principles learned from the history of science that a theory is only overthrown by a better theory, never merely by contradictory facts. Attempts are first made to reconcile the contradictory facts to the existing conceptual scheme by some modification of the concept. Only the combination of a new concept with facts contradictory to the old ideas finally brings about a scientific revolution. When once this has taken place, then in a few short years discovery follows discovery and the branch of science in question progresses by leaps and bounds."

The revolution brought about by Einstein has been so profound that we should have some knowledge of the ideas that have emerged from his theory: ideas like the equivalence of mass and energy, which has been dramatically confirmed by the atom bomb; the definition of the speed of light as the top limiting velocity in the universe; and the fundamental reexamination of our measurements of space and time. These are some of the new concepts that are discussed in the readings in this part. In addition, the selections describe some of the reasons that led to the new theory and the experimental confirmations of it. The selection from Einstein is included to give the reader a feeling for the type of thinking he used in developing his theory. Within the limitations of a short introductory book with a nonmathematical approach, it is not possible to give a complete account of Einstein's theory. Readers who feel interested in gaining a better grasp of the theory itself will find suggestions for further reading at the end of this part. In the context of these readings, the most important points to understand are how theories are conceived, how they evolve, and how they are often incorporated into broader conceptual schemes. The story of Newton and Einstein is illustrative of this process. Studying the life history of a theory will help toward an appreciation of the nature of scientific theories in general.

In Part 2 and again in Part 4 we discussed the fact that scientific method cannnot prove a theory to be definitely and absolutely true. At best it can show that there is a good probability that the theory represents a true description of reality. Yet, at any time, facts may appear that disprove it. Thus a scientific theory is forever "on trial," and it is this feature of the scientific process that prompted Gilbert Lewis to say that the concept of ultimate truth ". . . does not seem useful to science except in the sense of a horizon toward which we may proceed." Since this is true, should theories serve only as aids to scientific progress? Are they too transitory to have any deeper significance, or does each new synthesis discover a greater unity in nature and lead mankind to a new level of understanding?

NEWTON'S THEORY OF GRAVITY

RULES OF CORRECT REASONING IN PHILOSOPHY*
by Sir Isaac Newton (1686)

Rule I. We are to admit no more causes of natural things than such as are both true and sufficient to explain their appearances.

To this purpose the philosophers say that nature does nothing in vain, and more is in vain when less will serve; for Nature is pleased with simplicity, and affects not the pomp of superfluous causes.

Rule II. Therefore to the same natural effects we must, as far as possible, assign the same causes.

As to respiration in a man and in a beast; the descent of stones in Europe and in America; the light of our culinary fire and of the sun; the reflection of light in the earth, and in the planets.

Rule III. The qualities of bodies, which admit neither intensification nor remission of degrees, and which are found to belong to all bodies within the reach of our experiments, are to be esteemed the universal qualities of all bodies whatsoever.

For since the qualities of bodies are only known to us by experiments, we are to hold for universal all such as universally agree with experiments; and such as are not liable to diminution can never be quite taken away. We are certainly not to relinquish the evidence of experiments for the sake of dreams and vain fictions of our own devising; nor are we to recede from the analogy of Nature, which is wont to be simple, and always consonant to itself.

* From Sir Isaac Newton, *Principia Mathematica*, book III, edited by Florian Cajori, from the translation by Andrew Motte, University of California Press, Berkeley, Calif., 1934. Reprinted by permission.

THE DAWN OF UNIVERSAL MECHANICS†
by W. P. D. Wightman (1951)

On Christmas Day of the year 1642 (in which Galileo died) there was born, near Grantham in Lincolnshire, a delicate babe who, during a vigorous life of nearly eighty-five years, extended the laws of motion of Galileo into realms undreamed of by their discoverer; and, triumphing over the immense mathematical difficulties, reduced all the phenomena of motion to manifestations of one simple law. Young Isaac Newton quickly threw off the weakness of infancy, and at an early age took advantage of a stormy night to measure the force of the gale by pacing out the lengths of leaps taken with the aid of the wind and in opposition to it. The story is interesting in that it indicates clearly the germ of the work—the application of calculation to actual

† From William P. D. Wightman, *The Growth of Scientific Ideas*, Yale University Press, New Haven, Conn., 1951. Reprinted by permission of Yale University Press and Oliver & Boyd Ltd., Edinburgh and London.

experiments with the familiar but little understood forces of nature—by which he gained imperishable fame.

. . . But we must pass over these early years and picture him, as the French philosopher Voltaire, bids us, sitting in his garden at Woolsthorpe where, driven from Cambridge by threat of the Great Plague, he was passing the summer of 1665 in speculating concerning the motions of the heavenly bodies. Suddenly his attention was arrested by the fall of an apple to the ground. To no one before had such a familiar event seemed in any way connected with the motion of the heavenly bodies; to speak plainly, we cannot be sure that it was the fall of an *apple* which set Newton's mind to work, though his friend Stukeley also said that Newton told him so. In any case we have Newton's own written testimony that it was in 1665 that he began to think of "gravity extending to ye orb of the moon,"[1] and further, that before he set about the calculations he marked the significance of the fact that this force of gravity extended to the deepest mine shafts and the highest mountains—why not then, his bold imagination hinted, to the moon itself?

Before we attempt to trace in outline the use he made of the materials which others had provided, and to learn something of the new intellectual weapons which he himself forged, it is imperative that we clearly discern what it was that Newton was seeking. One thing it certainly was not, though in our childhood we may often have been told so, namely *why* an apple falls to the ground. Nor was it even why the moon moves as it does. His immediate purpose was in fact just that which in another connexion Galileo had proclaimed as the business of science, namely the demonstration that whatever may be the nature of the cause of an apple's fall to the ground, it is a cause of the *same nature* which determines the motion of the moon. Later, when he came to write his Preface to the First Edition of the *Principia*, he was to announce his belief that "the whole burden of philosophy [of nature] seems to consist in this—from the phenomena of motions to investigate the forces of nature, and then from these forces to demonstrate the other phenomena."

We must further understand that the search itself had been made possible only by Galileo's far-reaching studies; for so long as with the Greeks it was assumed that the motion of the moon in a circle round the earth was the most natural thing imaginable, there was clearly no problem to solve. But unless the moon is governed by influences entirely different from those apparently determining the behaviour of terrestrial bodies, its motion is anything but "natural"; for it should move in a straight line. Now Galileo taught us to distinguish as *forces* those natural influences which cause a body to diverge from rectilinear motion; hence some force must be acting on the moon. It was the genius of Newton to assume that

since we know of no influences acting on the moon and the planets other than those acting on terrestrial bodies, it is worth while trying to prove that these will suffice to account for the behaviour of the former. Later in life he expressed this ideal—the tacitly accepted ideal of all *modern* science—in the following words: "We are to admit no more causes of natural things than such as are both true and sufficient to explain their appearances." . . . To accomplish this task alone would have enshrined him among the immortals; actually it was but a small part of his ultimate achievement.

To follow Newton step by step on his arduous task would take us far too long. . . . Indeed modern research has made it seem very probable that Newton himself was far from "moving in a straight line" towards a clearly envisaged goal. He worked on the problem at least three times in his life, and on two of these occasions seems to have lost interest in it for years at a time. It will nevertheless be most profitable to appreciate what the central problems were; for in so doing we can gain an insight into the true nature of mathematical physics such as entirely eludes anyone who is content to hear merely the bald statement of the results.

Let us then examine the *facts* as they were known at the time of Newton's first attack on the problem of the moon's orbit. The moon was known to describe an orbit—approximately circular—about the earth as centre. This was not of course a direct fact of observation, but an interpretation of such facts, and of whose truth no competent astronomer doubted. It was also known that the radius of the moon's orbit was about sixty times the radius of the earth itself. . . . The only other facts needed by Newton were the period of revolution of the moon—rather more than twenty-seven days—and the distance fallen in one second by a body near the earth's surface when unimpeded by the air—a distance of approximately sixteen feet.

These were the only *facts* used by Newton; to extract from them the relation which he believed to hold between the motion of the moon and that of an object near the earth's

---

[1] It is significant for the history of thought that his youthful attempts to master Euclid were prompted by his inability to solve a problem in *astrology!*

surface, he had to propose a method of *measuring* forces. To do this he assumed the truth of Galileo's law of inertia, and explicitly stated what was only *implicit* in Galileo's law of falling bodies. It is a strange thing that it never seems to have occurred to Galileo that if bodies left to themselves remain in a state of rest or uniform rectilinear motion, then it is natural to *measure* forces by the changes of motion which these produce in a given body: in other words, by the accelerations which the body undergoes. . . . In taking this next step Newton completed the work which Galileo had begun.

Newton's statement of this Second Law of Motion was to the effect that forces are proportional to the changes of motion which they produce, whether that change is in the speed with which the body "covers the ground" or of the direction in which it is moving; for it is a simple fact of experience that a weight can be twirled on the end of a string at a steady "speed" only if a constant force be applied. The modern statement of the law is therefore that "forces are proportional to the accelerations they produce," acceleration being defined as rate of change of *velocity*, which in turn means *speed in a given direction*.

Motion in a circle therefore may be regarded as equivalent to one in a straight line with which is compounded an acceleration towards the centre. Newton easily proved, as had his contemporary Huygens, that this acceleration is in fact proportional to v^2/r, where v is the speed with which the body is moving in the circle, and r the radius of the circle. Thus if we accept Galileo's and Newton's conception of force, it follows inevitably that any body moving in a circle must be acted upon by a force which accelerates it towards the centre of the circle. Now it is a fact that the moon is constantly moving round the earth in a path which is approximately a circle centred at the earth, therefore there must be a force acting on the moon accelerating it towards the earth; is it not the most natural, though not of course the only possible, assumption that the earth is itself the origin of the force? The only convincing manner of answering this question in the

affirmative is to show that there is a precise numerical relationship between the supposed force of the earth on the moon and that on the apple. For numbers, like money, "talk"; that is, there is no disputing their testimony.

The next question therefore is the form of this supposed relationship. Here Newton made use of a hypothesis, probably first asserted by Bullialdus a few years before Newton's birth, and certainly familiar to Newton's contemporaries, Halley, Wren and Hooke, that the power of one body, say the sun, to attract another, say a planet, would, if it exists at all, be inversely proportional to the square of the distance between them. That this suggestion was put forward by Bullialdus, of whom probably most people—even some men of science—have never even heard, only goes to show how mistaken is the oft-expressed opinion that the great advances in scientific thought are the exclusive products of individual geniuses.

In order to show that his hypothesis was true, Newton had therefore to solve the comparatively easy problem (certain "simplifying assumptions" being made) of showing that if f_m, f_a, are respectively the forces acting on the moon and on the apple, which are respectively at distances d_m, d_a from the earth, then $f_m/f_a = d_a^2/d_m^2$. The first simplifying assumption is that the moon's orbit is circular, the second is that the distance of each body "from the earth" is to be taken as its distance from the centre of the earth; for neither the moon nor the earth can be regarded as a geometrical point, that is as negligibly small compared with the distance between them. And the difficulty naturally becomes far greater when bodies near the earth's surface are being considered. This is probably one of the subsidiary problems which Newton later referred to as being "more difficult than I was aware of." He referred to it in a slightly different connexion in III, 8 of the *Principia*; and his inability to solve it at that time, rather than the possible inaccuracy of his information regarding the diameter of the earth, probably accounted for his abandoning the formal proof of the whole project. Nevertheless it appears that he *did* make a provisional calculation, probably on such lines as these (Figure 7-1):

If a be the acceleration of the moon towards the earth, then $a = v^2/r$ and by Galileo's law (p. 126), s, the distance fallen $= \frac{1}{2}at^2 = \frac{1}{2}a = \frac{1}{2}v^2/r$ in one second. Now

$$v = \frac{\text{length of orbit}}{\text{time taken to describe it}}$$

$$= \frac{2\pi r}{t}$$

$$\therefore s = \frac{1}{2}\frac{v^2}{r}$$

$$= \frac{1}{2} \cdot \frac{4\pi^2 r^2}{t^2} \cdot \frac{1}{r}$$

$$= \frac{2\pi^2 r}{t^2}$$

$$= \frac{2 \times 3 \cdot 14^2 \times 240,000 \times 1760 \times 3}{(27.3 \times 24 \times 60 \times 60)^2} \text{ feet,}$$

27.3 being the number of *days* taken by the moon to describe its orbit of 240,000 *miles* radius.

The above fraction (in which the quantities used are those of to-day approximated to three significant figures) works out at .00449 ft.

Now if $f_m/f_a = d_a^2/d_m^2$, then, since force is proportional to acceleration, $s_m/s_a = d_a^2/d_m^2$, where s_m, s_a, are the respective distances fallen in one second by the moon and the apple. But the moon is known to be almost exactly sixty times as far from the centre of the earth as is the apple, so $s_a/s_m = 60^2/1$, that is, the distance fallen by the apple *should* be 3,600 times the distance fallen by the moon, i.e.

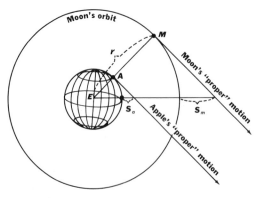

Figure 7-1

$0.00449 \times 3600 = 16.2$ ft. The actual value found by experiment is 16.1 ft. Newton probably got 15.5 ft. for the former quantity, which would justify his remark that he "found the answer pretty nearly."

While Newton, perhaps dissatisfied with the number of simplifying assumptions he had been compelled to adopt, took no further steps to make his view public, a similar problem was taking shape in the minds of many of his contemporaries both in England and on the Continent. This was whether it could be proved that, on the assumption that the force between the sun and a planet is inversely proportional to the square of the distance between them, the planet would necessarily move according to Kepler's First Law. By 1684 several members of the newly formed Royal Society seem to have proved independently that if it could be assumed, as was unfortunately only roughly true, that the orbits of the planets are circles, then the inverse square hypothesis is implicit in Kepler's *Third* law. . . .

Of course no one pretended that this result *proved* the truth of the inverse square hypothesis, but the agreement was too striking to be merely a "fluke." One of these brilliant men, Robert Hooke, who in the intervals of assisting in the rebuilding of London after the fire, found time to invent carriage springs, to make one of the first efficient compound microscopes and to come very near to discovering oxygen, claimed that he could deduce a similar relationship for elliptic orbits, but on being asked to deliver it for inspection, temporised in a manner which suggested that the task was in reality beyond his mathematical powers. The events following on this unworthy display of duplicity were in their way as dramatic as anything in the history of human endeavour; for had it not been for the resolution of another of this group, Halley, the greatest single discovery ever made might never have been known to any but its discoverer. Halley however determined to consult Newton at Cambridge. So in August 1684 he called on Newton and, without mentioning the tentative views of Hooke and the others, bluntly asked him what would be the path of a planet on the assumption that the force acting on it decreased in the proportion of the square of its distance from the sun. To his astonishment and delight Newton replied that the planet would describe an ellipse. His delight was somewhat tempered when Newton failed to find the papers on which he had, so he said, worked out the proof. However in November the papers arrived, giving two proofs of the theorem that, in his own words, "by a centrifugal force reciprocally as the square of the distance, a planet must revolve in an ellipsis about the centre of the force placed in the lower umbilicus [focus] of the ellipsis and with a radius drawn to that centre describe areas proportional to the times." Newton later claimed to have obtained a proof in 1676, but had apparently lost interest in the subject! Now he set to work again and wrote a small treatise, *De Motu Corporum*, which Halley saw on a second visit to Cambridge. Fortunately for the world Halley realised that here was a "scoop" of the first order and, overcoming Newton's disinclination for publicity, persuaded him to send it to the Royal Society for publication.

The next year, under the stimulus of Halley's encouragement, Newton successfully proved that a spherical body such as the earth exercises its force of gravitation, whether on the moon or on an apple at its surface, in a manner which is mathematically equivalent to the force which would be exerted by the same body regarded as a mathematical point situated at its centre. To effect this wonderful result Newton had been faced by the task of calculating the combined effects of all the particles of matter of which the earth is composed. Such a task appeared impossible of fulfillment; in fact we may say that it was impossible until Newton himself had invented a new branch of mathematics—akin to what we now call the "integral calculus"—by which such problems involving the effect of an apparently infinite number of infinitesimal (that is "vanishingly" small) particles could be tackled. . . .

The Royal Society was delighted with what it saw of Newton's work, and at once ordered it to be completed and printed at the Society's expense. When the extent of the undertaking was realised however there seems to have been a cooling-off on the part of the well-to-do who largely composed the Society's membership. The exact reason for the delay will perhaps never be known, but the fact remains that Halley, a man of modest fortune and with a young family to bring up, undertook the expense and much of the labour of seeing the work through the press. The Royal Society took the credit for the publication, but posterity knows that it was to the vision and self-sacrifice of Halley that it owes the final publication in 1687 of the greatest single monument of human learning—*Philosophiae Naturalis Principia Mathematica.*

The Newtonian Revolution

. . . We must now take note of an important implication of the law of gravitation. We have seen that the moon's path round the earth can be accounted for on the assumption that the earth draws the moon towards itself with exactly the same force as it does an apple on its own surface, only providing that magnitude of the force falls off in the proportion of the square of the distance from the centre of the earth. The moon being about sixty times as far from the earth's centre as is the apple, it will in unit time "fall" towards the centre about one three-thousand-six-hundredth part of the distance fallen by the apple. But what enabled Newton to enunciate his Second Law of Motion where Galileo had failed was the fact that the former had grasped the part played by the *mass*—the unchanging degree of resistance to motion, which characterises every material body; what, indeed, constitutes its "materiality." If of two garden rollers standing on the same level path, the one requires exactly twice the effort to give it the same acceleration as the other, we say that the former has twice the *mass* of the latter. Ordinarily we work the other way round: knowing that one *weighs* twice as much as the other, we at once *infer* that it will take twice as much effort to give it the same acceleration. It is so much easier to weigh garden rollers than to set up experiments by which may be measured the forces necessary to give them equal accelerations.

Indeed it is one of the most difficult problems in mechanics to contrive the measurement of "naked" forces unassociated with lumps of matter. But it cannot be too strongly emphasised that though in practice we measure masses by weighing them, the two quantities refer to entirely distinct characteristics of matter.

Now in all that we have said so far about the force controlling the motions of the heavenly bodies, we have been able to get on perfectly well without any knowledge of their *masses*. How can we say that the force acting on the moon differs from that acting on the apple only in respect of the squares of their respective distances from the earth which attracts them? It is to be hoped that the watchful reader has been troubled with a feeling of uneasiness about this very point. Bearing in mind that the magnitude of a force causing motion is always proportional to the product of the mass of the body moved and its acceleration (by suitable choice of units it is *equal* to this product), he must have felt that to compare the forces acting on moon and apple by comparing their accelerations is a mere trifling with the problem, seeing that the *mass* of the moon is so enormously greater than that of the apple. . . . the argument holds equally well for a grain of sand and an aerial bomb. The whole of terrestrial mechanics rests on the observed fact that all bodies at a given point near the earth's surface are accelerated towards the centre at the same rate. The mass has nothing to do with it. Obviously if we are going to retain our original definition of a unit force (as that which causes unit acceleration in unit mass) we must ascribe to the particular force of gravity the curious property of being always proportional to the masses it is acting upon, providing of course that they are equidistant from the centre of the earth; for only thus can it come about that different masses are equally accelerated at the earth's surface. This is the course which Newton took, his actual words being: "There is a power of gravity tending to all bodies, proportional to the several quantities of matter they contain." (*Principia*, Bk. III, Prop. VII).

It is a curious fact that the men of science of Newton's day and for nearly two centuries thereafter never seem to have been particularly struck by this odd characteristic of the "force" of gravity. . . . The law of gravitation as applied by Newton is enunciated in our text books in the following words: "Every particle of matter attracts every other particle with a force which varies directly as the product of their masses, and inversely as the square of the distance between them." The implication is clearly that "matter" itself somehow "generates" this "force" and exerts it in some mystical way across millions of miles of empty space. It is significant that Newton himself is much more guarded in his views than modern text books give him credit for. In speaking of this force he avoids the word "attraction," and speaks instead of "bodies gravitating towards one another." And in a letter to a friend, Richard Bentley, he writes: "You sometimes speak of gravity as essential and inherent to matter. Pray do not ascribe that notion to me; for the cause of gravity is what I do not pretend to know. . . . It is inconceivable that inanimate brute matter should, without the mediation of something else, which is not material, operate upon, and effect other matter without mutual contact." The widely held belief that Newton regarded gravitation as an *innate* characteristic of matter seems to have been due to one or two less cautious sentences in the *Principia* and in Query 31 of the *Opticks* (which however he is careful to correct at the end of the sentence). But more particularly was it due to the remarks made in the "popular" Preface to the Second Edition of the *Principia*, written by Roger Cotes, the editor. It is probable that Newton all along was struggling against the pseudo-Aristotelian tendency to invoke "occult powers" to "explain" everything—the antithesis to what Newton recognised the nature of scientific enquiry to be. His final views on the nature of matter appear in the last pages of the *Opticks:* "It seems probable to me that God in the beginning form'd matter in solid, massy, hard impenetrable, moveable Particles . . . and that these primitive Particles, being Solids, are incomparably harder than any porous Bodies compounded of them; even so very hard as never to wear or break in pieces; no ordinary power being able to divide what God himself made one in the first Creation." The innate qualities enumerated here do not include gravitation.

When following long established custom we speak of the earth's attraction for the apple and for the moon, we have in fact not a shred of evidence that any "force" such as is exerted by a tow-rope on a barge exists between them. If, however, we decide, as is implied by Galileo, that whenever a body suffers an acceleration, there must be a force acting on it, then we must inevitably deduce the existence of a force between earth and apple. And if further we decide, as did Newton, to measure forces by the acceleration they produce in unit masses, then we must infer that since all bodies fall with constant and equal accelerations at the same point on the earth's surface, the "force" which we have inferred to act on them must be proportional to their masses: this conclusion is inescapable *on the assumptions that we have made.*

This aspect of Newton's work is of great importance in assessing its ultimate validity, that is, as "science's last word." . . .

So far our discussion has been simplified by regarding the sun as "attracting" the planets, and the earth as "attracting" the moon and the apple. But Newton made it perfectly clear that the power of gravitation extends to every particle of matter; it is only for convenience that we have singled out one body—the greater—from the pair under consideration. The moon "attracts" the earth with the same force as that which the earth exerts upon it. To an observer on the sun, we may believe, the earth would not appear indifferent to this action: its path in space would not remain the same were the moon suddenly to be blotted out of existence.

The calculation of this mutual effect is made possible by Newton's Third Law of Motion: "To every action there is always opposed an equal reaction: or the mutual actions of two bodies upon each other are always equal, and directed to contrary parts." The operation of this law is a fact of daily experience. It is impossible to step from an unmoored rowing boat on to a landing stage without moving the boat in the opposite direction. We may believe that the same would be equally true of a man disembarking from the "Queen Mary"; but the effect is masked, even apart from the mooring ropes and rigid gangways, by the enormous mass of the ship compared with that of the man. By "action" Newton clearly meant what in the Second Law he had called "quantity of motion"—what we now call "momentum," that is the product of mass and velocity. Thus if any body is to alter its momentum it can do so only by altering that of some other body or bodies to an equal amount "directed to contrary parts." The propellent charge which sets the shell in motion can do so only by giving the gun an equal and opposite "motion." By using the mathematical device of a minus sign for a "contrary" motion—a convention which became familiar in later years—we are able to express Newton's Third Law in concise quantitative terms: "The algebraic sum of the momenta of an isolated system of bodies is a constant quantity." This is the first of the "conservation laws"—. . . .

Let us now pause for a moment to see what exactly was Newton's contribution to the growth of scientific ideas about matter and motion, and in what way it was in advance of all previous ideas in the same connexion. The simple idea which in Newton's skilled hands wove together the movements of all observable bodies was no more than this: All moving objects, whether planets or cannon balls, are composed of particles of something distinguished by two characteristics, namely an innate resistance to change of motion, the degree of which resistance is called the *mass* of the particle, and a tendency to gravitate together as if impelled by a force which varies directly as the product of the masses and inversely as the square of the distance between them. The "stuff" thus characterised is what we still call "matter."[2]

Thus stated, the Newtonian revolution

[2] The critical reader may wonder how the unit of mass is to be measured without dragging in force and so making the argument circular. Newton left this point in an unsatisfactory state. It is too difficult to deal with in detail here.

sounds prosaic enough. Why then do we hail it as probably the greatest single achievement of the human intellect? It leaves us completely ignorant as to why an apple falls to earth; for to suppose this problem solved by saying "because the earth attracts the apple" is grievously to err. Such a "solution" is no better than that of Aristotle to the effect that the "earthy nature of the apple is seeking its natural place." The law of gravitation, like the laws of motion of Galileo, does not tell us why bodies move towards each other, but precisely how their movement is determined. And it tells us more; for it discovers . . . what is essential in the motion of all material bodies, namely the mere fact that they *are* material. Whether we keep strictly to Newton's own words or whether we simplify the *verbal expression* of the law by speaking of an actual "attraction," matters but little. Provided we bear in mind what we mean by a "force" in the science of physics, we are compelled to say that all material bodies move as if impelled by a force operating according to Newton's law. Whether the operation of that force is "caused" by matter itself, or whether with Newton we prefer to await the results of further research, the consequences predicted by the law remain completely unchanged. And that is after all what "science" since Galileo's day has stood for. . . . The future was to reveal that nothing but the refinement of the mathematical technique was necessary to enable man to calculate the amounts of the known disturbances and thus to seek for, as yet unobserved, causes of residual disturbances. The law of gravitation not only explains, it also foretells.

Although a century had to pass after the death of Newton before the law of gravitation was used as an instrument of discovery, it must be realised that Newton himself was able to show that many carefully observed but as yet unexplained phenomena were just as inevitable consequences of this universal characteristic of matter as was the nearly circular path of the moon. Thus he began the proof of the extremely complex problem of showing that the oceanic tides are mainly the result of the varying "pulls" of the sun and moon on

the mass of water as they change their stations relative to one another. But perhaps the most beautiful interpretation of all was the demonstration that the precession of the equinoxes* (discovered by Hipparchos nearly two thousand years earlier— . . .), the so-called "inequalities" of the moon's motion, some already known to astronomers, but one of which was foretold by Newton; and the motions of the tides—all are manifestations of the same phenomenon, namely a disturbance of the simple gravitational reaction between two bodies by the action of a . . . *third* body. . . . Thus the moon instead of moving in an ellipse round the earth, according to Kepler's three laws, really "wobbles" to a small but precisely determinable extent. The plane containing the earth's orbit about the sun is inclined to that of the moon about the earth, otherwise there would be an eclipse of the sun at every "new moon" and of the moon at every "full moon." Now the sun is about four hundred times as far from the moon as is the earth, but it is vastly more massive; so its "pull" on the moon imposes an additional periodic motion on that body. The actual nature of this motion was *proved* by Newton to involve a gradual revolution of the *axis* of the moon's *orbit*, occupying about eighteen years; this is the principal cause of the recurring cycles of eclipse shown to the Chaldean astronomers as the "Saros" at least 2,500 years ago. By a superb use of the "principle of continuity" Newton extended this argument to the case of a ring of satellites, then to a ring of fluid surrounding the central body. . . . The last case of this sequence was that of a *solid ring* such as exists in the equatorial region of the earth. There will be similar rotation of the axis of this ring which, being rigidly connected to the sphere, will cause the axis of the latter also to revolve—and so the pole of the heavens will describe a circle and the equinoxes will precess! . . .

In Newton's hands the law of gravitation not only interpreted all the known motions of material bodies but actually foretold the existence of several others which were later ob-

* See footnote 5, p. 52.

served by astronomers. In this Newton was helped, rather more than he gave him credit for, by the Astronomer Royal, Flamsteed. But the greatest triumph subsequent to Newton's death came towards the end of the eighteenth century, when by its application it became increasingly more probable that a hitherto unknown planet existed in the solar system. The whole story is one of the great romances of science; we have space here only to show how it illustrates one of the most valuable scientific methods.

On 13th March 1781, Sir William Herschel, by profession a musician but who became one of the most brilliant observational astronomers, noticed among a group of small stars one whose size increased progressively with the magnification employed in his telescope (the almost "infinitely" distant stars actually become smaller but at the same time *brighter* when viewed through an instrument of higher magnifying power). On succeeding nights its changed position relative to the "fixed" stars confirmed his view that the body might be a comet. Later however, other observations showed its movements to be those not of a comet but of a planet; and in due course it was established that the body had been observed many times during the previous hundred years. This fact enabled mathematicians to determine . . . the constants by which its orbit about the sun could be determined. But before very long Uranus, for such was the name given to the new planet, began to wander seriously from the strait and narrow path which men had assigned to it. Here was a chance to put Newton's law to the most crucial test by, as it were, "turning it inside out."

To Newton, . . . the problems of celestial mechanics were always of the form: "Given such and such bodies, to deduce their relative motions." But in the case of Uranus the problem was: "Given such and such irregularities in the motion of one body to deduce the position and magnitude of some unknown body which is the cause thereof." Such a piece of investigation is an illustration of what logicians call "the method of residues"; for before any attempt could be made to seek the position of the unknown body, all the possible effects of known bodies, such as Jupiter and Saturn, had to be calculated and allowed for: the residual effect must then be due to some undetermined cause.

To this task the young Cambridge mathematician, J. C. Adams, and the experienced Frenchman, Leverrier, applied themselves, each in complete ignorance of the fact that the other was seeking the same goal. On 23rd September 1846, the Berlin astronomer, Galle, found the planet which was the cause of the trouble very near the spot where Leverrier told him to look. Within a few days the Cambridge Astronomer, Challis, was able to prove that he had observed the planet in the same region of the sky but in different positions relative to the stars on 30th July, 4th August and 12th August. The new planet was called Neptune. It is perhaps too much to say that but for a purely abstract dynamical law it would never have been recognised by human eye; but it is certain that its discovery would have been indefinitely postponed. The light of Neptune is thus a reflection of the light of Newton's thought which shone with such power as actually to bring new material bodies within the range of human ken.

By assuming the truth of the law of gravitation it had been possible to deduce the existence of a massive body far beyond the orbit of Saturn but still within the confines of the solar system. In 1862 however an American astronomer, Alvan Clark, observed a new star whose existence, unknown to him, had been deduced from the observed irregularities in the motion of another star. In all that we have said about the heavens thus far we have assumed the immobility of the stars—Newton, as we know, took the "frame of the fixed stars" as his frame of reference to which all motions could be referred as absolute. . . .

The most sensational triumph however was still to come. The German mathematician, Bessel, . . . had in 1834 made so many observations on Sirius, the brightest star in the heavens, as to suspect that its proper motion (that is, its own motion among all the other stars which by this time had come to be recognised as moving at high speeds) was irregular. So just as a new *planet* had been "invented" to account for the irregular behaviour of Uranus which was troubling astronomers at the same time, Bessel, having in ten years failed to detect any cause for the "wandering" of Sirius, "invented" a new and invisible *star*. In a letter to Sir John Herschel (William's son) he wrote: "I adhere to the conviction that Procyon [the 'Little Dog' star, another wanderer, quite separate from Sirius] and Sirius form real binary systems, consisting of a visible and an invisible star. There is no reason to suppose luminosity an essential quality of cosmical bodies. The visibility of countless stars is no argument against the invisibility of countless others."

What a change from the Ionian conception of the stars as being jets of flame bursting through, or fixed to, the crystal sphere which rotates about the earth! Bessel's remarks exemplify in the clearest manner the Newtonian revolution in which "bodies celestial" differ not at all in their effects from "bodies terrestrial"; their presence being deductible from the assumption that, being fashioned from "matter," they will be subject to the law of gravitation now seen as *universally* valid . . . in 1862 Alvan Clark, knowing nothing of the predictions of Bessel and the more accurate ones of Peters, stumbled by accident upon a faint star in the proximity of Sirius *just where the mathematicians said it ought to be at that time to account for the irregularity in the motion of Sirius itself.* This dark companion, though as massive as our sun, has only one five-hundredth of the intrinsic brightness of the latter.

It is interesting to note that the . . . greatest advances in the secure establishment of the law of gravitation were the results of "accidents." William Herschel, examining the smaller stars, discovers a "comet" which turns out to be a planet, whose irregular behaviour leads to the discovery of another planet. Once again the same indefatigable "amateur," . . . discovers the physical connexion between certain double stars, and so paves the way for the precise verification of the *universality* of the law of gravitation, and of the discovery

of dim bodies thousands of millions of miles beyond the reach of our solar system.

These "accidental" discoveries are gravely misunderstood by people not trained in scientific method. William Herschel was an *"amateur"* only in the literal French sense of the word: he *loved* astronomy so passionately as to conquer physical weakness to the extent of sitting at his telescope or polishing his mirrors all night after an ordinary day's work in his profession of music. He was a man of prodigious determination and unusual talent. "He studied science when he could" as George Forbes says in his *History of Astronomy*; but he studied to such good effect that his mind was prepared to make the best use of any "accidental" observation which he might happen to make. "Those that have eyes to see, let them see." . . .

So ends our study of the greatest sweep of human imagination, from the fall of an apple to the revolution of an invisible star! Every movement in the universe determined by the application of one simple law, so that "given the distribution of the masses and velocities of all the material particles of the universe at any one instant of time, it is *theoretically* possible to foretell their precise arrangement at any future time." "Theoretically," because the mathematical difficulties would far surpass the compass of any human mind however gifted. But even with that qualification this dictum of Laplace has raised philosophical doubts which seem to strike at the root of man's whole conception of the universe; for since every man's body consists of material particles, *their* motion, no less than that of the particles of inanimate matter, must inevitably follow a course already fully predictable to anyone possessed of sufficient knowledge and mathematical skill. And if this be so, then must all human efforts be in vain, all appearance of choice illusory; for the fabric of history which time weaves must be as completely determined as the melody which will emerge from a given gramophone record. Laplace and his contemporaries overlooked the fact that his deduction, like the gramophone record, bears within itself no mark to indicate why it should not be played backwards; but such a possibility makes nonsense of history.

The gradual realisation by the cultured world of this implication of the Newtonian revolution had, and is still having, the profoundest effect on the morals and ideals of Western civilisation. Thus the march of science leads us to positions whence we gain new views of spiritual realms as well as changing catastrophically our physical environment.

In the next chapter we shall briefly consider whether in the light of modern knowledge and criticism the Newtonian world-picture is quite as rigid in its outlines as it appeared to the thinkers of the eighteenth century.

Is the Law of Gravitation True?

In the summer of 1919 two topics produced a great deal of discussion in the more serious newspapers: one was the signing of the so-called "Peace Treaties," which left Europe on the brink of war for twenty years, and the other was the announcement that a handful of men of science had returned from a Pacific island with some photographs of a solar eclipse, from which conclusions had been drawn casting grave doubts on the absolute truth of the law of gravitation. Once again it seems the reader has been asked to spend an unconscionable amount of time and trouble being initiated into a scientific discovery which is not true. It is the purpose of this chapter to try to clear up this unsatisfactory situation.

At the present day most people fall into three groups in respect of their attitude towards science. The first group regard science as a messy business, whose study is undesirable for "nice" people; they are dying out fast, though unfortunately not quite fast enough. Of the other two groups, one accepts every statement of "Science," as our forefathers accepted "Holy Writ," as absolute truth, to doubt which is a special kind of blasphemy; while the other, bewildered by the constant rewriting of text books which are out of date almost before publication, regard "Science" as their forefathers did the "Evil One," as the spirit of confusion and deceit.

As we have already seen in connexion with the motions of the heavenly bodies only the study of its history can give us the clue to the unravelling of the apparent confusion in scientific knowledge. A method of interpretation which was perfectly true at the time of its enunciation has to be remodelled—often drastically—in the light of new knowledge. For knowledge is for ever *growing*—not merely accumulating like a heap of pebbles, but changing in outline and perspective like a living thing; the old writer knew what he was talking about when he wrote of the "tree of knowledge." The kind of knowledge we call science is a system of laws of nature. Laws are *concise* statements of how we believe nature *works*. To achieve this conciseness we have to make use of *general ideas*. The law of gravitation is of universal application simply because it purposely *excludes from consideration* all those properties of natural bodies except the universal property, that is, mass. The sun is so hot that the earth would be completely evaporated were it to approach it; the moon is so cold that its atmosphere is largely liquified and partly solidified. But by regarding these bodies as mere lumps of nondescript "stuff," each having a certain measurable resistance to change of motion (i.e. mass) and a certain orientation in space with regard to the other two, we find that their subsequent *motions* can be calculated by means of the law of gravitation. The temperature has nothing to do with it.

The law of gravitation therefore boils down to this: Give certain masses at certain known distances from each other, and whose relative velocities are known, we can calculate their subsequent motions.[3] Put in this way, the law of gravitation was absolutely true when it was enunciated, and is very nearly true to-day when the precision of measurement has greatly improved. Nor is it conceivable that it will ever be otherwise.

How can a law be "true" in 1687 and only "very nearly true" in 1948? It is not a question of a possible alteration in the way nature

---

[3] The mathematical difficulties become very grave for all possible cases of three bodies and, for four or more, almost beyond the power of man to handle.

"works"; whether this be so or not is beside the point. What we are here concerned with is the fact that we have "grown out of" the law of gravitation in two ways.

In the first place there was an irregularity in the motion of the planet Mercury which Newton's theory of the solar system failed to clear up [Figure 7-2]. This irregularity was observed only by virtue of an increase in the precision of instruments; latter-day astronomers "knew more" than Newton *could* have known. That was the first growing pain. But there was a more fundamental one.

If we refer to the "boiled down" gravitation law stated above, we shall observe that from this law we can calculate *motions* from *motions*. To do this we assume the truth of "laws of motion" connecting forces and masses; from which assumption it inevitably follows that the "force" of gravitation on any body *is always proportional to the mass of that body*. . . . Newton, in order to express his theory in words, had had to invent new general ideas, such as "mass," and adapt old ones such as "force" and "motion"; and that while the new ones were clear and adequate, the old ones passed into his use with all the confused associations of the ages. We have already seen that "force" has a very unscientific vagueness about it, but "motion" is in an even worse position.

After all, what do we mean by "motion"? We shall at once be told "change of position." But when, seated in a stationary train, we see a neighbouring train slowly begin to move,

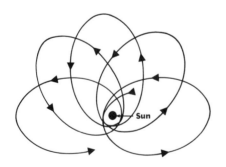

After Lincoln Barnett

Figure 7-2. The rotation of Mercury's elliptical orbit, greatly exaggerated here, was an irregularity not explained by Newton's theory of the universe. The ellipse actually advances 43 seconds of arc per century.

how do we know which has "really" moved? Only by checking our position with respect to the platform. This Newton fully realised: a body "really" moves when it has changed its position with reference to the "fixed" stars. He realised moreover that this matter of a *fixed frame of reference* to which all motions are to be referred is so essential a part of his whole mechanical system that he dealt with it in the famous Introductory Scholium to the First Book of the *Principia*. To avoid any possibility of misunderstanding it is necessary to quote the whole Scholium here:

Hitherto I have laid down the definitions of such words as are less known, and explained the sense in which I would have them to be understood in the following discourse. I do not define time, space, place and motion, as being well known to all. Only I must observe that the vulgar conceive those quantities under no other notions but from the relation they bear to sensible objects. And thence arise certain prejudices, for the removing of which it will be convenient to distinguish them into absolute and relative, true and apparent, mathematical and common.

(1) Absolute, true, and mathematical time, of itself, and from its own nature flows equably without regard to anything external, and by another name is called duration: relative, apparent, and common time, is some sensible and external (whether accurate or unequable) measure of duration by the means of motion, which is commonly used instead of true time: such as an hour, a day, a month, a year.

(2) Absolute space, in its own nature, without regard to anything external, remains similar and immovable. Relative space is some movable dimension or measure of the absolute spaces; which our senses determine by its position to bodies; and which is vulgarly taken for immovable space; such is the dimension of a subterranean, an aerial, or celestial space, determined by its position in respect of the earth. Absolute and relative space, are the same in figure and magnitude; but they do not remain always numerically the same. For if the earth, for instance, moves, a space of our air, which relatively and in respect of the earth remains always the same, will at one time be one part of the absolute space into which the air passes; at another time it will be another part of the same, and so, absolutely understood, it will be perpetually mutable.

Although a full discussion of this difficult matter would take us too long and too deep, yet since the answer to the question set at the head of this chapter depends on a clear understanding of the implications of Newton's assumptions, a brief exposition must be attempted.

The most important point to be noted is Newton's tacit departure from his own ideal of scientific enquiry: he *assumes* the existence of "absolute" time and space "without regard to anything external"—in other words, without any evidence from sensory experience, such as the "vulgar" base their ideas of time on. It is equally important to notice that Newton *had* to assume just this if he was to construct his mechanical System of the World. Finally we must not blame Newton for failing to haul himself up by his braces out of the climate of opinion into which he was born, and so to realise that "when once you tamper with your basic concepts," as Whitehead puts it, "philosophy is merely the marshalling of one main source of evidence and cannot be neglected." The liquidation of the Aristotelian physics involved the liquidation of the Aristotelian metaphysics of the immutable heavens; but Newton was not the man to do it. He was too great a man of science to attempt the impossible. The scientific advance has to proceed like that of an army—by jumps to tactical strong points, sometimes without the clearance of strategic minefields.

As soon as men of science realised that the "fixed" stars, so far from being "fixed" are moving relative to each other they began to look for another "platform." The most promising candidate was the "ether" whose undulations were supposed to constitute light. Unfortunately Michelson and Morley could find no evidence for the existence of the "ether" under conditions which should have rendered it easily observable. So the search had to start again. A few optimists are still searching, but most have given up the task as meaningless. Now if we can never be sure that a body has "really" moved, we can never be sure on which of two "moving" bodies a force is acting, for which reason it is hardly worth bothering about "force" at all. Following this train of thought, and taking as a fundamental property of nature the fact that weight and mass, though different properties are always equal in the same place, Professor Albert Einstein developed a system of dynamics (i.e. of the nature of motion) from which a new law of gravitation emerged. This law precisely accounted for the irregularity in the motion of Mercury which Newton's law had failed to do. But physicists rightly held that the "truth" of the law could not be finally established until, like Newton's and Galileo's laws, it had been shown that consequences *deduced* from it by pure reasoning were actually to be observed in nature. That is why the British eclipse expedition under the late Sir Arthur Eddington set out in 1919 to photograph some stars whose light was passing close to the eclipsed sun. The data they obtained were within the limits calculated on the basis of Einstein's theory.

Newton's law of gravitation is more "true" than Aristotle's for two reasons, because it enables us to control the movements of earthly bodies and to foretell the positions of heavenly bodies with a marvellous degree of exactitude, which the latter's was powerless to attempt, and also because Newton's concept of the relation between mass and acceleration was more precisely definable (and consequently "usable") than Aristotle's "natures."

Einstein's law of gravitation was derived from a consideration of the metrical properties of the "space" in which bodies move. As Professor Bridgman puts it, he was enquiring "into the meaning of simultaneity, and he was finding the meaning by analysing the physical operations employed in applying the concept in any concrete instance." Newton had taken such ideas as simultaneity for granted. With the knowledge of the critical importance of the nature of light signals for the timing of physical events, Einstein saw that such an assumption was too simple-minded. His "analysis of the physical operations" yielded first the Special Theory of Relativity, concerned with measurement between bodies moving at *different* but *uniform* velocities. Later came the General Theory which included the case of bodies moving with velocities mutually *accelerated*. The result of this was to render the concept of *force* redundant.

Einstein's law of gravitation is "truer" than Newton's for reasons similar to those which made Newton's "truer" than Aristotle's. It is more than likely that history will repeat itself and Einstein's beautiful theory be found after all to be not quite "true." But no theory which can reveal to us new secrets of the universe can be "false," though it may be "out of date." We do not regard the "Cutty Sark" as falsely contrived merely because it could not equal the performance of the "Queen Mary." The latter ship is in the main a development of the older; but the "steam wind" which presses upon her turbine plates by being more controllable, is more economically applied. The "Cutty Sark" was the wonder of her age; the "Queen Mary" can do all that she did and more; but thousands of people still derive pleasure in using the graceful methods of the old "sea bird" rather than the more powerful ones of the modern machine. Similarly for all our everyday uses, whether for the design of engines or for the writing of the "time table" of the planets, we use and shall long continue to use Newton's law, which is sufficiently exact to meet all purposes except those in which we are probing more deeply into the heart of the universe.

One question remains on which we may close this rather difficult discussion. If Einstein's dynamics is "truer" than Newton's, why do we waste so much time in teaching the latter in our schools? As well ask, why waste a child's time with instruction in the use of the foot rule, when the vernier calipers give us a much more accurate estimate of length? Because over-refinement tends merely to obscure the simple ideas of length and number which every human being must acquire. Einstein's dynamics are Newtonian dynamics subjected to intense refinement. One result of this refinement has been the removal of confusion in the general ideas which Newton, living in an age when Aristotelian views were still accepted by many learned men, had not entirely escaped. The author is one of those who would like to see our school text books subjected to the same refining influence; for there is much in time which reflects Newton's failure in this respect. It will be the chief service of the modern critical study of the history of science to present scientific knowledge as a growing tree which depends for its vigour as much on its roots in the past as upon its fresh young branches; but from which for true health all dead and rotten wood needs to be drastically pruned. In other words it will teach us that new theories do not replace old ones because they are more *true*; but grow out of and embrace the older because they are more adequate.

EINSTEIN'S THEORY OF RELATIVITY

THE UNIVERSE AND DR. EINSTEIN*
by Lincoln Barnett (1957)

In his great treatise *On Human Understanding* philosopher John Locke wrote three hundred years ago: "A company of chessmen standing on the same squares of the chess-

* From Lincoln Barnett, *The Universe and Dr. Einstein*, 2d ed., William Sloane Associates, New York, 1957. Copyright 1948 by Harper & Row, Publishers, New York: copyright 1948 by Lincoln Barnett; copyright 1957 by Lincoln Barnett. Reprinted by permission of William Sloane Associates.

board where we left them, we say, are all in the same place or unmoved: though perhaps the chessboard has been in the meantime carried out of one room into another. . . . The chessboard, we also say, is in the same place if it remain in the same part of the cabin, though perhaps the ship which it is in sails all the while; and the ship is said to be in the same place supposing it kept the same distance with the neighboring land, though perhaps the earth has turned around; and so chessmen and board and ship have every one changed place in respect to remoter bodies."

Embodied in this little picture of the moving but unmoved chessmen is one principle of relativity—relativity of position. But this suggests another idea—relativity of motion. Anyone who has ever ridden on a railroad train knows how rapidly another train flashes by when it is traveling in the opposite direction, and conversely how it may look almost motionless when it is moving in the same direction. A variation of this effect can be very deceptive in an enclosed station like Grand Central Terminal in New York. Once in a while a train gets under way so gently that passengers feel no recoil whatever. Then if they happen to look out the window and see another train slide past on the next track, they have no way of knowing which train is in motion and which is at rest; nor can they tell how fast either one is moving or in what direction. The only way they can judge their situation is by looking out the other side of the car for some fixed body of reference like the station platform or a signal light. Sir Isaac Newton was aware of these tricks of motion, only he thought in terms of ships. He knew that on a calm day at sea a sailor can shave himself or drink soup as comfortably as when his ship is lying motionless in harbor. The water in his basin, the soup in his bowl, will remain unruffled whether the ship is making five knots, 15 knots, or 25 knots. So unless he peers out at the sea it will be impossible for him to know how fast his ship is moving or indeed if it is moving at all. Of course if the sea should get rough or the ship change course abruptly, then he will sense his state of motion. But granted the idealized conditions of a glass-calm sea and a silent ship, nothing that happens below decks—no amount of observation or mechanical experiment performed *inside* the ship—will disclose its velocity through the sea. The physical principle suggested by these considerations was formulated by Newton in 1687. "The

motions of bodies included in a given space," he wrote, "are the same among themselves, whether that space is at rest or moves uniformly forward in a straight line." This is known as the Newtonian or Galilean Relativity Principle. It can also be phrased in more general terms: mechanical laws which are valid in one place are equally valid in any other place which moves uniformly relative to the first.*

The philosophical importance of this principle lies in what it says about the universe. Since the aim of science is to explain the world we live in, as a whole and in all its parts, it is essential to the scientist that he have confidence in the harmony of nature. He must believe that physical laws revealed to him on earth are in truth universal laws. . . .

In the next two centuries it appeared probable that Newton's view would prevail. For with the development of the wave theory of light scientists found it necessary to endow empty space with certain mechanical properties—to assume, indeed, that space was some kind of substance. Even before Newton's time the French philosopher, Descartes, had argued that the mere separation of bodies by distance proved the existence of a medium between them. And to eighteenth and nineteenth century physicists it was obvious that if light consisted of waves, there must be some medium to support them, just as water propagates the waves of the sea and air transmits the vibrations we call sound. Hence when experiments showed that light can travel in a vacuum, scientists evolved a hypothetical substance called "ether" which they decided must pervade all space and matter. Later on Faraday propounded another kind of ether as the carrier of electric and magnetic forces. When Maxwell finally identified light as an electromagnetic disturbance the case for the ether seemed assured.

A universe permeated with an invisible medium in which the stars wandered and through which light traveled like vibrations in a bowl of jelly was the end product of Newtonian physics. It provided a mechanical model for all known phenomena of nature,

* See p. 124. Ed.

and it provided the fixed frame of reference, the absolute and immovable space, which Newton's cosmology required. Yet the ether presented certain problems, not the least of which was that its actual existence had never been proved. To discover once and for all whether there really was any such thing as ether, two American physicists, A. A. Michelson and E. W. Morley, performed a classic experiment in Cleveland in the year 1881.

The principle underlying their experiment was quite simple. They reasoned that if all space is simply a motionless sea of ether, then the earth's motion through the ether should be detectable and measurable in the same way that sailors measure the velocity of a ship through the sea. As Newton pointed out, it is impossible to detect the movement of a ship through calm waters by any mechanical experiment performed *inside* the ship. Sailors ascertain a ship's speed by throwing a log overboard and watching the unreeling of the knots on the log line. Hence to detect the earth's motion through the ether sea, Michelson and Morley threw a "log" overboard, and the log was a beam of light. For if light really is propagated through the ether, then its velocity should be affected by the ether stream arising from the earth's movement. Specifically a light ray projected in the direction of the earth's movement should be slightly retarded by the ether flow, just as a swimmer is retarded by a current when going upstream. The difference would be slight, for the velocity of light (which was accurately determined in 1849) is 186,284 miles a second, while the velocity of the earth in its orbit around the sun is only 20 miles a second. Hence a light ray sent *against* the ether stream should travel at the rate of 186,264 miles a second, while one sent *with* the ether stream should be clocked at 186,304 miles a second. With these ideas in mind Michelson and Morley constructed an instrument of such great delicacy that it could detect a variation of even a fraction of a mile per second in the enormous velocity of light (Figure 7-3). This instrument, which they called an "interferometer" consisted of a group of mirrors so arranged that a light beam could be split in two and

Figure 7-3. The Michelson-Morley interferometer was an arrangement of mirrors designed so that a beam transmitted from the light source was divided and sent in two directions at the same time. This was done by a mirror, A, whose face was only thinly silvered, so that part of the beam could pass through to the mirror C, the remainder being reflected at right angles toward mirror B. Mirrors B and C then reflected the rays back to mirror A where, reunited, they proceeded to the observing telescope T. Since the beam ACT had to pass through the thickness of glass behind the reflecting face of mirror A three times, a clear glass plate of equal thickness was placed between A and B to intercept beam ABT and compensate for the resulting retardation. The whole apparatus was rotated in different directions so that the beams ABT and ACT could be sent with, against, and at right angles to the postulated ether stream. At first it might appear that a trip "downstream," for example, from B to A, should compensate in time for an "upstream" trip from A to B. But this is not so. To row a boat one mile upstream and another mile downstream takes longer than rowing two miles in still water or across current, even with allowance for drift. Had there been any acceleration or retardation of either beam by the ether stream, the optical apparatus at T would have detected it.

flashed in different directions at the same time. The whole experiment was planned and executed with such painstaking precision that the result could not be doubted. And the result was simply this: there was no difference whatsoever in the velocity of the light beams regardless of their direction.

The Michelson-Morley experiment confronted scientists with an embarrassing alternative. On the one hand they could scrap the ether theory which had explained so many things about electricity, magnetism, and light. Or if they insisted on retaining the ether they had to abandon the still more venerable Copernican theory that the earth is in motion. To many physicists it seemed almost easier to believe that the earth stood still than that waves—light waves, electromagnetic waves— could exist without a medium to sustain them.

It was a serious dilemma and one that split scientific thought for a quarter century. Many new hypotheses were advanced and rejected. The experiment was tried again by Morley and by others, with the same conclusion; the apparent velocity of the earth through the ether was zero.

The Solution

Among those who pondered the enigma of the Michelson-Morley experiment was a young patent office examiner in Berne, named Albert Einstein. In 1905, when he was just twenty-six years old, he published a short paper suggesting an answer to the riddle in terms that opened up a new world of physical thought. He began by rejecting the ether theory and with it the whole idea of space as a fixed system or framework, absolutely at rest, within which it is possible to distinguish absolute from relative motion. The one indisputable fact established by the Michelson-Morley experiment was that the velocity of light is unaffected by the motion of the earth. Einstein seized on this as a revelation of universal law. If the velocity of light is constant regardless of the earth's motion, he reasoned, it must be constant regardless of the motion of any sun, moon, star, meteor, or other system moving anywhere in the universe. From this he drew a broader generalization, and asserted that the laws of nature are the same for all uniformly moving systems. This simple statement is the essence of Einstein's Special Theory of Relativity. It incorporates the Galilean Relativity Principle which stated that mechanical laws are the same for all uniformly moving systems. But its phrasing is more comprehensive; for Einstein was thinking not only of mechanical laws but of the laws governing light and other electromagnetic phenomena. So he lumped them together in one fundamental postulate: all the phenomena of nature, all the laws of nature, are the same for all systems that move uniformly relative to one another.

On the surface there is nothing very startling in this declaration. It simply reiterates the scientist's faith in the universal harmony of natural law. It also advises the scientist to stop looking for any absolute, stationary frame of reference in the universe. The universe is a restless place: stars, nebulae, galaxies, and all the vast gravitational systems of outer space are incessantly in motion. But their movements can be described only with respect to each other, for in space there are no directions and no boundaries. It is futile moreover for the scientist to try to discover the "true" velocity of any system by using light as a measuring rod, for the velocity of light is constant throughout the universe and is unaffected either by the motion of its source or the motion of the receiver. Nature offers no absolute standards of comparison; and space is—as another great German mathematician, Leibnitz, clearly saw two centuries before Einstein—simply "the order or relation of things among themselves." Without things occupying it, it is nothing.

Along with absolute space, Einstein discarded the concept of absolute time—of a steady, unvarying, inexorable universal time flow, streaming from the infinite past to the infinite future. Much of the obscurity that has surrounded the Theory of Relativity stems from man's reluctance to recognize that sense of time, like sense of color, is a form of perception. Just as there is no such thing as color without an eye to discern it, so an instant or an hour or a day is nothing without an event to mark it. And just as space is simply a possible order of material objects, so time is simply a possible order of events. The subjectivity of time is best explained in Einstein's own words. "The experiences of an individual," he says, "appear to us arranged in a series of events; in this series the single events which we remember appear to be ordered according to the criterion of 'earlier' and 'later.' There exists, therefore, for the individual, an I-time, or subjective time. This in itself is not measurable. I can, indeed, associate numbers with the events, in such a way that a greater number is associated with the later event than with an earlier one. This association I can define by means of a clock by comparing the order of events furnished by the clock with the order of the given series of events. We understand by a clock something which provides a series of events which can be counted."

By referring our own experiences to a clock (or a calendar) we make time an objective concept. Yet the time intervals provided by a clock or a calendar are by no means absolute quantities imposed on the entire universe by divine edict. All the clocks ever used by man have been geared to our solar system. What we call an hour is actually a measurement in space—an arc of 15 degrees in the apparent daily rotation of the celestial sphere. And what we call a year is simply a measure of the earth's progress in its orbit around the sun. An inhabitant of Mercury, however, would have very different notions of time. For Mercury makes its trip around the sun in 88 of our days, and in that same period rotates just once on its axis. So on Mercury a year and a day amount to the same thing. But it is when science ranges beyond the neighborhood of the sun that all our terrestrial ideas of time become meaningless. For Relativity tells us there is no such thing as a fixed interval of time independent of the system to which it is referred. There is indeed no such thing as simultaneity, there is no such thing as "now," independent of a system of reference. For example a man in New York may telephone a friend in London, and although it is 7:00 P.M. in New York and midnight in London, we may say that they are talking "at the same time." But that is because they are both residents of the same planet, and their clocks are geared to the same astronomical system. A more complicated situation arises if we try to ascertain, for example, what is happening on the star Arcturus "right now." Arcturus is 38 light years away. A light year is the distance light travels in one year, or roughly six trillion miles. If we should try to communicate with Arcturus by radio "right now" it would take 38 years for our message to reach its destination and another 38 years for us to receive a reply.[1] And when we look at Arcturus and say that we see it "now," in 1957, we are actually seeing a ghost—an image projected on our optic nerves by light rays that left their source in 1919. Whether Arcturus even exists "now" nature forbids us to know until 1995.

Despite such reflections it is difficult for earthbound man to accept the idea that *this very instant* which he calls "now" cannot apply to the universe as a whole. Yet in the Special Theory of Relativity Einstein proves by an unanswerable sequence of example and deduction that it is nonsense to think of events taking place simultaneously in unrelated systems.

[1] Radio waves travel at the same speed as light waves.

RELATIVITY, THE SPECIAL THEORY*
by Albert Einstein (1916)

In your schooldays most of you who read this book made acquaintance with the noble building of Euclid's geometry, and you remember—perhaps with more respect than love—the magnificent structure, on the lofty staircase of which you were chased about for uncounted hours by conscientious teachers. By reason of your past experience, you would certainly regard everyone with disdain who should pronounce even the most out-of-the-

* From Albert Einstein, *Relativity: The Special and General Theory*, trans. by Robert W. Lawson, 1931. Reprinted by permission of Peter Smith, Publishers, Gloucester, Mass., and Methuen & Co., Ltd., London.

way proposition of this science to be untrue. But perhaps this feeling of proud certainty would leave you immediately if someone were to ask you: "What, then, do you mean by the assertion that these propositions are true?" Let us proceed to give this question a little consideration.

Geometry sets out from certain conceptions such as "plane," "point," and "straight line," with which we are able to associate more or less definite ideas, and from certain simple propositions (axioms) which, in virtue of these ideas, we are inclined to accept as "true." Then, on the basis of a logical process, the justification of which we feel ourselves compelled to admit, all remaining propositions are shown to follow from these axioms, i.e., they are proven.

A proposition is then correct ("true") when it has been derived in the recognized manner from the axioms. The question of the "truth" of the individual geometrical propositions is thus reduced to one of the "truth" of the axioms. Now it has long been known that the last question is not only unanswerable by the methods of geometry, but that it is in itself entirely without meaning. We cannot ask whether it is true that only one straight line goes through two points. We can only say that Euclidean geometry deals with things called "straight lines," to each of which is ascribed the property of being uniquely determined by two points situated on it. The concept "true" does not tally with the assertions of pure geometry, because by the word "true" we are eventually in the habit of designating always the correspondence with a "real" object; geometry, however, is not concerned with the relation of the ideas involved in it to objects of experience, but only with the logical connection of these ideas among themselves.

Every description of the scene of an event or of the position of an object in space is based on the specification of the point on a rigid body (body of reference) with which that event or object coincides. This applies not only to scientific description, but also to everyday life. If I analyze the place specification "Times Square, New York,"[1] I arrive at the following result. The earth is the rigid body to which the specification of place refers; "Times Square, New York," is a well-defined point, to which a name has been assigned, and with which the event coincides in space.

This primitive method of place specification deals only with places on the surface of rigid bodies, and is dependent on the existence of points on this surface which are distinguishable from each other. But we can free ourselves from both of these limitations without altering the nature of our specification of position. If, for instance, a cloud is hovering over Times Square, then we can determine its position relative to the surface of the earth by erecting a pole perpendicularly on the Square, so that it reaches the cloud. The length of the pole measured with the standard measuring rod, combined with the specification of the position of the foot of the pole, supplies us with a complete place specification. On the basis of this illustration, we are able to see the manner in which a refinement of the conception of position has been developed.

We thus obtain the following result: Every description of events in space involves the use of a rigid body to which such events have to be referred. The resulting relationship takes for granted that the laws of Euclidean geometry hold for "distances," the "distance" being represented physically by means of the convention of two marks on a rigid body.

"The purpose of mechanics is to describe how bodies change their position in space with time." I should load my conscience with grave sins against the sacred spirit of lucidity were I to formulate the aims of mechanics in this way, without serious reflection and detailed explanations. Let us proceed to disclose these sins.

It is not clear what is to be understood here by "position" and "space." I stand at the window of a railway carriage which is traveling uniformly, and drop a stone on the embankment, without throwing it. Then, disregarding the influence of the air resistance, I see the stone descend in a straight line. A pedestrian who observes the misdeed from the footpath notices that the stone falls to earth in a parabolic curve. I now ask: Do the "positions" traversed by the stone lie "in reality" on a straight line or on a parabola? Moreover, what is meant here by motion "in space"? From the considerations of the previous section the answer is self-evident. In the first place, we entirely shun the vague word "space," of which, we must honestly acknowledge, we cannot form the slightest conception, and we replace it by "motion relative to a practically rigid body of reference." The positions relative to the body of reference (railway carriage or embankment) have already been defined in detail in the preceding section. If instead of "body of reference" we insert "system of co-ordinates," which is a useful idea for mathematical description, we are in a position to say: The stone traverses a straight line relative to a system of co-ordinates rigidly attached to the carriage, but relative to a system of co-ordinates rigidly attached to the ground (embankment) it describes a parabola. With the aid of this example it is clearly seen that there is no such thing as an independently existing trajectory (literally, "path-curve"[2]), but only a trajectory relative to a particular body of reference.

In order to have a *complete* description of the motion we must specify how the body alters its position *with time;* i.e., for every point on the trajectory it must be stated at what time the body is situated there. These data must be supplemented by such a definition of time that, in virtue of this definition, these time values can be regarded essentially as magnitudes (results of measurements) capable of observation. If we take our stand on the ground of classical mechanics, we can satisfy this requirement for our illustration in the following manner. We imagine two clocks of identical construction; the man at the railway carriage window is holding one of them, and the man on the footpath the other. Each of the observers determines the position on his own reference body occupied by the stone at each tick of the clock he is holding in his hand. In this connection we have not taken account of the inaccuracy involved by the finiteness of the velocity of propagation of light. With this and with a second difficulty prevailing here we shall have to deal in detail later.

As long as one was convinced that all natural phenomena were capable of representation with the help of classical mechanics, there was no need to doubt the validity of this principle of relativity. But in view of the more recent development of electrodynamics and optics, it became more and more evident

that classical mechanics affords an insufficient foundation for the physical description of all natural phenomena. At this juncture the question of the validity of the principle of relativity became ripe for discussion, and it did not appear impossible that the answer to this question might be in the negative.

Now in virtue of its motion in an orbit round the sun, our earth is comparable with a railway carriage traveling with a velocity of about 30 kilometers per second. If the principle of relativity were not valid we should therefore expect that the direction of motion of the earth at any moment would enter into the laws of nature, and also that physical systems in their behavior would be dependent on the orientation in space with respect to the earth.

However, the most careful observations have never revealed such anisotropic properties in terrestrial physical space, i.e., a physical non-equivalence of different directions.* This is very powerful argument in favor of the principle of relativity.

There is hardly a simpler law in physics than that according to which light is propagated in empty space. Every child at school knows, or believes he knows, that this propagation takes place in straight lines with a velocity $c = 300,000$ km./sec. At all events we know with great exactness that this velocity is the same for all colors, because if this were not the case, the minimum of emission would not be observed simultaneously for different colors during the eclipse of a fixed star by its dark neighbor. By means of similar considerations based on observations of double stars, the Dutch astronomer De Sitter was also able to show that the velocity of propagation of light cannot depend on the velocity of motion of the body emitting the light. The assumption that this velocity of propagation is dependent on the direction "in space" is in itself improbable.

At this juncture the theory of relativity entered the arena. As a result of an analysis of the physical conceptions of time and space, it became evident that *in reality there is not*

[2] That is, a curve along which the body moves.

* The reference here is to the negative results of the Michelson-Morley experiment described on p. 230. Ed.

the least incompatibility between the principle of relativity and the law of propagation of light, and that by systematically holding fast to both these laws a logically rigid theory could be arrived at. This theory has been called the *special theory of relativity* to distinguish it from the extended theory, with which we shall deal later.

Lightning has struck the rails on our railway embankment at two places A and B far distant from each other. I make the additional assertion that these two lightning flashes occurred simultaneously. If I ask you whether there is sense in this statement, you will answer my question with a decided "Yes." But if I now approach you with the request to explain to me the sense of the statement more precisely, you find after some consideration that the answer to this question is not so easy as it appears at first sight.

Are two events (e.g., the two strokes of lightning A and B) which are simultaneous with reference to the *railway embankment* also simultaneous *relatively to the train?* We shall show directly that the answer must be in the negative (Figure 7-4).

When we say that the lightning strokes A and B are simultaneous with respect to the embankment, we mean: the rays of light emitted at the places A and B where the lightning occurs, meet each other at the mid-point M of the length A → B of the embankment. But the events A and B also correspond to positions A and B on the train. Let M′ be the mid-point of the distance A → B on the traveling train. Just when the flashes[3] of lightning occur, this point M′ naturally coincides with the point M, but it moves toward the right, with the velocity *v* of the train. If an observer sitting in the position M′ in the train did not

[3] As judged from the embankment.

possess this velocity, then he would remain permanently at M, and the light rays emitted by the flashes of lightning A and B would reach him simultaneously, i.e., they would meet just where he is situated. Now in reality (considered with reference to the railway embankment) he is hastening toward the beam of light coming from B, whilst he is riding on ahead of the beam of light coming from A. Hence the observer will see the beam of light emitted from B earlier than he will see that emitted from A. Observers who take the railway train as their reference body must therefore come to the conclusion that the lightning flash B took place earlier than the lightning flash A. We thus arrive at the important result:

Events which are simultaneous with reference to the embankment are not simultaneous with respect to the train, and vice versa (relativity of simultaneity).

Our train of thought in the foregoing pages can be epitomized in the following manner. Experience has led to the conviction that, on the one hand, the principle of relativity holds true, and that on the other hand the velocity of transmission of light *in vacuo* has to be considered equal to a constant *c*. By uniting these two postulates we obtained the law of transformation for the rectangular co-ordinates *x, y, z,* and the time *t* of the events which constitute the processes of nature. In this connection we did not obtain the Galilei transformation, but, differing from classical mechanics, the *Lorentz transformation.* General laws of nature are covariant with respect to Lorentz transformations.

It is clear from our previous considerations that the (special) theory of relativity has grown out of electrodynamics and optics. In these fields it has not appreciably altered the predictions of theory, but it has considerably

Figure 7-4

simplified the theoretical structure, i.e., the derivation of laws, and—what is incomparably more important—it has considerably reduced the number of independent hypotheses forming the basis of theory. The special theory of relativity has rendered the Maxwell-Lorentz theory so plausible that the latter would have been generally accepted by physicists even if experiment had decided less unequivocally in its favor.

Classical mechanics required to be modified before it could come into line with the demands of the special theory of relativity. For the main part, however, this modification affects only the laws for rapid motions, in which the velocities of matter v are not very small as compared with the velocity of light. We have experience of such rapid motions only in the case of electrons and ions; for other motions the variations from the laws of classical mechanics are too small to make themselves evident in practice. We shall not consider the motion of stars until we come to speak of the general theory of relativity.

Let me add a final remark of a fundamental nature. The success of the Faraday-Maxwell interpretation of electromagnetic action at a distance resulted in physicists becoming convinced that there are no such things as instantaneous actions at a distance (not involving an intermediary medium) of the type of Newton's law of gravitation. According to the theory of relativity, action at a distance with the velocity of light always takes the place of instantaneous action at a distance or of action at a distance with an infinite velocity of transmission.

THE UNIVERSE AND DR. EINSTEIN (Continued)*
by Lincoln Barnett (1957)

Einstein found what he wanted in a series of equations developed by the great Dutch physicist, H. A. Lorentz, in connection with a specific theory of his own. Although its original application is of interest now chiefly to scientific historians, the Lorentz transformation lives on as part of the mathematical framework of Relativity. To understand what it says, however, it is first necessary to perceive the flaws in the old principle of the addition of velocities. . . .

The paradox of the lightning flashes dramatizes one of the subtlest and most difficult concepts in Einstein's philosophy: the relativity of simultaneity. It shows that man cannot assume that his subjective sense of "now" applies to all parts of the universe. For, Einstein points out, "every reference body (or coordinate system) has its own particular time; unless we are told the reference body to which the statement of time refers, there is no meaning in a statement of the time of an

* Barnett, *op. cit.*

event." The fallacy in the old principle of the addition of velocities lies therefore in its tacit assumption that the duration of an event is independent of the state of motion of the system of reference. In the case of the man pacing the deck of a ship, for example, it was assumed that if he walked three miles in one hour as timed by a clock on the moving ship, his rate would be just the same timed by a stationary clock anchored somehow in the sea. It was further assumed that the distance he traversed in one hour would have the same value whether it was measured relative to the deck of the ship (the moving system) or relative to the sea (the stationary system). This constitutes a second fallacy in the addition of velocities—for distance, like time, is a relative concept, and there is no such thing as a space interval independent of the state of motion of the system of reference.

Einstein asserted, therefore, that the scientist who wishes to describe the phenomena of nature in terms that are consistent for all systems throughout the universe must regard measurements of time and distance as variable quantities. The equations comprising the Lorentz transformation do just that. They preserve the velocity of light as a universal constant, but modify all measurements of time and distance according to the velocity of each system of reference.[1]

So although Lorentz had originally developed his equations to meet a specific problem, Einstein made them the basis of a tremendous generalization and to the edifice of Relativity another axiom: the laws of nature preserve their uniformity in all systems when related by the Lorentz transformation. Stated thus, in the abstract language of mathematics the significance of this axiom can scarcely be apparent to the layman. But in physics an equation is never a pure abstraction; it is simply a kind of shorthand expression which the scientist finds convenient to describe the phenomena of nature. Sometimes it is also a Rosetta Stone in which the theoretical physicist can decipher secret realms of knowledge. And so by deduction from the message written in the equations of the Lorentz transformation, Einstein discovered a number of new

and extraordinary truths about the physical universe.

These truths can be described in very concrete terms. For once he had evolved the philosophical and mathematical bases of Relativity, Einstein had to bring them into the laboratory, where abstractions like time and space are harnessed by means of clocks and measuring rods. And so translating his basic ideas about time and space into the language of the laboratory, he pointed out some hitherto unsuspected properties of clocks and rods. For example: a clock attached to any moving system runs at a different rhythm from a stationary clock; and a measuring rod attached to any moving system changes its length according to the velocity of the system. Specifically the clock slows down as its velocity increases, and the measuring rod shrinks in the direction of its motion. These peculiar changes have nothing to do with the construction of the clock or the composition of the rod. The clock can be a pendulum clock, a spring clock, or an hour glass. The measuring rod can be a wooden ruler, a metal yardstick, or a ten-mile cable. The slowing of the clock and the contraction of the rod are not mechanical phenomena; an observer riding along with the clock and the measuring rod would not notice these changes. But a stationary observer, i.e., stationary relative to the moving system, would find that the moving clock has slowed down with respect to his stationary clock, and that the moving rod has contracted with respect to his stationary units of measurement.

This singular behavior of moving clocks and yardsticks accounts for the constant velocity of light. It explains why all observers in all systems everywhere, regardless of their state of motion, will always find that light strikes their instruments and departs from their instruments at precisely the same velocity. For as their own velocity approaches that of light, their clocks slow down, their yardsticks contract, and all their measurements are reduced to the values obtained by a relatively stationary observer. The laws governing these contractions are defined by the Lorentz transformation and they are very simple: the

[1] The Lorentz transformation relates distances and times observed on moving systems with those observed on systems relatively at rest. Suppose, for example, that a system, or reference body, is moving in a certain direction, then *according to the old principle of the addition of velocities*, a distance or length x', measured with respect to the moving system along the direction of motion, is related to length x, measured with respect to a relatively stationary system, by the equation $x' = x \pm vt$, where v is the velocity of the moving system and t is the time. Dimensions y' and z', measured with respect to the moving system at right angles to x' and at right angles to each other (i.e., height and breadth), are related to dimensions y and z on the relatively stationary system by $y' = y$, and $z' = z$. And finally a time interval t', clocked with respect to the moving system, is related to time interval t, clocked with respect to the relatively stationary system, by $t' = t$. In other words, distances and times are not affected, *in classical physics*, by the velocity of the system in question. *But it is this presupposition which leads to the paradox of the lightning flashes.* The Lorentz transformation reduces the distances and times observed on moving systems to the conditions of the stationary observer, keeping the velocity of light c a constant for all observers. Here are the equations of the Lorentz transformation which have supplanted the older and evidently inadequate relationships cited above:

$$x' = \frac{x - vt}{\sqrt{1 - (v^2/c^2)}}$$
$$y' = y$$
$$z' = z$$
$$t' = \frac{t - (v/c^2)x}{\sqrt{1 - (v^2/c^2)}}$$

It will be noted that, as in the old transformation law, dimensions y' and z' are unaffected by motion. It will also be seen that if the velocity of the moving system v is small relative to the velocity of light c, then the equations of the Lorentz transformation reduce themselves to the relations of the old principle of the addition of velocities. But as the magnitude of v approaches that of c, then the values of x' and t' are radically changed.

greater the speed, the greater the contraction. A yardstick moving with 90 per cent the velocity of light would shrink to about half its length; thereafter the rate of contraction becomes more rapid; and if the stick should attain the velocity of light, it would shrink away to nothing at all. Similarly a clock traveling with the velocity of light would stop completely. From this it follows that nothing can ever move faster than light, no matter what forces are applied. Thus Relativity reveals another fundamental law of nature: the velocity of light is the top limiting velocity in the universe.

At first meeting these facts are difficult to digest but that is simply because classical physics assumed, unjustifiably, that an object preserves the same dimensions whether it is in motion or at rest and that a clock keeps the same rhythm in motion and at rest. Common sense dictates that this must be so. But as Einstein has pointed out, common sense is actually nothing more than a deposit of prejudices laid down in the mind prior to the age of eighteen. Every new idea one encounters in later years must combat this accretion of "self-evident" concepts. And it is because of Einstein's unwillingness ever to accept any unproven principle as self-evident that he was able to penetrate closer to the underlying realities of nature than any scientist before him. Why, he asked, is it any more strange to assume that moving clocks slow down and moving rods contract, than to assume that they don't? The reason classical physics took the latter view for granted is that man, in his everyday experience, never encounters velocities great enough to make these changes manifest. In an automobile, an airplane, even in a V-2 rocket, the slowing down of a watch is immeasurable. It is only when velocities approximate that of light that relativistic effects can be detected. The equations of the Lorentz transformation show very plainly that at ordinary speeds the modification of time and space intervals amounts practically to zero. Relativity does not therefore contradict classical physics. It simply regards the old concepts as limiting cases that apply solely to the familiar experiences of man.

Einstein thus surmounts the barrier reared by man's impulse to define reality solely as he perceives it through the screen of his sense. . . . Relativity shows that we cannot foretell the phenomena accompanying great velocities from the sluggish behavior of objects visible to man's indolent eye. Nor may we assume that the laws of Relativity deal with exceptional occurrences; on the contrary they provide a comprehensive picture of an incredibly complex universe in which the simple mechanical events of our earthly experience are the exceptions. The present-day scientist, coping with the tremendous velocities that prevail in the fast universe of the atom or with the immensities of sidereal space and time, finds the old Newtonian laws inadequate. But Relativity provides him in every instance with a complete and accurate description of nature.

Whenever Einstein's postulates have been put to test, their validity has been amply confirmed. Remarkable proof of the relativistic retardation of time intervals came out of an experiment performed by H. E. Ives of the Bell Telephone Laboratories in 1936. A radiating atom may be regarded as a kind of clock in that it emits light of a definite frequency and wave-length which can be measured with great precision by means of a spectroscope. Ives compared the light emitted by hydrogen atoms moving at high velocities with that emitted by hydrogen atoms at rest, and found that the frequency of vibration of the moving atoms was reduced in exact accordance with the predictions of Einstein's equations. Someday science may devise a far more interesting test of the same principle. Since any periodic motion serves to measure time, the human heart, Einstein has pointed out, is also a kind of clock. Hence, according to Relativity, the heartbeat of a person traveling with a velocity close to that of light would be relatively slowed, along with his respiration and all other physiological processes. He would not notice this retardation because his watch would slow down in the same degree. But judged by a stationary timekeeper he would "grow old" less rapidly.

In order to describe the mechanics of the physical universe, three quantities are required: time, distance, and mass. Since time and distance are relative quantities one might guess that the mass of a body also varies with its state of motion. And indeed the most important practical results of Relativity have arisen from this principle—the relativity of mass.

In its popular sense, "mass" is just another word for "weight." But as used by the physicist, it denotes a rather different and more fundamental property of matter: namely, resistance to a change of motion. A greater force is necessary to move or stop a freight car than a velocipede; the freight car resists a change in its motion more stubbornly than the velocipede because it has greater mass. In classical physics the mass of any body is a fixed and unchanging property. Thus the mass of a freight car should remain the same whether it is at rest on a siding, rolling across country at 60 miles an hour, or hurtling through outer space at 60,000 miles a second. But Relativity asserts that the mass of a moving body is by no means constant, but increases with its velocity relative to an observer. The old physics failed to discover this fact simply because man's senses and instruments are too crude to note the infinitesimal increases of mass produced by the feeble accelerations of ordinary experience. They become perceptible only when bodies attain velocities relatively close to that of light. (This phenomenon, incidentally, does not conflict with the relativistic contraction of length.* One is tempted to ask: how can an object become smaller and at the same time get heavier? The contraction, it should be noted, is only in the direction of motion; width and breadth are unaffected. Moreover mass is not merely "heaviness" but resistance to a change in motion.)

Einstein's equation giving the increase of mass with velocity is similar in form to the other equations of Relativity but vastly more important in its consequences:

$$m = \frac{m_0}{\sqrt{1 - v^2/c^2}}$$

Here m stands for the mass of a body moving with velocity v, m_0 for its mass when at rest,

* See "FitzGerald-Lorentz contraction," in Glossary. Ed.

and c for the velocity of light. Anyone who has ever studied elementary algebra can readily see that if v is small, as are all the velocities of ordinary experience, then the difference between m_0 and m is practically zero. But when v approaches the value of c then the increase of mass becomes very great, reaching infinity when the velocity of the moving body reaches the velocity of light. Since a body of infinite mass would offer infinite resistance to motion the conclusion is once again reached that no material body can travel with the speed of light.

Of all aspects of Relativity the principle of increase of mass has been most often verified and most fruitfully applied by experimental physicists. Electrons moving in powerful electrical fields and beta particles ejected from the nuclei of radioactive substances attain velocities ranging up to 99 per cent that of light. For atomic physicists concerned with these great speeds, the increase of mass predicted by Relativity is no arguable theory but an empirical fact their calculations cannot ignore. In fact the mechanics of the proton-synchroton and other new super-energy machines must be designed to allow for the increasing mass of particles as their speed approaches the velocity of light, in order to make them operate at all.

By further deduction from his principle of Relativity of mass, Einstein arrived at a conclusion of incalculable importance to the world. His train of reasoning ran somewhat as follows: since the mass of a moving body increases as its motion increases, and since motion is a form of energy (kinetic energy), then the increased mass of a moving body comes from its increased energy. In short, energy has mass! By a few comparatively simple mathematical steps, Einstein found the value of the equivalent mass m in any unit of energy E and expressed it by the equation $m = E/c^2$. Given this relation a high school freshman can take the remaining algebraic step necessary to write the most important and certainly the most famous equation in history: $E = mc^2$.

The part played by this equation in the development of the atomic bomb is familiar to most newspaper readers. It states in the shorthand of physics that the energy contained in any particle of matter is equal to the mass of that body multiplied by the square of the velocity of light, the proper units being chosen in each case. This extraordinary relationship becomes more vivid when its terms are translated into concrete values: i.e., one kilogram of coal (about two pounds), if converted *entirely* into energy, would yield 25 billion kilowatt hours of electricity or as much as all the power plants in the U.S. could generate by running steadily for two months.

$E = mc^2$ provides the answer to many of the long-standing mysteries of physics. It explains how radioactive substances like radium and uranium are able to eject particles at enormous velocities and to go on doing so for millions of years. It explains how the sun and all the stars can go on radiating light and heat for billions of years; for if our sun were being consumed by ordinary processes of combustion, the earth would have died in frozen darkness eons ago. It reveals the magnitude of the energy that slumbers in the nuclei of atoms, and forecasts how many grams of uranium must go into a bomb in order to destroy a city. Finally it discloses some fundamental truths about physical reality. Prior to Relativity scientists had pictured the universe as a vessel containing two distinct elements, matter and energy—the former inert, tangible, and characterized by a property called mass, and the latter active, invisible, and without mass. But Einstein showed that mass and energy are equivalent: the property called mass is simply concentrated energy. In other words matter is energy and energy is matter, and the distinction is simply one of temporary state.

In the light of this broad principle many puzzles of nature are resolved. The baffling interplay of matter and radiation which appears sometimes to be a concourse of particles and sometimes a meeting of waves, becomes more understandable. The dual role of the electron as a unit of matter and a unit of electricity, the wave electron, the photon, waves of matter, waves of probability, a universe of waves—all these seem less paradoxical. For all these concepts simply describe different manifestations of the same underlying reality, and it no longer makes sense to ask what any one of them "really" is. Matter and energy are interchangeable. If matter sheds its mass and travels with the speed of light we call it radiation or energy. And conversely if energy congeals and takes on a different form we call it matter. Heretofore science could only note their ephemeral properties and relations as they touched the perceptions of earth-bound man. But since July 16, 1945 man has been able to transform one into the other. For on that night at Alamogordo, New Mexico, man for the first time transmuted a substantial quantity of matter into the light, heat, sound, and motion which we call energy.

Yet the fundamental mystery remains. The whole march of science toward the unification of concepts—the reduction of all matter to elements and then to a few types of particles, the reduction of "forces" to the single concept "energy," and then the reduction of matter *and* energy to a single basic quantity—leads still to the unknown.

RELATIVITY, THE GENERAL THEORY*
by Albert Einstein (1916)

The non-mathematician is seized by a mysterious shuddering when he hears of "four-dimensional" things, by a feeling not unlike that awakened by thoughts of the occult. And yet there is no more commonplace statement than that the world in which we live is a four-dimensional space-time continuum.

That we have not been accustomed to regard the world in this sense as a four-dimensional continuum is due to the fact that in physics, before the advent of the theory of

* *Einstein, op. cit.*

relativity, time played a different and more independent role, as compared with the space co-ordinates. It is for this reason that we have been in the habit of treating time as an independent continuum. As a matter of fact, according to classical mechanics, time is absolute, i.e., it is independent of the position and the condition of motion of the system of co-ordinates.

Since the introduction of the special principle of relativity has been justified, every intellect which strives after generalization must feel the temptation to venture the step toward the general principle of relativity. But a simple and apparently quite reliable consideration seems to suggest that, for the present at any rate, there is little hope of success in such an attempt. Let us imagine ourselves transferred to our old friend the railway carriage, which is traveling at a uniform rate. As long as it is moving uniformly, the occupant of the carriage is not sensible of its motion, and it is for this reason that he can without reluctance interpret the facts of the case as indicating that the carriage is at rest but the embankment in motion. Moreover, according to the special principle of relativity, this interpretation is quite justified also from a physical point of view.

If the motion of the carriage is now changed into a non-uniform motion, as for instance by a powerful application of the brakes, then the occupant of the carriage experiences a correspondingly powerful jerk forward. The retarded motion is manifested in the mechanical behavior of bodies relative to the person in the railway carriage. The mechanical behavior is different from that of the case previously considered, and for this reason it would appear to be impossible that the same mechanical laws hold relatively to the non-uniformly moving carriage, as hold with reference to the carriage when at rest or in uniform motion.

"If we pick up a stone and then let it go, why does it fall to the ground?" The usual answer to this question is: "Because it is attracted by the earth." Modern physics formulates the answer rather differently. The action of the earth on the stone takes place indirectly. The earth produces in its surroundings a gravitational field, which acts on the stone and produces its motion of fall.

In contrast to electric and magnetic fields, the gravitational field exhibits a most remarkable property, which is of fundamental importance for what follows. Bodies which are moving under the sole influence of a gravitational field receive an acceleration, *which does not in the least depend either on the material or on the physical state of the body.* For instance, a piece of lead and a piece of wood fall in exactly the same manner in a gravitational field (*in vacuo*) when they start off from rest or with the same initial velocity.

We obtain a new result of fundamental importance when we carry out the analogous consideration for a ray of light. We conclude *that, in general, rays of light are propagated curvilinearly in gravitational fields.* In two respects this result is of great importance.

In the first place, it can be compared with the reality. Although a detailed examination of the question shows that the curvature of light rays required by the general theory of relativity is only exceedingly small for the gravitational fields at our disposal in practice, its estimated magnitude for light rays passing the sun at grazing incidence is nevertheless 1.7 seconds of arc. This ought to manifest itself in the following way. As seen from the earth, certain fixed stars appear to be in the neighborhood of the sun, and are thus capable of observation during total eclipse of the sun. At such times these stars ought to appear to be displaced outward from the sun by an amount indicated above, as compared with their apparent position in the sky when the sun is situated at another part of the heavens. The examination of the correctness or otherwise of this deduction is a problem of the greatest importance, the early solution of which is to be expected of astronomers.[1]

To establish a relationship between time and space in the physical world it is necessary to consider the behavior of the clocks and measuring rods with which we might measure

[1] By means of the star photographs of two expeditions equipped by a Joint Committee of the Royal and Royal Astronomical Societies, the existence of the deflection of light demanded by theory was first confirmed during the solar eclipse of May 29, 1919. [See Figures 7-5 and 7-6. Ed.]

them. The problem of accurate and meaningful measurement turns out to be especially complicated when the timepieces and measuring rods are moving rapidly—say rotating at the speed of light—from the point of view of the observer. Hence it becomes necessary to specify the position of objects and events in the physical world by means of a mathematical system which does not depend on the rigid-body geometry of Euclid for definition of length or the straight-line co-ordinate system established by Descartes (Cartesian co-ordinates) for marking their position. Fortunately, the great mathematician, Gauss, had worked out his own system of co-ordinates (Gaussian co-ordinates) by which positions (that is, the distances between points) can be established by saying in effect that they are to be found at the intersections of two or more named curves. Since the four-dimensional space-time continuum of relativity is not rigidly Euclidean in character, it is extremely convenient to use Gaussian co-ordinates instead of a rigid body of reference to determine the time and place of an event or object in nature.

The following statement corresponds to the fundamental idea of the general principle of relativity: *"All Gaussian co-ordinate systems are essentially equivalent for the formulation of the general laws of nature."*

In gravitational fields there are no such things as rigid bodies with Euclidean properties; thus the fictitious rigid body of reference is of no avail in the general theory of relativity. The motion of clocks is also influenced by gravitational fields, and in such a way that a physical definition of time which is made directly with the aid of clocks has by no means the same degree of plausibility as in the special theory of relativity.

For this reason non-rigid reference bodies are used, which are as a whole not only moving in any way whatsoever, but which also suffer alterations in form *ad lib*, during their motion. Clocks, for which the law of motion is of any kind, however irregular, serve for the definition of time. We have to imagine each of these clocks fixed at a point on the non-rigid reference body. These clocks satisfy only the one condition, that the "readings" which are observed simultaneously on adjacent clocks (in space) differ from each other by an indefinitely small amount.

If we confine the application of the theory to the case where the gravitational fields can be regarded as being weak, and in which all masses move with respect to the co-ordinate system with velocities which are small compared with the velocity of light, we then obtain as a first approximation the Newtonian theory. Thus the latter theory is obtained here without any particular assumption, whereas Newton had to introduce the hypothesis that the force of attraction between mutually attracting material points is inversely proportional to the square of the distance between them. If we increase the accuracy of the calculation, deviations from the theory of Newton make their appearance, practically all of which must nevertheless escape the test of observation owing to their smallness.

We must draw attention here to one of these deviations. According to Newton's theory, a planet moves round the sun in an ellipse, which would permanently maintain its position with respect to the fixed stars, if we could disregard the motion of the fixed stars themselves and the action of the other planets under consideration. Thus, if we correct the observed motion of the planets for these two influences, and if Newton's theory be strictly correct, we ought to obtain for the orbit of the planet an ellipse, which is fixed with reference to the fixed stars. This deduction, which can be tested with great accuracy, has been confirmed for all the planets save one, with the precision that is capable of being obtained by the delicacy of observation attainable at the present time. The sole exception is Mercury, the planet which lies nearest the sun. Since the time of Leverrier, it has been known that the ellipse corresponding to the orbit of Mercury, after it has been corrected for the influences mentioned above, is not stationary with respect to the fixed stars, but that it rotates exceedingly slowly in the plane of the orbit and in the sense of the orbital motion. The value obtained for this rotary movement of the orbital ellipse was forty-three seconds of arc per century, an amount ensured to be correct to within a few seconds of arc. This effect can be explained by means of classical mechanics only on the assumption of hypotheses which have little probability, and which were devised solely for this purpose.

On the basis of the general theory of relativity, it is found that the ellipse of every planet round the sun must necessarily rotate in the manner indicated above; that for all the planets, with the exception of Mercury, this rotation is too small to be detected with the delicacy of observation possible at the present time; but that in the case of Mercury it must amount to forty-three seconds of arc per century, a result which is strictly in agreement with observation [Figure 7-2].

If we ponder over the question as to how the universe, considered as a whole, is to be regarded, the first answer that suggests itself to us is surely this: As regards space (and time) the universe is infinite. There are stars everywhere, so that the density of matter, although very variable in detail, is nevertheless on the average everywhere the same. In other words: However far we might travel through space, we should find everywhere an attenuated swarm of fixed stars of approximately the same kind of density.

This view is not in harmony with the theory of Newton. The latter theory rather requires that the universe should have a kind of center in which the density of the stars is a maximum, and that as we proceed outward from this center the group density of the stars should diminish, until finally, at great distances, it is succeeded by an infinite region of emptiness. This stellar universe ought to be a finite island in the infinite ocean of space.

This conception is in itself not very satisfactory. It is less satisfactory because it leads to the result that the light emitted by the stars and also individual stars of the stellar system are perpetually passing out into infinite space, never to return, and without ever again coming into interaction with other objects of nature. Such a finite material universe would be destined to become gradually but systematically impoverished.

But speculations on the structure of the universe also move in quite another direction. The development of non-Euclidean geometry led to the recognition of the fact that we can cast doubt on the *infiniteness* of our space without coming into conflict with the laws of thought or with experience (Riemann, Helmholtz).

In the first place, we imagine an existence in two-dimensional space. Flat beings with flat implements, and in particular flat rigid measuring rods, are free to move in a *plane* [Figure 7-8, top]. For them nothing exists outside of this plane: that which they observe to happen to themselves and to their flat "things" is the all-inclusive reality of their plane. In particular, the constructions of plane Euclidean geometry can be carried out by means of the rods. In contrast to ours, the universe of these beings is two-dimensional; but, like ours, it extends to infinity. In their universe there is room for an infinite number of identical squares made up of rods, i.e., its volume (surface) is infinite. If these beings say their universe is "plane," there is sense in the statement, because they mean that they can perform the constructions of plane Euclidean geometry with their rods. In this connection the individual rods always represent the same distance, independently of their position.

Let us consider now a second two-dimensional existence, but this time on a spherical surface instead of on a plane [Figure 7-8, bottom]. The flat beings with their measuring rods and other objects fit exactly on this surface and they are unable to leave it. Their whole universe of observation extends exclusively over the surface of the sphere. Are these beings able to regard the geometry of their universe as being plane geometry and their rods withal as the realization of "distance"? They cannot do this. For if they attempt to realize a straight line, they will obtain a curve, which we "three-dimensional beings" designate as a great circle, i.e., a self-contained line of definite finite length, which can be measured up by means of a measuring rod. Similarly, this universe has a finite area that can be compared with the area of a square constructed with rods. The great charm resulting from this consideration lies in the recognition of the fact that *the universe of these beings is finite and yet has no limits.*

But the spherical-surface beings do not need to go on a world tour in order to perceive that they are not living in a Euclidean universe. They can convince themselves of this on every part of their "world," provided they do not use too small a piece of it.

To this two-dimensional sphere universe there is a three-dimensional analogy, namely, the three-dimensional spherical space which was discovered by Riemann. Its points are likewise all equivalent. It possesses a finite volume, which is determined by its "radius."

According to the general theory of relativity, the geometrical properties of space are not independent, but they are determined by matter. Thus we can draw conclusions about the geometrical structure of the universe only if we base our considerations on the state of the matter as being something that is known. We know from experience that, for a suitably chosen co-ordinate system, the velocities of the stars are small as compared with the velocity of transmission of light. We can thus as a rough approximation arrive at a conclusion as to the nature of the universe as a whole if we treat the matter as being at rest.

We already know from our previous discussion that the behavior of measuring rods and clocks is influenced by gravitational fields, i.e., by the distribution of matter. This in itself is sufficient to exclude the possibility of the exact validity of Euclidean geometry in our universe. But it is conceivable that our universe differs only slightly from a Euclidean one, and this notion seems all the more probable, since calculations show that the metrics of surrounding space is influenced only to an exceedingly small extent by masses even of the magnitude of our sun [Figures 7-5 and 7-6]. We might imagine that, as regards geometry, our universe behaves analogously to a surface which is irregularly curved in its individual parts, but which nowhere departs appreciably from a plane: something like the rippled surface of a lake [Figure 7-7, top]. Such a universe might fittingly be called a quasi-Euclidean universe. As regards its space it would be infinite. But calculation shows that in a quasi-Euclidean universe the average density of matter would necessarily be nil. Thus such a universe could not be inhabited by matter everywhere; it would present to us that unsatisfactory picture which we portrayed.

If we are to have in the universe an average density of matter which differs from zero, however small may be that difference, then the universe cannot be quasi-Euclidean. On the contrary, the results of calculation indicate that if matter be distributed uniformly, the universe would necessarily be spherical (or elliptical) [Figure 7-7, middle]. Since in reality the detailed distribution of matter is not uniform, the real universe will deviate in individual parts from the spherical, i.e., the universe will be quasi-spherical [Figure 7-7, bottom]. But it will be necessarily finite. In fact, the theory (of relativity) supplies us with a simple connection between the space expanse of the universe and the average density of matter in it.*

* After publishing this essay in 1916, Einstein worked on several other models of the universe, illustrated in Figure 7-7 and discussed further in Part 8. Ed.

ILLUSTRATIONS OF RELATIVITY*
by George Gamow (1947)

Einstein came to the remarkable conclusion that the phenomenon of gravity is merely the effect of the curvature of the four-dimensional

* From *One, Two, Three . . . Infinity* by George Gamow. Copyright 1947 by George Gamow. Reprinted by permission of The Viking Press, Inc.

space-time world (Figures 7-5 and 7-6). In fact we may now discard as inadequate the old statement that the sun exercises a certain force that acts directly on the planets making them describe circular orbits around it. It

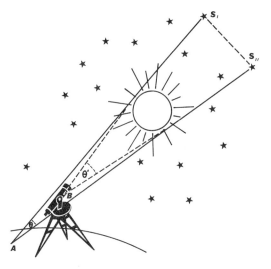

After George Gamow

Figure 7-5. The light rays from two stars S$_I$ and S$_{II}$ located (at the moment of observation) at opposite sides of the sun disk converge into a theodolite, which measures the angle between them. The experiment is then repeated later when the sun is out of the way, and the two angles are compared. If they are different we have proof that the mass of the sun changes the curvature of the space around it, deflecting the rays of light from their original paths. Such an experiment was originally suggested by Einstein to test his theory. The reader may understand the situation somewhat better by comparing it with its two-dimensional analogy shown in Figure 7-6. Obviously there was a practical barrier to carrying out Einstein's suggestion under ordinary conditions: because of the brilliance of the solar disk, you cannot see the stars around it; but during a total solar eclipse the stars are clearly visible in the daytime. In 1919, taking advantage of this fact, a British astronomical expedition to the Principe Islands (West Africa), from which the total solar eclipse of that year could best be observed, actually made the test. The difference of angular distances between the two stars with and without the sun between them was found to be 1.61 in. ± 0.30 in. as compared with 1.75 in. predicted by Einstein's theory. Similar results were obtained by various expeditions at later dates.

would be more accurate to say that the mass of the sun curves the space-time world around it, and the world-lines of planets look the way they do only because they are geodesical lines running through the curved space.

In Figure 7-7 we give a two-dimensional illustration of the flat space with "pimples," and two possible types of curved spaces. The so-called "positively curved" space corresponds to the surface of a sphere or any other closed geometrical figure, and bends "the same way" regardless of the direction in which one goes. The opposite type of

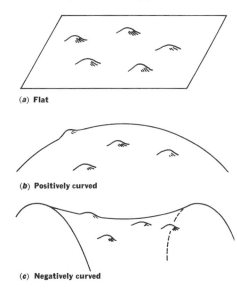

(a) Flat

(b) Positively curved

(c) Negatively curved

After George Gamow

Figure 7-7. Three views of space.

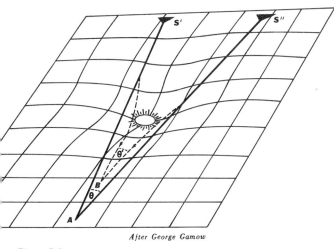

After George Gamow

Figure 7-6

"negatively curved" space bends up in one direction, but down in another, and resembles closely the surface of a western saddle. The difference between the two types of curvatures can be clearly realized if you cut out two pieces of leather, one from a football, another from the saddle, and try to straighten them out on a table. You will notice that neither can be straightened out without stretching or shrinking it, but, whereas the periphery of the football piece must be stretched, that of the saddle piece must be shrunk. The football piece has not enough material around the center to flatten it out; the saddle piece has too much, and it gets folded whenever we try to make it flat and smooth.

We can state the same point in still another way. Suppose we count the number of pimples located within one, two, three, etc. inches (counted along the surface) from a certain point. On the flat uncurved surface the number of pimples will increase as the square of the distances, that is, as 1, 4, 9, etc. On a spherical surface the number of pimples will increase more slowly than that, and on a "saddle" surface more rapidly. Thus the two-dimensional shadow scientists living in the surface, and thus having no way of looking at it from outside to notice its shape, will be still able to detect the curvature by counting the number of pimples that fall within the circles of different radii (Figure 7-8). It may be also noticed here that the difference between the positive and negative curvatures shows itself in the measurements of the angles in corresponding triangles. As we have seen

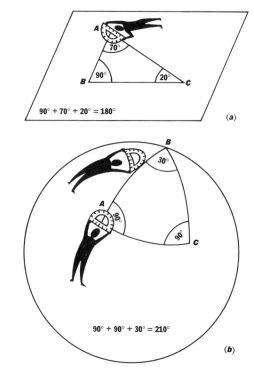

Figure 7-8. Two-dimensional scientists of the flat and curved "surface worlds" check the Euclidian theorem about the sum of the angles in a triangle.

After George Gamow

in the previous section the sum of angles of a triangle drawn on the surface of a sphere is always larger than 180°. If you try to draw a triangle on the saddle surface you will find that the sum of its angles is always less than 180°.

The above results obtained specifically in regard to curved surfaces can be generalized in regard to curved three-dimensional spaces according to the following table:

Type of space	Behavior at large distances	Angle-sum of a triangle	Volume of a sphere increases
Positively curved (sphere analogue)	Closes on itself	$> 180°$	Slower than cube of the radius
Flat (plane analogue)	Extends into infinity	$= 180°$	As the cube of the radius
Negatively curved (saddle analogue)	Extends into infinity	$< 180°$	Faster than cube of the radius

THEORY AND COMMON SENSE

"I can't believe *that*," said Alice.

"Can't you?" the Queen said, in a pitying tone. "Try again: draw a long breath, and shut your eyes."

Alice laughed. "There's no use trying," she said: "One can't believe impossible things."

"I daresay you haven't had much practice," said the Queen. "When I was your age, I always did it for half-an-hour a day. Why, sometimes I've believed as many as six impossible things before breakfast."

Lewis Carroll
Through the Looking Glass (1871)

From the point of view of the physicist, a theory . . . is a policy rather than a creed; its object is to connect or coordinate apparently diverse phenomena and above all to suggest, stimulate, and direct experiment.

J. J. Thompson
The Corpuscular Theory of Matter (1907)

Not that we may not, to explain any phenomena of nature, make use of any probable hypotheses whatsoever: hypotheses, if they are well made, are at least great helps to the memory, and often direct us to new discoveries. But my meaning is, that we should not take up any one too hastily (which the mind, that would always penetrate into the causes of things, and have principles to rest on, is very apt to do,) till we have very well examined particulars, and made several experiments, in that thing which we would explain by our hypothesis, and see whether it will agree to them all; whether our principles will carry us quite through, and not be as inconsistent with one phenomenon of nature, as they seem to accommodate and explain another. And at least that we take care that the name of *principles* deceive us not, nor impose on us, by making us receive that for an unquestionable truth, which is really at best but a very doubtful conjecture; such as are most (I had almost said all) of the hypotheses in natural philosophy.

John Locke
Concerning Human Understanding (1690)

Often the very fact that the words of science are the same as those of our common life and tongue can be more misleading than enlightening, more frustrating to understanding than recognizably technical jargon. For the words of science—relativity, if you will, or atom, or mutation, or action—have been given a refinement, a precision, and in the end a wholly altered meaning.

Thus we may well be cautious if we inquire as to whether there are direct connections, and if so of what sort, between the truths that science uncovers and the way men think about things in general—their metaphysics—their ideas about what is real and what is primary; their epistemology—their understanding of what makes human knowledge; their ethics—their ways of thinking, talking, judging, and acting in human problems of right and wrong, of good and evil. . . .

[Nevertheless] it is my thesis that generally the new things we have learned in science . . . do provide us with valid and relevant and greatly needed analogies to human problems lying outside the present domain of science or its present borderlands.

J. Robert Oppenheimer
Science and the Common Understanding (1955)

Nature is more intricately organized and cross-linked than our theories, so that each model or likeness that we try scores some striking successes and then falls short. All that we can do, at any state of our factual knowledge, is to prefer that code which makes what we know most orderly. That is, we choose those concepts which organize the messages of nature most coherently. We achieve this, in my view, by maximizing their content of information or meaning. This is the test for the inductions by which we try to generalize from our particular experience and to gain a basis for foresight.

Charles Darwin said sadly at the end of his life that

My mind seems to have become a kind of machine for grinding general laws out of large collections of facts.

Darwin was too modest. If such a machine can indeed be made, we do not know how to make it. Indeed, we do not know anything like it, except a man. For the discovery of laws is a complex induction like the solving of a cryptogram which, so far as we know, a machine procedure can help but not complete. It depends on an imaginative act, seeing the structure of the solution in a likeness, and seizing a likeness where none was expected.

J. Bronowski
Science as Foresight (1955)

COMMON SENSE AND THE UNIVERSE*
by Stephen Leacock (1942)

I

Speaking last December [1941] at the annual convention of the American Association for the Advancement of Science, and speaking, as it were, in the name of the great 100-inch telescope under his control, Professor Edwin Hubble, of the Mount Wilson Observatory, California, made the glad announcement that the universe is not expanding.† This was good news indeed, if not to the general public who had no reason to suspect that it was expanding, at least to those of us who humbly attempt to "follow science." For some twenty-

* From Stephen Leacock, "Common Sense and the Universe," in Stephen Leacock, *Last Leaves*, Dodd, Mead & Company, Inc., New York, 1945. Reprinted by permission of Dodd, Mead & Company, Inc., and McClelland and Stewart Limited, Toronto.

† This conclusion has subsequently been reversed. See p. 274.

five years past, indeed ever since the promulgation of this terrific idea in a paper published by Professor W. de Sitter in 1917, we had lived as best we could in an expanding universe, one in which everything, at terrific speed kept getting further away from everything else. It suggested to us the disappointed lover in the romance who leaped on his horse and rode madly off in all directions. The idea was majestic in its sheer size, but it somehow gave an uncomfortable sensation.

Yet we had to believe it. Thus, for example, we had it on the authority of Dr. Spencer Jones, the British Astronomer Royal, as recently as in his new and fascinating book of 1940, *Life on Other Worlds,* that "a distant universe in the constellation of Boötes has been found to be receding with a velocity of 24,300 miles a second. We can infer that this nebula is at a distance of 230,000,000 light-years." I may perhaps remind my fellow followers of science that a light-year means the distance traveled in one year by light, moving at 186,000 miles a second. In other words, this "distant universe" is now 1,049,970,980,-000,000,000,000 miles away.

Some distance! as Mr. Churchill would say.

But now it appears that that distant universe has *not* been receding at all; in fact, it isn't away out there. Heaven knows where it is. Bring it back. Yet not only did the astronomers assert the expansion but they proved it, from the behavior of the red band in the spectrum, which blushed a deeper red at the revelation of it, like the conscious water that "saw its God and blushed" at Cana in Galilee long ago. One of the most distinguished and intelligible of our astronomers, Sir Arthur Eddington, had written a book about it, *The Expanding Universe,* to bring it down to our level. Astronomers at large accepted this universal explosion in all directions as calmly as they once accepted the universal fall of gravitation, or the universal death in the cold under Carnot's Second Law of Thermodynamics.

But the relief brought by Professor Hubble is tempered on reflection by certain doubts and afterthoughts. It is not that I venture

any disbelief or disrespect toward science, for that is as atrocious in our day as disbelief in the Trinity in the days of Isaac Newton. But we begin to doubt whether science can quite keep on believing in and respecting itself. If we expand today and contract tomorrow; if we undergo all the doubled-up agonies of the curvature of space only to have the kink called off . . . if we get reconciled to dying a martyr's death at one general, distributed temperature of 459 degrees below zero, the same for all, only to find that the world is perhaps unexpectedly warming up again—then we ask, where are we? To which, of course, Einstein answers "Nowhere," since there is no place to be. So we must pick up our little book again, follow science, and wait for the next astronomical convention.

Let us take this case of the famous Second Law of Thermodynamics, that inexorable scroll of fate which condemned the universe —or at least all life in it—to die of cold. I look back now with regret to the needless tears I have wasted over that, the generous sympathy for the last little band of survivors, dying at 459 degrees below our zero ($-273°$ centigrade), the absolute zero of cold when the molecules cease to move and heat ends. No stove will light at that, for the wood is as cold as the stove, and the match is as cold as both, and the dead fingers motionless.

I remember meeting this inexorable law for the first time in reading, as a little boy, a piece of "popular science" entitled *Our Great Timepiece Running Down.* It was by Richard Proctor, whose science-bogeys were as terrifying as Mrs. Crow's *Night Thoughts,* only slower in action. The sun, it appeared, was cooling; soon it would be all over. Lord Kelvin presently ratified this. Being Scotch, he didn't mind damnation and he gave the sun and the whole solar system only ninety million years more to live.

This famous law was first clearly enunciated in 1824 by the great French physicist, Nicolas Carnot. It showed that all bodies in the universe kept changing their temperature —hot things heated cold, and cold things chilled hot. Thus they pooled their temperature. Like the division of a rich estate among a flock of poor relations, it meant poverty for all. We must all share ultimately the cold of absolute space.

It is true that a gleam came when Ernest Rutherford and others, working on radioactivity, discovered that there might be a contrary process of "stoking up." Atoms exploding into radioactivity would keep the home fires burning in the sun for a long time. This glad news meant that the sun was both much older and much younger than Lord Kelvin had ever thought it was. But even at that it was only a respite. The best they could offer was 1,500,000,000 years. After that we freeze. . . .

At this point I may perhaps pause to explain that the purpose of this article is not to make fun of science, nor to express disbelief in it, but only to suggest its limits. What I want to say is that when the scientist steps out from recording phenomena and offers a general statement of the nature of what is called "reality," the ultimate nature of space, of time, of the beginning of things, of life, of a universe, then he stands exactly where you and I do, and the three of us stand where Plato did—and long before him, Rodin's primitive thinker.

Consider this. Professor Hubble, like Joshua, has called upon the universe to be still. All is quiet. The universe rests, motionless, in the night sky. The mad rush is over. Every star in every galaxy, every island universe, is at least right where it is. But the old difficulty remains: Does it go forever, this world in the sky, or does it stop? Such an alternative has posed itself as a problem for every one of us, somewhere about the age of twelve. We cannot imagine that the stars go on forever. It's unthinkable. But we equally cannot imagine that they come to a stop and that beyond them is nothing, and then more nothing. Unending nothing is as incomprehensible as unending something. This alternative I cannot fathom, nor can Professor Hubble, nor can anyone ever hope to.

Let me turn back in order to make my point of view a little clearer. I propose to traverse again the path along which modern science has dragged those who have tried to follow it for about a century past. It was at first a path singularly easy to tread, provided that one could throw aside the inherited burden of superstition, false belief, and prejudice. For the direction seemed verified and assured all along by the corroboration of science by actual physical results. Who could doubt electricity after the telegraph? Or doubt the theory of light after photography? Or the theory of electricity when read under electric light? At every turn, each new advance of science unveiled new power, new mechanism of life—and of death. To "doubt science" was to be like the farmer at the circus who doubted the giraffe. Science, of course, had somehow to tuck into the same bed as Theology, but it was the theologian who protested. Science just said, "Lie over."

Let us follow then this path.

II

When mediaeval superstition was replaced by the new learning, mathematics, astronomy, and physics were the first sciences to get organized and definite. By the opening of the nineteenth century they were well set; the solar system was humming away so drowsily that Laplace was able to assure Napoleon that he didn't need God to watch over it. Gravitation worked like clockwork and clockwork worked like gravitation. Chemistry, which, like electricity, was nothing but a set of experiments in Benjamin Franklin's time, turned into a science after Lavoisier had discovered that fire was not a thing but a process, something happening to things— an idea so far above the common thought that they guillotined him for it in 1794. Dalton followed and showed that all things could be broken up into a set of very, very small atoms, grouped into molecules all acting according to plan. With Faraday and Maxwell, electricity, which turned out to be the same as magnetism, or interchangeable with it, fell into its place in the new order of science.

By about 1880 it seemed as if the world of science was fairly well explained. Metaphysics still talked in its sleep. Theology still preached sermons. It took issue with much of the new science, especially with geology and the new evolutionary science of life that went with the new physical world. But science paid little attention.

For the whole thing was so amazingly simple. There you had your space and time, two things too obvious to explain. Here you had your matter, made up of solid little atoms, infinitely small but really just like birdseed. All this was set going by and with the Law of Gravitation. Once started, the nebulous world condensed into suns, the suns threw off planets, the planets cooled, life resulted and presently became conscious, conscious life got higher up and higher up till you had apes, then Bishop Wilberforce, and then Professor Huxley.

A few little mysteries remained, such as the question of what space and matter and time and life and consciousness really were. But all this was conveniently called by Herbert Spencer the *Unknowable,* and then locked in a cupboard and left there.

Everything was thus reduced to a sort of Dead Certainty. Just one awkward skeleton remained in the cupboard. And that was the peculiar, mysterious aspect of electricity, which was not exactly a thing and yet more than an idea. There was also, and electricity only helped to make it worse, the old puzzle about "action at a distance." How does gravitation pull all the way from here to the sun? And if there is *nothing* in space, how does light get across from the sun in eight minutes, and even all the way from Sirius in eight years?

Even the invention of "ether" as a sort of universal jelly that could have ripples shaken across it proved a little unconvincing.

Then, just at the turn of the century the whole structure began to crumble.

The first note of warning that something was going wrong came with the discovery of X-rays. Sir William Crookes, accidentally leaving round tubes of rarefied gas, stumbled on "radiant matter," or "matter in the fourth state," as accidentally as Columbus discovered America. The British Government knighted him at once (1897) but it was too late. The thing had started. Then came Guglielmo

Marconi with the revelation of more waves, and universal at that. Light, the world had learned to accept, because we can see it, but this was fun in the dark.

There followed the researches of the radioactivity school and, above all, those of Ernest Rutherford which revolutionized the theory of matter. I knew Rutherford well as we were colleagues at McGill for seven years. I am quite sure that he had no original intention of upsetting the foundations of the universe. Yet that is what he did and he was in due course very properly raised to the peerage for it.

When Rutherford was done with the atom all the solidity was pretty well knocked out of it.

Till these researches began, people commonly thought of atoms as something like birdseed, little round solid particles, ever so little, billions to an inch. They were small. But they were there. You could weigh them. You could apply to them all the laws of Isaac Newton about weight and velocity and mass and gravitation—in other words, the whole of first-year physics. . . .

One must not confuse Rutherford's work on atoms with Einstein's theories of space and time. Rutherford worked all his life without reference to Einstein. Even in his later days at the Cavendish Laboratory at Cambridge when he began, ungratefully, to smash up the atom that had made him, he needed nothing from Einstein. I once asked Rutherford—it was at the height of the popular interest in Einstein, in 1923—what he thought of Einstein's relativity. "Oh, that stuff!" he said. "We never bother with that in our work!" His admirable biographer, Professor A. S. Eve, tells us that when the German physicist Wien told Rutherford that no Anglo-Saxon could understand relativity Rutherford answered, "No, they have too much sense."

But it was Einstein who made the real trouble. He announced in 1905 that there was no such thing as absolute rest. After that there never was. But it was not till just after the Great War that the reading public caught on to Einstein and little books on "relativity" covered the bookstalls.

Einstein knocked out space and time as Rutherford knocked out matter. The general viewpoint of relativity toward space is very simple. Einstein explains that there is no such place as *here*. "But," you answer, "I'm here; here is where I am right now." But you're moving, you're spinning round as the earth spins; and you and the earth are both spinning round the sun, and the sun is rushing through space towards a distant galaxy, and the galaxy itself it beating it away at 26,000 miles a second. Now where is that spot that is here! How did you mark it? You remember the story of the two idiots who were out fishing, and one said, "We should have marked that place where we got all the fish," and the other said, "I did, I marked it on the boat." Well, that's it. That's *here*.

You can see it better still if you imagine the universe swept absolutely empty: nothing in it, not even *you*. Now put a *point* in it, just one point. Where is it? Why, obviously it's nowhere. If you say it's right there, where do you mean by there? In which direction is there? In *that* direction? Oh! hold on, you're sticking yourself in to make a direction. It's in *no* direction; there aren't any directions. Now put in another point. Which is which? You can't tell. They *both* are. One is on the right, you say, and one on the left. You keep out of that space! There's no right and no left.

The discovery by Einstein of the curvature of space was greeted by the physicists with the burst of applause that greets a winning home-run at baseball. That brilliant writer just mentioned, Sir Arthur Eddington, who can handle space and time with the imagery of a poet, and even infiltrate humor into gravitation, as when he says that a man in an elevator falling twenty stories has an ideal opportunity to study gravitation—Sir Arthur Eddington is loud in his acclaim. Without this curve, it appears, things won't fit into their place. The fly on the globe, as long as he thinks it flat (like Mercator's map), finds things shifted as by some unaccountable demon to all sorts of wrong distances. Once he gets the idea of a sphere everything comes straight. So with our space. The mystery of gravitation puzzles us, except those who have the luck to fall in an elevator, and even for them knowledge comes too late. They weren't falling at all: just curving. "Admit a curvature of the world," wrote Eddington in his Gifford Lectures of 1927, "and the mysterious agency disappears. Einstein has exorcised this demon."

But it appears now, fourteen years later, that Einstein doesn't care if space is curved or not. He can take it either way. A prominent physicist of today, head of the department in one of the greatest universities of the world, wrote me on this point: "Einstein had stronger hopes that a general theory which involved the assumption of a property of space, akin to what is ordinarily called curvature, would be more useful than he now believes to be the case." Plain talk for a professor. Most people just say Einstein has given up curved space. It's as if Sir Isaac Newton years after he had said, with a yawn, "Oh, about that apple—perhaps it wasn't falling."

QUESTIONS TO CONSIDER

In Part 5 we saw how increase in the degree of observational accuracy led to new laws and theories. How does this principle apply to the readings in this part?

What was the dilemma that called for a new scientific theory at the turn of the century?

Why is a ". . . theory only overthrown by a better theory, never merely by contradictory facts" (Conant quotation, page 213).

Does Einstein's theory uncover a deeper unity in nature?

Do you agree with Oppenheimer when he says ". . . the new things we have learned in science . . . do provide us with valid and greatly needed analogies to human problems," or does this kind of application seem unsuitable to you in view of the changing nature of scientific theories?

SUGGESTIONS FOR FURTHER READING

On Newton

* Bronowski, J.: *The Common Sense of Science*, Vintage Books, Random House, Inc., New York, 1953, chap. III. An interesting discussion of Newton's model and its effect on the concepts of cause and order in the universe.

* Burtt, E. A.: *The Metaphysical Foundations of Modern Science*, Anchor Books, Doubleday & Company, Inc., Garden City, N.Y., 1954, chap. VII. A detailed and philosophical analysis of Newton's methods and ideas.

* Butterfield, Herbert: *The Origins of Modern Science*, The Macmillan Company, New York, 1957, chap. 8. The history of the modern theory of gravitation.

* Lodge, Oliver: *Pioneers of Science*, Dover Publications, Inc., New York, lectures VII, VIII, and IX. These three chapters deal in detail with Newtonian physics. Some mathematics is used but the treatment is not difficult.

On Relativity

* Barnett, Lincoln: *The Universe and Dr. Einstein*, Mentor Books, New American Library of World Literature, Inc., New York, 1958. In addition to the selection we have used, the reader may find the rest of this book helpful in explaining relativity.

* Durell, Clement V.: *Readable Relativity*, Harper Torchbooks, Harper & Row, Publishers, New York. One of the best simple mathematical accounts of relativity. It explains both the special and general theory using only elementary algebra and geometry.

* Einstein, A., and L. Infeld: *The Evolution of Physics*, Simon and Schuster, Inc., New York, 1961, chap. III. An excellent popular presentation of relativity by Einstein and one of his coworkers in research. It is told in simple language avoiding all highly technical terms and mathematical formulae.

* Paperback edition.

* Gamow, George: *One, Two, Three, . . . Infinity*, Mentor Books, New American Library of World Literature, Inc., New York, 1947, part II, chaps. III–V. A vivid and interesting account for the layman of the principles of relativity and the fourth dimension.

———: *Matter, Earth and Sky*, Prentice-Hall, Inc., Englewood Cliffs, N.J., 1958, part 1. Another very good description for the general reader of the concepts of relativity (Special Theory, chap. 7, and General Theory, chap. 12).

* Russell, Bertrand: *The A B C of Relativity*, Mentor Books, New American Library of World Literature, Inc., New York, 1959. One of the best simple but authoritative books on relativity for the layman.

Did creation occur as a single event billions of years ago, or is it going on around us all the time? This question, of great philosophical significance, is debated by two opposing schools of modern cosmology. The selections in this part show a scientific idea in the making and offer a new appreciation of the impact that scientific theories can have on other areas of human thought.

Gamow

Lovell

INTRODUCTION

The readings in this part bring us up to the frontiers of modern cosmology in the description of the two principal theories of the origin of the universe. They begin with a selection from Gamow, which fills in the background concerning present scientific knowledge of the galaxies: measurements of their size, rotation, and speed of recession, the geometry of space-time to which the reader was introduced in Part 7. One of the most revolutionary and reorienting concepts since the time of Copernicus is that our planet has been further displaced from the center of the universe and is now believed to occupy a very peripheral position in the spiral arm of an ordinary galaxy. This discovery, George Gamow says, comes as ". . . a slap in the face of human pride." This peripheral position hampers our investigation of the universe. Dark clouds prevent us from seeing the center of our galaxy and the part of the universe that lies beyond it. In these readings we see how science has overcome this difficulty and continues to find methods of gaining new knowledge of the universe. So far no barrier has remained "insurmountable" for long.

The latest tool in astronomical research—the radio telescope—was discovered just at the moment when we seemed to have approached the theoretical limits of the older methods. One of the limits of optical telescopes is due to the unsteadiness of our atmosphere, but this does not affect the radio telescope to the same degree because the longer wavelengths that it receives are less affected by slight fluctuations in the atmosphere. The long radio wavelengths are also not deflected as much by small dust particles as are the waves of visible light, and therefore the radio telescope is able to penetrate the clouds that lie between us and the center of the galaxy. Another limitation of the optical telescope is due to the faintness of the signals from the most distant sources. This difficulty, too, may be overcome by the radio telescope because of the unusually strong signals coming from what appear to be colliding galaxies, many of them far beyond the range of our optical telescopes. For these reasons the radio telescope may widen our horizons severalfold. It is important to remember that we are "seeing" farther back in time as we look farther out into space, so that our knowledge of the universe may be increased in all four dimensions as the new radio telescopes begin scanning the skies and as the information is evaluated by astronomers. However, we may encounter another barrier out where the galaxies are receding so fast that their radiation can never reach us. "Then,"

Hoyle

Bondi

Dingle

Lovell tells us, "we must be content. No further striving or inventions of man will enable us to probe the conditions which existed in the epochs of history beyond these few thousand years. They are gone forever beyond the fundamental limits of observability.

"At this point we reach the second stage of our inquiry, where we appeal to cosmological theory. The question is this. Can we formulate a theory in terms of known physical laws whose predictions agree so well with the present observable universe that we can predict the past and future?" Lovell goes on to show that there are at least two theories that fulfill these conditions: the evolutionary theory, sometimes referred to as the "big bang" theory and the steady-state or continuous creation theory. At the present state of our knowledge both these theories fit the framework of known facts. The situation depicted here is reminiscent of cosmological theory at the time of Ptolemy and Aristarchus, when two very different theories could be made to explain the observed facts, and the decision between them was frought with deep philosophical significance.

We have already seen one case in which science was forced to accept simultaneously two opposing theories. The facts demonstrated that no choice could be made between the two theories of light; they were both necessary to explain the observations and experiments. In Part 7 we saw how one theory, Newton's law of gravitation, was shown to be a special case of the larger synthesis of Einstein. Now in these readings we see a scientific decision actually in the making, an argument being hotly debated by both sides, and we realize that it is not always possible for scientists to remain aloof and impartial. Scientists are men who have convictions and are willing to do battle for them.

In the absence of decisive facts, the arguments for the two rival theories of cosmology revolve around a discussion about the nature of the assumptions on which they are based. However they also emphasize the possibility that observational tests within the next years, particularly with radio telescopes, may provide evidence that will decide between the two theories, which are so different in their conceptions of the universe. The unraveling of this mystery will be exciting and deeply significant for modern man, having far-reaching implications for our religious and philosophical beliefs. As Fred Hoyle once said, "The Universe is everything; both living and inanimate things; both atoms and galaxies; and if the spiritual exists as well as the material, of spiritual things also . . . for by its very nature the Universe is the totality of all things."

THE GALAXIES

Open wide the door for us, so that we may look out into the immeasurable starry universe; show us that other worlds like ours occupy the ethereal realms; make clear to us how the motion of all worlds is engendered by forces; teach us to march forward to greater knowledge of nature.

Giordano Bruno (1548–1600)

TOWARD THE LIMITS OF THE UNKNOWN*
by George Gamow (1962)

More than a century ago the famous British astronomer, William Herschel, observing the stellar sky through his large self-made telescope, was struck by the fact that most of the stars that are ordinarily invisible to the naked eye appear within the faintly luminous belt cutting across the night sky and known as the Milky Way. And it is to him that the science of astronomy owes the recognition of the fact that the Milky Way is not ordinary nebulosity or merely a belt of gas clouds spreading across space, but is actually formed from a multitude of stars that are so far away and consequently so faint that our eye cannot recognize them separately.

Using stronger and stronger telescopes we have been able to see the Milky Way as a larger and larger number of separate stars, but the main bulk of them still remains in the hazy background. It would be, however, erroneous to think that in the region of the Milky Way the stars are distributed any more densely than in any other part of the sky. It is, in fact, not the denser distribution of stars but the greater depth of stellar distribution in this direction that makes it possible to see what seems to be a larger number of stars in a given space than anywhere else in the sky. In the direction of the Milky Way the stars extend as far as the eye (strengthened by telescopes) can see, whereas in any other

* From *One, Two, Three . . . Infinity* by George Gamow. Copyright 1947 by George Gamow. Reprinted by permission of The Viking Press, Inc., and revised for this book, 1962.

direction the distribution of stars does not extend to the end of visibility, and beyond them we encounter mostly the almost empty space.

Looking in the direction of the Milky Way it is as though we are looking through a deep forest where the branches of numerous trees overlap each other forming a continuous background, whereas in other directions we see patches of the empty space between the stars, as we would see the patches of the blue sky through the foliage overhead.

Thus the stellar universe, to which our sun belongs as one insignificant member, occupies a flattened area in space, extending for large distances in the plane of the Milky Way, and being comparatively thin in the direction perpendicular to it.

A more detailed study by generations of astronomers led to the conclusion that our stellar system includes about 40,000,000,000 individual stars, distributed within a lens-shaped area about 100,000 light-years in diameter and some 5,000 to 10,000 light-years thick. And one result of this study comes as a slap in the face of human pride—the knowledge that our sun is not at all at the center of this giant stellar society but rather close to its outer edge.

In Figure 8-1 we try to convey to our readers the way this giant beehive of stars actually looks. By the way, we have not mentioned yet that in more scientific language the system of the Milky Way is known as the *Galaxy* (Latin of course!). The size of the Galaxy is here reduced by a factor of a hundred billion billions, though the number of points that represent separate stars are considerably fewer than forty billions, for, as one puts it, typographical reasons.

One of the most characteristic properties of the giant swarm of stars forming the galactic system is that it is in a state of rapid rotation similar to that which moves our planetary system. Just as Venus, Earth, Jupiter, and other planets move along almost circular orbits around the sun, the billions of stars forming the system of the Milky Way move around what is known as the galactic center. This center of galactic rotation is located in the direction of the constellation of Sagittarius (the Archer), and in fact if you follow the foggy shape of the Milky Way across the sky you will notice that approaching this constellation it becomes much broader, indicating that you are looking toward the central thicker part of the lens-shaped mass. (Our astronomer in Figure 8-1 is looking in this direction.)

What does the galactic center look like? We do not know that, since unfortunately it is screened from our sight by heavy clouds

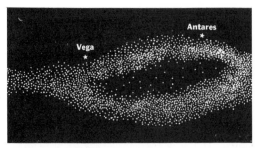

Figure 8-2. Looking toward the galactic center it would seem that the mythical celestial road branches into two one-way traffic lanes.

of dark interstellar material hanging in space. In fact, looking at the broadened part of the Milky Way in the region of Sagittarius[1] you would think first that the mythical celestial road branches here into two "one-way traffic lanes." But it is not an actual branching, and this impression is given simply by a dark cloud of interstellar dust and gases hanging in space right in the middle of the broadening between us and the galactic center. Thus whereas the darkness on both sides of the Milky Way is due to the background of the dark empty space, the blackness in the middle is produced by the dark opaque cloud. A few stars in the dark central patch are actually in the foreground, between us and the cloud (Figure 8-2).

It is, of course, a pity that we cannot see the mysterious galactic center around which our sun is spinning, along with billions of other stars. But in a way we know how it must look, from the observation of other stellar systems or galaxies scattered through space far beyond the outermost limit of our Milky Way. It is not some supergiant star keeping in subordination all the other members of the stellar system, as the sun reigns over the family of planets. The study of the central parts of other galaxies (which we will discuss a little later) indicates that they also consist of large multitudes of stars with the only difference that here the stars are crowded much more densely than in the outlying parts to which our sun belongs. If we think of the planetary system as an autocratic state where the Sun rules the planets, the Galaxy of stars may be likened to a kind of democracy in

Figure 8-1. An astronomer looking at the stellar system of the Milky Way reduced 100,000,000,000,000,000,000 times. The head of the astronomer is approximately in the position occupied by our sun.

[1] Which can be best observed on a clear night in early summer.

Figure 8-3. Great nebula in Andromeda.

which some members occupy influential central places while the others have to be satisfied with more humble positions on the outskirts of their society [Figure 8-3].

As said above, all the stars including our sun rotate in giant circles around the center of the galactic system. How can this be proved, how large are the radii of these stellar orbits, and how long does it take to make a complete circuit?

All these questions were answered a few decades ago by the Dutch astronomer Oort, who applied to the system of stars known as the Milky Way observations very similar to those made by Copernicus in considering the planetary system.

Let us remember first Copernicus' argument. It had been observed by the ancients, the Babylonians, the Egyptians, and others, that the big planets like Saturn or Jupiter seemed to move across the sky in a rather peculiar way. They seemed to proceed along an ellipse in the way the sun does, then suddenly to stop, to back, and after a second reversal of motion, to continue their way in the original direction. In the lower part of

Figure 8-4 we show schematically such a loop as described by Saturn over a period of about two years. (The period of Saturn's complete circuit is 29½ years.) Since, on account of religious prejudices that dictated the statement that our Earth is the center of the universe, all planets and the sun itself were believed to move around the Earth, the above described peculiarities of motion had to be explained by the supposition that planetary orbits have very peculiar shapes with a number of loops in them.

But Copernicus knew better, and by a stroke of genius, he explained the mysterious looping phenomenon as due to the fact that the Earth as well as all other planets move along simple circles around the Sun. This explanation of the looping effect can be easily understood after studying the schematic picture at the top of Figure 8-4.

The sun is in the center, the Earth (small sphere) moves along the smaller circle, and Saturn (with a ring) moves along the larger circle in the same direction as the Earth. Numbers 1, 2, 3, 4, 5 represent different positions of the Earth in the course of a year, and the corresponding positions of Saturn which, as we remember, moves much more slowly. The parts of vertical lines from the different positions of the Earth represent the direction to some fixed star. By drawing lines from the various Earth positions to the

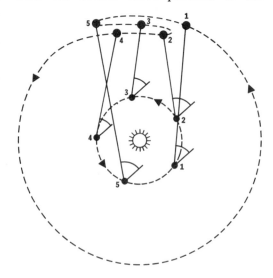

Figure 8-4

corresponding Saturn positions we see that the angle formed by the two directions (to Saturn and to the fixed star) first increases, then decreases, and then increases again. Thus the seeming phenomenon of looping does not represent any peculiarity of Saturn's motion but arises from the fact that we observe this motion from different angles on the moving Earth.

The Oort argument about the rotation of the Galaxy of stars may be understood after inspection of Figure 8-5. Here in the lower part of the picture we see the galactic center (with dark clouds and all!) and there are plenty of stars all around it through the entire field of the figure. The three circles represent the orbits of stars at different distances from the center, the middle circle being the orbit of our sun.

Let us consider eight stars (shown with rays to distinguish them from other points), two of which are moving along the same orbit as the sun, but one slightly ahead and one slightly behind it, the others located on somewhat larger and somewhat smaller orbits as shown in the figure. We must remember that owing to the laws of gravity the outer stars have lower and the inner stars higher velocity than the stars on solar orbits (this is indicated in the figure by the arrows of different lengths).

How will the motion of these eight stars look if observed from the sun, or, what is of course the same, from the Earth? We are speaking here about the motion along the line of sight, which can be most conveniently observed by means of the so-called Doppler effect.[2] It is clear, first of all, that the two stars (marked D and E) that move along the same orbit and with the same speed as the sun will seem stationary to a solar (or terrestrial) observer. The same is true of the other two stars (B and G) located along the radius, since they move parallel to the sun, so that there is no component of velocity along the line of sight.

Now what about the stars A and C on the outer circle? Since they both move more slowly than the sun we must conclude, as clearly seen in this picture, that the star A

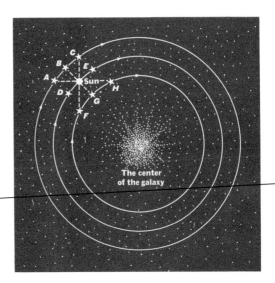

Figure 8-5

is lagging behind, whereas the star C is being overtaken by the sun. The distance to the star A will increase, while the distance to C will decrease, and the light coming from two stars must show respectively the red and violet Doppler effect. For the stars F and H on the inner circle the situation will be reversed, and we must have a violet Doppler effect for F and a red one for H.

It is assumed that the phenomenon just described could be caused only by a circular motion of the stars, and the existence of that circular motion makes it possible for us not only to prove this assumption but also to estimate the radius of stellar orbits and the velocity of stellar motion. By collecting the observational material on the observed apparent motion of stars all over the sky, Oort was able to prove that the expected phenomenon of red and violet Doppler effect really exists, thus proving beyond any doubt the rotation of the Galaxy. . . .

The exact measurements of the Oort effect of stellar motion now makes it possible to measure the orbits of stars and determine the period of rotation. Using this method of calculation it has been learned that the radius of the solar orbit having its center in Sagittarius is 30,000 light-years, that is, about two

[2] See the discussion of the Doppler effect on p. 265. [Also pp. 195–196.

thirds the radius of the outermost orbit of the entire galactic system. The time necessary for the sun to move a complete circle around the galactic center is some 200 million years. It is a long time, of course, but remembering that our stellar system is at least 5 billion years old, we find that during its entire life our sun with its family of planets has made 25 or more complete rotations. If, following the terminology of the terrestrial year, we call the period of solar rotation "a solar year" we can say that our universe is only 25 years old. Indeed things happen slowly in the world of stars, and a solar year is quite a convenient unit for time measurements in the history of the universe!

As we have already mentioned above, our Galaxy is not the only isolated society of stars floating in the vast spaces of the universe. Telescopic studies reveal the existence, far away in space, of many other giant groups very similar to that to which our sun belongs. The nearest of them, the famous Andromeda Nebula, can be seen even by the naked eye. It appears to us as a small, faint, rather elongated nebulosity. In Figures 8-6 and 8-7 are shown photographs, taken through the large telescope of the Mt. Wilson Observatory, of two such celestial objects. The two objects shown in these photographs are: the Nebula in Coma Berenices seen straight on the edge, and the Nebula in Ursus Major seen from the top. We notice that, as a part of the characteristic lens-shape ascribed to our Galaxy, these nebulae possess a typical spiral structure; hence the name "spiral nebulae." There are many indications that our own stellar structure is similarly a spiral, but it is very difficult to determine the shape of a structure when you are inside it. As a matter of fact, our sun is most probably located at the very end of one of the spiral arms of the "Great Nebula of the Milky Way."

For a long time astronomers did not realize that the spiral nebulae are giant stellar systems similar to our Milky Way, and confused them with ordinary diffuse nebulae like that in the constellation of Orionis, which represent the large clouds of interstellar dust

floating between the stars inside our Galaxy. Later, however, it was found that these foggy spiral-shaped objects are not fog at all, but are made of separate stars, which can be seen as tiny individual points when the largest magnifications are used. But they are so far away that no parallactic measurements can indicate their actual distance.

Thus it would seem at first that we had reached the limit of our means for measuring celestial distances. But no! In science, when we come to an insuperable difficulty the delay is usually only temporary; something always happens that permits us to go still farther. In this case a quite new "measuring rod" was found by the Harvard astronomer Harlow Shapley in the so-called pulsating stars or Cepheides.[3]

There are stars and stars. While most of them glow quietly in the sky, there are a few that constantly change their luminosity from bright to dim, and from dim to bright in regularly spaced cycles. The giant bodies of these stars pulsate as regularly as the heart beats, and along with this pulsation goes a periodic change of their brightness.[4] The larger the star, the longer is the period of its pulsation, just as it takes a long pendulum more time to complete its swing than a short one. The really small ones (that is, small as stars go) complete their period in the course of a few hours, whereas the real giants take years and years to go through one pulsation. Now, since the bigger stars are also the brighter, there is an apparent correlation between the period of stellar pulsation, and the average brightness of the star. This relation can be established by observing the Cepheides, which are sufficiently close to us so that their distance and consequently actual brightness may be directly measured.

If now you find a pulsating star that lies beyond the limit of parallactic measurements, all you have to do is to watch the star through the telescope and observe the time consumed

[3] So called after the star δ-Cepheus, in which the phenomenon of pulsation was first discovered.
[4] One must not confuse these pulsating stars with the so-called eclipsing variables, which actually represent systems of two stars rotating around each other and periodically eclipsing one another.

by its pulsation period. Knowing the period, you will know its actual brightness, and comparing it with its apparent brightness you can tell at once how far away it is. This ingenious method was successfully used by Shapley for measuring particularly large distances within the Milky Way and has been most useful in estimating the general dimensions of our stellar system.

When Shapley applied the same method to measuring the distance to several pulsating stars found imbedded in the giant body of the Andromeda Nebula, he was in for a big surprise! The distance from the Earth to these stars, which, of course, must be the same as the distance to the Andromeda Nebula itself, turned out to be . . . much larger than the estimated diameter of the stellar system of Milky Way. And the size of Andromeda Nebula came out only a little smaller than the size of our entire Galaxy. The two spiral nebulae shown in our Plates (Figures 8-6 and 8-7) are still farther away and their diameters are comparable to that of the Andromeda.*

This discovery dealt the death blow to the earlier assumptions that the spiral nebulae are comparatively "small things" located within our Galaxy, and established them as independent galaxies of stars very similar to our own system, the Milky Way. No astronomer would now doubt that to an observer located on some small planet circling one of the billions of stars that form the Great Andromeda Nebula, our own Milky Way would look much as the Andromeda Nebula looks to us [Figures 8-3 and 8-8].

The further studies of these distant stellar societies, which we owe mostly to Dr. E. Hubble, the celebrated galaxy-gazer of Mt. Wilson Observatory, reveal a great many facts of great interest and importance. It was found first of all that the galaxies, which appear more numerous through a good telescope than the ordinary stars do to the naked eye, do not all have necessarily spiral form, but present a great variety of different types.

* The distance to Andromeda is estimated at about two million light years. Ed.

There are *spherical galaxies*, which look like regular discs with diffused boundaries; there are *elliptical galaxies* [Figure 8-9] with different degrees of elongation. The spirals themselves differ from each other by the "tightness with which they are wound up." There are also very peculiar shapes known as "barred spirals."

It is a fact of extreme importance that all the varieties of the observed galactic shapes can be arranged in a regular sequence (Figure 8-10), which presumably corresponds to different stages of the evolution of these giant stellar societies.

Although we are still far from understanding the details of galactic evolution, it seems very probable that it is due to the process of progressive contraction. It is well known that when a slowly rotating spherical body of gas undergoes a steady contraction, its speed of rotation increases, and its shape becomes that of a flattened ellipsoid. At a certain stage of contraction, when the ratio of the polar radius to the equatorial radius becomes equal to $7/10$, the rotating body must assume a lenticular shape with a sharp edge running along its equator. Still further contraction keeps this lenticular shape intact, but the gases forming the rotating body begin to flow away into surrounding space all along the sharp equatorial edge, leading to the formation of a thin gaseous veil in the equatorial plane.

All the above statements have been proved mathematically by the celebrated English physicist and astronomer Sir James Jeans for a rotating gas sphere, but they can also be applied without any alterations to the giant stellar clouds that we call galaxies. In fact, we can consider such a clustering of the billions of stars as a flock of gas in which the role of molecules is now played by individual stars.

In comparing the theoretical calculations of Jeans with Hubble's empirical classification of galaxies, we find that these giant stellar societies follow exactly the course of evolution described by the theory. In particular we find that the most elongated shape of elliptic nebulae is that corresponding to

Figure 8-7. A spiral nebula in Ursa Major, a distant island universe, seen from above.

Figure 8-6.   Spiral nebula in Coma Berenices.

Figure 8-8.   Edge of Andromeda.

Figure 8-9.   An elliptical galaxy.

Spherical   Elliptic   Transitional   Closed spiral   Opened spiral

Figure 8-10. The various phases of normal galactic evolution.

the radius-ratio of 7/10 (E7), and that it is the first case in which we notice a sharp equatorial edge. The spirals that develop in the later stages of evolution are apparently formed from the material ejected by the rapid rotation, although up to the present we do not have a completely satisfactory explanation of why and how these spiral forms are formed and what causes the difference between the simple and the barred spirals.

Much is still to be learned from further study of the structure, motion, and stellar content in the different parts of galactic societies of stars. A very interesting result was, for example, obtained a couple of years ago by a Mt. Wilson astronomer, W. Baade, who was able to show that, whereas the central bodies (nuclei) of spiral nebulae are formed by the same type of stars as the spherical and elliptic galaxies, the arms themselves show a rather different type of stellar population. This "spiral-arm" type of stellar population differs from the population of the central region by the presence of very hot and bright stars, the so-called "Blue Giants," which are absent in the central regions as well as in the spherical and elliptic galaxies. Since, . . . the Blue Giants most probably represent the most recently formed stars, it is reasonable to assume that the spiral arms are so to speak the breeding grounds for new stellar populations. One could imagine that a large part of the material ejected from the equatorial bulge of a contracting elliptic galaxy is formed by primordial gases that come out into the cold intergalactic space and condense into the separate large lumps of matter, which through subsequent contraction become very hot and very bright. . . .

We must state here, first of all that the method of distance measurements based on pulsating stars, though giving excellent results when applied to quite a number of galaxies that lie in the neighborhood of our Milky Way, fails when we proceed into the depth of space, since we soon reach distances at which no separate stars may be distinguished and the galaxies look like tiny elongated nebulosities even through the strongest telescopes. Beyond this point we can rely on the visible size, since it is fairly well established that, unlike stars, all galaxies of a given type are of about the same size. If you know that all people are of the same height, that there are no giants or dwarfs, you can always say how far a man is from you by observing his apparent size.

Using this method for estimating distances in the far-outflung realm of galaxies, Dr. Hubble was able to prove that the galaxies are scattered more or less uniformly through space as far as the eye (fortified by the most highly powered telescope) can see. We say "more or less" because there are many cases in which the galaxies cluster in large groups containing sometimes many thousands of members, in the same way as the separate stars cluster in galaxies.

Our own galaxy, Milky Way, is apparently one member of a comparatively small group of galaxies numbering in its membership three spirals (including ours, and the Andromeda Nebula) and six elliptical and four irregular nebulae (two of which are Magellanic clouds).

However, save for such occasional clustering, the galaxies, as seen through the 200-inch telescope of the Palomar Mountain Observatory, are scattered rather uniformly through space . . . the visible horizons of the universe contain almost one billion individual stellar worlds! . . .

Studying the spectra of the light coming from these distant galaxies, Mt. Wilson's astronomer E. Hubble noticed that the spectral lines are shifted slightly towards the red end of the spectrum, and that this so-called "red shift" is stronger in the more distant galaxies. In fact, it was found that the "red shift" observed in different galaxies is directly proportional to their distance from us.

The most natural way to explain this phenomenon is to assume that *all galaxies recede from us with a speed that increases with their distance from us.* This explanation is based on the so-called "Doppler effect," which makes the light coming from a source that is approaching us change its color toward the violet end of the spectrum, and light from a receding source change toward the red. Of course, to obtain a noticeable shift the relative velocity of the source in relation to the position of the observer must be rather large. When Prof. R. W. Wood was arrested for going through a red traffic signal in Baltimore and told the judge that, because of this phenomenon, the light he saw looked green to him, since he was approaching it in the car, the professor was simply pulling the judge's leg. Had the judge known more about physics, he would have asked Professor Wood to calculate the speed with which he must have been driving in order to see green in a red light, and then would have fined him for speeding.

Returning to the problem of the "red shift" observed in galaxies, we come to what is at first sight a rather awkward conclusion. It looks as though all of the galaxies in the universe were running away from our Milky Way as if it were a galactic Monster of Frankenstein! What then are the horrible properties of our own stellar system, and why does it seem to be so unpopular among all other galaxies? If you think a little about this question, you will easily come to the conclusion that there is nothing particularly wrong with our Milky Way, and that, in fact, other galaxies do not run away from it exclusively but rather that all run away from one another. Imagine a rubber balloon with a polka-dot pattern painted on its surface (Figure 8-11). If you will begin to inflate it, gradually stretching its surface to a large and larger size, the distances between individual dots will continually increase so that an insect sitting on any one of the dots would receive the impression that all other dots are "running away" from it. Moreover the recession velocities of different dots on the expanding balloon will be directly proportional to their distance from the insect's observation point.

This example must make it quite clear that the recession of galaxies observed by Hubble has nothing to do with the particular properties or position of our own galaxy, but must be interpreted simply as due to *the general uniform expansion of the system of galaxies scattered through the space of the universe.*

From the observed velocity of the expansion and the present distances between the neighboring galaxies one easily calculates that *this expansion must have started at least five billion years ago.* . . .

We are now prepared to answer the fundamental question concerning the size of our universe. *Shall we consider the universe as extending into infinity and conclude that bigger and better telescopes will always reveal to the inquiring eye of an astronomer new and hitherto unexplored regions of space, or must we believe, on the contrary, that the universe occupies some very big but nevertheless finite volume, and is, at least in principle, explorable down to the last star?*

When we speak of the possibility that our universe is of "finite size," we do not mean, of course, that somewhere at a distance of several billion light-years the explorer of space will encounter a blank wall on which is posted the notice "No trespassing."

In fact, . . . *space can be finite without being necessarily limited by a boundary.* It can simply curve around and "close on itself," so that a hypothetical space explorer, trying to steer his rocket ship as straight as possible will describe a geodesic line in space and come back to the point from which he started.

The situation would be, of course, quite similar to an ancient Greek explorer who travels *west* from his native city of Athens, and, after a long journey, finds himself entering the eastern gates of the city.

And just as the curvature of the Earth's

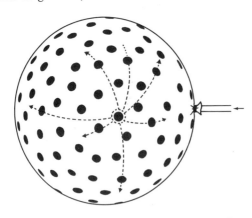

Figure 8-11. The dots run away from one another when the rubber balloon is expanding.

surface can be established without a trip around the world, simply by studying the geometry of only a comparatively small part of it, the question about the curvature of the three-dimensional space of the universe can be answered by similar measurements . . . one must distinguish between two kinds of curvature: the positive one corresponding to the closed space of finite volume, and the negative one corresponding to the saddle-like opened infinite space [Figure 7-7]. The difference between these two types of space lies in the fact that, whereas in the *closed space* the number of uniformly scattered objects falling within a given distance from the observer increases more slowly than the cube of that distance, the opposite is true in *opened space*. . . .

Now we can ask ourselves what kind of forces are responsible for the expansion of the universe, and whether this expansion will ever stop or even become contraction. Is there any possibility that the expanding masses of the universe will turn back on us and squeeze our stellar system, the Milky Way, the sun, the Earth, and the humanity on earth into a pulp with nuclear density?

According to conclusions based upon the best available information, this will never happen. Long ago, in the early stages of its evolution, the expanding universe broke all of the ties that might have held it together and is now expanding into infinity obedient

to the simple law of inertia. The ties we have just mentioned were formed by gravity forces which tended to prevent the masses of the universe from drawing apart. . . .

It seems that at present the kinetic energy of receding galaxies is several times greater than their mutual potential gravitational energy, from which it would follow that *our universe is expanding into infinity without any chance of ever being pulled more closely together again by the forces of gravity.* It must be remembered, however, that most of the numerical data pertaining to the universe as a whole are not very exact,[1] and it is possible that future studies will reverse this conclusion. But even if the expanding universe does suddenly stop in its tracks, and turn back in a movement of compression, it will be billions of years before that terrible day envisioned by the Negro Spiritual, "when the stars begin to fall," and we are crushed under the weight of collapsing galaxies!

[1] It must be mentioned here that the above-described method of estimating the age of the universe is based on the knowledge of the distances of faraway galaxies. Since at large distances no stars, and in particular no Cepheids, can be seen, even through the largest telescopes, these distances are estimated on the basis of the inverse square law for the observed brightness of light sources. Thus, if one galaxy seems 25 times fainter than another, it is considered to be 5 times farther away. This method presupposes, however, that the intrinsic brightness of a galaxy does not change with its age, which may not be true. In fact, younger galaxies probably contain many very bright fast-evolving stars which mostly disappear in older galaxies. Looking far out in space, we look far back in time and see distant galaxies as they were in the distant past. This may lead to an underestimate of their intrinsic brightness, resulting in an underestimate of their distance. Since radioastronomers (see next section) observe galactic collisions as far away as 9 billion light-years, the figure obtained on the basis of the red shift must probably be increased.

RADIO ASTRONOMY

RADIO TELESCOPES*
by A. C. B. Lovell (1959)

The succession of telescopes of ever-increasing size which have been constructed has continued to reveal more and more distant nebu-

* From A. C. B. Lovell, *The Individual and the Universe.* Copyright 1958, 1959 by A. C. B. Lovell. Reprinted by permission of Harper & Row, Publishers, New York, and Oxford University Press, Fair Lawn, N.J. This work was originally presented as the Reith Lectures and broadcast over the BBC in the autumn of 1958.

lae of stars. However, it seems likely that we have nearly reached the culmination of this line of development with the 200-inch telescope on Palomar Mountain in America which began its programme of work about 15 years ago. Culmination, because it seems possible that optical telescopes of this order of size may represent the largest which it is worth while building on earth. Even under the excellent atmospheric conditions which exist on Palomar, the unsteadiness of the atmosphere limits the realization of the maximum penetration of this telescope to a few dozen nights during the year.

This telescope can photograph star systems which are so far away that the light has taken over two thousand million* years to reach us, but when I discuss the problem of the origin of the universe you will realize that this distance is a most tantalizing limit. The desire to find out what lies beyond is very great— some knowledge of the star systems at twice this distance might well give us the key to unlock the secrets of the evolution of the entire universe. You will therefore understand that those of us who seek this knowledge seize with a particular passion any prospects of surmounting the hindrances of our earthbound environment. And indeed we have been born in a fortunate and exciting epoch. Out of the cataclysm of the world war have emerged two technical developments which are creating a revolution in astronomical observations— radio astronomy and the earth satellite.

When I think of the enormous scientific and technological problems which had to be solved I still stand in awe when I reflect that at this moment[1] at least four objects launched by man are relentlessly circling this earth. They have carried scientific instruments above the dense regions of the earth's atmosphere and are sending back by radio the information about the conditions in the environment of the earth which hitherto we have only been able to probe remotely and by inference. The astronomer whose interest lies in the problems of the solar system has already gathered a rich harvest of results about the complex of radiations and particles which exist in space and which are normally absorbed or transformed by processes in the upper regions of the atmosphere. Soon, telescopes will be carried into these regions and man's vision will

be freed from the disturbing effects of the atmosphere. Limitless possibilities are now emerging; indeed, we seem to be on the verge of another epoch of discovery which may well parallel that of the radio telescope.

In the ordinary course of events our knowledge of the universe comes to us because the sun and the stars emit light. Less than 30 years ago Jansky, an American engineer, discovered almost by accident that radio waves were reaching the earth from outer space. But although his proof that they were coming from regions of space outside the solar system was quite decisive, he could not find out much more about these radio waves. Radio waves and light waves travel through space with the same speed, 186,000 miles a second, but are distinguished by the difference in wavelength. The light which reaches us from the stars has a wavelength measurable in millionths of a centimetre whereas the wavelength of the radio waves is measured in metres. To detect these radio waves we need a special kind of telescope, now commonly known as a radio telescope, which is in effect, a very large version of the common television aerial. The urge to build big radio telescopes is the same as the driving force behind the construction of large optical telescopes, namely, the desire to penetrate far into space. Because of the long wavelength of the radio waves the radio telescopes have to be very much larger than optical telescopes. Even with the enormous instruments now in operation the radio-astronomer's view of the heavens is ill-defined compared with that given by a small optical telescope [Figure 8-12]. This factor greatly increases the difficulty of correlating the universe which we study with radio telescopes with the stars and galaxies visible to our eyes.

It is hardly surprising that Jansky and those who followed him were unable to relate their radio signals with the stellar objects perceived by our normal senses, and for a long time the idea existed that these radio waves were coming from the hydrogen gas which fills the space between the stars. For years Jansky's discovery remained almost unknown, and this unexpected gift of nature to man lay disregarded by the world's astronomers. My

---

* Throughout these selections, Professor Lovell uses the British "billion." The British "billion" is a million million, whereas the American 'billion" is a thousand million. Ed.
[1] The moment in question was at the time of the original broadcast on 23 November, 1958, when the Vanguard satellite, Explorer IV, Sputnik 3, and its carrier rocket were all in orbit.

own introduction to this work was accidental —a casual remark by a colleague during the endless wartime discussions on how to get a few more miles of range out of our radar. Yet within four years I was wanting most desperately the telescope which now towers over the Cheshire plain. You see, the wartime developments in radar had placed in our hands equipment of a sensitivity and excellence far greater than anything previously available. As soon as these new techniques were used to study the radio waves from the sky one realized that Jansky's discovery had opened an entirely new avenue for the exploration of space.

The improved definition and sensitivity of the equipment soon showed that some of the radio emission was concentrated in particular parts of the sky. The idea that the interstellar hydrogen gas emitted the radio waves turned out to be only a small part of the story. The real situation was much more exciting. The concentration of the radio emissions into localized sources does not seem to occur in any regions of the heavens in which there are prominent visible objects. On the other hand, if we turn our radio telescopes towards the bright stars like Sirius or Capella we cannot record any radio waves from them. Indeed, we face a paradox which has sometimes made us reflect on those heavenly bodies of Lucretius 'which glide devoid of light forevermore.' However, we do not believe that these newly discovered radio sources are dark stars. Our difficulty in relating them to the universe of our ordinary vision arises, we think, partly because the objects which emit radio waves are very faint and generally peculiar, and partly because the radio waves come from distant regions which are beyond the range of the optical telescopes.

Before I talk further about this situation it would, I think, be helpful if I described the results of our attempts to detect radio emissions from the more common stars and galaxies. To begin with, the sun is a very strong radio source—so strong indeed that it sometimes hinders the observations of the more distant signals, in the same way that its light blocks out stars from the ordinary telescopes.

Figure 8-12. Radio telescope at Parkes, New South Wales, Australia, which came into operation late in 1961.

One of the earliest of the post-war surprises was the discovery by Appleton and Hey that the sun spots and flares which occasionally appear on the solar surface are associated with great and irregular increases in the solar radio emissions. These solar eruptions are often accompanied by disturbing terrestrial events such as the appearance of the aurora borealis and the fadeouts in transatlantic radio-communications. When the sun is quiet, or undisturbed by spots, then the radio waves from the sun are much less intense. They are generated in the solar corona, that highly tenuous region of the sun extending far outside the photosphere which is the disk of the sun which we see normally [Figure 6-13]. For the radio astronomer the size of the sun depends on the wavelength which he uses to study it. At a radio wavelength of a few centimetres we find that the sun is about the same size as the sun which we see with our eyes, but as the wavelength we use increases so does the size of the sun as seen by the radio astronomer. At a few metres' wavelength its radius is several times greater than the optical radius. If our eyes were sensitive to these radio wavelengths the sun would appear to be enormous and probably flattened, not spherical as it now appears. The subjective basis for our knowledge of the sun introduces a nice point for philosophical argument.

Of the planets in our solar system, Jupiter at least behaves abnormally as far as the radio astronomer is concerned. About four years ago scientists in Washington got some unexpected deflections on the chart connected to their radio telescope. For a long time they thought it was some local interference but after a few months the same kind of interference began to appear in the middle of the night and eventually they realized that the signals were coming from the planet Jupiter. Now these results are very surprising, since, unlike the sun, Jupiter does not have the kind of hot atmosphere conducive to the generation of radio waves. It now seems possible that these signals come from the planetary surface, and recent work has indicated that if this is the case only a few places on the surface are responsible. It is interesting to speculate on the events which might generate these signals, since the energies involved are enormous. In fact, it is difficult to establish a parallel with anything which might happen on earth. One has to think in terms of the energy of ten or more hydrogen bombs, or giant volcanic eruptions like the explosion of Krakatau. We may well have to wait for the close approach of a space probe to Jupiter before this problem can be settled.

After these remarks about the radio emissions from the sun and Jupiter you may be somewhat puzzled by my earlier reference to the difficulty of detecting radio waves from the common visible objects in the universe. The sun is a common star, and one might therefore expect other stars in the Milky Way to emit similar radio waves. Indeed, they might well do so, but even the nearest star is over 200,000 times farther from us than the sun. If the sun were at that distance its radio waves would be 50,000 million times more difficult to detect and that presents us with an almost insuperable problem. Actually if these distant stars also have occasional great outbursts, then the radio waves emitted on these occasions might just be detectable by a large instrument like the telescope at Jodrell Bank. Such a search is in progress, but whatever the result it is clear that any radio emissions of this kind from common stars do not make any significant contribution to the radio waves which are emanating from the regions of the Milky Way.

When we turn our radio telescopes in the direction of the Milky Way we are studying radio waves which have been on their journey for many thousands of years. As I said in my first lecture, the Milky Way is an assemblage of ten thousand million stars arranged in the form of a flattened disk across which light would take 100,000 years to travel. As for the radio waves from the Milky Way, the only conclusive statement which I would be prepared to make is that they certainly do not originate in these stars. The Milky Way as revealed to the radio telescopes is not such a flattened disk. It is surrounded by a halo, or corona, of radio emission. The existence of this corona was inferred a year or so ago by the Russian astronomer, Schlovsky, whose idea was confirmed by the measurements of the radio astronomers in Cambridge, and this summer two of my colleagues using the Jodrell Bank telescope have found evidence for similar haloes around the distant extragalactic nebulae; that is to say, nebulae outside the Milky Way. We do not yet know how to interpret these discoveries because there is nothing visible in the optical telescopes outside the main stellar structure of these nebulae. Hoyle and Gold are convinced that the radio waves in these regions are emanating from high-energy particles moving in extensive magnetic fields, and that those same particles are the source of the cosmic radiation. If this linkage can be substantiated a most important step will have been made in our understanding of some fundamental astrophysical processes.

When we consider the radio emissions which come from the regions of the Milky Way defined by the assemblage of stars, we find a complicated situation which is not yet fully understood. Two features are of particular interest. Between the stars it has for long been realized that there must exist great clouds of hydrogen gas, but this gas is in a neutral state and does not emit light and so cannot be seen with ordinary telescopes. However, the neutral hydrogen atom emits radio waves on a particular wavelength of 21 centimetres, and these interstellar hydrogen clouds can be detected and measured with the radio telescopes. The story of the detection of these 21-centimetre emissions is an epic of modern science. In the terrible circumstances of the German occupation Van de Hulst, a young research student in Holland, made the calculations which led him to predict the existence of these radio waves. He showed that although for any one hydrogen atom the process of emission is only likely to take place once in eleven million years, the numbers of atoms in the interstellar clouds are so great that the emission should be detectable. Years of peace were required to develop the right equipment, and then in 1951 these weak radio waves were detected—an event which represented a triumph of technical skill and a brilliant vindication of Van de Hulst's prediction.

The astronomers in Leiden under their director, Jan Oort, seized on this unparalleled opportunity of piercing the secrets of the structure of the Milky Way. The large optical telescopes are powerless to penetrate the interstellar dust clouds which obscure the structural details of the system—and you must remember that we are placed in an unprivileged position on the edge of the galactic disk. The dust presents little handicap to the passage of the 21-centimetre waves, and during the last few years Oort and his staff have produced results of almost unbelievable detail and elegance describing parts of the Milky Way which men will never see.

The second feature of the radio waves which come from within the confines of the Milky Way is that the smooth background of radio emission is punctuated by very strong sources which stand out for the radio telescope in the same way that the bright visual stars stand out from the diffuse light of the Milky Way. I have already emphasized that

the common bright stars do not emit radio waves—at least they have not yet been detected—and the solution to the origin of these strong sources of radio waves cannot be found in the common stars. There are a few cases where these radio sources have been identified with unusual objects which can be seen in the optical telescopes. The most spectacular is the Crab Nebula [Figure 8-13], 4,000 light years away. This nebula is the gaseous remains of an exploding star or supernova outburst seen by Chinese astronomers 900 years ago in A.D. 1054. The millions of tons of hydrogenous material of the star disintegrated in a catastrophic explosion, and at present we see the gaseous shell of the explosion still moving out through space at the rate of 70 million miles a day. This gas is at a high temperature and in a great state of turmoil, and we believe that these conditions are responsible for the radio emission. There are two other well-established cases of supernova outbursts in the galactic system—those observed by Tycho Brahe in 1572 and by Kepler in 1604. The visible remnants of these

Mount Wilson and Mount Palomar Observatories

Figure 8-13.   Crab nebula.

are difficult to see in the telescope, but both have been identified as radio sources.

The most powerful of the radio sources in the Milky Way lies in the constellation of Cassiopeia, and this was very difficult to link up with any visible object. A few years ago after protracted research the American astronomers on Palomar succeeded in photographing a strange object coincident with the radio source. It is a diffuse and faintly luminous region of gas covering an area of sky which is much larger than that occupied by a star. The object contains filaments of gas in extremely violent motion. Recently, less intense sources have been associated with similar regions of diffuse gas in Gemini and Auriga. No one yet knows where these stand in the sequence of stellar evolution; they may be old supernovae or, alternatively, the beginning of the concentrations of gas which ultimately form stars. One thing seems certain, they are so faint and diffuse that they are unlikely to have been recognized as significant stellar objects but for their strong radio emissions.

From these remarks you will see that the radio emission generated in the Milky Way system has complex origins, such as the diffuse regions of turbulent gas which give us localized radio sources, of which some at least are supernova; the clouds of neutral hydrogen gas; the corona around the system where no matter can be seen; and probably emission from ionized hydrogen which contributes to the background radiation. But when we inspect our records we find many thousands of radio sources which seem to be distributed uniformly over the sky. Most of these are much weaker than those which I have just described in relation to the Milky Way, and their uniform distribution leads us to believe that they are external and lie at great distances from the local galaxy. Of course, the extragalactic star systems, of which there may be a hundred or even a thousand million in the field of view of the large optical telescopes, have an overall uniform distribution in space—at least within the two thousand million light years to which the telescopes

penetrate. It would therefore be natural to look for a close association between these nebulae and the radio sources.

When this is done, only a very limited number of associations can be found. The great spiral nebula in Andromeda at a distance of 2 million light years is one, but until a few months ago not more than a dozen out of all the millions of these normal extragalactic star systems had been related to the radio sources. This is entirely consistent with the strength of the radio waves emitted by the Milky Way system. If the extragalactic systems radiate in a similar way, then on account of their great distances from us only a small number would be detectable. The consistency of this picture has recently been firmly established by Hanbury Brown and Hazard using the new Jodrell Bank telescope with which they have been able to make detailed studies of several dozens of these normal extragalactic nebulae. Amongst all the confusion which still exists we can, I think, say that the spiral nebulae in the universe emit radio waves in the same way as our own spiral Milky Way system, but that very few of them can be detected with present day radio telescopes.

We are therefore still left with this problem of the thousands of radio sources which are detected by our radio telescopes, and we now believe that the solution of this puzzle may lie in one of the most remarkable of all the discoveries in radio astronomy. Some years ago Ryle and his colleagues in Cambridge made a very accurate measurement of the position of one of the stronger of these unidentified sources which lies in the constellation of Cygnus. These measurements were sufficiently accurate for the American astronomers to use the 200-inch telescope on Palomar to make an exhaustive search of this region of the sky. They found there a remarkable event in which two great extragalactic nebulae seem to have collided with one another. This collision, which is at a distance of 700 million light years, is nearly at the limit of clear definition of the world's biggest optical telescope, and yet the radio waves are relatively strong—so strong that even if the nebulae were ten times farther away we could still detect them as a radio source. We do not yet understand why two nebulae in collision like this produce radio waves which are far more intense than those they would produce separately. For our present argument the important fact is that the strength of the radio emission is out of all proportion to the visibility of the nebulae in the optical sense [Figure 8-14].

The relevance of this event to the problem of our unidentified radio sources depends on the question as to whether this collision of galaxies is unique. If one surveys the space around the Milky Way system, then it is very empty—there is not another galaxy of stars closer than a million or so light years, and this is a fairly average distance between galaxies. In this case the chances of collision are negligible. On the other hand, in the great clusters of galaxies which exist far out in space one might find a thousand galaxies separated by a mere thirty thousand light years. This still gives us a separation of a million million million miles between the galaxies and that, by ordinary standards, is a safe distance. But the galaxies in the clusters are moving about at a speed of over 2,000 miles a second, and this makes the chance of collision a substantial one.

We believe that the majority of these radio sources which lie outside the Milky Way may be colliding galaxies—a belief which has been strengthened by the discovery of a few more similar associations. We believe also that our failure to identify more of these radio sources with visible events arises because the collisions are taking place at very great distances, beyond the range of the optical telescopes. This view is now being freely discussed, but the precise interpretation of the current results from Cambridge and Sydney, where so much of this work has been done, is hotly disputed. The problem is of the very greatest significance to cosmology, and I must reserve further discussion until we consider the question of the origin of the universe.

On the issue of the collisions of galaxies I should perhaps say that I have adopted the interpretation which the American astrono-

Mount Wilson and Mount Palomar Observatories

Figure 8-14. Galaxy NGC 5128, which is associated with an intense radio source in Centaurus; it is believed to represent the collision of two galaxies in a remote part of the universe.

mers place on their own photographs. In the case of the two best examples in Cygnus and Perseus the photographs show the entwinement of two galactic systems. Ambartzumian, the distinguished Soviet astronomer, has argued that these are not collisions, but cases where the nucleus of a single galaxy has divided to form two separate systems, and that the photographs show the galaxies in process of separation. He believes that the parts of the divided nucleus are receding from one another with a speed of many hundreds of miles a second, and that very violent processes continue for tens of millions of years. The radio emission he believes to be a result of these violent processes involving the collision of masses of interstellar matter and the ejection of high-energy particles from the atmospheres of very young stars.

Earlier in this talk I referred to the great desire to find out what the universe is like beyond the present two thousand million light year limit of the optical telescopes, and it is natural to inquire if our present-day radio telescopes have yet penetrated to these remote regions of space and time. Unfortunately it is a question to which at present there is no decisive answer. One can, however, say this. If the interpretation of the unidentified radio sources which I have given during the last few minutes is correct, then some recent measurements of the strength and size of a few of those sources which have been made at Jodrell Bank implies that we are dealing with events at distances of many thousands of millions of light years. Indeed, we may now be in the process of probing the ultimate depths of space and time.

TWO THEORIES OF THE ORIGIN OF THE UNIVERSE

THE EVOLUTIONARY THEORY*
by A. C. B. Lovell (1959)

I want to talk to you about the problem of the origin of the universe. I suppose it would hardly be an exaggeration to say that this is the greatest challenge to the intellect which faces man, and I cannot pretend that I have any new solution to offer you. However, you may have gathered from my earlier talks that today the air is alive with a new hope and expectancy, because our new instruments may be reaching out so far into space that we may soon be able to speak with more confidence. I am going to set out the problem as I see it, and I hope you will get an idea of these vast cosmological issues and of the implications of the alternative solutions which lie ahead. At the end I shall tell you what I think about it all as an ordinary human being.

We have seen that observational astronomy tells us about the universe as it exists out to distances of about two thousand million light years. At that distance we are seeing the universe as it existed two thousand million years ago. Within this vast area of space and time we can study the innumerable stars and galaxies, and from these observations we can attempt to infer the probable nature and extent of the cosmos beyond the range of observations.

I think there are three stages in which we might consider this problem. The first stage is to inquire whether the observations are likely to be extended in the future to even greater distances and thereby penetrate even farther into past history than the present two thousand million years. The second stage is an appeal to cosmological theory, an inquiry as to the extent to which the present observations agree with any particular cosmology and the nature of the past and future as predicted by these theories. Finally, we shall reach a stage where theories based on our present conceptions of physical laws have nothing further to say. At this point we pass from physics to metaphysics, from astronomy to theology, where the corporate views of science merge into the beliefs of the individual.

The vast region of space and time enclosed by the present observations includes several hundred million galaxies of stars. As far as we can see, the overall large-scale structure of the universe within these limits has a high degree of uniformity. When we look at these distant regions we find that the light is reddened, indicating that the galaxies are receding from us. As far as we can see, the red shift of the most distant nebulae is still increasing linearly with distance. There is no indication that we are seeing anything but a small part of the total universe. However, in the second stage of our inquiry we shall see that an observational test between rival cosmological theories demands a still further penetration, and an extension of the present observational limit is a matter of some ur-

* Lovell, op. cit.

gency in cosmology. Unfortunately there are fundamental difficulties introduced by the recession of the galaxies which no device of man will ever surmount. At the present observable limit of the large optical telescopes the galaxies are receding with a speed of about one-fifth of the velocity of light. From this aspect alone we face a limit to future progress. Even if no other effects intervened we could never obtain information about those farther regions of space where the velocities of recession of the galaxies reach the speed of light. The light from the more distant galaxies will never reach us. In Eddington's phrase 'Light is like a runner on an expanding track with the winning post receding faster than he can run.'

There are, moreover, further difficulties which will hinder the approach to this fundamental limit. If the remote galaxies were stationary, then all the light emitted, say, in one second would reach our telescopes. But the galaxies are moving away with speeds which are an appreciable fraction of the velocity of light, and as the speed increases less and less of the light actually emitted by the galaxies in one second reaches our instruments. This degradation of the intensity of the light coupled with the accompanying shift in wavelength to the red end of the spectrum worsens still further the technical difficulties of these observations.

The radio telescopes may well be in a stronger position with respect to these hindrances. To begin with, the collisions of galaxies, which I described in an earlier lecture, generate very powerful radio emissions, and the shifts in wavelength which accompany the recession do not present the same observational difficulties as in the optical case. In fact, the present belief is that many of the objects already studied by their radio emissions lie at distances which exceed considerably the present two thousand million light years' limit of the optical telescopes. Therefore, we can, I think, answer the first stage of our inquiry with some degree of certainty in the following way. The present observable horizon of the universe will be pushed back by a limited amount in the near future, per-

haps to a few thousand million light years. Then we must be content. No further strivings or inventions of man will enable us to probe the conditions which existed in epochs of history beyond these few thousand million years. They are gone for ever beyond the fundamental limits of observability.

At this point we reach the second stage of our inquiry, where we appeal to cosmological theory. The question is this. Can we formulate a theory in terms of known physical laws whose predictions agree so well with the present observable universe that we can predict the past and future?

Indeed, when we turn to the cosmological theories which are today seriously considered by astronomers we find a most absorbing state of affairs. Not one, but several theories can explain from acceptable postulates the present observable state of the universe. These predictions bring us face to face with the ultimate problem of the origin of the universe in ways which are startlingly different. But the new techniques in astronomy may be on the verge of producing observational data which may be decisively in favour of one or other of these cosmologies. At least one of these alternatives would, I think, present theology with a very serious dilemma. In fact, if the full implications of the theory eventually receive the support of astronomical observations it is difficult to see how certain fundamental doctrines could be maintained in their present harmonious relation with our physical knowledge of the universe.

First of all, though, I want to discuss the cosmological theories which are generally classed as the evolutionary models of the universe. I think it would be correct to say that these theories, which are a consequence of Einstein's general theory of relativity, are regarded with the most favour by the majority of contemporary astronomers. In passing, perhaps I should add that in the light of our present knowledge it does not seem worth while discussing for our present purpose any of the cosmological theories which preceded the introduction of the theory of general relativity in 1915. The application of Newton's theory of gravitation, in which the attraction between bodies varies inversely as the square of their distance apart, to the large-scale structure of the universe would require that the universe had a centre in which the spatial density of stars and galaxies was a maximum. As we proceed outwards from this centre the spatial density should diminish, until finally at great distances it should be succeeded by an infinite region of emptiness. The observed uniformity in the large-scale structure of the universe is clearly at variance with these ideas. Neither does any theory based on Newton's laws of universal attraction and conservation of mass offer hope of explaining the observed expansion and recession of the nebulae. On the other hand, in Einstein's theory of general relativity gravitation is not explained in terms of a force but of the deformation of space near massive bodies. In our ordinary life we treat space as though it were flat, or Euclidean, in the sense that the geometrical properties obey the axioms of Euclid as we were taught in school. For example, the three angles of a triangle add up to two right angles. According to Einstein's theory, however, these simple conceptions must be abandoned, and though in ordinary circumstances the differences are insignificant, nevertheless when we consider the properties of space near a massive star, for example, the conceptions of a flat space no longer apply . . . [Figure 7-6].

Einstein attempted to apply his new ideas of the gravitational curvature of space-time to the universe as a whole. In this case the curvature of space would be influenced not only by one star, but by countless stars and galaxies. However, in the large-scale view, as we have seen, the distribution has a high degree of uniformity, and the problem of the overall curvature of space can be related to the average density of the matter in the universe. In working out the equations Einstein was unable to find any solution which described a static universe. We must remember that this was a decade before the discovery of the recession of the nebulae, and any cosmological theory which did not provide for a static cosmos could have been little more than a curiosity.

Faced with this dilemma, Einstein realized in 1917 that the difficulties could be surmounted by the introduction of a new term in his equations. This is the famous λ term, or the cosmical constant, over which there was to be so much future dispute. This new term appears in the equations as an arbitrary universal constant. Its interpretation in terms of a physical model of the universe is that it introduces an effect analogous to repulsion. This cosmic repulsion increases with the distance between bodies, and is to be regarded as superimposed on the usual forces of Newtonian attraction. Thus at great distances the repulsion outweighs the attraction, and in the equilibrium condition the Newtonian attraction and cosmical repulsion are in exact balance.

We cannot follow in detail the subsequent developments, which are of the utmost complexity. Some years after the introduction of these ideas the whole situation was altered in dramatic fashion by the discovery that the universe was non-static but was expanding. At about the same time the Russian mathematician, Friedman, found other solutions of Einstein's equations which predicted either an expanding or contracting universe. In fact, now it has for long been realized that the equations of general relativity cannot define an unique universe because there are three unknowns in the equations, whereas observationally we have only two sets of data. The possible types of non-static universes fall into three main families determined by the various possible combinations of the sign of the cosmical constant and the space curvature. These are a universe which starts from a point origin at a finite time in the past and expands continuously to become infinitely large after an infinite time, a universe whose radius has a certain finite value at the initial moment of time, and thence expands to become infinite after an infinite time, and lastly a universe which expands from zero radius to a certain maximum and then collapses to zero again, this process of oscillation being capable of indefinite repetition. Within each of these three main categories a large number of possible models can be constructed differing in various points of detail. For the past thirty years cosmologists have sought for arguments based on the observed characteristics of the universe which would identify the actual universe with one of the theoretical models.

All that I propose to do here is to give some examples of these evolutionary models, one of which is today believed by many cosmologists to describe the past history with some degree of certainty. The first example is a solution discovered by the Abbé Lemaître in 1927 and developed by Eddington. I have already said that by introducing the cosmical constant Einstein was able to specify a static condition of the universe in which the Newtonian attraction and cosmical repulsion are in exact balance. However, this equilibrium is unstable. If something upsets the balance so that the attraction is weakened, then cosmical repulsion has the upper hand and an expansion begins. As the material of the universe separates, the distance between the bodies becomes greater, the attraction still further weakens, the cosmical repulsion ever increases, and the expansion becomes faster. On the other hand, if the equilibrium was upset in the other way so that the forces of attraction became superior, then the reverse would occur and the system would contract continuously. Eddington's view was that in the initial stage the universe consisted of a uniform distribution of protons and electrons, by our standards very diffuse. This proton-electron gas comprised the entire primeval universe, which would have had a radius of about a thousand million light years. At some stage an event or series of events must have occurred in this diffuse gas which determined that the universe was launched on a career of expansion and not contraction. There were many views as to how this might have happened. Eddington held that the accumulation of irregularities in the gas started the evolutionary tendency. Soon, condensations formed in the gas and those ultimately became the galaxies of stars. On these views the present radius of the universe must be about five times that of the initial static primeval universe.

In the light of modern knowledge this theory receives little support. The time scale of its evolution is too short, and one cannot find a compelling reason why the primeval gas should have been disturbed in such a way as to determine that the universe was launched on a career of expansion rather than contraction. The initial condition is a special case, ephemeral and fortuitous. As far as the laws of physics are concerned, one can only say that by chance the initial disturbances were such as to determine the history of the universe. One cannot feel very happy that such a chance occurrence some thousands of millions of years ago should have determined the fundamental features of the universe. Moreover, although originally the theory as expounded by Jeans and Eddington undoubtedly had attractive features for some theologians, I feel now that this might well have been enhanced by feelings of relief that the vastness, uniformity, and organization of the universe which had just been revealed still remained outside the conceivable laws of physics in its initial state. Indeed, when considering these initial conditions Jeans spoke in terms of 'the finger of God agitating the ether,' implying a divine intervention at a predictable time in past history after which the laws of physics became applicable. This degree of familiarity with divine processes is, I think, undesirable theologically, and for science it evades the problem by obscuring the ultimate cosmological issue.

Moreover, there is another problem which must be faced. The event which we have considered in the unstable static assemblage of primeval gas predetermined the subsequent history of the universe. One must still inquire how long the gas existed in this condition of unstable equilibrium and how the primeval gas originated. Science has nothing to say on this issue. Indeed, it seems that the theory requires the exercise of yet another divine act at some indeterminate time before the occurrence which set off the gas on its career of condensation and expansion.

Of course, this particular model is now of little more than historical interest as being one of the first of the evolutionary theories based on general relativity to receive serious attention. It provides, however, a remarkable example of the influence in cosmology of the predilection of the individual. When faced with the various possible cosmological models which we have outlined, Eddington said this: 'Since I cannot avoid introducing this question of a beginning, it has seemed to me that the most satisfactory theory would be one which made the beginning not too unaesthetically abrupt. This condition can only be satisfied by an Einstein universe with all the major forces balanced.' He continues, 'Perhaps it will be objected that, if one looks far enough back, this theory does not really dispense with an abrupt beginning, the whole universe must come into being at one instant in order that it may start in balance. I do not regard it in that way. To my mind undifferentiated sameness and nothingness cannot be distinguished philosophically.' In this way Eddington attempted to rationalize the basis on which to build the universe.

I have already mentioned the Abbé Lemaître. His original work in 1927, published in a little-known journal, was discovered by Eddington. Although Eddington remained faithful to this idea that the universe evolved from the static but unstable Einstein universe, the conception was soon abandoned by Lemaître himself. For the past twenty-five years Lemaître's name has been associated with another model whose origin recedes even farther back in time than the static Einstein state. Of all cosmologies, it is, perhaps, by far the most thoroughly studied. We shall see later that during the last few years a tremendous clash has occurred with other opinions, but at the present time there are no known features of the observable universe which are incompatible with Lemaître's evolutionary cosmology. Lemaître's model is typical of one of the groups of theories inherent in general relativity, according to which the universe originated at a finite time in the past and expands to an infinite size at an infinite future time.

Perhaps we can most easily visualize this conception by taking the universe as we see it now and inquiring quite simply what might have been the situation long ago. The observations of the distant galaxies show that their light and radio emission is shifted in wavelength so that as received on the earth the light is redder and the radio waves longer in wavelength than those which are actually emitted. The interpretation of this shift is that we are separating from the galaxies at a very high speed, and that the speed of recession increases as we move out into space. At the limits of present-day observation the speed of recession is about thirty-seven thousand miles per second, which is a fifth of the velocity of light. The observation which gives us this figure is of a cluster of galaxies in Hydra photographed in the two-hundred-inch telescope. The so-called cosmological principle which is inherent in Lemaître's theory implies that if human beings equipped with similar instruments existed on a planet in this Hydra cluster of galaxies, then they would see the cluster of galaxies to which we belong at the limit of their powers of observation, and the velocity of recession would also be thirty-seven thousand miles per second. It is important to rid ourselves of any idea that because all around us we find galaxies in recession, then we are the centre of the recessional movement. This is not the case. It is an impression which we obtain because we can see only a small part of the total universe.

To return to this cluster of galaxies in Hydra. We are now seeing it as it was two thousand million years ago moving away at a rate of thirty-seven thousand miles a second. What is the likely past history of this and all other similar galaxies? Up to a point this question is not too difficult to answer. For example, a minute ago we were two million miles closer to this cluster than we are now. A year ago we were over a billion miles closer. If we recede back into history in this manner we realize that the galaxies such as Hydra which are now almost beyond our view must have been very much closer to us in the remote past. In fact, if we proceed in this way, then we reach a time of about eight or nine thousand million years ago when all the galaxies must have been very close together indeed. Of course, the galaxies themselves have evolved during this time, but the primeval material from which they were formed must have existed in a space which is very small compared with the universe today.

With important reservations which I shall deal with now, this in essence is the fundamental concept of Lemaître's theory, namely, that the universe originated from a dense and small conglomerate which Lemaître calls the primeval atom. I shall return in a moment to the conditions which might have existed at the beginning, and to the possible events which might have initiated the disruption and expansion of the primeval atom. It is in fact necessary to emphasize that the theory does not demand the formation of the galaxies in the first phase of the expansion. The primeval atom contained the entire material of the universe, and its density must have been inconceivably high—at least a hundred million tons per cubic centimetre. The initial momentum of the expansion dispersed this material, and after thousands of millions of years the conditions applicable to the so-called Einstein universe would have been reached. Then the size of the universe was about a thousand million light years and the density would have been comparable to that with which we are familiar on earth. According to Lemaître, at this stage the initial impetus of the expansion was nearly exhausted and the universe began to settle down into the nearly static condition which we have previously considered, where the forces of gravitational attraction and cosmical repulsion were in balance. The mathematical treatment indicates that the universe must have stayed for a long time in this condition. It is during this phase that the great clusters of galaxies began to form from the primeval material. Then the conditions of near equilibrium were again upset, the forces of cosmical repulsion began to win over those of gravitational attraction, and the universe was launched on the career of expansion which after nine thousand million years brought it to the state which we witness today.

The time scale determined by tracing back the past history of the galaxies brings us not to the beginning of time and space, but merely to a condition which existed a few thousand million years ago when the universe was probably about one-tenth of its present size and consisted of the original gaseous clouds from which the clusters of galaxies began to form. The processes of the formation and evolution of the galaxies from this early stage are the subject of very detailed mathematical treatment. There is, as present, every reason to believe that a satisfactory explanation of the evolution of the universe from that condition can be given in terms of the known laws of physics. But when we pass on to consider the even earlier stages, difficulties and uncertainties appear. How much farther do we have to go back in time to the condition of the primeval atom? The theory does not determine this with any precision, because the delay which the universe suffered during the equilibrium phase when the gaseous clouds were forming into galaxies cannot be specified. One can, however, say this—that the explosion or disintegration of the primeval atom must have occurred between twenty thousand million and sixty thousand million years ago. In other words the period of about nine thousand million years ago, when the galaxies began to form and the present period of expansion began, represents a comparatively recent phase in the history of the universe. . . .

I shall talk about the alternative view which science can offer on the origin of the universe, but before doing this I want to dwell a moment on the implications of this evolutionary theory. The time scale, although vast, is conceivable in human terms. From the initial moment of time when the primeval atom disintegrated, astronomy and mathematics can attempt to describe the subsequent history of the universe to the state which we observe today. Moreover, there is every chance that in the foreseeable future man will produce experimental tests which will either substantiate or destroy this picture. But when we inquire what the primeval atom was like, how it disintegrated and by what means and at what time it was created we begin to cross the boundaries of physics into the realms of philosophy and theology. The important thing at that stage is what you and I think about this situation, this beginning of all time and space.

As a scientist I cannot discuss this problem of the creation of the primeval atom because it precedes the moment when I can ever hope to infer from observations the conditions which existed. If, indeed, the universe began in this way, then the concepts of space and time with which we deal originated at some moment between twenty thousand million and sixty thousand million years ago. Time, in the sense of being measured by any clock, did not exist before that moment, and space, in the sense of being measured by any yardstick, was contained entirely within the primeval atom. The vast regions of space which we survey today are just a small part of those which were originally the space of that small conglomerate.

We can, of course, speculate on the issues of the creation of the primeval atom and its initial condition, but it is the philosopher who must first build a scheme which is self-consistent and which leads us smoothly into beginning of space-time where the mathematician can take over. Or one can simply refuse to discuss the question. If we wish to be materialistic, then we adopt the same attitude of mind as the materialist adopts in more common situations. The materialist will begin in the present case at the initiation of space-time when the primeval atom disintegrated....

With an effort of imagination the human mind can trace its way back through the thousands of millions of years of time and space, and we can attempt to describe in common concepts the condition of the primeval atom. The primeval atom was unstable and must have disintegrated as soon as it came into existence. There we reach the great barrier of thought because we begin to struggle with the concepts of time and space before they existed in terms of our everyday experience. I feel as though I've suddenly driven into a great fog barrier where the familiar world has disappeared.

I think one can say that philosophically the essential problem in the conception of the beginning of the universe is the transfer from that state of indeterminacy to the condition of determinacy, after the beginning of space and time when the macroscopic laws of physics apply. When viewed in this way we see that the problem bears a remarkable similarity to one with which we are familiar. This is the indeterminacy which the quantum theory of physics introduces into the behaviour of individual atoms, compared with the determinacy which exists in events where large numbers of atoms are involved. The process of thought by which we reduce the multiplicity of the entire universe to its singular condition of the primeval atom is equivalent in principle to the reduction of the chair in which you are sitting to one of its individual atoms. Not in the evolutionary sense of course, but in the sense that quantum theory and the principle of uncertainty explains why the behaviour of the individual atom is indeterminate and why it is impossible for you to find out the condition of the atom with any precision, because you will disturb it in the very process of investigation. In fact, the application of the fundamental concepts of quantum theory to the cosmological problem enables us to begin the struggle with the barrier which arises whenever we think about the beginning of space and time.

The primeval atom was a singular state of the universe, as incapable of precise specification by physical methods as the familiar individual particle in the uncertainty principle of modern physics. When the primeval atom disintegrated the state of multiplicity set in and the universe became determinate in a macroscopic sense. Philosophically, space and time had a natural beginning when the condition of multiplicity occurred, but the beginning itself is quite inaccessible. In fact, in the beginning the entire universe of the primeval atom was effectively a single quantum unit in the sense that only one of the future innumerable potential states existed. I am aware that this discussion is merely a line of metaphysical thought. Its importance lies in the parallel with the fundamental difficulties and basic indeterminacies in modern quantum theory. If future advances should occur in these directions, then it may become possible to speak with more certainty about the condition of the original cosmological quantum. In the light of our present knowledge of atomic physics it is possible only to surmise the kind of condition which might have existed. I suggested earlier that the density of matter in this primeval atom was inconceivably high. This is arrived at by a simple arithmetical deduction from the probable total mass of the universe as we see it now, and by assuming that the radius of the primeval atom was not greater than, say, a few million miles. However, it is possible that the primeval atom was not like this, but that it consisted of intense radiation and corpuscular rays which formed the primeval gas during the first phases of the expansion. In fact, it is a fundamental concept of Lemaître's theory that the cosmic radiation which we observe today is a relic of this early state. A characteristic of this picture of evolution is the long time-scale involved in the transformation of the intense energy of the original primeval atom, first into the gaseous clouds of hydrogen and then by processes, which awaited the high temperatures and pressures which arose when stars began to form, into the other elements with which we are familiar today. If pressed to describe this primeval atom in conventional terms one would, I think, refer to a gigantic neutron. By radioactive decay this neutron suffered a tremendous explosion. Protons, electrons, alpha particles, and other fundamental particles emerged from it at great velocity and continued to fill all space nearly uniformly as this basic material expanded for many thousands of millions of years until the clusters of galaxies began to form.

An alternative picture of the condition of the primeval atom has been given by Gamow, who believes that it consisted entirely of high-temperature thermal radiation. Five minutes after the expansion began the temperature of the universe was a thousand million degrees, after a day it had fallen to forty million degrees—say, nearly to the temperature of the centre of the sun; after ten million years it had fallen to an average temperature, which we call room temperature. On this theory of Gamow all the chemical elements which we

deal with today must have been formed within the first thirty minutes of the life of the universe.

Gamow differs from Lemaître in other important respects. In Lemaître's theory the force of the initial disintegration was exhausted after a few thousand million years, and the expansion which we witness today came into play only as a result of the forces of cosmical repulsion which developed when the galaxies began to form. In Gamow's theory the force of the initial explosion was so great that the expansion of the universe is attained without invoking the force of cosmical repulsion. In other words, the beginning in the Gamow theory is close to the nine thousand million years which we deduce by tracing back the history of the galaxies, and there is no protracted period in the state of diffuse gas with all the major forces balanced as in Lemaître's theory.

The most distinguished living exponent of the evolutionary theory of the origin of the universe is himself in Holy Orders. For him and for all who associate their universe with God, the creation of the primeval atom was a divine act outside the limits of scientific knowledge and indeed of scientific investigation. The probable condition of intense radiation in the primeval atom is entirely consistent with the divine command "Let there be light." It would, of course, be wrong of me to suggest that this view of the origin of the universe demands necessarily the possibility of creation of matter by a divine act. On the contrary, those who reject God adopt a strictly materialistic attitude to the problem of the creation of the primeval atom. They would argue that the creation of the primeval material had no explanation within the framework of contemporary scientific knowledge, but would escape from the dilemma by reserving the possibility that science would, if given the opportunity of studying these initial conditions, find a satisfactory solution. Or they would evade the problem of a beginning altogether by following a further line of thought due to Gamow that the primeval atom was not the beginning, but merely a state of maximum contraction of a universe which had previously existed for an eternity of time.* I think, however, that for theology, there is one important observation to make. If the universe was created and evolved in the manner just described, then the conception that the creation of the primeval material was a divine act can never be attacked by scientific investigation. A set of conditions which existed over twenty thousand million years ago, and which can never return again, is for ever beyond investigation.

The theory which we have discussed envisages a once for all creation in the remote past followed by a steady evolution to the present conditions. The alternative to this theory is that the creation of matter is taking place continuously and that although stars and galaxies evolve from this basic material, the universe, when considered as a large-scale structure, is in a steady state. We can illustrate this view by considering the future history of the galaxies which are now near the limit of observation. We are receding at great speed from these galaxies. In a billion years' time the galaxies will have passed for ever from our field of view and other galaxies which are now closer to us will have moved out to our observable horizon. So much is common ground on both the evolutionary and steady-state theories. The sharp distinction arises when we compare the picture of the universe within the observable horizon now and in a billion years' time. On the evolutionary theory more and more galaxies move out of our field of view, and the number of galaxies which we can see with our instruments will for ever decrease. In other words, the average spatial density of the universe is decreasing. On the steady-state theory this is not the case. Although individual galaxies re-

cede beyond the observable horizon, others are always being created to take their place. In a billion years' time the universe will look to us very much as it does now. The individual galaxies will have changed, but their average spatial density remains the same, because matter is always in creation throughout all of space. The cosmological principle of the evolutionary theory in which the universe would appear to be the same to any observer, wherever he was situated in space, has become the perfect cosmological principle according to which the universe is the same throughout all space and time.

The implications of this point of view are, of course, profound. For example, there cannot have been a beginning in any scale of time at all. If we trace back in time the history of the galaxies, they dissolve into gas and then into uncreated matter as they move in towards us, whereas others come into view from beyond the observable horizon. At a time of twenty thousand million years ago the evolutionary models picture the universe as a concentrated conglomerate of gas, whereas the steady-state universe would have appeared as it does today. Indeed, however far we go back in time, there is no stage at which we can say that the universe, as a whole, had a beginning. In the only language at our command we can say that the history of the universe on the steady-state theory extends to an infinite time in the past.

Whereas there is hope that we can put our inferences about the past to an experimental test, we can discuss the future only in terms of the predictions of cosmological theory. Here again there are great differences between the evolutionary and steady-state models. The predictions of the steady-state theory are quite clear. The universe has an infinite extent in space and an infinite future in time. There is, of course, a limit to the observable universe from any one place in it determined by the speed of expansion. But if an intelligent being exists at our observable limit he would find himself surrounded by a similar universe of galaxies and so on without end. Neither does the theory of continuous creation place any limitation on the future extent in time. In the

* Gamow in his book *One, Two, Three . . . Infinity* states it this way: "The universe is now expanding because in some previous period of its history (of which, of course, no record has been left), it contracted from infinity into a very dense state and then rebounded, as it were, propelled by the strong elastic forces inherent in compressed matter. . . . We can now send our imagination flying beyond any limits, and ask ourselves whether during the precompressive stages of the universe everything that is now happening was happening in reverse order. Were you reading this book from the last page to the first some six or eight billion years ago? . . . Interesting as they are, such questions cannot be answered from the purely scientific point of view, since the maximum compression of the universe, which squeezed all matter into a uniform nuclear fluid, must have completely obliterated all the records of the earlier compressive stages." Ed.

same way that a billion years ago the universe would look the same as it does now, so in a billion years of future existence the overall large-scale picture will be unchanged.

The future on the evolutionary models is quite different. The total content of matter was fixed once and for all at the time of creation. The expansion is thinning out the galaxies, and in a billion years our view of space would indeed be vastly different from what it is today. In some variations of the evolutionary theory the process of expansion is expected to reverse when the spatial density has fallen to a certain value, and then the contraction of space would bring the ageing galaxies into view again. But even in such variations of the evolutionary models the ultimate death of the universe seems inescapable, because the energy with which the universe was imbued at its creation is relentlessly becoming less available.

The finite limitations of space, time, and content in some of the evolutionary models lead one to ask whether our universe is, in fact, the entire cosmos. It is a question which at present cannot be discussed with profit. There is no feature of the theory which would preclude the existence of other universes created at different times, but unless we are hopelessly wrong in our interpretation of our observations of the universe we see, there is no conceivable way in which we can ever penetrate the regions of time and space where they might exist.

The conflict between the steady-state and evolutionary theories is of the very greatest significance to cosmology and to human thought. The evolutionary theory places the creation of matter at a definite moment in the remote past, beyond human investigation. Although the steady-state theory has no solution to the problem of the creation of matter,* it is important to appreciate that if this theory is correct, then the primeval gas is being cre-

*Fred Hoyle in his book *Frontiers of Astronomy* says on this point: "There is an impulse to ask where originated material comes from. But such a question is entirely meaningless within the terms of reference of science. Why is there gravitation? Why do electric fields exist? Why is the Universe? These queries are on a par with asking where newly originated matter comes from and they are just as meaningless and unprofitable. . . . We can ask questions quite freely about the consequences of the laws of physics. But if we ask why the laws of physics are as they are, we shall receive only the answer that the laws of physics have consequences that agree with observation." Ed.

ated now, at this moment, and hence is open to human investigation. On the whole, I think it must be incontestable that the steady-state theory is more materialistic than the evolutionary theory. It could be said that the creation process is a divine act which is proceeding continuously, and which is beyond the conception of the human mind. On the other hand, it cannot be denied that this may be a somewhat perilous attitude for the simple reason that the tools of science can probe the regions of space where this creation is occurring. In fact, in the equations of the cosmologists a creation term already exists. Philosophically, it is, I think, important to emphasize the approachability of the creation of hydrogen which is inherent in these modern theories of continuous creation. Otherwise the metaphysical impact would not be severe. In this sense the concept was stated long ago by Kant in these words ". . . the remaining part of the succession of eternity is always infinite," he said, "and that which has flowed is finite, the sphere of developed nature is always but an infinitely small part of that totality which has the seed of future worlds in itself, and which strives to evolve itself out of the crude state of chaos through longer or shorter periods. The creation," he went on, "is never finished or complete. It has, indeed, once begun, but it will never cease," But, of course, Kant's doctrine was egocentric, in the sense that God had completed the creation in the part of the cosmos which we can see. In the contemporary theories of continuous creation the processes of formation should still be occurring all around us, and are therefore open to human investigation.

I think it is true to say that during the last few years the cosmological issue has crystallized into a conflict between these evolutionary and steady-state theories of the origin of the universe. The variations in detail within these two broad principles are numerous. Many of these differences are highly abstract, but in so far as the stream of human thought is concerned these internal variations are of small consequence compared with the major issue as to whether creation is occurring now and throughout all time in the past and in the future, or whether the fundamental material of the universe was created in its entirety some billions of years ago.

It seems possible that we may be on the verge of settling by experimental observation which of these two principles is correct. In fact, the group of young cosmologists* who have promulgated the theories of continuous creation have always emphasized that, as distinct from the theoretical arguments which have surrounded the variations of evolutionary cosmology in the last thirty years, the new theories should be capable of direct experimental test. For example, if with our telescopes we could penetrate so far into space that we could see a cluster of galaxies from which the light had taken nine thousand million years to reach us, then it would be possible to reach a clear decision. For at that time in the past on the evolutionary theory the clusters of galaxies were only just beginning to form from the primeval gas. Well, of course, such a straightforward observation is impossible because of the limited range of our telescopes. I said earlier that the most distant object yet identified in the telescopes is the cluster of galaxies in Hydra at about two thousand million light years. Although the light from this cluster has been travelling through space for two thousand million years, it is too close to us in time and space to be of use in distinguishing between the two theories.

It is, however, on the verge of the regions of space and time where the universe would be expected to be significantly different if creation was still in progress compared with the conditions in an evolutionary universe. If time and space had a beginning, then when the universe was only a few thousand million years old it would be much more compact than it is today. The galaxies would be in existence, but they would be packed closer together compared with their spatial density today. The spatial density today—by which I mean the number of galaxies within, say, fifty or a hundred million light years of the Milky Way—can be determined by the large telescopes. If we could count the number in a

similar volume of space at a distance of several thousand million light years we should in effect be making a count of the galaxies as they existed several thousand million years ago. If creation is still taking place, then on the steady-state theories this number should be the same as today. If the evolutionary model is correct, then the spatial density at this distance in time and space will be much greater [Figure 8-15].

The possibility of carrying out this decisive observational test excites the imagination. Unfortunately it seems likely that the hindrances introduced by the atmosphere of the earth will prevent the great optical telescopes from penetrating to the required regions of space. It may well be that only when optical telescopes can be carried in earth satellites or erected on the moon will it be possible to look back into the past to this extent. Before the advent of such futuristic enterprises it seems likely that the great radio telescopes will give us the answer we require. You may remember that in a previous talk I referred to the collisions of galaxies which, for reasons not yet understood, generate radio waves which can easily be picked up in the radio telescopes, although the light from these galaxies is so faint that they are near the limit of the normally observable universe. We can already study galaxies in collision at such distances that they must be far beyond the range of the optical telescopes. We believe that these investigations are already taking us so far out in space and so far back in time that the radio waves have been on their journey for a few thousand million years. The circumstantial evidence for this belief in the origin of many of the unidentified radio sources is very strong, and if this is confirmed we have the tools with which human beings can bring the cosmological issues to a decisive test.

The concept of continuous creation also presents us with another opportunity to make an even more direct and decisive test. If the theory is correct, then the hydrogen gas which forms the primeval material of the galaxies must be in creation at a considerable rate. The theory demands the appearance of hydrogen at the rate of several billion trillion tons

---

* Fred Hoyle, Hermann Bondi, and Thomas Gold have been the most prominent advocates of this theory. Ed.

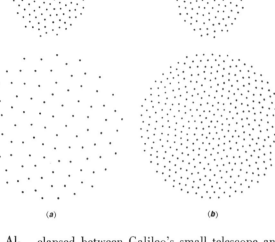

After Scientific American

Figure 8-15. Evolutionary and steady-state views are compared in these diagrams. At left is a schematic view of an evolutionary universe. At the top is a sample of the universe with the galaxies represented by dots. At the bottom is a picture of the same galaxies after the passage of time. The galaxies have merely receded from one another. At right is the same kind of view of a steady-state universe. At the top is a sample of the universe. At the bottom is a picture of the volume occupied by the same galaxies after the passage of time. In that time, however, new galaxies have been created, maintaining the density of the galaxies as before.

(a)   *(b)*

per second in the observable universe. Although this figure is vast, in fact, by ordinary human concepts of terrestrial space the rate is exceedingly slow. It represents the creation of only a few atoms of hydrogen per cubic mile of space per year. The presence of this hydrogen in intergalactic space may well be detectable in the near future by the radio telescopes.

As individuals we must therefore face the possibility that within the next few years astronomers may be able to speak with unanimity about the ultimate cosmological problem. Only the materialist can turn aside unmoved by this prospect. For others, a settlement of this cosmological issue might mean an affirmation or rejection of deeply embedded philosophical and theological beliefs.

So far I have tried to present the contemporary background without prejudice, but no doubt before I finish you will expect me to say a word about my own personal views. At the moment our outlook in astronomy is optimistic. A new epoch has been opened by the development of radio telescopes, and we are perhaps within a generation of an even more astonishing one because of the inherent possibilities of astronomical observations from earth satellites or the moon. We can only guess as to the nature of the remote regions which might be photographed by telescopes removed from their earth-bound environment. In the case of radio telescopes this development is still very young. Three hundred years

elapsed between Galileo's small telescope and the inauguration of the 200-inch telescope on Palomar Mountain. In the development of radio telescopes we have not covered a tenth of that time-span. I think therefore that our present optimism may well be of the kind which comes from the initial deployment of great new instruments and techniques. I have no doubt that within a few years these instruments will enable us to resolve the conflict which I have described between the evolutionary and steady-state models. In this process new difficulties will certainly appear, and these might make my present description of the universe as out of date as the static egocentric description which was in vogue in the first twenty years of this century. When we are dealing with time-spans of thousands of millions of years it would be sheer impudence to suggest that the views of the cosmos which have evolved from the techniques developed in our age possess any degree of finality. My present attitude to the scientific aspects of the problem is therefore neutral in the sense that I do not believe that there yet exist any observational data which are decisively in favour of any particular contemporary cosmology. The optimism with which I believe that we are on the verge of producing the necessary observational data is tempered with a deep apprehension, born of bitter experience, that the decisive experiment nearly always extends one's horizon into regions of new doubts and difficulties.

The Evolutionary Theory   285

On the question of the creation of the primeval material of the universe it seems to me unlikely that there can ever be a scientific description, whether in terms of the evolutionary or steady-state theories. If the idea of continuous creation is substantiated, then science will have penetrated very far indeed into the ultimate processes of the universe. It might then appear that a completely materialistic framework would have been established, but it does not seem to me that this is the case. If one imagines a scientific device which is so perfect that it could record the appearance of a single hydrogen atom as demanded by the continuous creation theory, then the scientific description of the process would still be imperfect. The same basic and quite fundamental difficulty would appear, as I have described in the case of the primeval atom, in the further effort to obtain information about the nature of the energy input which gave rise to the created atom.

If I were pressed on this problem of creation I would say, therefore, that any cosmology must eventually move over into metaphysics for reasons which are inherent in modern scientific theory. The epoch of this transfer may be now and at all future time, or it may have been twenty thousand million years ago. In respect of creation the most that we can hope from our future scientific observations is a precise determination of this epoch. I must emphasize that this is a personal view. The attitudes of my professional colleagues to this problem would be varied. Some would no doubt approve of this or a similar line of metaphysical thought. Others would not be willing to face even this fundamental limit to scientific knowledge, although,

as I have said, an analogous limitation occurs in modern scientific theory which describes the well-known processes of atomic behaviour. Some, I am afraid, will be aghast at my temerity in discussing the issues at all. As far as this group is concerned, all that I say is that I sometimes envy their ability to evade by neglect such a problem which can tear the individual's mind asunder.

On the question of the validity of combining a metaphysical and physical process as a description of creation, this, as I said earlier, is the individual's problem. In my own case, I have lived my days as a scientist, but science has never claimed the whole of my existence. Some, at least, of the influence of my upbringing and environment has survived the conflict, so that I find no difficulty in accepting this conclusion. I am certainly not competent to discuss this problem of knowledge outside that acquired by my scientific tools, and my outlook is essentially a simple one. Simple in the sense that I am no more surprised or distressed at the limitation of science when faced with this great problem of creation than I am at the limitation of the spectroscope in describing the radiance of a sunset or at the theory of counterpoint in describing the beauty of a fugue.

When I began my talks I mentioned the mixture of fear and humility with which I approached the task. Now you see the irony of the modern astronomer's life in its entirety. The devices of a world war have been forged, with the help of the fear of another, into a system of scientific experiments which take us back through time and space to deal with the problems of the origin of the universe.

WHY IS IT DARK AT NIGHT?*
by Hermann Bondi (1959)

One of the bases of modern cosmology is known as Olbers' paradox, which makes the darkness of the night sky appear as a curious

* From *The Universe at Large* by Hermann Bondi. Copyright © 1959 by The Illustrated London News and Sketch Ltd. Reprinted by permission of Doubleday & Company, Inc.

phenomenon. The argument leading up to this is so simple and attractive and beautiful that it may not be out of place to consider it here in full.

When one looks at the sky at night one

notices that there are some very bright stars, more medium bright ones and very large numbers of faint ones. It is easy to see that this phenomenon might be accounted for by the fact that the bright-looking stars happen to be near; the medium bright ones rather farther away, and the faint ones a good deal farther away still. In this way one would not only account for the variations in brightness but also for the fact that there are more of the faint ones than of the medium bright ones, and more of the medium bright ones than of the very bright ones, for there is more space farther away than nearby. One can now speculate about stars yet farther away, so far away, in fact, that they cannot be seen individually, not by the naked eye, nor even by the telescope. The question then arises of whether these very distant stars, though they would individually be too faint to be seen, might not be so exceedingly numerous as to provide an even background illumination of the night sky? This is the question that the German astronomer Olbers asked 130-odd years ago. The argument will now be presented in the light of the astronomical knowledge of 1826, without considering any of the phenomena discovered by modern astronomy.

Olbers' Paradox

Olbers then attempted to calculate what the brightness of the background of the sky should be on this basis. He immediately realized that in trying to consider effects from regions too far away to be seen in detail, he was forced to make assumptions about what the depths of the universe were like. He then made a set of assumptions which looks so plausible even nowadays that they may well serve as a model of what the beginning of a scientific investigation should be like. He first assumed, in the light of the knowledge of his day (1826), that the distant regions of the universe would be very much like our own. He expected there would be stars there, with the same average distance between them as between near stars. He expected that while each star would have an intrinsic brightness of its own, there would be an average bright-

ness of stars very much like that in our astronomical neighborhood. In other words, he assumed that we get a typical view of the universe. This is in full accord with the ideas that have been current since the days of Copernicus, that there is nothing special, nothing pre-selected about our position in the scheme of things. This is a convenient assumption from a scientific point of view and a very fruitful one because we can assume that what goes on around us holds elsewhere as well, if not in detail at least on the average.

Unfortunately, this assumption is not sufficient for the calculation Olbers wished to make. For light travels at a finite speed: at a high speed, it is true, but a finite one nevertheless. The light we now receive from many distant regions was sent out by the objects there a long time ago, having spent the intervening period on its journey from there to here. What is important for us, therefore, in trying to calculate the amount of light we get from the depths of the universe, is not how much the stars there radiate *now*, but how much they radiated at the time when the light which we receive now was sent out by them. We have to make a guess about the variation of astronomical conditions, not only with space, but also with time. And here, again, Olbers made the simplest of all possible assumptions, for he assumed time to matter as little as space. In other words, he supposed that not only in other parts of the universe, but also at other times, there would be stars, that their brightness would be the same as it is in our astronomical neighborhood, and similarly, their average distance apart would be the same as it is near us. Next, Olbers assumed, very naturally, that the laws of physics, as we know them from here, apply elsewhere and at other times. In particular, he assumed that the laws of the propagation of light—the way light spreads out after leaving its source—applied over these vast regions just as much as they apply in our rooms here. This, again, is the most obvious, most convenient and most fruitful assumption one can make. It would seem a stupid thing to set out on a voyage of discovery into the depths of the universe by first throwing away all the knowledge we have gained in our vicinity. Finally, Olbers made an assumption which is of the utmost importance, but he made it implicitly. He was not aware of the fact that he was making an assumption at all. Scientists know very well that this is the most dangerous kind of assumption. This assumption was that there were no large, systematic motions in the universe; that the universe was static.

The Mathematics of Starlight

On the basis of these four assumptions, it is easy to work out the background light of the sky. Imagine a vast, spherical shell surrounding us (Figure 8-16). The thickness of the shell is supposed to be small compared with its radius; but the whole shell is supposed to be so enormous that there are vast numbers of stars within the shell. How many stars are there in this shell? In order to work this out we have to know the volume of the shell. If we call the radius of the shell R and its thickness H, then we see readily that the surface of the sphere on which the shell is built is $4\pi R^2$ and thus the volume of the shell is, to a sufficient approximation,

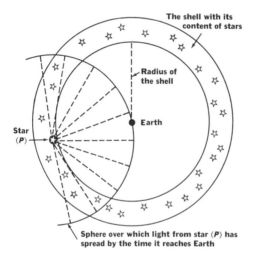

The shell with its content of stars

Radius of the shell

Earth

Star (P)

Sphere over which light from star (P) has spread by the time it reaches Earth

Figure 8-16. Each star gives off a large amount of light, but only a small fraction reaches our earth. But there are so many millions of stars, a large amount of light should reach us. If we consider shells of equal thickness, equal amounts of light should reach us from each shell. If this were so, the sky should be bright and there would be neither light nor day nor any life on earth.

$4\pi R^2 H$. If, now, N is the number of stars per unit volume, then the number of stars in the shell of volume $4\pi R^2 H$ will be $4\pi R^2 HN$. How much light will all the stars in the shell send out? If the average rate at which an individual star sends out light is L, then all the stars in the shell put together will send out $4\pi R^2 HNL$. However, what interests us is not how much light all these stars send out, but how much light we receive from them. Consider the light of an individual star in the shell. By the time the light from it reaches us, it will have traveled through a distance R: and so it will have spread out over a sphere of surface $4\pi R^2$. That is to say, the light of each individual star has to be divided by $4\pi R^2$ to tell us the intensity of light from it which is received here. This is true of all the stars in the shell, and therefore, the total light we receive from all the stars in the shell is the total light they send out divided by $4\pi R^2$. This division leads to the cancellation of the factor $4\pi R^2$ and we are left with HNL.

It will be seen that this does not involve the radius of the shell at all. The amount of light we receive from any shell of equal thickness is the same irrespective of the radius of the shell. If, therefore, we add shell after shell, then, since we get the same amount of light from each shell, the amount received will go up and up without limit. On this basis, we should be receiving an infinite amount of light from all the shells stretching out to infinity. However, this argument not only leads to an absurd conclusion, but is not quite right. For each star, in addition to sending out light, obstructs the light from the stars beyond it. In other words, we will not be receiving light from stars in the very distant shells because there will generally be a star in between us and there—a nearer star—which will intercept the light. Of course, it will be realized that stars send out very much light, considering how small a surface they have. Therefore, this obscuring or shadowing effect is not very strong; it will prevent the sum from going up to infinity, but it still leads to our getting from all these shells of stars a flood of light equal to 50,000 times sunlight when the sun is in the zenith. On this basis, then, it should be incredibly bright both day and night. Everything would be burned up; it would correspond to a temperature of over 10,000 degrees Fahrenheit. Naturally, this remarkable result astonished Olbers, and he tried to find a way out. He thought that this flood of light might be stopped by obscuring clouds of matter in space between us and these distant stars. However, this way of escape does not work. For, if there were such a cloud, it would be getting hot owing to the very fact that it was absorbing light from stars; and it would go on getting hotter and hotter until it radiated by its glow as much light as it received from the stars. And then it would not be a shield worth having any longer. Other ways out have been tried, but none of them works. We are, therefore, inevitably led to the result that, on the basis of Olbers' assumptions, we should be receiving a flood of light which is not, in fact, observed.

Expansion and Dimness

This little argument may well serve as a prototype of scientific arguments. We start with a theory, the set of assumptions that Olbers made. We have deduced from them by a logical argument consequences that are susceptible to observation, namely, the brightness of the sky. We have found that the forecasts of the theory do not agree with observation, and thus the assumptions on which the theory is based must be wrong. We know, as a result of Olbers' work, that whatever may be going on in the depths of the universe, they cannot be constructed in accordance with his assumptions. By this method of empirical dis-

proof, we have discovered something about the universe and so have made cosmology a science.

In order to escape from this paradox, we have to drop at least one of his assumptions. In the light of modern knowledge described in the previous chapter, the reader will have no difficulty in spotting the assumption that has to be dropped. It is the one that the universe is static. If the universe is expanding, then the distant stars will be moving away from us at highest speeds, and, it is well known from ordinary physics that light emitted by a receding source is reduced in intensity compared with light emitted by a source at rest. With an expanding universe, such as the one we live in, it may indeed be dark at night, for the light from the distant shells is tremendously weakened by the fact that the luminous objects in them are rushing away from us at high speed. Thus, the darkness of the night sky, the most obvious of all astronomical observations, leads us almost directly to the expansion of the universe, this remarkable and outstanding phenomenon discovered by modern astronomy.

Other changes made by modern astronomy in Olbers' assumptions are relatively minor. It is true that we know that our stars do not go on and on, but form a large stellar system, our galaxy; but we also know that beyond our galaxy there are millions and millions of other galaxies, all more or less like ours. We could, therefore, put Olbers' argument into modern language by changing the reference to stars going on and on in space to galaxies going on and on. The substance of the argument would not be affected.

THE STEADY-STATE THEORY OF THE UNIVERSE*
by Hermann Bondi (1960)

In cosmology, one is considering an extrapolation of physics as we know it here to a very much larger scale of phenomenon. What we

* From Hermann Bondi et al., *Rival Theories of Cosmology*, Oxford University Press, Fair Lawn, N.J., 1960. Reprinted by permission.

have learnt in the laboratory is to be applied to the universe at large. Clearly, there are dangers and difficulties in making such an enormous extrapolation. . . .

Can we really suppose that physical processes go on elsewhere as they do in our neighbourhood? Clearly, the answer to this question will depend on whether we are in a very special place in the universe or whether ours is a typical one. If our position in the universe in space and time is typical, then we can feel confident that our locally acquired knowledge is applicable elsewhere. If, on the other hand, the universe were very different elsewhere or at other times from what it is here and now, then we would need to know which aspects of our physical knowledge were truly permanent and which of them had just caught a mood of the moment of the universe. If we assume that all the physics we know is unchangeable, although the universe is changing, then we make a possible but quite arbitrary assumption.

Of course, it may be necessary to consider the very difficult problems of the variation of physics in a varying universe; but before we enter the enormous complication of this question, we first try to see whether our universe might not happen to be one that is the same everywhere and at all times when viewed on a sufficiently large scale. In examining this possibility, we by no means claim that this must be the case; but we do say that this is so straightforward a possibility that it should be disproved before we begin to consider more complicated situations.

We are thus led to consider a model of the universe which is uniform on a large scale, both in space and in time. This model is known as the steady-state model. It is a useful model because in it we can be sure that physics, as we know it here, applies everywhere else. Moreover, as I shall explain later in this talk, it is a model that makes many forecasts that can be checked by experiment and observation. Therefore, it is a testable and, accordingly, a useful scientific theory. It follows immediately from the assumptions of the steady-state theory that the universe must be expanding, for otherwise, as a simple argument shows, we would be drowned by a flood of light from the most distant regions. In order to be consistent with the assumption of uniformity the motion of

expansion must be such that there is a velocity of recession proportional to distance. The effect of the recession will then prevent the flood of light. This indeed is the type of motion that is being observed.

Next, if we have such a motion, then it would seem at first sight that the mean density in the universe must be diminishing, because if the distances between the galaxies are increasing all the time, it follows that the same matter now fills a larger volume. However, this would be in flagrant contradiction with the postulate that the universe is the same at all times. The only way out of this difficulty is to suppose that there is a process of continual creation going on—a process by which, in the enormous spaces between the galaxies, new matter constantly appears. This new matter condenses and forms new galaxies to fill the increasing spaces between the older ones.

Furthermore, every star ages since it converts hydrogen into helium in order to supply the energy the star radiates into space. As each star in the galaxy goes through these changes, the galaxy itself ages. However, the *average* age of galaxies is kept down since new galaxies constantly form in the increasing spaces between the old ones. It is for this reason, in order to keep the average age constant, that we require the new matter to be laid down in the vast intergalactic spaces. Only in this way can new galaxies be formed so that the average distance between galaxies stays constant, although, because of the expansion of the universe, the distance between existing galaxies is all the time increasing. Old galaxies, as they move farther and farther away, become less and less observable.

The whole picture of the steady-state universe is, therefore, very much like a picture of a stationary human population. Each individual is born, grows up, grows old and dies, but the average age stays the same owing to the fact that, all the time, new individuals are being born. We have, in the steady-state theory, a very similar picture of the universe of galaxies. Old galaxies die by drifting into regions where they are harder and harder to observe, and new galaxies are formed all the time in the spaces between the old ones. In this way, we arrive at a universe that is on the large scale uniform and unchanging. Moreover, it is the only model of this type. Of course, it deviates from ordinary physics in assuming this phenomenon of continual creation of matter which is, indeed, a major infringement of present formulations of physics. Dr. Bonnor has argued that this process of continual creation violates the principle of conservation of energy which has withstood all the revolutions in physics in the last sixty years and which most physicists would be prepared to give up only if the most compelling reasons were presented; but this seems to me to be unsound. The principle of conservation of mass and energy, like all physical principles, is based on observation. These observations, like all experiments and observations, have a certain measure of inaccuracy in them. We do not know from the laboratory experiments that matter is absolutely conserved; we only know that it is conserved to within a very small margin. The simplest formulation of this experimental result seems to be to claim that matter must be absolutely conserved. But this is purely a mathematical abstraction from certain observational results that may contain, indeed are bound to contain, errors.

Now, in fact, the mean density in the universe is so low, and the time scale of the universe is so large, by comparison with terrestrial circumstances, that the process of continual creation required by the steady-state theory predicts the creation of only one hydrogen atom in a space the size of an ordinary living-room once every few million years. It is quite clear that this process, therefore, is in no way in conflict with the experiments on which the principle of the conservation of matter and energy is based. It is only in conflict with what was thought to be the simplest formulation of these experimental results, namely that matter and energy were precisely conserved. The steady-state theory has shown, however, that much simplicity can be gained in cosmology by the alternative formulation of a small amount of continual creation, with conservation beyond that. This may, therefore, be the formulation with the greatest overall simplicity. There is thus no reason whatever, on the basis of any available evidence, to put the steady-state theory out of court because it requires this process of continual creation. This would be indeed a prejudice, and not a scientific argument.

Finally, as I said at the beginning, we must see how testable this theory is. How many forecasts does it make that can be checked by observation and experiment? There is a whole class of observations based on a very simple consideration. When we see the most distant galaxies that we can observe, then we look at them, not as they are now, but as they were a long time ago, for the light that travelled from them to us took a long time to cover the distance between them and us.

In the case of the most distant galaxies visible in optical telescopes this time is probably 5,000,000,000 years. If the universe as a whole is evolving, . . . then, presumably, all the galaxies originated at more or less the same time. In particular, we can definitely say that in such a universe no galaxies originated very recently. According to relativistic theories, then, we see the distant galaxies at an earlier stage in their evolution than the near ones which we see as they are now, more or less. Therefore, one would expect some variations with distance in the appearance of the galaxy, or the colour of light that it sends out, or in the degree of clustering, or possibly in the likelihood that it is a strong emitter of radio waves observable by radio astronomy. Accordingly, if one looks out into space and compares the shapes of distant galaxies with those of near galaxies, or compares in the same manner any other of the characteristics I mentioned, then either one will or one will not find a variation with distance. On the basis of the steady-state theory, time does not matter. A long time ago the universe looked just the same as it does now. Accordingly, no such variation can occur in the picture of the steady-state theory. In the evolutionary pictures one would expect precisely such a variation. Therefore, if these observations are made and any variation is found, then the steady-state theory is stone dead. If no such variation is found, it does not necessarily mean that the evolutionary theories are wrong, because one can always say that the period of time into which we can look back is too short for any such changes to show themselves. Some such observations are within the range of existing equipment, or equipment now in process of being built. Indeed, from the point of view of the steady-state theory we have the very satisfactory situation that although two different observations of this type have been claimed to disprove the steady-state theory, in both cases it has since been shown that they involved far greater observational errors than had originally been believed. In one case the absence of any such variation has now been established, in the other no definite conclusions can be drawn at present. However, many of these tests may be practicable in the near future. . . .

Enough has happened in the twelve years that this theory has existed to show that it gives us a useful way of looking at the universe, a way that inspires new observations and is vulnerable to them.

EVIDENCE FROM THE RADIO TELESCOPE*
by George Gamow (1962)

Radio emission from the colliding galaxies is so intensive that the radio telescope can observe them at distances four times as large as those at which the galaxies themselves can be seen through the largest optical telescope. Within that volume one expects to find about one thousand colliding galactic pairs, a sample large enough for statistical studies. The British radio astronomer, Martin Ryle, undertook the construction of such a giant radio telescope, which occupies nearly five acres of ground near Cambridge University, and published his results early in 1961 in the *Monthly Notices* of the Royal Astronomical Society. The main point of investigation was the study of the distribution of colliding galaxies in the space of the Universe up to a distance of about 8 billion light years. The farther they are away from us the fainter is the radio signal, and a basic law of physics states that the observed intensity decreases in inverse proportion to the square of the distance. (Thus, being moved twice as far away, a candle will look four times fainter, and 10 times away it will look 100 times fainter.) On the other hand, if the sources are distributed uniformly through space, their number within a sphere of a given radius will increase as the volume of the sphere, i.e., as the cube of its radius (twice the radius, eightfold the volume; 10 times the radius, 1,000 times the volume). Thus if we plot the number of sources with the observed intensity below a certain upper limit against that limit, the numbers should increase in inverse proportion to the square root of the cube of that limit. Indeed, the sources which appear to us 100 times fainter must be located 10 times farther away in space. But if the radius of a sphere is 10 times larger its volume, and also the number of sources within it, must be 1,000 times larger. Similarly, 10,000 times fainter sources must be located 100 times farther away, so that the total number of sources located closer to us than this limit must be 1,000,000 times larger. This theoretically expected relation is shown by a broken line (marked: slope—1.5) in the diagram (Figure 8-17) which is taken from the article of Ryle and his collaborator P. F.

* Reprinted from *The Great Ideas Today 1962* by permission of the publisher, Encyclopaedia Britannica, Inc.

Scott. The readers familiar with logarithms will notice that the plot is constructed on the logarithmic scale, i.e. by making on both axes the marks for 10, 100, 1,000, at equal distances. In this case the expected relation should be a straight line sloping to the right as shown in the figure. The circles and crosses represent the direct results of the observation and a few vertical lines indicate the limits of the possible observational error.

We notice at once that the observed points do not fall on the expected line (broken) but rather on another line (continuous) with a larger slope. It seems that the sources are located closer to each other at greater distances (lower observed intensities) and become less crowded closer to us. . . . What is true for colliding galaxies must also be true for all other galaxies which are not in collision at present. . . .

If the [steady state] theory is correct, the regions of the Universe located far away from us must show the same picture as the nearby regions. Ryle's work seems to indicate that this is not the case, and speaks in favor of the [evolutionary] theory according to which the Universe originated from a highly

Figure 8-17. The number of observed galactic collisions plotted against their intensity (inverse square of the distance). If the universe were in a steady state, the observed points (circles and crosses) would fall on the broken line marked slope —1.5.

compressed state of matter many billions of years ago.

Cosmic Dispute*

"Your years of toil,"
Said Ryle to Hoyle,
  "Are wasted years, believe me.
The Steady State
Is out of date.
  Unless my eyes deceive me,

My telescope
Has dashed your hope.
  Your tenets are uprooted.
Let me be terse:
Our Universe
  Grows daily more diluted!"

Said Hoyle, "You quote
Lemaître, I note,
  And Gamow, coming after.
That crazy gang
And their Big Bang—
  They break me up with laughter.

You see, my friend,
It has no end
  And there was no beginning,
As Bondi, Gold,
And I will hold
  Until our hair is thinning."

"Not so!" cried Ryle
With rising bile
   And straining at the tether,
"Far galaxies
Are, as one sees,
More tightly packed together."

"You make me boil!"
Exploded Hoyle,
   His arguments arranging,
"New matter's born
Each night and morn.
   The picture is unchanging!"

     "Ah, let's have done,"
     They said as one,
       "Enough's enough. So be it!"—

     But will a feud
     Like this conclude,
       For who can referee it?

Barbara Gamow (1963)

A PRIORI ASSUMPTIONS*
by Herbert Dingle (1956)

From a purely logical point of view scientific cosmology would appear to have no justification, to be a gigantic impertinence. It is saved from this by a frank recognition by scientists of what it is and what its limitations are. The work of three centuries has shown that the scientific approach is on unassailable ground when it declares itself to be the best prescription yet devised for obtaining knowledge of the relations between phenomena. Whether or not its generalizations have any right to be regarded as the *truth*, they lead to further knowledge—which, so far as we can see, would be quite unobtainable otherwise. But they do this only on the condition that we abandon them the moment we see that they cease to hold. They originate in phenomena and they are at the mercy of phenomena.

The Aristotelian general principles, on the other hand, were conceived *a priori*, independently of phenomena, and phenomena were distorted at liberty so as to exemplify them. The problem was to "save the phenomena." The basic principles themselves could not be threatened; it was the phenomena that stood in need of salvation.

* From Herbert Dingle, "Cosmology and Science," *Scientific American*, September, 1956. Reprinted by permission.

Contrast with this the point of view that caused modern cosmologists to discard the Newtonian cosmology for the totally different Einsteinian cosmology—on the basis of the tiniest of differences between theory and observation. At the behest of measurements so fine that only in this age have they become possible at all, we have thrown over the whole picture of a universe in which bodies are pushed along by a conspiracy of alien forces and have substituted in its place a system of free bodies moving along the paths, which so to speak, offer them the easiest course. We are prepared to revise our principles to fit observation because man's whole experience in seeking knowledge has taught us that nature is far more likely to follow in the large the laws we observe her to follow in the small than to behave according to our intuitive ideas of decorum.

In most branches of science this philosophy has been adhered to unswervingly. The activities of experimental physicists, chemists and biologists are for the most part beyond reproach: we learn where we can, generalize from observation and extend the generalizations until they are found to fail, when we replace them by wider ones. But in cosmology this restraint does not always hold. Some cosmologists have returned to the discredited practice of inventing arbitrary general principles, with no justification except that they seem "right," and fitting phenomena to the requirements of the principles. We have been presented, for example, with a "cosmological principle" which demands that, on the large scale though not on the small (where it might readily be tested), every part of the universe must be exactly the same as any other. This has been extended to a "perfect cosmological principle" which says that the uniformity of the universe must *always* hold true, its general appearance being eternally the same. If the scientific procedure of generalizing from observation leads to anything inconsistent with this, it must be wrong. The principles are of necessity inviolable, and all phenomena must be interpreted in accordance with them. There could scarcely be a more complete return to a kind of philosophy which we once thought had been abandoned forever.

Anyone acquainted with the history of cosmology can recognize the cosmological principle and the perfect cosmological principle as having precisely the same nature as perfectly circular orbits and immutable heavens. Indeed, the perfect cosmological principle is largely identical with the Aristotelian principle of unchanging celestial regions.

We should not confuse the cosmological principle with valid scientific procedure of assuming, for purposes of investigation, that the rough approximation to homogeneity which we observe in space as far as we can see it extends to the whole of space. That is the normal type of scientific generalization, and it is usually made in relativistic cosmology in order to restrict the almost limitless field of investigation that would be open if all possibilities were taken into account. We calculate what it demands of the yet unexamined regions and hold ourselves ready to discard it if they should fail to meet those demands. The cosmological principle, however, alters observed facts to make them accord with its requirements. Observation appears to show that the density of matter in the universe is continually decreasing. This cannot be so, says the principle: unobservable matter must be in process of creation out of nothing in just the right amount to keep the density constant. The only reason for supposing its creation is that otherwise the perfect cosmological principle would be violated, and the only reason for supposing that this cannot happen is that a few mathematicians would not like it. It seems an insufficient reason.

ARBITRARY STARTING CONDITIONS*
by Fred Hoyle (1955)

It will be clear that the aim of the steady-state theory is to dispense with arbitrary conditions: arbitrary starting conditions leading to expansion and large scale uniformity, arbitrary conditions leading to the formation of galaxies. Instead of attributing the main features of the Universe to arbitrary fiat it is proposed that nothing less should be possible than a demonstration that all the main fea-

tures of the Universe are consequences of the laws of physics, entirely independent of any starting conditions.

The conventional outlook of present-day physics is that all physical laws are to be discovered by an examination of very small scale happenings in the laboratory, by the examination of the properties of atoms with particular reference to the nuclei of the atoms. Yet we have an example of a law of physics that was not discovered by experiments in the laboratory and whose relation to the field of atomic physics is still not understood. This is the law of gravitation. What we know about gravitation was discovered from a study of phenomena on the scale of our own solar system (this statement applies both to the work of Newton and of Einstein). Are we then to suppose that no further additions to the laws of physics are to be obtained through the study of the Universe on a scale larger than the solar system? The distance to Olbers' limit is more than 100,000,000,000,000 times greater than the distance of the Earth from the Sun. Is the study of the Universe on such a tremendous scale to be no more than an exercise in the application of what we have already learned on the Earth and within the solar system? We should certainly doubt whether this is so were it not for the fact that a great deal of what happens on a larger scale is very readily explicable in terms of our extremely locally derived knowledge. The behaviour of the whole of our Galaxy, of the stars in it, of their formation from gas clouds, of the motions and properties of the gas clouds, all appear entirely explicable in terms of locally derived knowledge. It is only when we come to phenomena on an extragalactic scale, on a scale greater than the clusters of galaxies, that we arrive at a situation where our locally derived knowledge apparently breaks down—for it seems fair to describe a recourse to a whole set of arbitrary starting conditions as a breakdown. The suspicion is that what we ought to be deriving as consequences of the laws of physics we are being obliged to accept as conditions arbitrarily imposed for no reasons that we understand. This procedure is quite characteristic of the outlook of primitive peoples, who in attempting to explain the local behaviour of the physical world are obliged in their ignorance of the laws of physics to have recourse to arbitrary starting conditions. These are given credence by postulating the existence of gods, gods of the sea who determine the arbitrary starting conditions that control the motion of the sea, gods of the mountains, gods of the forests, of the air, of the seasons of the year, of the Sun, of the Moon, and so forth. There is a strong hint that what

modern man has tried to do with the Universe is no better than what primitive man did with problems whose nature we now find simple but which once no doubt seemed just as complicated as the problems that remain unsolved today. In principle arbitrary starting conditions are to be avoided if any alternative attack is possible.

The argument leading to the steady-state theory is one such line of attack. Already the old requirement that the expansion of the Universe be imposed as a starting condition has been disposed of, but many problems remain—the average size of clusters of galaxies and the large scale uniformity of the Universe are two of them. . . .

One further remark must be made about the steady-state theory of the Universe. It is not a point in support of this theory that it contains conclusions for which we might happen to have an emotional preference. Herbert Dingle has quite correctly warned us recently against promoting a theory simply because we happen to like it. The grounds for the acceptance of a theory are its agreement with observation. The grounds for a serious discussion of a theory lie in the possibility of subjecting it to observational test. This condition the steady-state theory fulfils in good measure. . . . The steady-state theory must always be more subject to observational check than its rivals because by disposing of arbitrary starting conditions it removes a whole series of hypotheses that from their very nature are beyond test. The weakness of the superdense theory for instance is that it puts most of the important observational features of the Universe into its starting conditions— the reason for the expansion of the Universe, for its large scale uniformity, for the condensation of the galaxies, are put into the theory in a manner that cannot be tested. This is to miss what seems to be the whole point of a scientific theory, that its value depends on the possibility of disproving it: Gold has expressed this most aptly by saying that "for a theory to be of any value it must be vulnerable." Vulnerability supplies the conditions for success or failure in accordance with observational tests and it is on this that science, and indeed all rational argument, is based. The aim in science is not to build a theory that is so hedged in with protective conditions that nobody can get at it. The aim is to build a theory that is exposed to observational attack in as many directions as possible, and which then manages to survive.

Quite apart from its attempt to eliminate arbitrary starting conditions there is a further reason why the steady-state theory must be more vulnerable to observational attack than any other cosmological theory. In the steady-state theory all observable features must be consequences of processes that are still happening. In other theories most of the important features of the Universe are consequences of processes that are over and done with. In some cases there may be a possibility of examining the situation at an earlier time by observing light received from great distances (the light having started on its journey at a much earlier time, and therefore giving information about an earlier state of affairs). But this will not always be the case, and indeed no positive observation has so far been made that refers unequivocally to a significantly different epoch from the present. In the steady-state theory all processes must on the other hand still be happening and are therefore susceptible to observation. The steady-state theory therefore places observation on a stronger footing than any other theory, since according to the steady-state theory there is no aspect of cosmology that cannot (at any rate in principle) be directly verified. It is true that we must not accept a theory on the basis of an emotional preference but it is not an emotional preference to attempt to establish a theory that would place us in a position to obtain a complete understanding of the Universe. The stakes are high, and win or lose, are worth playing for.

The pertinent facts of the natural sciences, to which we have referred, are awaiting still further research and confirmation, and the theories founded on them are in need of further development and proof before they can provide a sure foundation for arguments which, of themselves, are outside the proper sphere of the natural sciences. This notwithstanding, it is worthy of note that modern scholars in these fields regard the idea of the creation of the universe as entirely compatible with their scientific conceptions and that they are even led spontaneously to this conclusion by their scientific research. Just a few decades ago, any such "hypothesis" was rejected as entirely irreconcilable with the present state of science.

Pope Pius XII
Address to the Pontifical Academy of Science (November 22, 1951)

Today there is a wide measure of agreement, which on the physical side of science approaches almost to unanimity, that the stream of knowledge is heading towards a non-mechanical reality; the universe begins to look more like a great thought than like a great machine. Mind no longer appears as an accidental intruder into the realm of matter; we are beginning to suspect that we ought rather to hail it as the creator and governor of the realm of matter—not of course our individual minds, but the mind in which the atoms out of which our individual minds have grown exist as thoughts. . . .

If the universe is a universe of thought, then its creation must have been an act of thought. Indeed the finiteness of time and space almost compel us, of themselves, to picture the creation as an act of thought, whose richness is measured by the immensity of these quantities. Time and space, which form the setting for the thought, must have come into being as part of this act. Primitive cosmologies pictured a creator working in space and time, forging sun, moon and stars out of already existent raw material. Modern scientific theory compels us to think of the creator as working outside time and space, which are part of his creation. Just as the artist is outside his canvas. "Non in tempore, sed cum tempore, finxit Deus mundum." Indeed, the doctrine dates back as far as Plato:

"Time and heavens came into being at the same instant, in order that, if they were ever to dissolve, they might be dissolved together. Such was the mind and thought of God in the creation of time."

And yet, so little do we understand time that perhaps we ought to compare the whole of time to the act of creation, the materialisation of the thought.

James Jeans
The Mysterious Universe (1930)

This picture of the universe as exploding fireworks which went off ten billion years ago invites us to consider the remarkable question of Miguel de Unamuno, whether the whole world—and we with it—be not possibly only a dream of God; whether prayer and ritual perhaps be nothing but attempts to make Him more drowsy, so that He does not awaken and stop our dreaming.

Pascual Jordan
Physics of the Twentieth Century (1944)

There was a monk indulging against the teaching of the Master in cosmological enquiries. In order to know where the worlds ends he began . . . interrogating the gods of the successive heavens. . . . Finally, the Great Brahma himself became manifest, and the monk asked him where the world ends. . . . The great Brahma took that monk by the arm, led him aside and said: "These gods, my servants, hold me to be such that there is nothing I cannot see, understand, realize. Therefore, I gave no answer in their presence. But I do not know where the world ends. . . ."

Dialogues of the Buddha (563–483 B.C.)

The Infinite*

Dear to me always was this lonely hill
And this hedge that excludes so large a part
Of the ultimate horizon from my view.
But as I sit and gaze, my thought conceives
Interminable vastnesses of space
Beyond it, and unearthly silences,
And profoundest calm; whereat my heart almost

Becomes dismayed. And as I hear the wind
Blustering through these branches, I find myself
Comparing with this sound that infinite silence;
And then I call to mind eternity,
And the ages that are dead, and this that now
Is living, and the noise of it. And so
In this immensity my thought sinks drowned:
And sweet it seems to shipwreck in this sea.

Conte Giacomo Leopardi (1798–1837)

* From R. C. Trevelyan, *Translations from Leopoldi*, Cambridge University Press, New York, 1941. Reprinted by permission.

QUESTIONS TO CONSIDER

What do scientists mean by creation? Is it a suitable subject for scientific investigation?

Both schools of cosmology accuse each other of being unscientific. Dingle says that the steady-state theory is based on an a priori assumption—like the perfect circles of Ptolomaic theory. Hoyle, on the other hand, says the evolutionary theory is based on arbitrary starting assumptions that are not subject to test and therefore are no better than the myths of primitive people. Which argument seems to you to be more valid? Why is it necessary to make so many broad assumptions in cosmology?

Hoyle and Bondi say that, by basing their theory on the perfect cosmological principle, they are making the simplest assumption. In a scientific theory is the simplest assumption always the best?

Is it useful to create theories that cannot be proved or disproved by the evidence that we now possess, or would it be better for astronomers to reserve judgment, to wait until more facts are available and then construct a theory that fits them?

Early returns from the radio telescope seem to favor the evolutionary theory (see Gamow, page 292). Is the evidence sufficient to decide between the two theories? When astronomers do decide between the two theories of creation, will the decision make any difference in your personal beliefs?

SUGGESTIONS FOR FURTHER READING

* Bondi, Hermann: *The Universe at Large*, Anchor Books, Doubleday & Company, Inc., Garden City, N.Y., 1960. A Science Study Series book giving a clear exposition of the theory of continuous creation, as well as a number of other subjects: radiation belts, tides, gravitation, motion, and magnetism.

* Bondi, H., et al.: *Rival Theories of Cosmology*, Oxford University Press, Fair Lawn, N.J., 1960. An interesting collection of essays presenting different sides of the "cosmic dispute."

* Gamow, George: *The Creation of the Universe*, Viking Press, Inc., New York, 1961. A very interesting presentation of Gamow's version of the evolutionary theory of the origin of the universe.

* Hoyle, Fred: *The Nature of the Universe*, Harper & Row, Publishers, New York, 1960. A description of the steady-state theory, easy and rewarding reading for the layman.

* ———: *Frontiers of Astronomy*, Harper & Row, Publishers, New York, 1955. A more technical book by the same author, giving a much more detailed description of stellar evolution.

Munitz, Milton K. (ed.): *Theories of the Universe*, The Free Press of Glencoe, New York, 1957. A very fine anthology of original writings from the myths of Babylonia to modern times.

* *The Universe*, A Scientific American Book, Simon and Schuster, Inc., New York. A reprint of a special issue (September, 1956) containing a number of excellent articles dealing with different phases of our knowledge of the universe.

* Paperback edition.

PART 9

IS THERE OTHER LIFE
IN THE UNIVERSE?

Science is a leap of the imagination. The selections in this part take the reader along on a speculative search for other life in the universe. They show how a change in theoretical concepts can create a new possibility that scientific imagination jumps in to explore, with results that may be very exciting from our human point of view.

Shapley

INTRODUCTION

A few decades ago the question of whether there might be life on other planets would have been relegated to writers of science fiction. Now, as the readings in this part testify, astronomers are agreed that the probability of life existing elsewhere in the universe is very high. The difference in attitude has been brought about by a change in the scientific theory of the origin of our solar system. If the planets were caused by a chance collision of two stars, as astronomers believed until recently, the event would have been rare enough to make it unlikely that there would be other planets in the proper zone to support life. But when the collision hypothesis was overthrown and the nebular hypothesis, which had first been proposed by Kant in 1755, was reestablished, the calculations concerning the uniqueness of planetary systems were drastically altered. According to the nebular hypothesis, all stars were formed in the same way as our sun and therefore could possess planetary systems. This theory makes the number of possible sites for life truly "astronomical," especially in view of the latest estimates of numbers of stars in the whole universe.

The change in concepts came about as the result of new evidence about the chemical constitution of matter in the universe—the discovery of larger amounts of hydrogen and helium in the bodies of the sun and stars. This evidence, which was made available by increased skill and precision in analyzing the spectra of the stars, led to a sweeping change of theoretical concepts and, as a corollary, to the conclusion that there might be billions of sites for life throughout the universe. Thus we see how an idea of enormous significance from our human point of view has occurred because of the reversal of a decision between two rival theories. This story may well serve as illustrative of the sudden way science can revolutionize our human views. It is advisable to remember also that the information and the theories in this field are still in

Su-Shu

Ovenden

a state of rapid development. Every year brings the discovery of new facts that may at any time bring about new theoretical interpretations. We recall J. J. Thompson's statement that ". . . from the point of view of the physicist a theory is a policy rather than a creed." In considering the human corollaries to scientific theories, it is well to keep in mind the dynamic and growing nature of science. Shapley, on page 345, says, "And as groping philosophers and scientists we are thankful for the mysteries that still lie beyond our grasp."

The central question of this part is an especially tantalizing mystery that is almost within our grasp today. With the possibility of space exploration it may be settled before many years have gone by. Scientifically, the problem of the existence of other life in the universe spans two fields of inquiry. One side of the problem involves the chemical and biological nature of life and the process of evolution. The other side is an astronomical problem, the existence of possible sites in which life could develop. Since our main focus in this book is on the broad aspects of the universe, the readings in this part concentrate on the second question. We have included only enough information on biology and chemistry to delineate the conditions necessary for the support of living things. Assuming the right site and enough time, the majority of scientists believe today that life would be inevitable. The question of whether this conclusion is justified cannot be profitably discussed within the context of these selections. It requires a background in biochemistry that is beyond the scope of this book. Several of the authors in this part believe that, given sufficient time, the process of evolution must lead eventually to the appearance of intelligent beings. Furthermore, there is a good probability that these beings may have reached a higher state of development than we have attained. There is enough support for this point of view so that impulses received by radio telescope are now being analyzed for messages from outer space. If such a message were found, it would surely be one of the most dramatic discoveries of all time.

A RECONSIDERATION OF MAN'S PLACE IN THE UNIVERSE

Sky, universe, all-embracing ether, and immeasurable space alive with movement—all these are of one nature. In space there are countless constellations, suns, and planets; we see only the suns because they give light; the planets remain invisible, for they are small and dark. There are also numberless earths circling around their suns, no worse and no less inhabited than this globe of ours. For no reasonable mind can assume that heavenly bodies which may be far more magnificent than ours would not bear upon them creatures similar or even superior to those upon our human Earth.

Giordano Bruno (1548–1600)

AN INQUIRY CONCERNING OTHER WORLDS*
by Harlow Shapley (1958)

We start with the following proposition: Is there not at this time a justification for a revised look at mankind as a world factor? Our prompt answer is "Yes!" To the scientist, rich in new knowledge, and to the puzzled layman, and perhaps to some philosophers, the answer is decidedly affirmative. An elementary reason for a reconsideration lies in the recognition in recent years of the "displacement" of the sun, earth, and other planets from a central place, or even a significant place, in the sidereal universe—in the placing of the observer in a very undistinguished location in a faint spiral arm of an ordinary galaxy.

This reason is elementary but momentous, for it concerns the replacement of the earlier *geocentric and heliocentric* theories of the universe by the *eccentric* arrangement that now we all accept. By this move we have made a long forward step in cosmic adjustment—a step that is unquestionably irreversible. We must get used to the fact that we are peripheral, that we move along with our star, the sun, in the outer part of a galaxy that is one among billions of star-rich galaxies.

If there is some grandeur in our position

in space and time, I fail to find it. Our glory must lie elsewhere. Also, should we not openly question the rather vain and tedious dogma that man somehow is something very special, something superior? He may be. I hope he is. But certainly it is not in his location in space, or in his times; not in his energy content or chemical composition. He is not at all outstanding in the four basic material entities—space, time, matter, energy. Nothing unique and worthy of boast in his size, activity, composition, or his epoch in cosmic chronology. He is of course an intricate and interesting phenomenon, but we should not get sentimental about him. . . .

Before we can propose ourselves and our destiny as significant concerns of the universe, we should turn our attention to the possible existence and general spread of protoplasm throughout stellar spaces and cosmic times. We can no longer be content with the hypothesis that living organisms are of this earth only. But before we ponder on the life spread, we should inquire into the prevalence of suitable sites for biological operations. The initial question is not whether such sites are presently inhabited. First we ask: Are there other habitable celestial bodies—bodies that would be hospitable if life were

* From Harlow Shapley, *Of Stars and Men.* Reprinted by permission of the Beacon Press, copyright © 1958 by Harlow Shapley.

After George Gamow

Figure 9-1. Space and time scales of the universe. The relative sizes of various objects in everyday life, in the macrocosm, and in the microcosm are shown in a decimal logarithmic scale, i.e., in the scale in which each factor of 10 is represented by one division of the yardstick. The sizes range from the diameter of an electron, and other elementary particles that are about 0.00001 angstrom, to the diameter of giant stellar galaxies, which often measure 100,000 light-years across. It is interesting to notice that the size of the human head is just about halfway between the size of an atom and the size of the sun, or halfway between the size of an atomic nucleus and the diameter of the planetary system (on the logarithmic scale in both cases, of course).

An Inquiry Concerning Other Worlds   305

there? No field of inquiry is more fascinating than a search for humanity, or something like humanity, in the mystery-filled happy land beyond the barriers of interstellar space. But are there such happy lands? . . .

Human bodies are constructs of commonly known chemical elements, and nothing else. . . . The element oxygen accounts for about sixty-five per cent of our bodies; eighteen per cent is carbon, ten per cent hydrogen, three per cent nitrogen, two per cent calcium, and another two per cent includes silicon, phosphorus, sodium, sulphur, iron, and a dozen other elements—all common to the crust of the earth and to the flames of the sun. The percentages vary somewhat from rat to leech, from watery octopus to crusty coral. There is more than average calcium in the bony vertebrates, more silicon in the brachiopods, more H_2O in the jellyfish; but all animals employ all the common atoms. The elements uncommon to the rocks, like gold, platinum, and radium, are also uncommon to man.

The stars are composed of the same stuff as that which constitutes the sun and is found in the earth's crust. They are built of the same materials as those that compose terrestrial organisms. As far as we can tell, the same physical laws prevail everywhere. The same rules apply at the center of the Milky Way, in the remote galaxies, and among the stars of the solar neighborhood.

In view of a common cosmic physics and chemistry, should we not also expect to find animals and plants everywhere? It seems completely reasonable; and soon we shall say that it seems inevitable. But to demonstrate the actual presence of organic life in other planetary systems is now impossible for us because the stars are so remote and we, as earth-bound searchers of the sky, are yet too feeble in the face of stellar realities. To establish, however, through statistical analysis the high probability of planets suitable for living organisms is not difficult. A statistical argument, in fact, is more convincing than would be a marginal observation.

It will clarify the discussion if we start with two routine reminders: (1) by life we mean what here we terrestrials recognize as life—a biochemical operation involving carbon and nitrogen and making use of water in the liquid state (other kinds are imaginable; e.g., one where silicon replaces carbon, or where sulphur's participation is like that of oxygen. Such is imaginable, but unlikely); and (2) Mars and Venus are therefore the only other planets of our solar system that are at all suitable for living organisms. The evidences are good that Martian life is low and lichen-like, if it exists at all, and the surface of Venus is an unsolved problem, with the odds against living organisms because of the lethal chemistry of the atmosphere.

Among the many definitions of life is the cold rigid version; "material organizations perpetuating their organization." The emphasis is on "perpetuating." We might better put it: "the perpetuation by a material organization of its organization." The definition can quite properly refer both to individuals and to species, and also to societies. They are all alive. They all die, if we suitably define death. The lively deathless atoms of our breath and bodies, however, are not, in this defining, alive.

Life is tough, tenacious, and also persistent when we give it time to adjust to varying environments. We find it in geysers and hot springs. Some flowers bloom under the snow. Both plants and animals on occasion endure for long periods on hot deserts. Some seeds can withstand desiccation and extreme cold indefinitely. Life as we know it on the earth has wide adaptability; but there are limits, and one of them is the heat and radiation near a star's surface, where the molecules constituting protoplasm would be dissociated.

In our consideration of the spread of life throughout the universe, we must therefore immediately drop all thoughts of living organisms on the trillions of radiant stars. The flames of the sun are rich in the lively atoms of oxygen, carbon, hydrogen, nitrogen, and calcium—the principal constituents of living matter—but physical liveliness and organic livingness are quite different behaviors. At the surfaces of some of the cool stars, like Antares and Betelgeuse, and in the cooling sunspots, we find a few familiar molecules, in addition to the scores of kinds of atoms; but there is nothing that is as complicated and tender as the proteins—those molecular aggregates that underlie the simplest life. And of course the stars harbor no water in the liquid state.

The stars are out of it, therefore, and they probably represent more than half of all the material in the universe. Most of the rest is believed to be in the form of interstellar gas, with a bit of dust. The dust is of the sort that shows up as meteors, when in collision with the earth's atmosphere, and appears also as remote dark nebulosities that interrupt and make patchy the glow of the Milky Way. No life exists on these minute meteoric specks, or on the relatively larger meteorites, and for several reasons. Among the reasons: (1) the masses are too small to hold gravitationally an atmosphere (even our moon cannot maintain the oxygen and carbon dioxide necessary for breathing animals and plants); (2) moreover, the meteors out between the stars are too cold for liquid water; and (3) they are all too unprotected against the lethal ultraviolet radiation from hot stars.

How about life on the comets? The same general argument holds as for meteors and meteorites, since the comets are simply assemblages of dusty fragmented meteoric materials, infused with escaping gases. In addition, most of the large comets of the solar system are, when brightest, too near the sun for living organisms and the rest of the time too frigidly remote in the outer parts of their orbits.

In our search for life we are therefore left with the planets, and those on which it can occur and survive must be neither too near their stars nor so remote from them that the cold is unrelieved. They should not be too small to hold an oxygen atmosphere, unless we are content to settle for primitive anaerobic life. (A few types of low organisms thrive in the absence of elemental oxygen.)

The life-bearing planets must also have nonpoisonous atmospheres, salutary waters, and agreeable rocky crusts; but given time enough, organisms could no doubt become adjusted to environments that would be poisonous and impossible for life such as that now developed on the earth.

Finally, the propitious planets that are suitable in size, temperature, and chemistry must also have orbits of low eccentricity. Highly eccentric orbits, like those of most comets, would bring their planets too near the star at periastron a part of the year, and then too far out at apastron. The resulting temperature oscillations would be too much for comfort, perhaps even too much for the origins and persistence of early life. Also, in the interests of avoiding too great differences in temperature from night to day, it would be best if the planets rotate rapidly and their rotational axes be highly inclined (as is ours) to their orbital planes.

With the foregoing requirements in mind we ask if there are many really suitable planetary systems, and the companion question: How are planets born?

ORIGIN OF THE SOLAR SYSTEM AND THEORIES OF STELLAR EVOLUTION

THE BIRTH OF PLANETS*
by George Gamow (1962)

For us, the people living in the seven parts of the World (counting Admiral Byrd for

* From *One, Two, Three . . . Infinity* by George Gamow. Copyright 1947 by George Gamow. Reprinted by permission of The Viking Press, Inc., and revised for this book, 1962.

Antarctica) the expression "solid ground" is practically synonymous with the idea of stability and permanence. As far as we are concerned all the familiar features of the Earth's surface, its continents and oceans, its mountains and rivers could have existed since the beginning of time. True, the data of historical geology indicate that the face of the Earth is gradually changing, that large areas of the continents may become submerged by the waters of the oceans, whereas submerged areas may come to the surface.

We also know that the old mountains are gradually being washed away by the rain, and that new mountain ridges rise from time to time as the result of tectonic activity, but all these changes are still only the changes of the solid crust of our globe.

It isn't, however, difficult to see that there must have been a time when no such solid crust existed at all, and when our Earth was a glowing globe of melted rocks. In fact, the study of the Earth's interior indicates that most of its body is still in a molten state, and that the "solid ground" of which we speak so casually is actually only a comparatively thin sheet floating on the surface of the molten magma. The simplest way to arrive at this conclusion is to remember that the temperature measured at different depths under the surface of the Earth increases at the rate of about 30°C per kilometer of depth (or 16°F per thousand feet) so that, for example, in the world's deepest mine (a gold mine in Robinson Deep, South Africa) the walls are so hot than an air-conditioning plant had to be installed to prevent the miners from being roasted alive.

At such a rate of increase, the temperature of the Earth must reach the melting point of rocks (between 1200°C and 1800°C) at a depth of only 50 km. (approx. 31 miles) beneath the surface, that is, at less than 1 per cent of the total distance from the center. All the material farther below, forming more than 97 per cent of the Earth's body, must be in a completely molten state.

It is clear that such a situation could not have existed forever, and that we are still observing a certain stage in a process of gradual cooling that started once upon a time when the Earth was a completely molten body, and will terminate some time in the distant future with the complete solidification of the Earth's body all the way to the center. A rough estimate of the rate of cooling and growth of the solid crust indicates that the cooling process must have begun several billion years ago.

The same figure can be obtained by estimating the age of rocks forming the crust of the Earth. Although at first sight rocks exhibit no variable features, thus giving rise to the expression "unchangeable as a rock," many of them actually contain a sort of natural clock, which indicates to the experienced eye of a geologist the length of time that has passed since they solidified from their former molten state.

This age-betraying geological clock is represented by a minute amount of uranium and thorium, which are often found in various rocks taken from the surface and from different depths within the Earth. . . . the atoms of these elements are subject to a slow spontaneous radioactive decay ending with the formation of the stable element lead.

To determine the age of a rock containing these radioactive elements we need only to measure the amount of lead that has been accumulated over the centuries as the result of radioactive decay.

In fact, as long as the material of the rock was in the molten state, the products of radioactive disintegration could have been continuously removed from the place of their origin by the process of diffusion and convection in the molten material. But as soon as the material solidified into a rock, the accumulation of lead alongside the radioactive element must have begun, and its amount can give us an exact idea of how long it was going on, in exactly the same way as the comparative numbers of empty beer cans scattered between the palms on two Pacific islands could have given to an enemy spy an idea of how long a garrison of marines had stayed on each island.

The general result of the survey of the accumulation of lead reveals an extremely important fact that: *no rocks found on the surface of the Earth exhibit an age of more than 3 billion years* (the oldest rocks known are those from the Black Hills of South Dakota, United States, 1.5 billion years old; from

Karelia, Finland, 1.9 billion years old; and from Rhodesia, South Africa, 2.7 billion years old), from which we must conclude that *the solid crust of the Earth was formed from previously molten material 3 or more billion years ago.* Recent studies of Clare C. Peterson in Sweden and Harrison Brown of California, United States, who studied the age of meteorites, indicate that the planetary system may be as much as 4.5 billion years old.

Thus we can picture the Earth several billion years ago as a completely molten spheroid surrounded by a thick atmosphere of air, water-vapors, and probably other extremely volatile substances.

How did this hot lump of cosmic matter come into being, what kind of forces were responsible for its formation, and who supplied the material for its construction? These questions, pertaining to the origin of our Globe as well as to the origin of every other planet of our solar system, have been the basic inquiries of scientific *Cosmogony* (the theory of the origin of the universe), the riddles that have occupied the brains of astronomers for many centuries.

The first attempt to answer these questions by scientific means was made in 1749 by the celebrated French naturalist George-Louis Leclerc, Comte de Buffon, in one of the forty-four volumes of his *Natural History.* Buffon saw the origin of the planetary system as the result of a collision between the sun and a comet that came from the depth of interstellar space. His imagination painted a vivid picture of a "comèt fatale" with a long brilli-

ant tail brushing the surface of our, at that time lonely, sun and tearing from its giant body a number of small "drops," which were sent spinning into space by the force of the impact (Figure 9-2, left).

A few decades later entirely different views concerning the origin of our planetary system were formulated by the famous German philosopher Immanuel Kant, who was more inclined to think that the sun made up its planetary system all by itself without the intervention of any other celestial body. Kant visualized the early state of the sun as a giant, comparatively cool, mass of gas occupying the entire volume of the present planetary system, and rotating slowly around its axis. The steady cooling of the sphere through radiation into the surrounding empty space must have led to its gradual contraction and to the corresponding increase of its rotational speed. The increasing centrifugal force resulting from such rotation must have led to the progressive flattening of the gaseous body of the primitive sun, and resulted in the ejection of a series of gaseous rings along its extended equator (Figure 9-2, right). Such a ring formation from the rotating masses can be demonstrated by the classical experiment performed by Plateau in which a large sphere of oil (not gaseous, as in the case of the sun) suspended within some other liquid with equal density and brought into rapid rotation by some auxiliary mechanical device begins to form rings of oil around itself when the speed of rotation exceeds a certain limit. The rings formed in this way were supposed to have

(a) **Buffon's collision hypothesis**   (b) **Kant's ring hypothesis**

Figure 9-2. Two schools of thought in cosmogony.

broken up later and to have condensed into various planets circling at different distances around the sun.

These views were later adopted and developed by the famous French mathematician Pierre-Simon, Marquis de Laplace, who presented them to the public in his book *Exposition du système du monde,* published in 1796. Although a great mathematician, Laplace did not attempt to give mathematical treatment to these ideas, but limited himself to a semi-popular qualitative discussion of the theory.

When such a mathematical treatment was first attempted sixty years later by the English physicist Clerk Maxwell, the cosmogonical views of Kant and Laplace ran into a wall of apparently insurmountable contradiction. It was, in fact, shown that if the material concentrated at present in various planets of the solar system was distributed uniformly through the entire space now occupied by it, the distribution of matter would have been so thin that the forces of gravity would have been absolutely unable to collect it into separate planets. Thus the rings thrown out from the contracting sun would forever remain rings like the ring of Saturn, which is known to be formed by innumerable small particles running on circular orbits around this planet and showing no tendency toward "coagulation" into one solid satellite.

The only escape from this difficulty would consist in the assumption that the primordial envelope of the sun contained much more matter (at least 100 times as much) than we now find in the planets, and that most of this matter fell on the sun, leaving only about 1 per cent to form planetary bodies.

Such an assumption would lead, however, to another no less serious contradiction. Indeed if so much material, which must originally have rotated with the same speed as the planets do, had fallen on the sun, it would inevitably have communicated to it an angular velocity 5000 times larger than that which it actually has. If this were the case, the sun would spin at a rate of 7 revolutions per hour instead of at 1 revolution in approximately 4 weeks.

These considerations seemed to spell death

to the Kant-Laplace views, and with the eyes of astronomers turning hopefully elsewhere, Buffon's collision theory was brought back to life by the works of the American scientists T. C. Chamberlin and F. R. Moulton, and the famous English scientist Sir James Jeans. Of course, the original views of Buffon were considerably modernized by certain essential knowledge that had been gained since they were formulated. The belief that the celestial body that had collided with the sun was a comet was now discarded, for the mass of a comet was by then known to be negligibly small even when compared with the mass of the moon. And so the assaulting body was now believed rather to be another star comparable to the sun in its size and mass.

However, the regenerated collision theory, which seemed at that time to represent the only escape from the fundamental difficulties of the Kant-Laplace hypothesis, likewise found itself treading on muddy ground. It was very difficult to understand why the fragments of the sun thrown out as a result of the vigorous punch delivered by another star would move along the almost circular orbits followed by all planets, instead of describing elongated elliptical trajectories.

To save the situation it was necessary to assume that, at the time the planets were formed by the impact of the passing star, the sun was surrounded by a uniformly rotating gaseous envelope, which helped to turn the originally elongated planetary orbits into regular circles. Since no such medium is now known to exist in the region occupied by the planets, it was assumed that it was later gradually dissipated into interstellar space, and that the faint luminosity known as *Zodiacal Light,* which at present extends from the sun in the elliptical plane, is all that is left from that past glory. But this picture, representing a kind of hybrid between the Kant-Laplace assumption of the original gaseous envelope of the sun and Buffon's collision hypothesis was very unsatisfactory. However, as the proverb says, one must choose the lesser of two evils, and the collision hypothesis of the origin of the planetary system was accepted as the correct one, being used until very recently in all scientific treatises, textbooks, and popular literature (including the author's two books *The Birth and Death of the Sun*, 1940, and *Biography of the Earth*, 1941).

It was only in the fall of 1943 that the young German physicist C. Weizsäcker cut through the Gordian Knot of the planetary theory. Using the new information collected by recent astrophysical research, he was able to show that all the old objections against the Kant-Laplace hypothesis can be easily removed, and that, proceeding along these lines, one can build a detailed theory of the origin of planets, explaining many important features of the planetary system that had not even been touched by any of the old theories.

The main point of Weizsäcker's work lies in the fact that during the last couple of decades astrophysicists have completely changed their minds about the chemical constitution of matter in the universe. It was generally believed before that the sun and all other stars were formed by the same percentage of chemical elements as those that we have learned from our Earth. Geochemical analysis teaches us that the body of the Earth is made up chiefly of oxygen (in the form of various oxides), silicon, iron, and smaller quantities of other heavier elements. Light gases such as hydrogen and helium (along with other so-called rare gases such as neon, argon, etc.) are present on the Earth in very small quantities.[1]

In the absence of any better evidence, astronomers had assumed that these gases were also very rare in the bodies of the sun and the other stars. However, the more detailed theoretical study of stellar structure led the Danish astrophysicist B. Stromgren to the conclusion that such an assumption is quite incorrect and that, in fact, at least 35 per cent of the material of our sun must be pure hydrogen. Later this estimate was increased to above 50 per cent, and it was also found that a considerable percentage of the other solar constituents is pure helium. Both the

theoretical studies of the solar interior (which recently culminated in the important work of M. Schwarzschild), and the more elaborate spectroscopic analysis of its surface, led astrophysicists to a striking conclusion that: *the common chemical elements that form the body of the Earth constitute only about 1 per cent of the solar mass, the rest being almost evenly divided between hydrogen and helium with a slight preponderance of the former.* Apparently this analysis also fits the constitution of the other stars.

Further, it is now known that *interstellar space is not quite empty*, but is filled by a mixture of gas and fine dust with a *mean density of about 1 mg matter in 1,000,000 cu miles space*, and this diffuse, highly rarefied material apparently has the same chemical constitution as have the sun and the other stars.

In spite of its incredibly low density the presence of this interstellar material can be easily proved, since it produces noticeable selective absorption of the light from stars so distant that it has to travel for hundreds of thousands of light-years through space before entering into our telescopes. The intensity and location of these "interstellar absorption lines" permits us to obtain good estimates of the density of that diffuse material and also to show that it consists almost exclusively of hydrogen and probably helium. In fact, the dust, formed by small particles (about 0.001 mm in diameter) of various "terrestrial" materials, constitutes not more than 1 per cent of its total mass.

To return to the basic idea of Weizsäcker's theory, we may say that this new knowledge concerning the chemical constitution of matter in the universe, plays directly into the hand of the Kant-Laplace hypothesis. In fact, if the primordial gaseous envelope of the sun was originally formed from such material, *only a small portion of it, representing heavier terrestrial elements, could have been used to build our Earth and other planets.* The rest of it, represented by noncondensible hydrogen and helium gases, must have been somehow removed, either by falling into the sun or by being dispersed into surrounding

[1] Hydrogen is found on our planet mostly in its union with oxygen in water. But everybody knows that although water covers three quarters of the Earth's surface the total water mass is very small compared with the mass of the entire body of the Earth.

interstellar space. Since the first possibility would result, as it was explained above, in much too rapid axial rotation of the sun, we have to accept another alternative, namely, that the gaseous "excess-material" was dispersed into space soon after the planets were formed from the "terrestrial" compound.

This brings us to the following picture of the formation of the planetary system. When our sun was first formed by the condensation of interstellar matter a large part of it, probably about a hundred times the present combined mass of planets, remained on the outside forming a giant rotating envelope. (The reason for such behavior can easily be found in the differences between the rotational states of various parts of interstellar gas condensing into the primitive sun.) This rapidly rotating envelope should be visualized as consisting of *noncondensible gases* (hydrogen, helium, and a smaller amount of other gases) and *dust-particles* of various terrestrial materials (such as iron oxides, silicon compounds, water droplets and ice crystals) which were floating inside the gas and carried along by its rotational motion. The formation of big lumps of "terrestrial" material, which we now call planets must have taken place as the result of collisions between dust particles and their gradual aggregation into larger and larger bodies. In Figure 9-3 we illustrate the results of such mutual collisions which must have taken place at velocities comparable to that of meteorites.

One must conclude, on the basis of logical reasoning, that at such velocities the collision of two particles of about equal mass would result in their mutual pulverization (Figure 9-3, left), a process leading not to the growth but rather to the destruction of larger lumps of matter. On the other hand, when a small particle collides with a much larger one (Figure 9-3, middle) it seems evident that it would bury itself in the body of the latter, thus forming a new, somewhat larger mass.

Obviously these two processes would result in the gradual disappearance of smaller particles and the aggregation of their material into larger bodies. In the later stages the process will be accelerated due to the fact that the larger lumps of matter will attract gravitationally the smaller particles passing by and add them to their own growing bodies. This is illustrated in Figure 9-3, right, which shows that in this case the capture-effectiveness of massive lumps of matter becomes considerably larger.

Weizsäcker was able to show that *the fine dust originally scattered through the entire region now occupied by the planetary system must have been aggregated into a few big lumps to form the planets, within a period of about a hundred million years.*

As long as the planets were growing by the accretion of variously sized pieces of cosmic matter on their way around the sun, the constant bombardment of their surfaces by fresh building material must have kept their bodies very hot. As soon, however, as the supply of stellar dust, pebbles, and larger rocks was exhausted, thus stopping the process of further growth, the radiation into interstellar space must have rapidly cooled the outer layers of the newly formed celestial

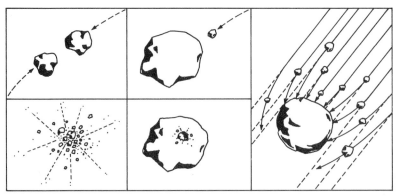

Figure 9-3

312   **Is There Other Life in the Universe?**

bodies, and led to the formation of the solid crust, which is even now growing thicker and thicker, as the slow internal cooling continues.

The next important point to be attacked by any theory of planetary origin is the explanation of the peculiar rule (known as the *Titus-Bode* rule) that governs the distance of different planets from the sun. In the table on this page these distances are listed for nine planets of the solar system, as well as for the belt of *planetoids,* which apparently corresponds to an exceptional case where separate pieces did not succeed in collecting themselves into a single big lump.

Name of the planet	Distance from the sun in terms of earth's distance from the sun	The ratio of the distance of each planet from the sun, to the distance from the sun of the planet listed above it
Mercury	0.387	
Venus	0.723	1.86
Earth	1.000	1.38
Mars	1.524	1.52
Planetoids	about 2.7	1.77
Jupiter	5.203	1.92
Saturn	9.539	1.83
Uranus	19.191	2.001
Neptune	30.07	1.56
Pluto	39.52	1.31

The figures in the last column are of especial interest. In spite of some variations, it is evident that none are very far from the numeral 2, which permits us to formulate the approximate rule: *the radius of each planetary orbit is roughly twice as large as that of the orbit nearest to it in the direction of the sun.*

It is interesting to notice that a similar rule holds also for the satellites of individual planets, a fact that can be demonstrated, for example, by the table below giving the relative distances of nine satellites of Saturn.

Name of satellite	Distance in terms of Saturn's radius	The ratio of increase in two successive distances
Mimas	3.11	
Enceladus	3.99	1.28
Tethys	4.94	1.24
Dione	6.33	1.28
Rhea	8.84	1.39
Titan	20.48	2.31
Hyperion	24.82	1.21
Japetus	59.68	2.40
Phoebe	216.8	3.63

As in the case of the planets themselves, we encounter here quite large deviations (especially for Phoebe!) but again there is hardly any doubt that there is a definite trend for regularity of the same type.

How can we explain the fact that the aggregation process that took place in the original dust cloud surrounding the sun did not result in the first place in just one big planet, and why the several big lumps were formed at these particular distances from the sun?

To answer this question we have to undertake a somewhat more detailed survey of motions that took place in the original dust cloud. We must remember first of all that every material body—whether it is a tiny dust particle, a small meteorite, or a big planet—that moves around the sun under the Newtonian law of attraction is bound to describe an elliptical orbit with the sun in the focus. If the material forming the planets was formerly in the form of separate particles, say, 0.0001 cm. in diameter, there must have been some 10^{45} particles moving along the elliptical orbits of all various sizes and elongations. It is clear that, in such heavy traffic, numerous collisions must have taken place between the individual particles, and that, as the result of such collisions, the motion of the entire swarm must have become to a certain extent organized. In fact, it is not difficult to understand that such collisions served either to pulverize the "traffic violators" or to force them to "detour" into less crowded "traffic lanes." . . . By careful analysis of the situation, Weizäcker was able to show that for the stability of such a system . . . the entire picture of motion must have looked very much like Figure 9-4. Such an arrangement would assure "safe traffic" within each individual ring, but, since these rings rotated with different periods, there must have been "traffic accidents" where one ring touched another. The large number of mutual collisions taking place in these boundary regions between the particles belonging to one ring and those belonging to neighboring rings must have been responsible for the aggregation process and for the growth of larger and larger lumps of matter at these particular distances from the sun. Thus, through a gradual thinning process within each ring, and

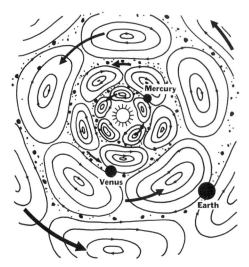

Figure 9-4. Dust-traffic lanes in the original solar envelope.

through the accumulation of matter at the boundary regions between them, the planets were finally formed.

The above described picture of the formation of the planetary system gives us a simple explanation of the old rule governing the radii of planetary orbits. In fact, simple geometrical considerations show that in the pattern of the type shown in Figure 9-4, *the radii of successive boundary lines between the neighboring rings form a simple geometrical progression, each of them being twice as large as the previous one.* We also see why this rule cannot be expected to be quite exact. In fact, it is not the result of some *strict law* governing the motion of particles in the original dust cloud, but must be rather considered as expressing a certain *tendency* in the otherwise irregular process of dust traffic.

The fact that the same rule also holds for the satellites of different planets of our system indicates that the process of satellite formation took place roughly along the same lines. When the original dust cloud surrounding the sun was broken up into separate groups of particles that were to form the individual planets, the process repeated itself in each case with most of the material concentrating in the center to form the body of the planet, and the rest of it circling around condensing gradually into a number of satellites.

With all our discussion of mutual collisions and the growth of dust particles, we have forgotten to tell what happened to the gaseous part of the primordial solar envelope that, as may be remembered, constituted originally about 99 per cent of its entire mass. The answer to this question is a comparatively simple one.

While the dust particles were colliding, forming larger and larger lumps of matter, the gases that were unable to participate in that process were gradually dissipating into interstellar space. It can be shown by comparatively simple calculations that the time necessary for such dissipation was about 100,000,000 years, that is, about the same as the period of planetary growth. Thus by the time the planets were finally formed, most of the hydrogen and helium that had formed the original solar envelope must have escaped from the solar system, leaving only the negligibly small traces referred to above as Zodiacal Light.

One important consequence of the Weizsäcker theory lies in the conclusion that *the formation of the planetary system was not an exceptional event, but one that must have taken place in the formation of practically all of the stars.* This statement stands in sharp contrast with the conclusions of the collision theory, which considered the process by which the planets were formed as very exceptional in cosmic history. . . .

If, as it appears now, . . . there must be millions of planets within our galaxy alone, . . . it would be at least strange if life—even in its highest forms—had failed to develop in these "inhabitable" worlds.

In fact, . . . the simplest forms of life, such as different kinds of viruses, actually are merely rather complicated molecules composed mainly of carbon, hydrogen, oxygen, and nitrogen atoms. Since these elements must be presented in sufficient abundance on the surface of any newly formed planet, we must believe that sooner or later after the formation of the solid crust of earth and the precipitation of atmospheric vapors forming the extensive water reservoirs, a few molecules of such type must have appeared, owing to an accidental combination of the necessary atoms in the necessary order. To be sure, the complexity of living molecules makes the probability of their accidental formation extremely small, and we can compare it with the probability of putting together a jigsaw puzzle by simply shaking the separate pieces in their box with the hope that they will accidentally arrange themselves in the proper way. But on the other hand we must not forget that there were an immense number of atoms continuously colliding with one another, and also a lot of time in which to achieve the necessary result. The fact that life appeared on our Earth rather soon after the formation of the crust indicates that, improbable as it seems, the accidental formation of a complex organic molecule required probably only a few hundred million years. Once the simplest forms of life appeared on the surface of the newly formed planet, the process of organic reproduction, and the

evolution would lead to the formation of more and more complicated forms of living organisms.[2] There is no telling whether the evolution of life on different "inhabitable" planets takes the same track as it did on our Earth. The study of life in different worlds would contribute essentially to our understanding of the evolutionary process.

But whereas we may be able to study the forms of life that may have developed on Mars and Venus (the best "inhabitable" planets of the solar system) in the not too distant future by means of an adventuresome trip to these planets on a "nuclear-power propelled space ship," the question about the possible existence and the forms of life in other stellar worlds hundreds and thousands of light-years away, will probably remain forever an unsolvable problem of science.

[2] More detailed discussion of the origin and evolution of life on our planet can be found in the author's forthcoming book *A Planet Called Earth* to be published by The Viking Press, Inc., in 1963.

THE PRIVATE LIFE OF THE STARS*
by George Gamow (1958)

Having a more or less complete picture of how the individual stars give birth to their families of planets, we may now ask ourselves about the stars themselves.

What is the life history of a star? What are the details of its birth, through what changes does it go during its long life, and what is its ultimate end?

We can start studying this question by looking first at our own sun, which is a rather typical member among the billions of stars forming the system of the Milky Way. We know, first of all, that our sun is a rather old star, since according to the data of paleontology it has been shining with unchanged intensity for a few billion years supporting the development of life on the Earth. No ordinary source could supply so much energy for such a long period of time, and the prob-

lem of solar radiation remained one of the most puzzling riddles of science until the discovery of radioactive transformations and the artificial transformation of elements revealed to us tremendous sources of energy hidden in the depths of atomic nuclei. . . . practically every chemical element represents an alchemical fuel with a potentially tremendous output of energy, and that this energy can be liberated by heating up these materials to millions of degrees. . . .

Thermonuclear Reactions

The discovery of radioactivity and the recognition of the fact that the energy stored within atomic nuclei exceeds, by a factor of a million, the energy liberated in ordinary chemical transformations, threw an entirely new light on the problem of solar energy sources. If the sun could have existed for several thousands of years fed by an ordinary chemi-

* From George Gamow, *Matter, Earth and Sky*, © 1958. Reprinted by permission of Prentice-Hall, Inc., publisher and Macmillan & Co., Ltd.

cal reaction (burning), nuclear energy sources are surely rich enough to supply an equal amount of energy for billions of years. The trouble is, however, that in natural radioactive decay the liberation of nuclear energy is extremely slow. In order to explain the observed mean rate of energy production in the sun, we would have to assume that the sun is composed almost entirely of uranium, thorium, and their decay products. Thus, we are forced to the conclusion that the liberation of nuclear energy inside the sun is not an ordinary radioactive decay, but rather some kind of induced nuclear transformation caused by the specific physical conditions in the solar interior. It is natural to expect that the factor responsible for the induced nuclear transformations is the tremendously high temperature existing in the solar interior. . . . And, indeed, the calculations carried out in this direction in 1929 by the Austrian physicist, F. G. Houtermans, and the British astronomer, R. Atkinson, led to the conclusion that at the temperatures existing in the solar interior, thermonuclear reaactions between hydrogen nuclei (protons) and the nuclei of other light elements can be expected to liberate sufficient amounts of nuclear energy to explain the observed radiation of the sun.

Carbon Cycle and H-H Reaction

Although the work of Houtermans and Atkinson proved, beyond any doubt, that the energy production inside the sun is due to thermonuclear reactions between hydrogen and some light elements, the exact nature of these reactions remained obscure for another decade because of the lack of experimental knowledge concerning the result of nuclear bombardment by fast protons. However, with the pioneering work of Cockcroft and Walton on artificially accelerated proton beams and subsequent work in this direction, enough material has been collected in this field to permit the solution of the solar energy problem. One possible solution was proposed in 1937 by H. Bethe in the United States and C. von Weizsäcker in Germany (independently of one another) and is known as the *carbon cycle*, while the other possibility was conceived by an American physicist, Charles Critchfield, and is known as the *H-H reaction*. The net total result of both reactions is the transformation of hydrogen into helium, but it is achieved in a different manner in each reaction.

In carbon cycles, the atom of carbon can be considered as a "nuclear catalyst" that helps unite four independent protons into a single α-particle by capturing them one by one and holding them together until the union is achieved. After 4 protons are caught and the newly formed α-particle is released, we get back the original carbon atom which can go again through the next cycle. The total period of the cycle is 6×10^6 years while the total energy liberated by the cycle is 4×10^{-5} erg, which yields for the rate of energy liberation per carbon atom the value of 2×10^{-19} erg/sec. Since, according to present data concerning the chemical composition of the sun, each gram of solar material contains 10^{-4} gm of carbon (5×10^{18} carbon atoms), this leads to the total rate of energy liberation of 1 erg/gm $\times$ sec, which is only one per cent of the observed production in the sun.

In the H-H reaction, the series of reactions takes 3×10^9 years and liberates 4×10^{-5} erg, leading to an energy production rate of 5×10^{-22} erg/sec per proton. Since hydrogen constitutes about 50 per cent of the solar material (2×10^{23} protons per gram), the total rate of energy liberation comes out to be 100 erg/gm $\times$ sec, in good agreement with the observed value.

The predominance of the H-H reaction over the carbon cycle in the sun, however, is not the general rule, and is reversed in many other stars. The point is that these two sets of thermonuclear reactions possess different sensitivities to temperature. While the rate of the H-H reaction increases comparatively slowly with increasing temperature, the rate of the carbon cycle goes up very rapidly. We shall see in the next chapter that the brightness of various stars depends essentially on their mass, which determines the temperatures in their deep interior: the more massive the star, the hotter it is inside and the more violent are the energy-producing thermonuclear reactions. Thus, if we take Sirius, for example, we find that its central temperature is 2.3×10^7 °K (compared with only 2.0×10^7 °K in the center of the sun). At this higher temperature the rate of energy production by the carbon cycle becomes considerably larger than that of the H-H reaction, so that it plays here the principal role. On the other hand, in all stars less massive than the sun (and 95 per cent of all stars belong to this group), the carbon cycle becomes quite unimportant and these stars draw their energy entirely from the H-H reaction.

The Future of Our Sun

Since the energy radiated by the sun is due to the continuous transformation of hydrogen into helium in its interior, the sun evidently cannot shine for an eternity and is bound to run out of fuel sometime in the future. It is estimated that during the 5 billion years of its existence our sun has used about one-half of its original supply of hydrogen, so that it still has enough nuclear fuel for another 5 billion years. What will happen 5 billion years from now when our sun comes close to the end of its resources? To answer this question we have to remember that thermonuclear reactions proceed almost exclusively near the center of the sun, where the temperature is the highest. Thus, the shortage of nuclear fuel will be felt first in the central regions of the sun, where all the originally available hydrogen will have been transformed into (unburnable) helium. We can easily visualize that this will result in a rearrangement of things in the solar interior in such a way that the high-temperature region will move to the interface between the "burned-out core" and the outer layers that still contain enough hydrogen to maintain a nuclear fire. The internal structure of the sun, therefore, will be transformed from a so-called *point source model* (energy source in the center) to a *shell source model* in which the energy is liberated in a thin spherical shell that separates the burned-out core from the rest of the solar body (Figure 9-5). As more

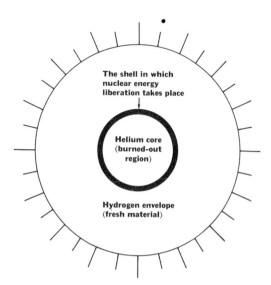

The shell in which nuclear energy liberation takes place

Helium core (burned-out region)

Hydrogen envelope (fresh material)

Figure 9-5. A shell source model of red giant stars.

and more hydrogen is consumed, the "shell" will move outwards from the center, as a ring of fire does that has been started by a carelessly dropped match in a dry grass field.

It was suggested by Charles Critchfield and the author, and later confirmed by the more detailed calculations of M. Schwarzschild and his associates, that the formation of such a shell source inside the sun (or any other star) must result in a steady growth of the star's body and in a gradual increase of its luminosity. In fact, within a few hundred million years after the shell source is formed the diameter of the sun is expected to become as large as the orbit of Venus, and its luminosity will increase by a factor of between 10 and 20, making the oceans on the earth boil violently. After this last effort, the sun will begin to shrink and fade out again, until it becomes quite faint and insignificant. But there is no reason for immediate panic—we still have five billion years to go.

Normal Stars, Stellar Giants, and Dwarfs

As we have mentioned before, different stars have different colors, ranging from a brilliant bluish hue to a dull red. This is, of course, due to the difference in their surface temperatures, and it makes it possible for us to learn about the physical conditions on their surfaces. More exactly, the surface temperatures of stars can be estimated by the study of the absorption lines in their spectra, in the same manner as it is done in the case of our sun. We find that, while the surface temperature of Capella is 6,500°K, i.e., about the same as that of our sun, the temperature of Rigel tops the 11,000°K mark. The reddish star, Antares, on the other hand, has a temperature of only about 3,000°K.

Knowing the surface temperature and the absolute brightness of a star, we can find its linear diameter, even though through the largest telescope the star appears no larger than a point. According to the Stefan-Boltzmann law, the temperature determines the amount of light emitted by a unit area of stellar surface. Thus, dividing the total light emission of a star by the emissivity per unit area, we can calculate the total surface, and, hence the diameter of the star. In this way we find that, whereas Sirius A is only 1.8 times larger than the sun, Capella and Antares are larger than the sun by factors of 12 and 450, respectively. On the other hand, Sirius B is much smaller than the sun, being, in fact, only slightly larger than the earth.

Plotting the magnitudes of a large number of stars against their surface temperatures (both in logarithmic scale) we obtain the very interesting diagram (Figure 9-6) associated with the name of a famous American astronomer, H. N. Russell. We find that most of the stars in this diagram fall within a narrow band known as the *main sequence*. Our sun, Sirius, Rigel, and many other stars belong to this sequence. As we go along this sequence towards brighter and brighter stars, the radius increases, but only moderately. If we check on the masses of the stars belonging to the main sequence (these masses can be estimated if the stars in question belong to a double system), we find that they also increase along the sequence. Thus, we conclude that the increase of radius is simply due to the increase of stellar mass and that the mean density of stars belonging to the main sequence varies but little.

An entirely different picture emerges if we take stars such as *Antares*, or *ε Aurigae*. The points representing these stars in the Russell diagram fall far to the right of the regular main sequence, indicating that these stars must have entirely different internal structures. This class of stars is known under the general name, *Red Giants*—red because they all have a low surface temperature and thus a red color, and giants because of their abnormally large geometrical dimensions and their very high luminosity [Figure 9-7]. Taking into account the measured masses of these stars (30 sun masses for Antares, and for 15 ε Aurigae), we find that their material is extremely rarefied. While the mean density of our sun is 1.6 with respect to water, the mean densities of Antares, and ε Aurigae are only 0.02, and 0.000003, respectively, as compared to atmospheric air.

In contrast to the Red Giants are the so-called *White Dwarfs*, which are located in the lower left corner of the Russell diagram. A typical representative of this class is the companion of Sirius (Sirius B) which having a mass almost equal to that of the sun, is only slightly larger than the earth [Figure 9-8]. Thus, its mean density must be 500,000 times greater than that of water!

Pulsating and Exploding Stars

While most of the stars are seen as luminous points, shining quietly with a constant light, there are many wide deviations from this general rule. To this class of unusual stars belong the stars known as *Cepheid variables*, or simply *Cepheids*, which are subject to periodic pulsations because of some as yet unknown reason. The giant bodies of these stars expand and contract with rhythmic regularity, and this periodic change of dimensions is accompanied by corresponding periodic changes of color and luminosity. The luminosity curve of δ Cephei, after which all this class of stars is named, is shown in Figure 9-9 and is distinctly different from the luminosity curve of an eclipsing variable. The interesting point about the Cepheids is that their pulsation period, which varies for different stars from a fraction of a day to several months, is directly correlated with their intrinsic brightness: *the brighter the star, the longer is its pulsation period*. This gives astronomers an invaluable method for the measurement of

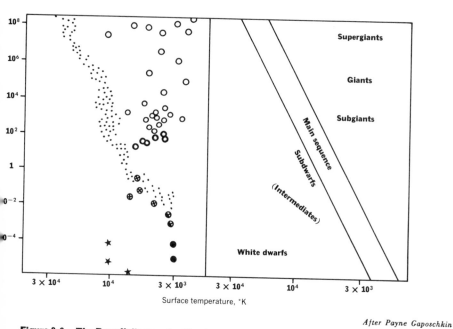

White dwarfs

Supergiants

Giants

Subgiants

Main sequence

Subdwarfs

(Intermediates)

| 3 × 10⁴ | 10⁴ | 3 × 10³ | 3 × 10⁴ | 10⁴ | 3 × 10³ |

Surface temperature, °K

After Payne Gaposchkin

Figure 9-6. The Russell diagram for the stars near the sun that form the spiral arms of our galaxy (see page 322).

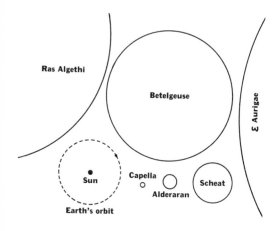

Ras Algethi

Betelgeuse

ε Aurigae

Sun

Capella

Alderaran

Scheat

Earth's orbit

Figure 9-7. Giant and supergiant stars compared with the size of our planetary system.

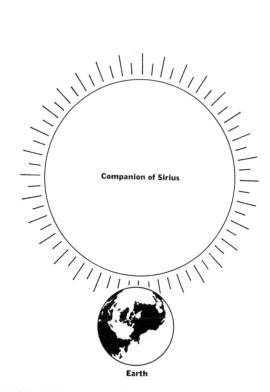

Companion of Sirius

Earth

Figure 9-8. White dwarf stars as compared with the earth.

The Private Life of the Stars   319

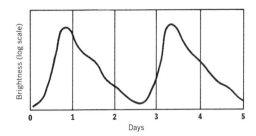

Figure 9-9. Luminosity changes of δ Cephei.

distances that are too large to be tackled by the parallax method. Indeed, by observing the changes of luminosity of a distant Cepheid variable, we obtain directly its pulsation period from which we can determine its absolute brightness. Comparing this brightness with the observed one, and using the inverse square law, we obtain a very exact measurement of the distance of that star from us.

Somewhat similar behavior is observed in the case of the so-called *U Geminorum stars*, named after a star in the constellation of Twins that was the first star of this type to be studied. Instead of going through smooth continuous changes of luminosity as Cepheids do, these stars remain completely tranquil for a longer or shorter period of time, and then burst in the process of a minor explosion. Some of these stars blow up every week and some others only every few months. It is interesting to note that the intensity of these periodic explosions increases in direct proportion to the interval between them.

The extreme case of the periodic explosions of the U Geminorum-type stars is probably represented by the so-called *novae* stellar explosions in which a star's brightness may increase overnight by a factor of many thousands, as compared with a factor of only 30 or 40 for typical U Geminorum stars. These violent stars were given the name, *novae*, i.e., "new ones," because it was originally believed that they were not in the sky before they were first seen. However, later observation proved that these "new stars" were actually not new at all, but rather old stars which, because of some catastrophic process, suddenly increased their luminosity. It is very likely, indeed, that the novae are rather similar to the U Geminorum-type stars except that they explode

only once in a few thousand years and with correspondingly higher intensity. About a hundred novae appear in our stellar system of the Milky Way each year, but very few of them are close enough to us to be seen by the naked eye.

But the real standouts among exploding stars are the so-called *supernovae*, which stand in about the same relation to ordinary novae as the H-bomb does to a small A-bomb. When a star becomes a supernova its luminosity increases by a factor of a few hundred million and at its maximum the exploding star may become as bright as the rest of the galaxy to which it belongs. The first historically recorded explosion of this type took place in the constellation of Taurus on July 4, 1054, and is described in detail in the chronicles of the Peiping Observatory. We read:

In the first year of the period Chihha, the fifth moon, the day Chi-chou [i.e. July 4, 1054], a great star appeared approximately several inches southeast of T'ien-Kuan [i.e. ζ Tauri]. After more than a year, it gradually became invisible.

If we look now at the point in the sky where the Chinese astronomers observed a new star nine centuries ago, we see a very interesting object known as the *Crab Nebula* [Figure 8-13]. It does look like an expanding smoke cloud caused by some vigorous explosion, and, indeed, comparing the older photographs of the Crab Nebula with more recent ones, we find that this nebulosity *is* expanding at the rate of 0.18 angular seconds per year. Since the present angular radius of the Crab Nebula is about 160″, we conclude that the expansion must have started about 900 years ago, which is in perfect agreement with the date of the new star in Taurus as given in Chinese chronicles.

Careful observations reveal that in the center of the Crab Nebula is a faint, but very hot, star, apparently all that is left of the star that must have blown up nine centuries ago. The mass of that star is estimated to be about 25 per cent larger than that of the sun, while the mass of the expanding nebulosity is about 10 per cent of solar mass. It may be added that the Crab Nebula is 5,000 light-years away from us, which means that, whereas the explosion was observed on the earth only nine centuries ago, it actually took place during the beginning of human civilization.

Since the time of the Chinese supernova, only two explosions of comparable violence have taken place among the stars of our Milky Way system. One of them occurred in the constellation of Cassiopeia in 1572 and was described by Tycho Brahe in his book, *De Stella Nuova;* one of the illustrations from this book is shown in Figure 9-10. Another similar explosion took place soon thereafter in the year 1604 and was observed by Tycho's assistant, Johannes Kepler. Since that time no new supernovae have appeared in our galaxy, and, considering that statistical data indicate that the average interval between the supernovae in a given galaxy is about 300 years, we may expect to see one in the sky pretty soon (i.e., within a month or within a century).

However, our stellar system of the Milky Way is only one of the billions of other similar stellar systems, known as *galaxies,* that float in space within the range of modern telescopes, and we have a much better chance to observe supernovae in these far-away stellar systems. As a matter of fact, a bright supernovae appeared in 1885 in our nearest cosmic neighbor, the Great Nebula in Andromeda. By constantly observing a few hundred of our neighboring galaxies, the Mount Wilson astronomers, W. Baade and F. Zwicky, were able to observe and to study the luminosities of a dozen supernovae going off in them.

The Evolution of Stars

Since the stars forming our system of the Milky Way are similar to our sun, differing from it essentially only in their mass, their evolutionary history must be similar to that of the sun, described in the previous chapter. Like the sun, the stars must have condensed once upon a time from a dilute mixture of gas and dust, and have finally reached the steady (main-sequence) state in which they consume their original hydrogen supply by means of carbon cycles or H-H reactions.

However, stars of different masses go through their evolutionary cycles at different rates. According to observationally established, and theoretically confirmed, *mass-luminosity relations,* the brightness of the stars, and hence their rate of hydrogen consumption, increases as the cube of their mass. Since the original supply of hydrogen in a star is apparently proportional to its mass, we must conclude that *the total life spans of different stars must be inversely proportional to the squares of their masses.* Thus, we speak about the "calendar age" of a star, which simply refers to the number of years it has existed, and of its "genetic age," which represents its age as the fraction of its total life span. Stars of the same calendar age may have entirely different genetic ages. Imagine a human being, a dog, and a mouse—all three having been born five years ago. The human being is still a baby; the dog is already a mature dog; and the mouse is a *dead* mouse since mice do not live that long. A similar situation exists in the world of stars, and, by observing the stars that are seen in the sky now, we may expect to find among them representative examples of all different stages of stellar evolution. Thus, our theoretical considerations concerning our sun's past

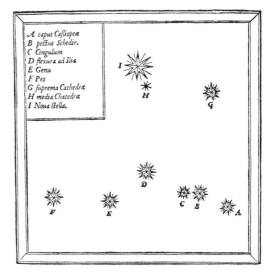

Figure 9-10. An illustration from Tycho Brahe's book "De Stella Nuova," indicating the position of a new star (marked by I) in the constellation of Cassiopeia.

Figure 9-11. The horsehead in Orion.

and future can be directly compared with the observed properties of stars that are at the present time passing through these evolutionary stages.

A very important fact about the stellar population of our system that was emphasized by the Mount Wilson astronomer, W. Baade, a number of years ago is that there exist two different types of stellar population. In the neighborhood of the sun, which Baade calls the "local swimming hole," the space between the stars is filled by a very diluted mixture of gas and dust that forms giant interstellar nebulae obscuring the stars located behind them (Figure 9-11). The density of this interstellar material is about 10^{-24} gm/cm³, which means that a cube of space 1,000 km on a side contains only one gram of matter. This material, the total mass of which is comparable to the total mass of the stars themselves, serves as the source for the formation of new stars by a slow condensation process. The continuous formation process of stars from the dilute interstellar material accounts for the fact that this type of stellar population contains very bright stars like Rigel, which, because of their very short life span, must be considered to have been born considerably later than our sun and its planetary system. It is interesting to notice that stars are apparently born in large groups that originate from large contracting nebulosities and then disperse in different directions as the children of one large family. This fact

was recently emphasized by a Russian astronomer, V. A. Ambarzumian, in his studies of the so-called *stellar associations* formed by dispersing groups of stars, all of the same comparatively small age.

In contrast to the above described stellar communities, known as *Population I*, there exists also stellar communities known as *Population II* that are characterized by the complete absence of any interstellar material. A typical example of such a stellar community is represented by the *globular clusters* (Figure 9-12) that float in space far away from us near the center of our stellar system. Apparently in this case the formation of the stars took place all at once in some distant past, with all the available material being completely utilized. All stars of Population II are of the same calendar age, and no new stars can be formed any more. Thus, while stellar Population I can be compared with the population of a city containing the members of all ages, from newborn babies to gray-haired veterans, stellar Population II resembles more the alumni of the class of 1912 (or any other year) of some large university. No new members are admitted, and the membership is gradually extinguished by the dying-out process.

Stellar Population II presents particular interest for the study of stellar evolution, since,

Figure 9-12. Globular star cluster in Hercules.

being of the same calendar age, the stars of different masses belonging to it show a clear picture of their genetic age differences. In Figure 9-13 we give the Russell diagram of the Population II stars forming a typical globular cluster like the one shown in Figure 9-12. Comparing it with the corresponding diagram of the Population I stars (Figure 9-6), we notice that the main sequence is sharply limited from above and that the stars that are more than 3.5 times more luminous (and more than 50 per cent more massive) than our sun are completely absent. These are the "dead mice" stars which, because of their fast fuel consumption, were completely extinguished a long time ago. The demarcation line between the existing and non-existing stars of the main sequence of Population II corresponds to stars with the calculated life span of about 5 billion years, a figure that must represent the age of our stellar system. This figure closely agrees with the estimated age of various other characteristic features of our universe, be it the oceans, the earth's crust, or the moon. It underlines once more the general belief of scientists today that *the universe as we know it now was formed about five billion years ago.*

Later Stages of Stellar Evolution

What happens to a star when all the hydrogen in its central regions is turned into helium? We have already mentioned in the previous chapter in relation to the future of our sun that such exhaustion of hydrogen is expected to result in the formation of an *energy-producing shell* at the base of the outer hydrogen-rich envelope, and that the growth of that shell should lead to a gradual increase of stellar radius and luminosity. The stars that come to that stage of their evolution are bound to take off from the main sequence of the Russell diagram and to travel toward its upper right corner. And, in fact, that is exactly what one observes in the case of globular star clusters. In Figure 9-13 we notice a narrow band that starts from the cut-off point of the main sequence and extends in the predicted direction; this band represents those stars that apparently have

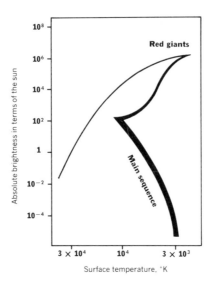

Figure 9-13. The Russell diagram of stars that form the central body of the Milky Way system and of globular clusters.

exhausted their central hydrogen supply and are in various stages of their shell-source development. Theoretical studies of this phase of stellar evolution indicate that a new kind of thermonuclear reaction begins to be of importance in addition to regular H → He transformations. In fact, the rapidly increasing central densities in shell-model stars begin to favor triple-collision processes in which the helium forming the isothermal core is transformed directly into carbon:

$$_2He^4 + \, _2He^4 + \, _2He^4 = \, _6C^{12} + \text{radiation}$$

This important reaction, first proposed by the American physicist E. E. Salpeter, is followed by other reactions, such as:

$$_6C^{12} + \, _2He^4 = \, _8O^{16} + \text{radiation}$$
$$_8O^{16} + \, _2He^4 = \, _{10}Ne^{20} + \text{radiation}$$
$$\text{etc.}$$

which gradually build up the original hydrogen of the stellar interior into more and more complex nuclei. This continuous build-up process is presumably terminated when nuclei of iron atoms are formed, since iron nuclei are the most stable nuclei among all chemical elements.

In order to maintain the high central temperature and density needed for the maintenance of the above described reactions, the star must begin to contract, and its luminosity gradually fades; this is responsible for the band in the Russell diagram for Population II that runs downward and to the left from the highest luminosity point reached by the evolving stars. During this descent into oblivion, stars pass through various unstable states and are subject to the pulsations and periodic minor explosions described earlier in this chapter.

Arriving at the end of their evolutionary track at the lower left corner of the Russell diagram, stars become internally unstable and blow up in the brilliant display of supernovae explosions.

LIFE OUTSIDE THE SOLAR SYSTEM

PROBABILITY OF LIFE*
by Harlow Shapley (1958)

On the basis of our sampling census of stars in our galaxy, and our sampling of galaxy population out to the limit attainable by present telescopes, we can readily compute that there are more than 10^{20} stars in the universe, each one competent of course through radiation to maintain the photochemical reactions that are the basis of plant and animal life. Perhaps only a few per cent of these are single stars with planetary potentialities. Perhaps only a few per cent of these few developed in such a way (nebular contraction) or had such a suitable experience in the past (collisional) that they would now possess persisting planets. Perhaps only a few per cent of these that succeed in having stable-orbited persisting planets would have one or more at the right distance from the central star; and of these rightly placed planets but one per cent have an orbit of suitable circularity to maintain sufficiently equable temperatures. We could go on with further restrictions to a few of the few of the few, because nonpoisonous airs and waters are also required, and that particular activity of carbon, oxygen, hydrogen, and nitrogen that we call "living" must get started. We could by such restrictions reduce the number of stars with livable and actually "inhabited" planets to nearly a nothing.

All these restrictions, however, get us practically nowhere in isolating ourselves as something unique and special, for there are too many stars. Three undeniable factors have entered our consideration—the ordinariness of our sun which has accomplished the creation of life on this planet; the evidence of the universality of the kind of chemistry and physics we know here; and the existence of more than 10^{20} opportunities for life, that is, the existence of more than one hundred thousand million billion stars.

Let us look once more at large numbers and work this argument over again. Suppose that because of doubling, clustering, secondary collisions, and the like, only one star in a thousand has a planetary system. Personally I would think that one in fifty would be a better estimate, and many of those who believe in the nebular contraction theory of stellar formation would say that at least one out of ten stars has planets. But to be conservative, we say that only one out of a thousand has a planetary system, and then assume that but one out of a thousand of those stars with systems of planets has one or more planets at the right distance from the star to provide the water and warmth that protoplasm requires. In our solar system we have two or three planets in such an interval of distance [Figure 9-14]. Further, let us suppose that only one out of a thousand of those stars with

* From Harlow Shapley, *Of Stars and Men.* Reprinted by permission of the Beacon Press, copyright © 1958 by Harlow Shapley.

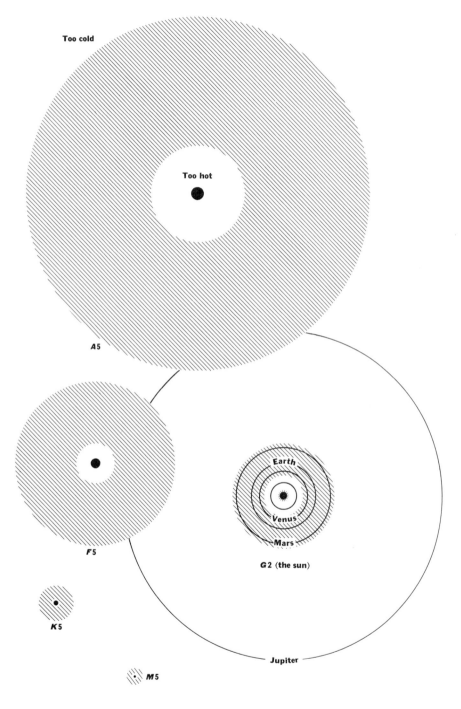

Too cold

Too hot

A5

F5

Earth

Venus

Mars

G2 (the sun)

K5

Jupiter

M5

Figure 9-14. **Thermally habitable zone of various types of star is represented by the hatched area around the star. Here the A5 spectral type has the largest zone, but the star does not remain stable long enough for evolution to take place on a planet near it. The habitable zone of our sun (a G2 type) extends from the orbit of Venus to the orbit of Mars. Tiny M5 star has the smallest zone.**

planets suitably distant has one large enough to hold an atmosphere; in our system we have at least seven planets out of nine with atmospheres. That will reduce our suitable planet to a one in a billion chance.

Let us make one other requirement of our suitable planet: the chemical composition of air and water must be of the sort that would develop the naturally arising complex inorganic molecules into the organic. Perhaps that happens but once in a thousand times?

Assembling all four of the one to a thousand chances (all grossly underestimated, I believe, but in the effort to establish our uniqueness in the world, and hence our "importance," we are making it as hard as possible to find other habitable planets), we come to the estimate that only one star out of 10^{12} meets all tests; that is, one star out of a million million. Where does that high improbability of proper planets leave us? Dividing the million million into the total number of stars, $10^{20} \div 10^{12}$, we get 10^8—that is a hundred million planetary systems suitable for organic life. This number is a minimum, and personally I would recommend, . . . its multi-

plication by at least a thousand times, possibly by a million.

To state a conclusion: The researches of recent times have enriched and clarified our concepts of habitable planets. Through discovering the true stellar nature of the spiral "nebulae," through the sounding of star-and-galaxy populated space to such great depths that the number of knowable stars rises to billions of times the number formerly surmised, and through the discovery of the expansion of the universe with its concomitant deduction that a few billion years ago the stars and planetary materials were much more densely and turbulently crowded together than in the present days of relative calm, we have strengthened our beliefs with respect to the existence of other "worlds." The present concept includes the identifying of our own world as the surface of planet No. 3, in the family of a run-of-the-mill yellowish star, situated in the outer part of a typical galaxy that contains billions of typical stars—this "home galaxy" being one item in an over-all system, the Metagalaxy, that numbers its galaxies in the multibillions.

LIFE OUTSIDE THE SOLAR SYSTEM*
by Su-Shu Huang (1960)

What is the probability that man will ever be able to visit the life-bearing planet of another star, or that the earth will receive a visitor from such a planet? Does the possibility justify taking measures now—in advance of a visit—to put existing technology to the task of scanning the sky for signals from intelligent organisms outside the solar system, or for transmitting signals in the hope they may be heard? If so, what sort of signals should be listened for or sent? . . .

For the present there is no hope of detecting on a photographic plate the existence of a planet of another star. Such planets as may attend even the nearest star are completely

* From Su-Shu Huang, "Life outside the Solar System," *Scientific American*, April, 1960, pp. 55–63. Reprinted by permission.

lost to view in the brilliance of the star's light. Some day there may be a telescope on a platform in space, free of the interfering effects of the earth's atmosphere. As has been suggested by Nancy G. Roman of the National Aeronautics and Space Administration, the instrument would produce a sharp star image that could be blocked out so that a planet near the star could be detected by means of a long photographic exposure. Even the subtle methods used to detect spectroscopic binaries (Figure 9-15) are not refined enough to find a planet, because the effect of a planet upon the motion of its parent star is so slight.

There is nonetheless other well-established evidence to support the contention that planets are common. In the first place, no sharp dis-

To observer

To observer

Yerkes Observatory

Figure 9-15. Spectroscopic detection of close binaries is depicted in these diagrams and spectra. At top, the stars are orbiting around their center of mass, the one at left moving toward the earth, the one at right, away from the earth. Spectral lines made by the star moving toward the earth shift toward the violet end of the spectrum, and lines from the star moving away shift toward the red end, splitting the spectral lines as seen in the upper spectrum below the diagrams. In the lower diagram, the binaries are moving across the line of vision as seen from the earth. This gives rise to the normal single spectral lines seen in the lower spectrum. Spectroscopic binaries are so close to- gether that no telescope can resolve them into separate bodies, and only their spectra enable us to detect them and to calculate their orbital movements.

Figure 9-16. The rotational velocity of stars on the main sequence diagrammed according to spectral type. The slow spin after type F5 may indicate that planets are present.

tinction can be drawn between binary or multiple stars and stars with planetary systems. According to Gerard P. Kuiper of the Yerkes Observatory, the mean distance of separation between the components of all binaries so far investigated is about 20 astronomical units. This is of the same order of magnitude as the distance between the sun and its major planets (Jupiter, Saturn, Uranus and Neptune). Kaj Aa. Strand at the U.S. Naval Observatory in Washington has studied small perturbations in the orbital motion of a star called 61 Cygni, which has a companion that is too faint to be directly observed. He has found that the mass of this unseen object is about a hundredth of that of the sun. This mass lies between that of stars and of Jupiter. It is therefore reasonable to believe that the masses of small stars in binary systems grade continuously down to the masses of planets. Since binaries are so common in our galaxy, it would seem that many stars that now appear to be alone actually possess planets.

Harold C. Urey of the Scripps Institution of Oceanography has found additional evidence for planets in a certain kind of meteorite. According to Urey, diamonds embedded in these objects show that they must at one time have been under high pressure in a body the size of the moon. Such moonlike objects, known as "prestellar nuclei," would enhance the formation of both stars and planets from a dust cloud. Any irregularity in the motions of a dust cloud should be expected to produce more than one such nucleus, and the formation of planets or multiple stars would follow as a normal consequence.

Finally, measurements of the angular momenta of many stars give every indication that planets exist outside the solar system. Otto Struve of the National Radio Astronomy Observatory has pointed out that main-sequence stars more massive than Type F5 [about 1.3 times the mass of our sun] usually rotate rapidly, but starting with this type the rotation of stars slows down abruptly. In other words, the average angular momentum per unit mass of the main-sequence stars exhibits a conspicuous break at Type F5 (Figure 9-16). The most reasonable explanation of this strange phenomenon is that unobservable planets have absorbed the angular momentum, just as Jupiter and other planets of the sun carry 98 per cent of the angular momentum of the solar system, leaving the sun with only 2 per cent and a comparatively long period (27 days) of rotation. If planets do indeed account for the slow spin of these otherwise sunlike stars, then planets appear just where life is more likely to flourish.

Thus it seems that intelligent life may be scattered throughout the Milky Way and the universe as a whole. In our immediate neighborhood, however, we may be its only representatives. The sun's nearest neighbor, Alpha Centauri, is only 4.3 light-years away. It is a triple system with two massive components (a G4 star and a K1) revolving around each other about 20 astronomical units apart; at a considerable distance is a small third star. The two larger bodies have highly eccentric orbits, and if there is a stable zone for a planet in this system, it is extremely hard to compute (Figure 9-17). Moreover, recent investigations indicate that the system may be much younger than the sun, so that higher forms of life might not have had time to evolve even if a habitable planet does exist in it.

Forty other stars are located within five parsecs (16.7 light-years) of the sun. Only

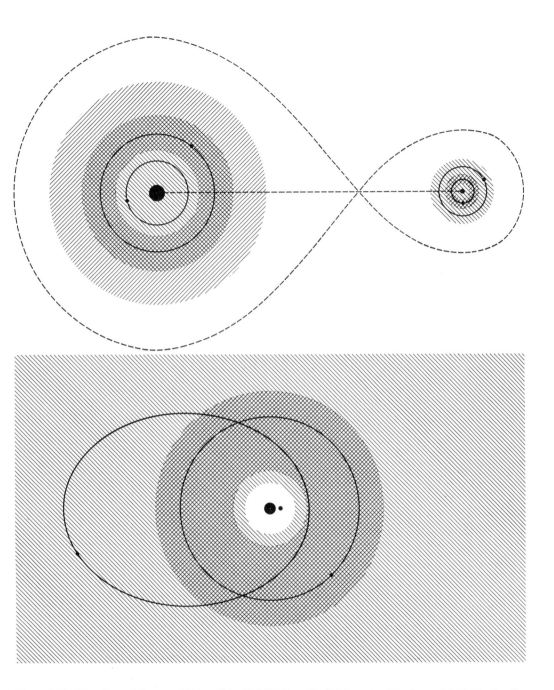

Figure 9-17. Planetary orbits around binary stars depicted in an idealized manner. The figure eight in the top diagram is simply a mathematical projection from which the dynamically stable planetary orbit is calculated for widely separated binaries. At bottom are close binaries. For a planet to bear life, its orbit would have to fall completely within both the dynamically stable zone (\\\ hatching) and the thermally habitable zone (/// hatching). At bottom the highly elliptical planetary orbit is dynamically stable, but it does not fall completely within the thermally habitable zone; the planet therefore could not harbor any life.

two—Epsilon Eridani (a K2 type) and Tau Ceti (G4)—seem to fulfill the conditions for the existence of advanced forms of life, and Epsilon Eridani may not be exactly on the main sequence. Tau Ceti is 10.8 light-years distant, has an apparent visual magnitude of 3.6, is located on the celestial sphere about 16 degrees south of its equator and appears above the horizon in the northern sky only in the winter.

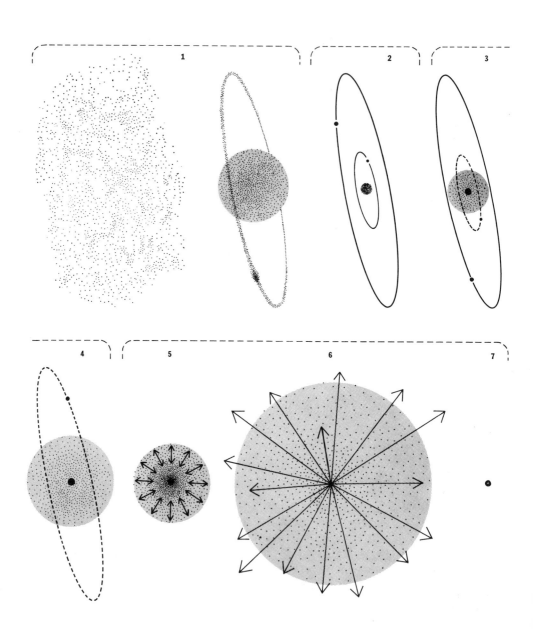

Figure 9-18. Possible evolution of a star 1.2 times the mass of the sun begins with a dust cloud condensing into a star and protoplanets (1), a process taking perhaps 10 million years. The star enters the "main sequence" (2) and remains there for approximately 8 billion years. Then it expands (3) into the red giant stage (4), first destroying life on its inner planet, then burning up the planets in turn. This period may last about 100 million years. Then the star may pulsate in luminosity every few hours (5) for thousands of years, finally exploding into a nova (6) and eventually collapsing into white dwarf (7). The time period for final stages (5, 6, and 7) is not known.

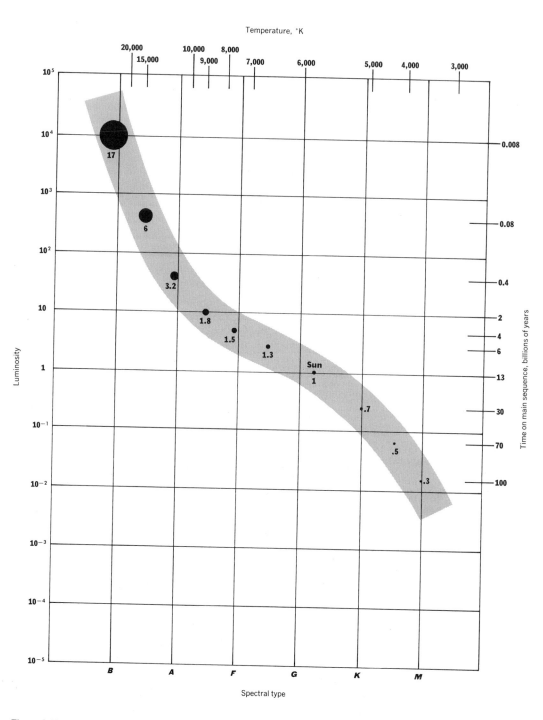

Figure 9-19. Typical stars on the main sequence are represented on this diagram. Vertical scale at left indicates luminosity, the sun being unity. Scale at right shows time on the main sequence. The numbers at top denote temperature in degrees Kelvin; the letters at bottom, spectral type. Small figures beneath each star give its mass with respect to the mass of the sun.

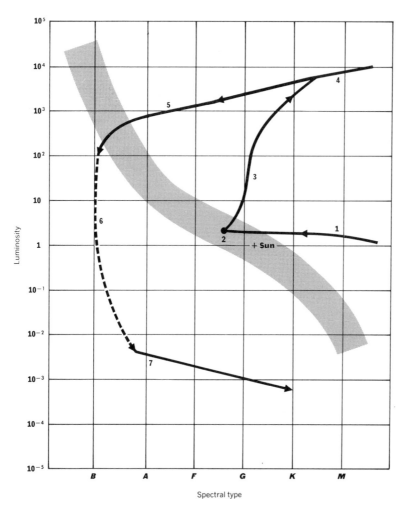

Figure 9-20. Evolutionary path of a star with a mass 1.2 times that of the sun is traced. The vertical scale is luminosity (the sun is unity); the horizontal scale, spectral type. The main sequence is outlined by the gray hatching. The numbers on the path correspond to the stages of stellar evolution depicted in the illustration at the top of Figure 9-19. At 1 the star is in the stage of gravitational contraction; at 2 it is on the main sequence; at 3 it is expanding; at 4 it is a red giant; at 5 it pulsates. The broken line (6) indicates uncertainty as to the path the star follows in reaching the white-dwarf stage (7).

Since intelligent life is probably not a rare phenomenon, and since at least one star in our vicinity meets the specifications of a life-fostering star, it may seem odd that we have had no visitors from other worlds. The idea would have drawn ridicule 20 years ago, but today it deserves consideration. There are, however, several reasons for believing that we have had no visitors from outer space. For one thing, the 10.8 light-years that separate us from Tau Ceti—astronomically a short distance—is an extremely long distance in terms of human experience. Even traveling at the speed of the artificial satellites that man

has launched, space voyagers would need hundreds of thousands of years to traverse it. It is possible that organisms from Tau Ceti might have a far longer life-span than man, but this supposition invokes radical assumptions that cannot be supported by present knowledge. Furthermore, if a meeting is to occur, our high technological civilization would have to be contemporary with that created by intelligent organisms on other planets. The cultural evolution that brought mankind to its present technical competence began only a few centuries ago. And even if human civilization endures for hundreds of thousands of years, it would be a brief episode in the time-scale of biological evolution. Therefore the chance that advanced civilizations might be flourishing at the present time on the planets of one or two nearby stars is excessively small.

Some workers have concluded, however, that the chance is good enough—and certainly intriguing enough—to institute radio surveillance of signals originating outside the solar system. Guiseppe Cocconi and Philip Morrison of Cornell University have pointed out that the most favorable wavelength would be one close to but outside of the 21-centimeter line emitted by hydrogen in space, because in this region of the spectrum the galactic noise and the noise produced in the earth's atmosphere are at a minimum. Moreover, this important wavelength would be of as much interest to astronomers on another planet as to those on earth. Cocconi and Morrison have urged that radiation picked up by the 600-foot radio telescope, now being built by the Navy in West Virginia, be analyzed for the presence of signals. According to them, that telescope will be capable of detect-

ing signals generated 10 light-years away by a technology no more advanced than our own. Meanwhile Frank D. Drake of the National Radio Astronomy Observatory, who makes a more generous estimate of the distance at which signals sent by intelligent organisms could be detected, is in charge of an actual project that is employing a smaller telescope to detect any radio signals transmitted by living beings in other "solar systems."

What kind of signals may we expect to receive or should we send out? Probably the most abstract and the most universal conception that any intelligent organisms anywhere would have devised is the sequence of cardinal numbers: 1, 2, 3, 4 and so on. The most likely signal would be a series of pulses indicating this sequence repeated at regular intervals. Such a signal may upon first consideration appear to be too simple for the sophisticated task of communicating with other beings far away among the stars. It would sound like baby talk. But after all interstellar communication is surely still in the baby-talk stage.

LIFE WITHIN OUR OWN SOLAR SYSTEM

THE SOLAR SYSTEM*
by Michael Ovenden (1962)

In examining the peculiar properties of the Earth, as a planet of the Sun, that seem to be necessary to sustain living creatures of the types found on the Earth, we have seen that the higher forms of life require an atmosphere containing oxygen, or else water in which oxygen has been dissolved. Plant life does not necessarily need this oxygen—indeed, the oxygen in the Earth's atmosphere may have originated from the activity of plant life at an earlier stage of the Earth's history—but does require available carbon

dioxide. It is the particular property of plants that they can absorb solar energy, and store it up as chemical energy by building from carbon dioxide and water heavier, larger chemical molecules.

But by far the most important requirement of life on Earth would seem to be an equable temperature. The range of temperature that allows for *active* life is very small, from about 20 degrees F to 140 degrees F. The upper temperature limit is the more important, for if the temperature is too high, the complex molecules upon which the chemical activity of life seems to depend begin to break up. The

* From Michael Ovenden, *Life in the Universe*, Copyright © 1962, Educational Services, Inc. Copyright © 1961 by the Illustrated London News and Sketch, Ltd. Reprinted by permission of Doubleday & Company, Inc.

lower limit is much less definite, for life may, at low temperatures, assume a latent form. Though not active at the low temperature, life does not die, but will recover and become active if the temperature is raised.

Measuring the Planets' Temperatures

In this chapter we look at the other planets of the solar system with these limitations in mind, and we consider first the temperature criterion. The temperature of a planet's surface depends, first, upon its distance from the source of heat and light, the Sun. If the planet had no atmosphere, and absorbed all the radiation falling upon it, then it would be easy to calculate the temperature at which the planet's surface would stabilize at any given distance from the Sun. It is important to notice that the temperature depends upon the property of the *planet*; space itself, in the solar system, can have no "temperature," only matter can. If an artificial planet were sent into the solar system, made of highly polished metal (so that it reflected all the radiation of the Sun falling on it, and absorbed none of it), then the interior of the artificial planet would remain completely cold, however near the Sun it went.

The temperature of the surface of a planet can be measured—approximately, at least—by using very sensitive detectors of heat. Such a sensitive detector is the *thermocouple* (Figure 9-21). If a circuit of wire is made, one half being of one metal and the other half of another metal, and the two junctions are kept at different temperatures, then a small electric current will flow through the circuit. If this current is measured, the difference in temperature of the two junctions can be measured.

Suppose, then, that we have such a thermocouple, and we keep one junction at the freezing point of water by immersing it in a mixture of water and ice. The other junction is placed in a telescope, so that the image of a planet falls on it. The thermocouple absorbs the energy of the heat and light from the planet, and heats up. From the small electric current that flows, we can tell how much energy is coming to us from the planet (if we allow for any absorption by the telescope itself). Now not all this energy will be heat radiation by the planet; some of it will be solar radiation that has been reflected by the planet. But whereas the heat radiation will be of long wavelengths in the far infrared, the

Figure 9-21. At top, the apparatus for measuring temperature with a thermocouple; at bottom, its application to a telescope.

solar radiation is mostly in the form of visible light. We can separate these two components of the radiation if we make observations first with the planet's radiation passing through a cell of water before it reaches the thermocouple, and then without the water cell. The water cell absorbs the heat rays from the planet, but is transparent to the visible light. . . . So, by subtracting the energy received with the water cell from the energy received without the water cell, we find the heat received from the planet, and from this we can calculate the planet's temperature.

Mercury and Venus

The planet nearest the Sun is Mercury, at a distance of 36 million miles. If we use the distance of the Earth from the Sun (93 million miles) as our unit of distance (the Astronomical Unit), then Mercury is nearly 0.4 Astronomical Units away from the Sun. It keeps the same face towards the Sun, and we would calculate its surface temperature on the sunward side to be about 700 degrees F. This is close to the measured value. The dark side of Mercury is so cold that no radiation can be detected from it.

The agreement between the calculated and observed temperatures shows that Mercury has no appreciable atmosphere. We would not expect it to have. A gas consists of a large number of molecules, which, as the gas is heated up, move faster and faster, colliding with each other. When the temperature is high enough, many of the molecules acquire speeds greater than the escape speed from the planet. They then fly off into space, just as a rocket which exceeds the escape speed from the Earth's surface will become an artificial planet. In the case of Mercury, its surface temperature is so high that if it ever had any atmosphere, this would long since have evaporated into space. Any atmosphere that remains must be very, very tenuous indeed compared with the density of the Earth's atmosphere. With a temperature so far exceeding the upper limit for active life, and with no appreciable atmosphere, Mercury seems a most unlikely abode for life at all resembling life as we know it on Earth (Figure 9-22).

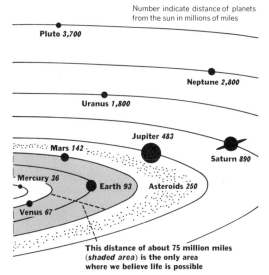

Number indicate distance of planets from the sun in millions of miles

Pluto *3,700*

Neptune *2,800*

Uranus *1,800*

Jupiter *483*

Mars *142*

Saturn *890*

Mercury *36*

Earth *93*

Asteroids *250*

Venus *67*

This distance of about 75 million miles (*shaded area*) is the only area where we believe life is possible

Figure 9-22. Life as we know it is possible only in a small region of the solar system.

We would expect Venus to have a temperature of about 450 degrees F at nearly three-quarters of an Astronomical Unit from the Sun. The observations give quite a different answer—about −40 degrees F. This is because Venus is covered with an extensive atmosphere, full of clouds. These clouds reflect nearly all the solar light and heat, and there is little left to heat the planet. But the same clouds will also bottle up any heat radiation from the planet, so that the actual temperature of the surface of Venus may be much higher than the observed temperature. What we are really observing is the temperature of the atmosphere of Venus above the cloud layer. In fact, this thick cloud layer prevents us from knowing anything about the surface conditions on Venus—we do not even know how rapidly Venus rotates, because we cannot see any permanent marking on the surface [Figure 9-23].

It is difficult also to know of what the clouds of Venus are composed. They appear very white, because they reflect so much solar radiation; this is the main reason why Venus can become the brightest object in the night sky. The method used to discover the chemical nature of the atmosphere of a planet is to look closely at the spectrum of the planet. If we pass the light of the Sun through a

Figure 9-23. The phases of Venus, displaying the true relative sizes of its disc at different points in the orbit.

prism, we see a colored rainbow band with some colors missing or faint. We usually pass the light through a slit, and the missing colors appear as dark lines in the solar spectrum. There are many tens of thousands of such lines, and the particular lines that appear depend upon the chemical nature and physical conditions of the atoms in the outer layers of the Sun. If a planet simply reflected the light of the Sun, then its spectrum should be an exact replica, albeit a faint replica, of the solar spectrum. But if the planet has an atmosphere, then the sunlight has had to pass twice through the planet's atmosphere before reaching us. We might hope to see new dark lines appearing in the planet's spectrum that were *not* in the Sun's spectrum, lines produced by the atoms of the planetary atmosphere.

The spectrum of Venus has been searched for such telltale lines, in the hope of identifying the atoms of the planet's atmosphere. But such searches have been inconclusive. In particular, the characteristic groups of lines that we know to be due to water vapor do not occur in the spectrum of Venus. (This is a difficult observation, because our own atmosphere contains water vapor, and produces dark water-vapor telluric lines in both the solar and planetary spectra.) At one time it was supposed that this negative observation

ruled out any possibility of the clouds' being ordinary water-vapor clouds, and many suggestions of alternative chemical constituents were made, such as solid carbon dioxide, and formaldehyde, a compound of carbon, oxygen and hydrogen. But if the temperature at the cloud level is as low as −40 degrees F, then the clouds might still be of water, but in a frozen state. If this be so, then on the surface of Venus water might exist in a free liquid state, and conditions on Venus might well be suited to the development of life. But this is just speculation. The clouds of Venus hide the secrets of the surface well, and Venus remains an enigma.

The Moon

The Earth's natural satellite, the Moon, should have an average temperature much the same as that of the Earth. But the mass of the Moon is only about an eightieth of the mass of the Earth, and so the escape velocity from the surface of the Moon is much less than that from the Earth. While the Earth has been able to retain its atmosphere over cosmic periods of time, the Moon has not. The Moon has no air, and consequently no free water lying on its surface. Also, because of aeons of tidal action by the Earth on the solid body of the Moon, the Moon keeps the same face always to the Earth (apart from a slight vestigial rotation called *libration*). Its day is, therefore, as long as a month on the Earth.

On the sunlit side of the Moon, at the middle of the lunar day, the temperature of the surface may exceed the boiling point of water (212 degrees F). At sunset on the Moon the temperature has dropped to −50 degrees F, and at midnight on the Moon is as low as −240 degrees F (Figure 9-24).

Just to step across from the sunlight into the shadow of a crater or mountain on the lunar surface would be to experience a drop of temperature of over 200 degrees F. Certainly the Moon seems to be no place for the development of active life. It is just possible, however, that simple organisms might be able to survive the cold of the lunar night and the heat of the lunar day in a latent form, to have a brief activity twice a month (at sunset

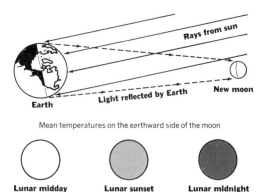

Mean temperatures on the earthward side of the moon

Lunar midday
up to 220°F

Lunar sunset
—50°F

Lunar midnight
as low as —240°F

Figure 9-24. The Moon is at best an inhospitable planet, as its earthward temperatures show. Remember that water boils at 212°F!

and sunrise on the Moon). Possibly the day is not far hence when instruments may be sent to the Moon to investigate, among other matters, whether such primitive life cells do exist there. For this reason, considerable care has been taken to sterilize the attempted and successful lunar probes, so that there should be no danger of taking simple life forms to the Moon from the Earth, to contaminate it before these interesting observations could be made.

Mars, Jupiter and Beyond

The next planet outward from the Earth is Mars, at one and a half Astronomical Units. Mars has a slight atmosphere, and its temperature (at its warmest parts) may rise above the freezing point of water. Of all the planets of the solar system, Mars is the most likely one on which to find other forms of life. Furthermore, observations of Mars give some ground for believing that life of a sort does exist on Mars. For this reason, I will devote my next chapter to Mars alone.

Beyond Mars we find the giant planet Jupiter, over five times as far from the Sun as the Earth is. Its surface temperature would be expected to be around —200 degrees F, and it is covered by a most extensive atmosphere of ammonia and methane, both gases being highly poisonous to Earth-like forms of life. As we proceed outward, we come to the other giant planets, Saturn, Uranus and Neptune; these planets are even colder than Jupiter, and all have thick atmospheres of a nature similar

to that of Jupiter (Figure 9-25). Some of the satellites of Saturn also have atmospheres of the same poisonous nature. The most distant planet, Pluto, is nearly forty times as far away from the Sun as the Earth is, and it takes 248 years to travel once round the Sun. So far away is the Sun from Pluto that the surface temperature of the planet can hardly exceed —350 degrees F. Any atmosphere that Pluto might have had must be frozen on its surface. Between the planets there are countless billions of small particles called meteors. Some of these may get swept up by the Earth's atmosphere, and burn up as "shooting stars." If the meteor is large enough, it may survive partly intact to the ground, where it falls as a meteorite. Fortunately, most meteorites are only like pebbles, but the rare missile from space may be several tons in weight. Such an object would devastate many square

Figure 9-25. The scale of our solar-system temperatures.

miles when it lands, and leave a large crater. Several such meteor craters are recognized on the Earth's surface. An object exceeding a quarter of a mile in diameter would be visible in space by the sunlight it reflects. It would be a minor planet, or asteroid. The orbits of over 2000 such asteroids, whose diameters range up to 500 miles, are known, and there is a concentration of them between the orbits of Mars and Jupiter. On many such small planets, the temperature conditions might be suitable for active life. None of them is large enough to retain an atmosphere, or free water, but it is perhaps not impossible that, if the requisite chemical elements are present in the soil of the asteroid, some forms of life might arise to utilize them. If we consider that active life is possible only over the range of temperature for which life as we know it on Earth can remain active, then we see that in only a very narrow zone within the solar system—not too near the Sun, nor yet too far away—could we expect to find active life. In fact, in the distance of 3700 million miles that separates Pluto from the Sun, active life is restricted to a band only 75 million miles wide (Figure 9-22). Only the Earth, Mars and Venus, together with a few asteroids, overlap this band. Truly, in this picture of the universe life seems to be balanced precariously on a tightrope.

The Planet Mars

If we are to find any evidence of life in the solar system outside the Earth, it is to the planet Mars that we must look. The restricted temperature range within which active life is possible limits the distance from the Sun for active life to a zone about 75 million miles wide. Within this zone lie Venus, Earth, and Mars, but Venus, as we have seen, is cov-ered with a dense cloud layer, and conditions on the surface are almost completely unknown.

Because of its greater distance from the Sun, the surface of Mars is, on the average, colder than the Earth. An average temperature for the planet as a whole would be about −40 degrees F, compared with +59 degrees F for the Earth. But the temperature on the surface of Mars can rise above the freezing point of water. At the poles of Mars during the appropriate summer season on the planet the temperature may rise as high as +70 degrees F, but in the winter the temperature will fall to −130 degrees F. The equatorial zone on Mars suffers a much smaller variation of temperature throughout the Martian year, although here again the temperature in summer may rise a few degrees above the freezing point of water. Remembering that at temperatures below the range for active life, life may become latent, we would expect that any life forms on Mars (that do not have their own built-in temperature control such as warm-blooded terrestrial creatures have) would spend much of their time in a latent state, becoming active and self-propagating only for a brief season when the temperature is high enough.

Mars takes nearly 700 of our days to move once around the Sun, and it rotates on its axis in about 24½ hours (Figure 9-26). The range of temperature throughout a day on Mars is, theoretically, much the same as that on the Earth's equator, say 80 degrees F. This figure, in fact, is reached over desert regions near the Earth's equator, but in most places the daily variation is much less because of the effects of the Earth's atmosphere. The atmosphere of Mars is much thinner, and so nearly the full daily variation of temperature would be experienced there.

The Martian Atmosphere

That Mars has an atmosphere is easily seen by comparing a photograph of Mars taken in red light with one taken in blue light [Figure 9-27]. The red photograph shows a number of dark markings, which are more or

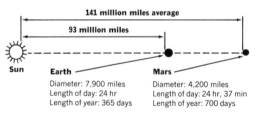

141 million miles average

93 million miles

Sun

Earth
Diameter: 7,900 miles
Length of day: 24 hr
Length of year: 365 days

Mars
Diameter: 4,200 miles
Length of day: 24 hr, 37 min
Length of year: 700 days

Figure 9-26

Mount Wilson and Mount Palomar Observatories

Figure 9-27. Mars, taken in blue light, left, and red light, right, with the 200-inch telescope.

less permanent. A blue photograph taken at the same time will (usually) show very few markings at all. This difference arises because the Martian atmosphere scatters away the blue light of the Sun, while the red light gets through to the surface undiffused. Photographs of the Earth taken from Mars would show a similar effect.

While the differing appearances of the red and blue photographs of Mars show that it has an atmosphere, it is not possible immediately to say whether the scattering is due to the gases of the atmosphere, or to particles suspended in the atmosphere. But very occasionally it is found that the surface markings do show up on blue photographs. This rare phenomenon is called "a blue clearing." It is not at all well understood, but it does prove that most of the scattering comes from particles within the Martian atmosphere, since it is impossible that for brief periods the atmosphere as a whole should disappear. But what

these particles are, and what causes their occasional absence from the Martian atmosphere, is, as yet, a mystery.

The spectrum of Mars has been examined carefully to discover the chemical nature of the Martian atmosphere. As has been discussed before, if the planet had no atmosphere, its spectrum would be a faint replica of the spectrum of the Sun, since the planet shines by reflecting sunlight. If the light from the Sun has had to pass through the planet's atmosphere, the atoms and molecules of this atmosphere may produce their own telltale absorptions. Unfortunately, the sunlight also has to pass through the Earth's atmosphere before it reaches our telescopes, and the terrestrial atmosphere produces its own absorption lines, which are much stronger than those owing to any planetary atmosphere. For this reason, it is difficult to detect in a planet's atmosphere any gases also in our own atmosphere. Extensive search has been made for evidence of water vapor in the Martian spectrum, but the search has been inconclusive just because of the heavy absorption produced by water vapor in the Earth's atmosphere. Another difficulty is that many likely gases, such as nitrogen, produce absorption lines in parts of the spectrum that are completely cut off by the Earth's atmosphere, in the ultraviolet. It may be possible, in the not too distant future, to observe the spectrum of Mars from a satellite-borne telescope above the Earth's atmosphere, when these difficulties will disappear.

However, the search of the Martian spectrum has not been without result. Positive evidence has been obtained for the presence of carbon dioxide in the Martian atmosphere. The total amount of CO_2 in the Martian atmosphere is about the same as in the Earth's atmosphere, but because the Martian atmosphere is much thinner, this corresponds to a higher percentage of CO_2, 0.2 per cent compared with 0.03 per cent for the Earth. The main constituent of the Martian atmosphere is probably nitrogen. Oxygen has not been definitely detected, and probably amounts to no more than 0.1 per cent of the atmosphere.

The total amount of atmosphere on Mars is less than a fifth of the terrestrial atmosphere, and at the planet's surface the pressure is less than a tenth of the surface pressure on Earth. But, owing to the smaller gravitational force on Mars, the density of the atmosphere drops off less rapidly with height than on the Earth. At heights above twenty miles, the atmosphere on Mars is actually more dense than the Earth's atmosphere at the same altitude. Since meteors burn up in the Earth's atmosphere at heights of about seventy miles, the thinner Martian atmosphere is actually a better protection from meteoric bombardment.

A Rusty Desert

The first thing that you would see on the surface of Mars when looking at it through a telescope would be the general orange-red color of the surface. The ruddy color of the planet, in fact, is easily noticed by the naked eye. The areas showing this red tint have been called "deserts," but it must not be sup-

posed that the deserts on Mars are just like the deserts on Earth. Much work has gone into the study of the spectrum of the Martian deserts. There is definite evidence that there are some silicates present—chemical substances similar to sand. But the main constituent is probably similar to limonite, a terrestrial mineral containing a great deal of red iron oxide. Because of the absence of oxygen in the planet's atmosphere, it is probable that any oxygen that might have been present has been used up in oxidizing the surface. Mars may be a *rusty* planet!

If we were to attempt to summarize the conditions on Mars, we would liken them to conditions in a terrestrial desert if it were transported to the poles, and raised into the stratosphere. While certain very primitive terrestrial forms of life, such as bacteria, might manage to survive on Mars, certainly no highly developed forms of terrestrial life could exist there without artificial aid. Yet, compared with other parts of the universe, conditions on Mars are very similar to those on Earth.

Seen through a telescope, the most prominent features of the Martian surface are the white polar caps. These caps are extensive in the Martian winter, and shrink and disappear in the Martian summer (the summer of one hemisphere occurring at the same time as the winter of the other). They are almost certainly composed of water, but here the similarity with the polar snowcaps on Earth ends, for the Martian polar caps are [probably] little more than thin layers of frost.

Blue-green Markings

A more careful study of Mars through a telescope reveals a number of irregularly shaped dark blue-green markings (Figure 9-28). They are more or less permanent—maps of Mars have been made, and the features named —but they are not exactly constant in shape or appearance. In particular, they show a variation of color with the changing seasons on Mars, in time with the melting of the polar caps. There have been many hypotheses put forward to explain these markings: for example, that they are composed of minerals that change color as the moisture from the polar caps reaches them. Recently, it was suggested that, because the general pattern of the markings seemed to follow the lines that one would expect for the prevailing winds on Mars, the markings might be composed of ash from volcanoes (although no volcano has ever been observed). But in my view, the hypothesis that best explains the great variety of observations that have been made of these marking is that they are vegetation that flourishes during the short Martian summer [Figure 9-29].

One of the most cogent arguments for this view is the fact that, although we not infrequently observe dust storms in the Martian atmosphere, the dark markings are not permanently obscured by them. The markings seem to have the power of *regeneration*. The Russian astronomer Tikhoff made many interesting comparisons of the spectrum of the dark markings on Mars with the spectra of terrestrial vegetation at various altitudes in the Pamirs. He found that at low level, where the climate was temperate, the plants reflected much of the sunlight in the infrared. However at higher altitudes, where the plants needed more warmth, they began to absorb the infrared solar rays. In fact, the greater the altitude, the greater the absorption in the infrared. The spectrum of the Martian markings was very similar to the spectrum of terrestrial vegetation at the highest altitudes.

To grow and develop, plants need oxygen at considerably higher pressure than is found on Mars. But plants have a means of overcoming this deficiency. They can form oxygen in the presence of sunlight by photosynthesis, and there is no reason why this photosynthesized oxygen should not be trapped by the plant, which would build up a "local environment" with a higher oxygen content. This is just what the leaves of terrestrial plants do, and, for that matter, the lungs of human beings. The composition of the atmosphere within your lungs is rather different from the composition of the outside air.

Attempts have been made to detect in the spectrum of the dark markings on Mars the characteristic absorption lines due to chloro-

Figure 9-28. Mars as observed and mapped in 1905. The "canals" of Mars, which some astronomers can see but others cannot, are mapped at left and the regional color variations at right.

phyll. This crucial test has not yet been successful, but the failure does not rule out the possibility of vegetation, since some plants on Earth, especially those in hard climates, do not show this spectrum. But although the chlorophyll spectrum has not been detected, lines that *are* found in the spectra of terrestrial plants, and that seem to be characteristic of molecules of living matter, have been detected. These lines are *not* present in the spectrum of the Martian deserts.

If we accept that the most satisfactory explanation of the dark markings on Mars is that they are vegetation, we might speculate on the nature of such vegetation (Figure 9-30). The hardiest plants on Earth are the lichens, organisms that consist of a fungus in close association with an alga. The fungus provides protection from the cold and serves as a trap for moisture. The algae build up essential organic material, and provide oxygen by photosynthesis. The fact that the general pattern of markings follows the supposed prevailing wind pattern might be explained if the plant life is propagated by spores or seeds.

Once a primitive form of life has gained hold upon a planet, we know of no limit to the complexity which life there might attain by evolution. Has intelligent life developed on Mars? This is a question to which we can give no answer at the present time. If we took our largest telescopes to Mars, and looked at the Earth, the smallest single object that we could just observe would be 100 miles across. Nothing that we could see would give any hint that intelligent life had developed on the Earth.

March 9

June 23

May 11

July 31

May 29

August 21

Figure 9-29. Mars' seasonal changes. Photographs of the same face of Mars taken at different Martian seasonal dates showing the gradual melting of the snow cap and the intensification of the blue-green areas from March 9 to August 21 (Martian dates). The development of the blue-green regions during Martian summer, reaching a maximum during this June and July, strikingly resembles the behavior of growing vegetation.

Martian Enigmas: "Canals" and Phobos

In the early years of this century there was much discussion about the so-called canals of Mars (Figure 9-28). Some skilled observers saw the surface of Mars covered with a network of fine, straight lines. If such a network of markings does exist, it is very difficult to think of a "natural" process that could cause them, and the suggestion that they were strips of vegetation growing along the banks of artificial canals was not unreasonable. Unfortunately, some equally skilled visual observers do not see these straight lines at all, and it is a well-known fact that the human eye tends to connect up a random set of markings at the limit of visibility with straight lines. The problem cannot be solved by photography, for, owing to the unsteadiness the Earth's atmosphere causes in the image of a planet, a photograph cannot show as fine a detail as can be seen by a trained visual observer. While some of the biggest "canals" did show up on the photographs, the existence of these broader objects is not, in any case, in dispute. But the reality of the fine network of lines remains a matter of controversy.

While a surface detail on Mars would have to be 100 miles across for it to be recognized as such, a luminous object, if sufficiently bright, could be seen, although the object is itself smaller than 100 miles. From the amount of sunlight that they reflect, we know that the satellites of Mars, Phobos and Deimos, are only a few miles in diameter (Figure 9-31). Phobos, the inner one, is so near the planet's surface that it goes around Mars in a period shorter than the rotation period of Mars. From the planet it would be seen to rise in the West and set in the East, like some of our own artificial satellites. It has, in fact, been suggested seriously that Phobos might be an artificial satellite of Mars. Long series of observations have shown that Phobos has been gradually getting ahead, in its orbit, compared with its path computed under the assumption that it is moving under the attraction of Mars. Terrestrial artificial satellites speed up in just this way because of the effect of the Earth's atmosphere, which eventually causes a satellite to spiral in and

Figure 9-30. Vegetation on Mars, if it exists, must open its leaves to the Sun in daytime, store water, and close its leaves in the Martian night for protection against the cold.

fall to Earth. But if Phobos is made of rocky material, like a natural satellite, then the required density of Martian atmosphere a few thousand miles above the planet's surface is vastly greater than is possible for the actual Martian atmosphere. For the actual atmosphere to produce the observed acceleration, the mean density of Phobos would have to be so low that it could not be other than a hollow spherical shell—a most unnatural satellite! To escape this difficulty, some astronomers have supposed that the acceleration of Phobos is due to tidal action by Mars, although this is possible only if the crust of Mars is of an entirely different composition from that of the Earth. Others have chosen the more startling hypothesis that Phobos is artificial. Only time will tell who is correct.

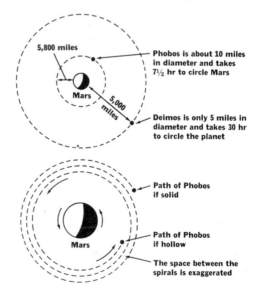

Figure 9-31. The Martian moons are late discoveries. Phobos' behavior is yet to be explained.

THE HUMAN RESPONSE

THE MYSTERIOUS UNIVERSE*
by Sir James Jeans (1930)

Standing on our microscopic fragment of a grain of sand, we attempt to discover the nature and purpose of the universe which surrounds our home in space and time. Our first impression is something akin to terror. We find the universe terrifying because of its vast meaningless distances, terrifying because of its inconceivably long vistas of time which dwarf human history to the twinkling of an eye, terrifying because of our extreme loneliness, and because of the material insignificance of our home in space—a millionth part of a grain of sand out of all the sea-sand in the world. But above all else, we find the universe terrifying because it appears to be indifferent to life like our own; emotion, ambition and achievement, art and religion all seem equally foreign to its plan. Perhaps indeed we ought to say it appears to be actively hostile to life like our own. For the most part, empty space is so cold that all life in it would be frozen; most of the matter in space is so hot as to make life on it impossible; space is traversed, and astronomical bodies continually bombarded, by radiation of a variety of kinds, much of which is probably inimical to, or even destructive of, life.

Into such a universe we have stumbled, if not exactly by mistake, at least as the result of what may properly be described as an accident. The use of such a word need not imply any surprise that our earth exists, for acci-

*From Sir James Jeans, *The Mysterious Universe*, Cambridge University Press, New York, 1930. Reprinted by permission of Cambridge University Press.

dents will happen, and if the universe goes on for long enough, every conceivable accident is likely to happen in time. It was, I think, Huxley who said that six monkeys, set to strum unintelligently on typewriters for millions of millions of years, would be bound in time to write all the books in the British Museum. If we examined the last page which a particular monkey had typed, and found that it had chanced, in its blind strumming, to type a Shakespeare sonnet, we should rightly regard the occurrence as a remarkable accident, but if we looked through all the millions of pages the monkeys had turned off in untold millions of years, we might be sure of finding a Shakespeare sonnet somewhere amongst them, the product of the blind play of chance. In the same way, millions of millions of stars wandering blindly through space for millions of millions of years are bound to meet with every sort of accident, and so are bound to produce a certain limited number of planetary systems in time. Yet the number of these must be very small in comparison with the total number of stars in the sky. . . .

Just for this reason it seems incredible that the universe can have been designed primarily to produce life like our own; had it been so, surely we might have expected to find a better proportion between the magnitude of the mechanism and the amount of the product. At first glance at least, life seems to be an utterly unimportant by-product; we living things are somehow off the main line.

A FREE MAN'S WORSHIP*
by Bertrand Russell (1903)

Such, in outline, but even more purposeless, more void of meaning, is the world which

*From Bertrand Russell, *Mysticism and Logic*, George Allen & Unwin, Ltd., London, 1903. Reprinted by permission of George Allen & Unwin, Ltd.

Science presents for our belief. Amid such a world, if anywhere, our ideals henceforward must find a home. That man is the product of causes which had no prevision of the end they were achieving; that his origin, his growth, his hopes and fears, his loves and his beliefs, are but the outcome of accidental collocations of atoms; that no fire, no heroism, no intensity of thought and feeling, can preserve an individual life beyond the grave; that all the labours of the ages, all the devotion, all the inspirations, all the noonday brightness of human genius, are destined to extinction in the vast death of the solar system, and that the whole temple of Man's achievement must inevitably be buried beneath the debris of a universe in ruins—all these things, if not quite beyond dispute, are yet so nearly certain, that no philosophy which rejects them can hope to stand. Only within the scaffolding of these truths, only on the firm foundation of unyielding despair, can the soul's habitation henceforth be safely built. . . .

Brief and powerless is Man's life; on him and all his race the slow, sure doom falls pitiless and dark. Blind to good and evil, reckless of destruction, omnipotent matter rolls on its relentless way; for Man, condemned to-day to lose his dearest, to-morrow himself to pass through the gate of darkness, it remains only to cherish, ere yet the blow falls, the lofty thoughts that ennoble his little day; disdaining the coward terrors of the slave of Fate, to worship at the shrine that his own hands have built; undismayed by the empire of chance, to preserve a mind free from the wanton tyranny that rules his outward life; proudly defiant of the irresistible forces that tolerate, for a moment, his knowledge and his condemnation, to sustain alone, a weary but unyielding Atlas, the world that his own ideals have fashioned despite the trampling march of unconscious power.

OF STARS AND MEN*
by Harlow Shapley (1958)

You may say that these are but speculations, insecurely founded, and that you choose to believe and reason and worship otherwise. And I must reply that you should follow your inclination. But you are invited to think seriously of the cosmic facts. Let us hope that an easement is not sought in comforting tradition alone, or in resort to crude irrationality. The new knowledge from many sources—from the test tube, from the extended radiation spectrum, the electron microscope, experimental agriculture, and the radio telescope; from mathematical equations and the cosmotrons—the revelations from all these make obsolete many of the earlier world views. The new discoveries and developments contribute to the unfolding of a magnificent universe; to be a participant is in itself a glory. With our confreres on distant planets; with our fellow animals and plants of land, air, and sea; with the rocks and waters of all planetary crusts, and the photons and atoms that make up the stars—with all these we are associated in an existence and an evolution that inspires respect and deep reverence. We cannot escape humility. And as groping philosophers and scientists we are thankful for the mysteries that still lie beyond our grasp.

There are those who would call this attitude their philosophy, their religion. They would be loath, I hope, to retreat from the galaxies to the earth; unwilling to come out of the cosmic depths and durations to concern themselves only with one organic form on the crust of one small planet, near a commonplace star, at the edge of one of the galaxies. They would hesitate to retreat to that one isolated spot in their search for the Ultimate. May their kind increase and prosper!

A PERSONAL VIEW*

by Fred Hoyle (1960)

With the clear understanding that what I am now going to say has no agreed basis among scientists but represents my own personal views, I shall try to sum up the general philosophic issues that seem to me to come out of our survey of the Universe.

It is my view that man's unguided imagination could never have chanced on such a structure as I have put before you. No literary genius could have invented a story one-hundredth part as fantastic as the sober facts that have been unearthed by astronomical science. You need only compare our inquiry into the nature of the Universe with the tales of such acknowledged masters as Jules Verne and H. G. Wells to see that fact outweighs fiction by an enormous margin. One is naturally led to wonder what the impact of the New Cosmology would have been on a man like Newton, who would have been able to take it in, details and all, in one clean sweep. I think that Newton would have been quite unprepared for any such revelation, and that it would have had a shattering effect on him. . . .

Next we come to a question that everyone, scientist and nonscientist alike, must have asked at some time. What is man's place in the Universe? I should like to make a start on this momentous issue by considering the view of the out-and-out materialists. The appeal of their argument is based on simplicity. The Universe is here, they say, so let us take it for granted. Then the Earth and other planets must arise in the way we have already discussed. On a suitably favored planet like the Earth, life would be very likely to arise, and once it had started, so the argument goes on, only the biological processes of mutation and natural selection are needed to produce living creatures as we know them. Such creatures are no more than ingenious machines that have evolved as strange by-products in an odd corner of the Universe. No important connection exists, so the argument concludes,

between these machines and the Universe as a whole, and this explains why all attempts by the machines themselves to find such a connection have failed.

Most people object to this argument for the not very good reason that they do not like to think of themselves as machines. But taking the argument at its face value, I see no point that can actually be disproved, except the claim of simplicity. The outlook of the materialists is not simple; it is really very complicated. The apparent simplicity is only achieved by taking the existence of the Universe for granted. For myself there is a great deal more about the Universe that I should like to know. Why is the Universe as it is and not something else? Why is the Universe here at all? It is true that at present we have no clue to the answers to questions such as these, and it may be that the materialists are right in saying that no meaning can be attached to them. But throughout the history of science, people have been asserting that such and such an issue is inherently beyond the scope of reasoned inquiry, and time after time they have been proved wrong. Two thousand years ago it would have been thought quite impossible to investigate the nature of the Universe to the extent I have been describing it to you in this book. And I dare say that you yourself would have said, not so very long ago, that it was impossible to learn anything about the way the Universe is created. All experience teaches us that no one has yet asked too much. . . .

If there is one important result that comes out of our inquiry into the nature of the Universe it is this: when by patient inquiry we learn the answer to any problem, we always find, both as a whole and in detail, that the answer thus revealed is finer in concept and design than anything we could ever have arrived at by a random guess. And this, I believe, will be the same for the deeper issues we have just been discussing. I think that all our present guesses are likely to prove but a very pale shadow of the real thing; and it is on this note that I must now finish. Perhaps the most majestic feature of our whole exist-ence is that while our intelligences are power-ful enough to penetrate deeply into the evolu-tion of this quite incredible Universe, we still have not the smallest clue to our own fate.

QUESTIONS TO CONSIDER

What reasons do we have for believing that there is other life in the universe? Is there any direct scientific evidence of life?

Shapley's calculation on pages 324 to 326 is based on a number of assumptions. Some of these assumptions are the same that Olbers used in making his compu-tations (see pages 287 to 288). Can you find any others?

After we have explored the moon, which planet would you choose to explore, and why?

Do you think we should send the message "1, 2, 3, 4" into outer space? If we received an answer, say "5, 6, 7, 8," eight years later, would we be able to locate the origin of the answer in space and time? Would it give us any other signifi-cant information about the universe? Why was this message suggested for communicating with other intelligent life? Are numbers likely to be universal?

SUGGESTIONS FOR FURTHER READING

Gamow, George: *Matter, Earth and Sky*, Prentice-Hall, Inc., Englewood Cliffs, N.J., 1958, chaps. 18, 19, and 20. A detailed and somewhat technical description of the planetary system, the sun, and the stellar system. The selec-tion in these readings was taken from chap. 20.

* Hoyle, Fred: *The Frontiers of Astronomy*, Harper & Row, Publishers, New York, 1955, chaps. 1–6. A study of the earth and the origin of the planetary system.

* Hurley, Patrick M.: *How Old Is the Earth?* Anchor Books, Doubleday & Company, Inc., Garden City, N.Y., 1959. An account of our present knowl-edge of the earth's history. Easy reading for the layman.

Hutchings, Edward, Jr. (ed.): *Frontiers of Science*, Basic Books, Inc., Pub-lishers, New York, 1958. A collection of essays on recent research. The fol-lowing essays are particularly interesting in connection with this part:

Salisbury, Frank: "The Inhabitants of Mars"

* Paperback edition.

Burbridge, Margaret, and Geoffrey Burbridge: "Cosmical Alchemy."
Sandage, Allan: "The Birth and Death of a Star."
Hutchings, Edward, Jr.: "The Size of the Universe."
Wilson, Albert G.: "Astronomy and Eschetology."

* Shapley, Harlow: *Of Stars and Men*, Washington Square Press, Pocket Books, Inc., New York, 1960. We have used several selections from this very stimulating and well-written book and strongly recommend reading it in its entirety.

* *The Universe*, A Scientific American Book, reprinted from the September, 1956, issue, Simon and Schuster, Inc., New York. The following articles are particularly pertinent to the subject matter of this part:

Fowler, William: "The Origin of the Elements."
Baade, Walter: "The Content of Galaxies."

* *The New Astronomy*, A Scientific American Book, Simon and Schuster, Inc., New York. A collection of articles on astronomy that appeared in *Scientific American* from 1948 to 1954.

PART 10

WHY EXPLORE SPACE?

The space age has dramatically brought to our attention the fact that science has become the concern of every citizen today. Because the race to conquer the new scientific frontier has become so involved with public policy, ". . . it will not be one man going to the moon, it will be an entire nation." These readings examine the question of how we, as a nation, should meet the challenge of the space age.

Ley

Lundin

Goodwin

Rabinowitch

INTRODUCTION

Today we stand on the verge of the realization of one of the oldest dreams of man. Since ancient times men have been challenged by thoughts of outer space; indeed it is the same challenge that has led to the development of knowledge about the universe. An understanding of the relative positions of the heavenly bodies, the nature of the earth's atmosphere, and the laws that govern the motion of all bodies: these concepts were necessary foundations for man's venture into space. In this sense the scientists we have been studying—Copernicus, Torricelli, Galileo, Kepler, and Newton—were the real pioneers of the space age. The desire to know, coupled with the urge to adventure and discovery, has led inevitably to the exploration of the universe. Space science is simply the most recent phase in this exploration.

Through the centuries of scientific advance men's imaginations have leaped out beyond actual knowledge to speculations and dreams about journeys to other worlds. There are mentions of space travel in early Egyptian and Persian literature, and, of course, we all recall the Greek myth of Icarus' ill-fated flight. Bruno believed in the existence of a plurality of worlds, and in 1634 Kepler wrote one of the first science fiction tales of a journey to the moon (*Somnium: Or the Astronomy of the Moon*). But these dreams of exploration remained pure fantasy. It was not until the beginning of the twentieth century that space travel became a practical possibility.

The major breakthrough that made outer space suddenly accessible was the development of rocket propulsion. Several pioneers working in different parts of the world were responsible for bringing the possibilities of rocket propulsion before the scientific world. The first man was a Russian, Konstantin Tiolkowski. In 1898 he wrote an article on the principles of rocket flight through space. This article did not immediately receive much attention from other scientists. Then in 1919 the Smithsonian Institution published a small pamphlet written by Robert Goddard, a professor of physics at Clark University, in Massachusetts. The pamphlet was entitled *A Method for Reaching Extreme Altitudes* and brought Goddard a grant to study the possibilities of rocket development. This study, like Tiolkowski's, created very little interest. Goddard, however, worked on alone for many years, supported by grants from the Guggenheim and Carnegie Foundations, and in 1935 one of his rockets reached an altitude of 7,500 feet. In the meantime, a German professor, Herman Oberth, had published a book on space flight (1923). This book did stimulate professional interest and started activity on an international front. The Russians rediscovered their prophet, Tiolkowski. Oberth and Willy Ley were instrumental in founding the German Rocket Society, which helped to create popular interest in the subject.

However, it was largely the impetus of the military applications and the advent of the Second World War that brought about rapid development in rocket design. The German research institute at Peenemünde, under the direction of Walter Dornberger and Wernher Von Braun, produced the V-2 rocket, which was the largest and most spectacular product of this war effort. The Russians were also proceeding with the development of a large rocket, and the United States had one project for a small, high-altitude rocket, which culminated, after the war, in the rocket called the WAC Corporal. At the end of the war the research and planning staff from Peenemünde surrendered to the American forces and was brought to America. The Russians captured the German production engineers of the V-2 rockets.

Throughout its short history the challenge of man's venture into space has been closely intertwined with national interest. Today the interdependence of the two aspects is dramatically apparent in the competition between the United States and the Soviet Union. In the public mind, the pure motivations arising from man's curiosity and the desire to explore are overshadowed by the drive for national prestige and the fear of losing the cold war with Russia. Certainly the immense outlay of money that is needed for space exploration would not be immediately forthcoming were it not for military and prestige factors. Some responsible citizens today doubt whether such a vast outlay of national resources is warranted to send a man to the moon. Other writers point out that both spiritually and materially science has always more than repaid the efforts that have gone into it. They say that the problem is not so much whether space should be explored—the advance of science makes this exploration inevitable—but how fast it should be attempted and who will take the lead. President Kennedy said in his address to Congress, of May 25, 1961, "This decision demands a major national commitment. . . . Every citizen of this country, as well as the members of Congress, should consider the matter carefully in making their judgment and . . . there is no sense in agreeing or desiring, that the United States take an affirmative position in outer space unless we are prepared to do the work and bear the burdens to make it successful. In a very real sense, it will not be one man going to the moon . . . it will be an entire nation."

Thus science has become a vast cooperative venture and the average citizen is inevitably more involved in it than he was in the days when it was pursued by small, privately supported groups or by individuals. The image of the lone scientist working quietly in his laboratory seems to have been replaced by bustling billion-dollar research centers employing thousands of workers. Has scientific method really changed so much in the last years that science can be mass-produced instead of demanding the time and solitude usually required for creative work? Or is it technology, the application of known scientific principles for practical ends, that is being mass-produced? We should not forget that the really important technical breakthrough that made space travel possible was made by men working alone: Goddard, Oberth, Tiolkowski. And the fundamental scientific principles on which the space age was built were conceived by Galileo, Kepler, and Newton several hundred years ago. The readings in this part concentrate on these fundamental ideas and show how they are being applied to the conquest of space.

In the race to compete with Soviet accomplishments, sight is sometimes lost of the avowed policy of the United States and the United Nations that the conquest of space should be undertaken as a cooperative effort between nations and that the benefits deriving from it should be freely available to the whole world. Rabinowitch expresses the hope that ". . . man's confrontation with the immensity of the universe could become an important step toward the realization of the common origin, common fate and common aspirations of all mankind."

THE SCIENCE OF SPACE TRAVEL

Science is the soul of the prosperity of nations and the living source of all progress. Undoubtedly the tiring discussions of politics seem to be our guide— empty appearances! What really leads us forward is a few scientific discoveries and their application.

Louis Pasteur (1822–1895)

WHERE DOES SPACE BEGIN?*
by Willy Ley (1958)

A few years ago the *New Yorker* ran a cartoon showing the interior of an airliner. A small boy inquired of the hostess, "Are we in outer space now?" while his mother looked exceedingly embarrassed. Actually the question was quite justified, for if that plane was flying at, say, 20,000 feet, its passengers were at least near the borders of space in some respects.

It all depends on the viewpoint, for there is no simple answer to the simple question: "Where does space begin?" Or, since it does depend on the viewpoint, there is no single answer to that question. There are several [Figure 10-1].

The earth, as everybody has learned in school at an early age, is a rocky ball moving around the sun in empty space. Its surface is protected by a thin film of atmosphere that has an amazing variety of jobs. It sees to it that not too much of the ultraviolet rays coming from the sun reaches the ground. It stops the majority of all meteorites from hitting the earth. It takes care of most cosmic rays. In addition to all that, it circulates water and acts as a blanket to keep the surface warm.

Considering this large variety of functions one can easily get the feeling that mother

earth must have provided an atmospheric blanket many hundreds of miles thick to protect the life on the ground and in the waters. Actually this amazing blanket is not only versatile, it is also quite thin. We are much closer to space than we think. At three miles up the comfortable air pressure of sea level has dropped to half of its sea-level value. At ten miles up the pressure is down to ten per cent of what it is at sea level. At twenty miles it is down to just one per cent.

So if you generously neglect that last remaining one per cent you might simply say that you are in space if you reach 100,000

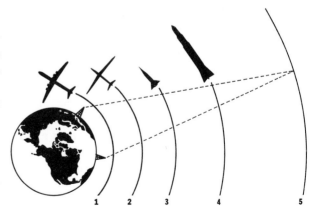

1 - Airplane passenger - 4 miles
2 - High altitude airplane pilot - 20 miles
3 - Aeronautical engineer - 35 miles
4 - Rocket engineer - 150 miles
5 - Radio engineer - 300 miles

Figure 10-1. The edges of space.

* From *Satellites, Rockets and Outer Space* (Newly Revised) by Willy Ley. Copyright © 1958, 1961, 1962 by Willy Ley, and copyright 1957, 1958 by Chicago Sun-Times, published by arrangement with The New American Library of World Literature, Inc., New York.

feet. Since rocket-propelled airplanes have flown higher than 100,000 feet, their pilots can claim to have been in space—and probably do. But unfortunately things are not that simple. It all depends on the effects you have in mind.

Radio engineers, as is well known, use certain layers in the upper atmosphere from which to bounce short radio waves in order to make contact with spots on the ground they could not contact otherwise. The highest of these so-called "ionized layers" is called the F_2 layer, which has been found as high as 300 miles. A radio engineer is, therefore, justified in saying that from his point of view there are 300 miles of atmosphere above his head. The air may be extremely thin that high up, but he can still find a layer that does something.

The rocket expert looks at the same question with something entirely different in mind. A rocket motor works best in a vacuum, where there is no air to slow down the exhaust blast of the rocket. By the same token so does the rocket body itself when unimpeded by any air resistance. In short, the expert looks for a place where there is no resistance left. If he finds no resistance whatever, he feels he is in space. And is happy about it.

Strangely enough, his own figure comes out much lower than the figure of the radio engineer. The artificial satellites have raised his original figure of 120 miles to about 160 miles. Above that there seems to be no measurable resistance left. So, to the rocket engineer space begins 160 miles up.

The aeronautical engineer again feels differently about the whole thing. He does want some air resistance because without air he cannot produce any "lift" with his wings. He will reason that he is in space if even a very fast-moving airplane cannot obtain any lift any longer. Just where that would take place depends on a number of things, like the assumed speed of the plane. But the figure will be somewhere near 35 miles; that is the height where space begins for the aeronautical engineer.

But all these people, radio men, rocket men and aeronautical men, are thinking in terms of machines. When the medical man enters the discussion he thinks in terms of people. And when you do that, space is awfully near. The first mile above sea level presents no problems whatever, as the inhabitants of Denver will be eager to testify. Two miles up is not much of a problem either; you merely have to (and can) get used to it.

At three miles you can still get along if you grew up at such a height or took enough time acclimatizing yourself, but flatlanders need extra oxygen. Of course, inside a building, or an airplane cabin, you can simply compress the external air until you get a pressure you like. That is still workable for another two miles. Even at five miles a man can expose himself to what is left of the atmosphere without fatal results. He does need oxygen and had better be warmly dressed since the temperature is around *minus* 40 degrees Fahrenheit. But it can be done.

Above five miles another factor comes in.

The boiling point of water, and of all other substances that are normally liquids, depends on air pressure. If the air pressure is lowered, the boiling point is lowered too; even on a not very high mountain it takes hours to boil potatoes; the water simply does not get hot enough.

To a physician the pilot is, among other things, a container holding liquids at a temperature near 100 degrees Fahrenheit. When the air pressure drops so low that 100 degrees Fahrenheit is the boiling point of water no oxygen mask will do any good any more. The body fluids will erupt, boiling, even though they haven't changed temperature, and death is inevitable. Moreover, it is the same kind of death that would strike a man far out in space, a million miles from earth.

The height at which the body fluids would start boiling is twelve miles and space medical researchers have called this altitude the "space equivalent altitude"; that is where space begins as far as the human body is concerned. Even before this height is reached full protection is needed, an airtight cabin, a package containing the friendly environment of the lower altitudes.

Such cabins were first built for animal capsules. Then for men. And, as the suborbital shots and the orbital flights with Mercury capsules have shown, the problem has been solved.*

We can go on from there.

Why Not Anti-gravity Screens?

At reasonably regular intervals, . . . somebody expresses his amazement at the lack of logic exhibited by people who plan artificial satellites and space travel in general. That engineers go ahead and spend hundreds of thousands of dollars of company or tax money designing and building rocket motors that can and do burn up 400 pounds of fuel per second. Why don't they spend their time and money, . . . on finding out how to counteract gravity? Once they know how, wouldn't everything be so much easier? Why bother with enormous rocket motors? Why not try to invent a gravity "screen" and use rocket motors only for steering?

Offhand, I can think of two reasons, both of which I consider fairly valid. The first one is that no one knows how to build a gravity screen. The second is that no one knows how to go about inventing one. To do so we'd have to know just what gravity really is. We don't. . . .

There is no explanation of what gravity really is. There is no known deviation from the rules, a deviation that might be a clue as to its nature. And as long as we don't even know what it is we certainly cannot know what to do about it. Maybe we'll find out one day. In the meantime we can do interesting things, in spite of gravity, by building large rockets.

* See "A Chronology of Space Exploration," p. 393, for later data. Ed.

ROCKETS†
by Harold L. Goodwin (1954)

A rocket stands on its vanes, ready to fire. It is being held down by the force of gravity. According to the First Law of Motion, it will remain at rest until acted upon by some new force. The rocket weighs 20 tons, fully loaded.

As the firing button is pushed, the rocket propellant starts to burn. The exhaust flares out of the rocket's engine, rapidly building up thrust. When the thrust of the rocket's engine is greater than the weight of the rocket, it will move.

The thrust exceeds 20 tons, and the rocket starts to climb. Its speed increases in accordance with the Second Law of Motion:‡ the acceleration of a rocket is always directly proportional to its thrust.

Inside the rocket engine, the propellant burns, generating hot exhaust gases. The molecules of the exhaust gases press with equal force on all the walls of the combustion chamber. Since the vent of this chamber is open, there is no push in that direction. The end result of the interaction of these various forces is movement of the rocket in the forward direction. This action can be easily demonstrated by inflating an ordinary balloon and letting it go. Notice how it moves as the air escapes (Figure 10-2).

The rocket propellant carries its own oxidizing supply. If it is a solid propellant, the oxygen is mixed right in with the combustible material in chemical combination. If it is a liquid propellant, the oxidizing agent is carried in a separate tank and mixed with the fuel as it goes into the combustion cham-

† From Harold Leland Goodwin, *The Science Book of Space Travel*, Franklin Watts, Inc., New York, 1954. Reprinted by permission.
‡ See footnote, p. 356. Ed.

Figure 10-2. **Direction of forces inside a rocket motor.**

Figure 10-3. A rocket follows the same principle of motion as the wagons, which move as a result of the recoil of shotgun and machine gun. The lower wagon continues to move with increasing speed because the machine gun fires and recoils almost continuously.

ber. Sometimes the oxidizer is liquid oxygen and the fuel is gasoline, or alcohol. Sometimes the oxygen is contained in a compound like nitric acid.

A familiar example of the Third Law of Motion* can be found in the field of artillery. A cannon is essentially a tube, open at one end. Sealed at the closed end is a projectile and a quantity of explosive. The explosive is ignited. The solid powder burns, generating hot exhaust gases which expand rapidly. The force exerted is very great; something has to give. The thing that gives is the projectile. Under the force of the expanding gas it is pushed violently through the tube and leaves at the open end. But the forces act in the opposite direction, too, and the cannon moves backward. Since the cannon has a much greater mass, it is not accelerated as much as the shell.

In earlier times, the "kick" of the cannon was absorbed by letting the piece push back its carriage. Now the force is absorbed by hydraulic buffers.

Imagine a cannon mounted on a carriage. It is obvious that the carriage would be rolled

---

* Newton's three laws of motion are restated here for your convenience. See pages 217 to 221 for more complete explanation. (1) Every body remains at rest or moves in a straight line with a constant velocity unless compelled to change its velocity by a resultant force acting on it. (2) The product "mass × acceleration" varies directly as the resultant force acting on the body and the acceleration is in the direction of that force. (3) To every action there is an equal and opposite reaction. Ed.

backward each time the cannon was fired. If friction and air resistance were removed, the backward speed of the carriage would increase with every shot. If the cannon were fired continuously, like a machine gun, the carriage would gain speed rapidly. Remove the projectiles, use only blank cartridges discharged continuously, and the analogy between cannon and rocket becomes even closer, with the muzzle of the cannon acting like the exhaust outlet of the rocket. . . . Figure 10-3).

A rocket might be considered a sort of gun which fires a continuous stream of burning gas, producing continuous recoil. Since the thrust generated by the burning gas is forward, and occurs inside the rocket's combustion chamber, the rocket moves (Figure 10-2). This movement is independent of the outside air, and the oxidizer in the fuel makes the rocket independent of the oxygen in the air. Hence the rocket will work in a vacuum. In fact, the air actually interferes with the rocket's motion; the rocket would operate more efficiently in vacuum than in air.

The rocket is the only power plant known to be independent of the atmosphere. Until some new method of propulsion is discovered, spaceships must be rockets. This means that Newton, in stating the Third Law of Motion, also pointed the way to space travel. . . .

In theory, there are two ways of overcoming gravity in order to reach space. An object can climb gradually, or, as in the case of a rocket, it can be given a mighty shove so that it will coast to infinity.

The first method envisions a vehicle that can climb to space at a controlled speed, perhaps maintaining a constant velocity—a scheme possible in theory, but impractical. Because of the fuel requirements, such a method is wasteful even if engineers can build a vehicle capable of carrying it out.

The second method envisions a vehicle which can accelerate to high velocity, gaining enough momentum, before its fuel is cut off or exhausted, to coast to infinity. Since this second method is practicable, it will be worth while to examine some of the factors involved.

Air resistance immediately comes to mind. However, rockets of spaceship size would lose very little of their velocity to air resistance. The major factor is gravity. Obviously, the less time the rocket has to spend fighting gravity, the greater the saving: time of travel can be reduced by getting the rocket to maximum velocity in the shortest possible time. But this requires high acceleration.

The rocket is limited in its ability to accelerate by the thrust of its motors; the larger the rocket, the less rapidly it gets away from the ground. It is interesting to see a big rocket take off. Most laymen tend to think of rockets in terms of the Fourth of July variety, or of the bazooka rockets or rocket barrages seen in war movies. Some of these small rockets have tremendous accelerations, equivalent to fifty times the value of gravity at the earth's surface. (This is expressed as 50g.) But the big rockets like the V-2's and Vikings take off in the most leisurely manner imaginable. The V-2 starts with an acceleration of 1g and reaches 6g at the point where its fuel is all burned. The Viking starts in the same manner and reaches 7g.

This comparatively leisurely rate of acceleration is a good thing, however. It means that the rocket does not reach maximum acceleration until most of the atmosphere is below it, a fact which makes air resistance of less importance. In addition, these accelerations are well within human tolerance. . . .

High accelerations and velocities, of course, are useful for reaching an objective. To defeat gravitational attraction a definite velocity known as *escape velocity* must be attained. Escape velocity has become a magic phrase in recent years. Any good physics handbook will provide the mathematical basis of computing escape velocity for the gravitational field of any heavenly body. But the simplest nonmathematical explanation is: *escape velocity is equal to the velocity with which an object would land on earth after falling from an infinite distance*. This definition does not take air resistance into account—but neither does the value given for escape velocity.

The value for escape velocity is 7.1 miles per second at the earth's surface. This figure is often rounded off for the sake of convenience to 7 miles per second, or 25,000 miles per hour. But these figures are less than the required velocity, and a calculation based on them might prove slightly misleading. For that reason, 26,000 miles per hour is a better round-off. This is the velocity a spaceship must reach if it is to take off from earth and travel a million miles into space. . . .

Three Steps to Space

There is a system used in getting to remote places like mountain tops or the North Pole, which may be useful in space travel. The method enabled a group of British mountain climbers to conquer Mount Everest in June 1953.

A large expedition starts off, laden with supplies. Then, at a given point, the large party stops and establishes a base camp. A smaller crew detaches itself from the main group and goes on. Some distance toward the objective, this second party also sets up a camp. A third and still smaller group, perhaps only two men, goes on to the objective.

The method is used when it is impractical for a large group to go the whole distance, and when the distance or other difficulties make it impossible for a small group to carry adequate supplies.

If gravity is pictured as a mountain to be overcome, an analogy is possible (Figure 10-4). The base of the mountain must be at

Figure 10-4. "Gravity mountain." The outline of the mountain shows the amount of energy required to overcome earth's gravity. The amount of energy needed decreases rapidly 100,000 miles from earth, shows little decrease until then.

sea level and the plateau at the top of the mountain a million miles away. Unlike the mountains which challenge climbers, the gravity mountain is steepest at the base. Then, as the top is approached, it becomes less and less precipitous, until the level top is reached which corresponds to a million miles—infinity.

In theory, the mountain could be mastered at a steady pace, if a properly designed and sufficiently powerful vehicle were available. Even a motorcycle could climb a steep hill at a steady pace, if the cycle were powerful enough. But in practice, in the sport of hill climbing, the cyclist gets a good start and hopes his momentum will help carry him over the hilltop.

A rocket uses momentum, too. As noted earlier, the Viking accelerates typically under power for a minute and 12 seconds, then coasts for 3 minutes and 14 seconds before reaching peak altitude. This may mean, depending on the payload and other factors, that the Viking accelerates to an altitude of 30 miles, then coasts another 100 miles.

To coast to the top of Gravity Mountain, a velocity of 7.1 miles per second must be achieved. This velocity is critical in space travel, and reaching it is the biggest problem confronting rocketeers today.

The factors in calculating rocket velocity are these: the weight, shape, and volume of the rocket, the weight and volume of propellant required, the weight and volume of the payload, the exhaust velocity of the gases gen-

erated by the burning of the propellant, air resistance, and gravitational acceleration.

In rocketry . . . the step principle . . . is not new. Fireworks operating on the principle have been manufactured for years. Both Hermann Oberth and Robert Goddard, the so-called fathers of space flight, recognized the value of the procedure in their early papers.

The first application of the step principle came in early 1949. A small American rocket, the WAC Corporal, was married to a German V-2. (The term "marriage" is customary in such cases.) Within a minute after the V-2 took off it had climbed to about 20 miles and was moving at a velocity of nearly a mile a second. Then the much smaller WAC Corporal fired, *adding its own velocity to that of the V-2.* In a little over half a minute the WAC had accelerated to a velocity of almost 1.4 miles per second and had burned up all its fuel.

Both the V-2 and the WAC Corporal continued to climb, coasting on the momentum given them by their accelerations. The V-2 rose to almost 100 miles before starting to fall back to earth. It landed five minutes after the take-off. Meanwhile the WAC Corporal continued to climb, and more than six minutes after the take-off reached a peak altitude of 250 miles. . . .

Combining two rockets, then, allowed one to reach an altitude no single-step rocket has attained. A rocket can have two, three, four, five, or more steps. In theory, it can have any number, but of course there are practical limits.

PRINCIPLES OF SPACE FLIGHT*
by Willy Ley (1962)

I know of no other science which has such a magnificent record of living up to its own predictions as rocket research has had. Tiolkowski, Goddard, and Oberth—in that chronological order—predicted that high-performance rockets would result from the utilization

of liquid fuels. Goddard, Oberth, and von Pirquet predicted that the first useful (peacetime) application of large liquid-fuel rockets would be the exploration of the upper atmosphere. All rocket men predicted that the application of the step principle would quickly lead to astonishing performances.

When, on July 29, 1955, the official an-

* From *Rockets, Missiles, and Space Travel* by Willy Ley. Copyright 1951, 1957 by Willy Ley. Reprinted by permission of The Viking Press, Inc., and revised for this book, 1962.

nouncement came from the White House that the United States would shoot an artificial satellite, the concept had a voluminous, if fairly short, history.

What Holds It Up?

But I know from much experience which question most people want to have answered first—the question "What holds it up?" An answer can be given in several ways. The simplest and, in some respects, the most "correct" answer is provided by Figure 10-5. A rocket shot from A to B is really the upper end of an ellipse which has one of its focal points coinciding with the center of the earth. One might say that this ellipse is "intersected" by the surface of the earth at A and B. The larger the ellipse, the farther apart A and B will be. If the ellipse grows large enough to encompass the whole earth the rocket will be in an orbit around the earth. To a mathematician or astronomer this explanation is "obvious," but I have found that it isn't quite that obvious to highway engineers, judges, medical doctors, and just plain interested laymen. For them another explanation—labeled in my mind as the "ballistic" explanation—usually does better.

Look at Figure 10-6. It shows the earth

Figure 10-6. Circular velocity diagram showing how a gun on an imaginary mountain of colossal height could increase projectile trajectory to a circular orbit.

with an imaginary mountain of colossal dimensions, the size having the purpose of putting its peak outside the atmosphere. If we imagine a number of guns placed on that mountain peak, with the barrels precisely horizontal, we can begin the explanation. The first imaginary gun we fire is supposed to have a muzzle velocity of ¼ mile per second. The projectile will slowly curve downward and strike the ground some distance away. The next imaginary gun is supposed to have a muzzle velocity of ½ mile per second. The same thing will happen but of course the projectile will carry over a longer distance. And the projectile from a third imaginary gun with a muzzle velocity of 1 mile per second will strike the ground still farther away.

The fact that a higher muzzle velocity produces a longer range is in itself well known to practically everybody. But why that is so is less well known. It can be understood quite easily by realizing that any projectile describes two motions simultaneously. The first of the two is due to muzzle velocity. If the second motion, caused by gravitational attraction, did not interfere, the first motion would be horizontal in a straight line. If the projectile had no muzzle velocity, it would describe only the second motion—a straight fall to the ground. Together the two motions produce a curve—the projectile moves sidewise and falls downward simultaneously.* The speed of fall does not vary from shot to shot,

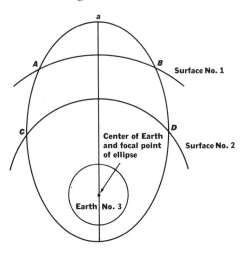

Figure 10-5. The origin of an earth-circling ellipse. A ballistic rocket traveling from A to B on Surface No. 1 actually describes a portion of an ellipse with the center of the earth in one of its focal points. As this ellipse grows larger (indicated here by a shrinking earth), a shot might travel from C to D on Surface No. 2. If the ellipse grows still more, the result is an orbit around Earth No. 3. Of course, this ellipse has to begin at some distance from the ground.

* See p. 127 for Galileo's analysis of this motion. Ed.

but the muzzle velocity can be changed. If the muzzle velocity is high, the curve will be shallow; if it is low, the curve will be steep.

If the muzzle velocity gets very high, the range is increased by another factor: the curvature of the earth. For low muzzle velocities, such as produce ranges of 10 miles or less, that factor does not show. The curvature of the earth, compared with the curvature of the projectile's trajectory, is so "shallow" that it can be considered a flat (plane) surface. But if the trajectory's curvature is shallow too, the curvature of the earth's surface will become more apparent. And in the end one curve will be as shallow as the other; the projectile, while falling, will never reach the ground. The earth's surface, in a manner of speaking, curves downward as fast as gravity causes the projectile to approach it.

In this case the projectile also "falls," as it did in the other cases, but it falls *around* the earth. If the experiment could be made directly at sea level one would find that the velocity required to produce a closed circle is 5 miles per second. Naturally it cannot be done at sea level because of air resistance. And at higher altitudes the velocity required to produce the closed circle, or near-circular ellipse, is somewhat less. Nature herself has demonstrated the case: the moon needs a velocity of only 1 kilometer or $\frac{2}{3}$ of a mile per second.* Obviously a certain orbit will belong to any velocity within the limits of 5 miles per second at sea level and $\frac{2}{3}$ of a mile per second at the distance of the moon.

Choice of Orbits

Equally obviously each of these many possible orbits will have a definite period of revolution. An orbit, say 8000 miles from the earth's surface is not only much longer than one 500 miles from the surface, the orbital rocket traveling in it will also move with a slower velocity. To return to the two examples used in the preceding paragraph, the "sea-level satellite," with its 5 miles per second, would sprint around the earth once in 83 minutes. The moon, on the other hand, with its low orbital velocity and its long orbit,

* See p. 217 for Newton's solution of this problem. Ed.

needs a month. Between these two limits literally anything is possible. For example:

CIRCULAR ORBITS*

| Distance from surface | | Period of revolution | | Orbital velocity, |
Miles	Km			miles/sec
346	557	96	minutes	4.69
470	756	1¾	hours	4.41
1,075	1,730	2	hours	4.39
3,200	5,150	3½	hours	3.58
4,000	6,430	4	hours	3.47
7,700	12,400	7	hours	2.90
22,300	35,900	24	hours	1.90

* These figures can be calculated from Kepler's laws. See Glossary. Ed.

The last item in this table is an orbit which holds a certain fascination. An artificial satellite in this orbit would need precisely one day for a complete revolution and if the plane of the orbit were made to coincide with the plane of the equator, it would appear motionless, always occupying the same spot in the sky like a fixed star. Since such a behavior permits very precise aiming of short-wave antennas, satellites in this 24-hour orbit will serve as long-range communication relays. But one must not confuse the low orbital velocity with the velocity needed to get to the orbit.

Naturally, the farther the orbit is from the surface of the earth the less velocity is needed to maintain an object in it (Figure 10-7). However, the farther the orbit is from the earth's surface, the more fuel is required to reach it from the ground; from the point of view of overall fuel expenditure a lower, nearer orbit is more advantageous. It is also more advantageous from the point of view of optical tracking, telemetering, and so forth. But while all these factors are in favor of a low orbit, one cannot just pick an arbitrary figure. The orbit has to be well outside the atmosphere, otherwise air resistance causes a loss of momentum and the satellite or rocket loses altitude, thereby experiencing more air resistance and in consequence more loss of momentum and altitude. In short, it tends to approach the ground along a spiral path. Actually it is vaporized by aerodynamic heating when it enters denser layers of the atmosphere.

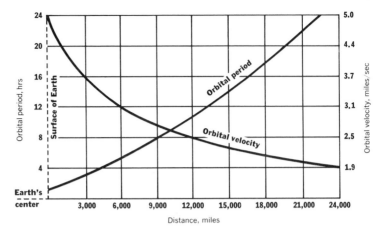

After Arthur C. Clarke

Figure 10-7. Orbital periods versus orbital distances. Figures at left indicate periods; at right, velocities; at bottom, distances in miles.

The orbits of satellites around the earth are elliptical. The lowest point in every such orbit is the place where third stage burn-out occurred [Figure 10-8]. The astronomical term for this point is "perigee" (from Greek *peri,* meaning "near" or "around" and *gaia,* the Greek word for earth). Since perigee altitude and final burn-out altitude are the same, the distance of the perigee can be established by the experimenters within fairly wide limits; for the first American shot it was 224 miles. The highest point in the orbit is 180 degrees away from the perigee and is called the apogee. For the first American shot the apogee was 1573 miles from the surface. The laws of celestial mechanics see to it that the perigee, the center of the earth, and the apogee are in a straight line (Figure 10-9).

The perigees of most satellites were low enough so that there was a certain amount of air resistance left. When the satellite comes back from apogee for the first time it has to slice through this upper atmosphere in order to pass through its perigee. This causes a small amount of drag and since the satellite travels on momentum its momentum is somewhat reduced. This means that the apogee of the second circuit around the earth is somewhat closer to the earth—the satellite lacks the energy to go quite as far away as it did the first time. For every revolution then, the apogee comes somewhat closer (Figure 10-9). The technical name for this phenomenon is "orbital decay;" the ellipse "decays" into a circle, once considered the "ideal" figure for orbits. The circle, of course, forms at the altitude the perigee then has, since the apogee has shrunk to that distance. The circle may not even achieve actual existence, for the orbit decays again, this time into a spiral path along which the satellite descends toward the "burn-up."

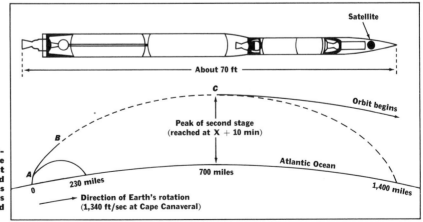

Figure 10-8. Take-off performance of the Vanguard satellite carrier. Brennschluss of the first stage is at A, that of the second stage at B; the third stage begins firing at C. The dotted line is the trajectory of the second stage after its Brennschluss.

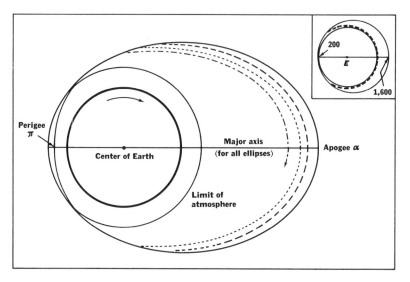

Figure 10-9. Orbital decay of an artificial satellite in a temporary orbit. For clarity, the eccentricity of the orbit, the amount of shrinkage per revolution, and the arbitrary limit of the atmosphere have been exaggerated. The insert at top right shows the correct eccentricity for an orbit with perigee at 200 miles and apogee at 1,600 miles. The dotted line in the insert shows the 250-mile level.

The area that can be seen from a satellite is quite large even from comparatively low altitudes. As the height increases the area grows too. An observer on the Discoverer I satellite at apogee (which was 605 miles) would have been able to see just about one-third of the surface of the earth (Figure 10-10). But as the table below worked out by Robert P. Haviland shows, an optimum

Figure 10-10. Visual angle from the satellite.

is reached at about 4000 miles. A further increase in distance does not help much after that. A television satellite should therefore circle the earth at a distance of between 2500 and 4000 miles to make about 40 per cent of the disk visible to the observer, but a different distance may be chosen for other reasons.

Acceleration and Weightlessness

The very introduction of a pilot changes the whole picture. Some things are easier with a pilot, who is more versatile than any guidance equipment (and also weighs much less than the more complicated versions of guidance equipment), and who can exercise judgment. If, on reentry, the temperature rises too high, the pilot can lift his ship out of the atmosphere again; he might be able to seek the shadow cone of the earth to radiate accumulated heat away faster (of course there are natural limitations)—in short, in many respects the presence of the pilot is a great improvement. On the other hand, the pilot is the most destructible part of the whole assembly, and the design has to be changed to coddle him, especially for the periods of acceleration and deceleration.

As regards the speed of movement, there

Vision angle β, degrees	Geocentric angle ϕ, degrees	Height h, miles	Slant range s, miles	Arc a, miles	Percent of earth visible
160	20	57.3	705	700	8
140	40	257	1,445	1,400	17
120	60	620	2,310	2,100	25
100	80	1,210	3,350	2,800	32
80	100	2,222	4,750	3,500	38
60	120	4,000	6,920	4,200	43
40	140	7,650	11,000	4,900	47
20	160	19,000	22,700	5,600	49
17	163	22,300	26,800	5,800	49.5

is no problem; plain speed does not matter at all; one doesn't even feel it. It took humanity centuries even to find out that it was moving around the sun at the rate of 18½ miles per second. The reason so many people think of "speed" as something to be endured is that they are impressed by what I call the "false speed sensations" engendered by ground travel. If you drive along a highway you feel the bumps of minor unevennesses of the ground; air whistles by; trees and road signs flash by. You are constantly assailed by an assembly of visual, auditory, and tactile sensations, all of which are the products not of the speed but of the road. A flight in a passenger liner shows the true facts to a large extent. If the weather is reasonably good about the only indication is the faint vibrations caused by the engines. And this is improved even more in a large

jet; in a flight in a B-47 I had to *tell* myself by looking at the instruments that we were racing across the sky at better than 400 miles per hour.

The first detailed calculation about the acceleration a man would have to stand to go into an orbit around the earth in a three-stage rocket was made by Dr. Wernher von Braun in 1952. The resulting curve is shown on Figure 10-11. This acceleration was tested in a large centrifuge and when the centrifuge came to a standstill the test subject stepped out in fine health. If he had really gone through this acceleration curve with a rocket he would have been moving at the rate of 5 miles per second. But he would also have been weightless. Why this is so is always somewhat difficult to explain. Of course it has nothing to do with being "beyond the pull of gravity." In the first place the gravitational

Figure 10-11. Accelerations experienced during the ascent of a hypothetical three-stage rocket ship. The two acceleration peaks of 9 g and 8 g are both of very short duration. The broken line indicates the velocity at any particular moment.

attraction of a body does not stop somewhere as does the sovereignty of a country. It is more like seeing a strong light from a greater and greater distance; it will look fainter but it is not gone at a certain distance. If too faint to be seen by the eye, it can still be seen with optical instruments. One can only say that there comes a distance where it is too faint to matter. In the case of the earth's gravitational field this point is 162,000 miles away, and that distance is merely the one at which the gravitational field of the sun is equally powerful.

Then, if the man is still deep in the earth's gravitational field, why does he seem to be weightless? The answer is that the human body, just as it has no organ for detecting speed, also lacks an organ to detect gravity. What the airman's feet feel when he stands at attention on a concrete runway is not gravity, but resistance to gravity. The runway prevents him from following the pull of gravity. If a mile-deep shaft suddenly opened below him he would come to a sad and sudden end on impact at the bottom. But until he reaches bottom he does not feel any pull because he is following it freely. There is no sensation of weight because there is nothing to prevent his fall. He is experiencing "zero-g."

So is the man in the rocket ship. His lack of weight sensations, which could be theoretically deduced, used to be termed "free fall," but since the word "fall" also suggests "down," while the rocket ship will be moving in any direction (but only very rarely "down"), noncommittal "zero-g" was substituted for "free fall."

The original use of the term free fall is also responsible, in my opinion, for several decades of assertions that zero-g would feel like "a never-ending fall" and that it was at least doubtful whether a man could adjust to this sensation. The very idea of a never-ending fall is frightening, of course, but the fact that it is a frightening idea which could be effectively presented does not necessarily render it a correct idea. I believe that this was just the outcome of a poor choice of words,

for it certainly is not the outcome of logical reasoning. It cannot be shown that the sensation of zero-g and the experience of falling must or even will be connected by the mind. It is much more likely that the word which will (inadequately) serve to describe the sensation is the word "floating."

Safe Return to Earth

To leave an orbit the velocity of the orbiting vessel must be reduced which is done by firing a rocket motor in the direction of the ship's movement. To accomplish this does not require any such maneuver as turning the ship around in space, as long as the assignment is just to return into the atmosphere and to land. (If the landing were to be accomplished at a specific time on a specific base the ship may have to be turned in space preparatory to the retarding blast.) Since the ship's "attitude," while circling the earth, remains the same, there must be a short period during every revolution where the rocket motor points in the direction of the movement (Figure 10-12, left). As the rocket blast slows the ship down it leaves its orbit and begins to follow an ellipse that brings it into the atmosphere. If, as could easily be done, the ship has traveled halfway around the earth along this ellipse before entering the atmosphere it will enter nose first (Figure 10-12, right), and then the long supersonic glide to kill its remaining speed will begin.

Building the Space Station

If we now imagine that an object had been jettisoned by the ship before the pilot started the retarding blast, this object would simply stay in the orbit. Another flight could add another object. This is the natural fact upon which the idea of building a large-size artificial satellite in space is based. This large artificial satellite, since it will be manned by a crew when finished, has another name which distinguishes it from unmanned artificial satellites. It is the Space Station.

The concept of a manned space station was introduced into scientific literature with Hermann Oberth's first book, beginning on page

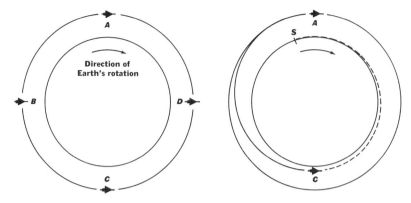

Figure 10-12. Attitudes of a manned ship in orbit and on the return flight. The diagram at left shows that the attitude of a ship (or rocket) in a permanent orbit remains unchanged. For the return flight (right), the pilot fires the rocket motor in position A and enters the atmosphere about 50 minutes later in position C. The broken line shows the supersonic glide; the speed of sound is passed at S. In this diagram, the ship's motion is opposite to the earth's rotation.

86.[1] In this, the last chapter of the short book, Oberth estimated that a rocket carrying two men would weigh at least 400 metric tons. Then he continued, "If we let such rockets of the largest size [mentioned] move around the earth in a circle they will behave like a small moon. Such rockets no longer need to be designed for landing. Contact between them and the earth can be maintained by means of smaller rockets so that the large ones (let's call them observing stations) can be rebuilt in the orbit the better to suit their purpose. If the continuing state of apparent weightlessness should have undesirable consequences, which, however, I doubt, one could connect two such rockets by wire ropes a few kilometers in length and make them rotate around each other."

This really is more than the mere germ of an idea; it is the whole concept without engineering detail: the ship which stays in space, not designed for landing; the supply by transport rockets; the gradual improvement with materials brought up by these transport rockets; the trick of having centrifugal force substitute for gravity, if needed.

[1] The idea had been anticipated in science fiction just twice and at a surprisingly early date. The first anticipation was by Edward Everett Hale in *The Brick Moon* (Boston: Little, Brown, 1899), first published in the *Atlantic Monthly* (1870–71), in which an artificial satellite 200 feet in diameter is to be launched for improving the establishing of longitude at sea. The brick structure is inadvertently launched ahead of time with thirty-seven construction workers aboard who can be provided with supplies from earth. The second was in Kurd Lasswitz's *Auf zwei Planeten* (1897) where space stations are described as the key to space travel.

To the Moon and Beyond

That our moon would be the first goal of a manned space trip has been taken for granted all along. The main reason why the moon is going to be the first place where a ship from earth will make "planetfall" (to update a nautical term) is its nearness. It is a trip of not quite a quarter million miles and unmanned rockets have spanned this distance in 35 hours.*

But nearness is not the only reason, our moon is an entirely different world. Its most numerous features are the thousands upon thousands of "craters." Most astronomers consider them the scars of the impacts of large meteorites, but there are a few who cling to the older idea of volcanism. Aside from the craters the most unusual feature of the moon are its dark areas which can easily be seen with the naked eye.

The dark areas on the moon have always intrigued the imagination. Folk tales and legends of many lands tried to make them mean something and described them as a hare, or as an old woman carrying firewood, or as a man doing something—or nothing— and invented stories why the hare, or the old woman, or whatever, were in the moon. Even before the invention of the telescope some philosophers voiced the opinion that the dark

* See Lunik II, "A Chronology of Space Exploration," p. 394. Ed.

areas must be land which somehow differed from the other land on the moon.

After the very first telescopes had been built, early astronomy took over from folklore and philosophy and stated that the dark areas differed indeed from other land, for they were the seas and oceans of the moon. Consequently they were all given Latin names like *Mare Imbrium*, which means "sea of rains," and are collectively referred to as *maria* (accent on the first syllable). Although the belief that they were actual seas did not last much longer than a century, these names are still in use.

Finding that they were not seas unfortunately brought with it the question "then what are they?" and to this day it has not really been answered. Looking at them through the telescope shows only two things. The large plains of the *maria* are quite dark and they are incredibly flat and smooth. Of course in every one of these plains you can find a crater or two and an occasional mountain peak, but in general they are flat as, well, as the oceans.

The standard answer about their nature has been, for many years, that they are old and enormous lava flows that cooled off and solidified into gigantic beds of hardened lava. This was a better answer than none at all, but the *mare* plains of the moon looked smoother even than frozen lava. The English astronomer Thomas Gold said so recently. And he advanced the idea that they could well be enormous dust bowls, depressions filled to the rim with very fine dust, possibly as much as a mile in depth.

That our moon must be a very dusty place has been recognized for some time. Meteorites of all sizes, but mostly tiny, must be pelting the moon continually. In striking they smash a piece of lunar rock into dust, and break up themselves in the process. Even more important may be the action of the cosmic rays, which ruin the crystalline structure of the rocks until they crumble into dust. But this must be self-limiting, for the dust, once formed, protects the rock underneath.

While all the astronomers are willing to concede a layer of dust over the whole moon —estimates vary from one half inch to about eight inches in thickness—Thomas Gold's suggestion of mile-deep dust bowls is too novel to be generally accepted. It is not impossible, however, and most of the *maria* look smooth enough to fit his explanation.

Whether this is correct is something we might learn even before the first manned expedition reaches the moon, for it is hoped that instrument packages can be "soft landed" on the moon within a few years. The manned landing is an official "Project" by now, called Project Apollo, which will use a three-man ship. Of course the first landing will be just that, the first landing of many more to come. A permanent settlement on the moon, mainly a research station and astronomical observatory will certainly be in existence before the Twentieth Century reaches its end.

Beyond the moon there are the planets, brought within reach perhaps, by the existence of the space station near which the ships that will go to them can be assembled. We can deal with them now, and—in the style of chapter headings in old books—"first with their general motions."

The Mechanics of Interplanetary Flight

There is a fundamental difference between a trip to the moon and a trip to one of the neighboring planets and it is not just a question of distance. True, the moon is on the average 240,000 miles away, while the minimum distance to Venus, our neighbor on the "inside" of the solar system, is about 20 million miles and the minimum distance to Mars, our neighbor on the "outside," is around 35 million miles. The fundamental difference lies elsewhere. The trip to the moon is really just a special case because earth and moon form a system of their own. In a certain sense they are a unit, and a rocket bridging the distance between these two "only" has to overcome the gravitational field of the earth first and that of the moon afterward. Although the sun is the "gravitational ruler" of the solar system, there is no reason to pay any attention either to the gravitational influence of the sun or to the orbital motion of the earth. Not that the attraction of the sun is unnoticeable at our distance of 93,000,000 miles. It is extremely powerful, but that does not matter, since the earth, the moon, and the ship are all subjected to it in the same manner. They are on the same potential of the sun's gravitational field. With regard to the sun all three move with about the same velocity and within narrow limits in the same direction, and because of that the presence of the sun can be disregarded.

An everyday example may make this clear. The straight ascent of a rocket with an immediate return to earth is like getting up from your seat in a railroad car, going to the window, and coming back. The ascent with a subsequent fall to the moon is like going to another car in the same train. For all these restricted movements it does not matter whether the train is standing still or is traveling at full speed, because your seat, the window, and the next car all move with the same speed. But setting out for Venus or Mars means leaving the train, and then the speed of the train becomes an important consideration.

The planets of our solar system all move in the same direction around the sun. They also move in almost the same plane; not quite the same plane, but with differences which are not large compared to the enormous size of the whole. Only the orbit of the planet Pluto at the edge of our solar system and the orbits of a few asteroids and of a number of comets are tilted at a steep angle. However, they do not move at the same speed; the inner planets are faster by far (Figure 10-13). They need the higher velocities to stay in their orbits—to counterbalance the more powerful attraction of the sun. The whole may be visualized as a whirlpool with sloping sides, the sun being in the center at the very deepest point. The innermost sections rotate at the highest speed, at some distance from the center the speed of rotation is perceptibly slower, while the outer portions, where the whirlpool slopes least, move rather slowly. At each point the speed of rotation is just sufficient to counteract the attraction of the sun, to prevent the bodies that are at that point from sliding down toward the center.

See Figure 10-14 and if you turn the book upside down the curve for the earth's field can be used to illustrate one-half of the "whirlpool." Of course this is just a device; one can visualize and even draw a whirlpool but one cannot draw a gravitational field.

Supposing now that a body moving in one of the outer slow parts were suddenly slowed down some more by an outward force. In such a case the body would not be able to maintain its orbit; it would start sliding down toward the center, the sun. Gaining speed while sliding down, it might acquire a new balance, but the thing which interests us at the moment is that it would be drawn toward the center if it lost some of its normal speed. Conversely one of the faster bodies, pushed to a still higher speed by an outside force, would move outward, overcoming the attraction of the central body.

This thought can be applied to actual conditions in the solar system with little alteration. Supposing we have a large rocket, capable of reaching a velocity of 7 miles per second relative to the earth. Before take-off that rocket is part of the earth, and its orbital velocity, as seen from the sun, is 18.5 miles per second. In a vertical take-off this rocket would either add its own velocity to that of the earth, or subtract it from that of the earth, depending only on the time of the day. Now the "front side" of the earth, the one

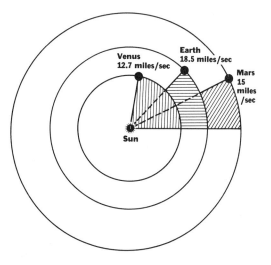

Figure 10-13. The movements of Venus, Earth and Mars during a fifty-day period.

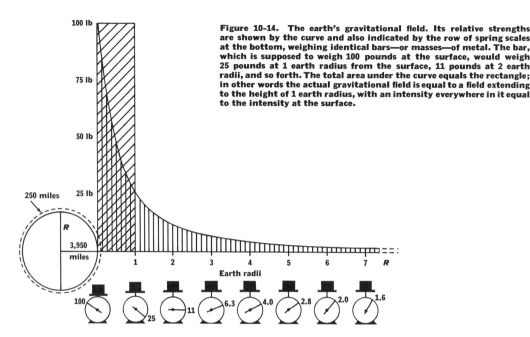

Figure 10-14. The earth's gravitational field. Its relative strengths are shown by the curve and also indicated by the row of spring scales at the bottom, weighing identical bars—or masses—of metal. The bar, which is supposed to weigh 100 pounds at the surface, would weigh 25 pounds at 1 earth radius from the surface, 11 pounds at 2 earth radii, and so forth. The total area under the curve equals the rectangle; in other words the actual gravitational field is equal to a field extending to the height of 1 earth radius, with an intensity everywhere in it equal to the intensity at the surface.

that points in the direction of its orbital movement, is the "dawn side." For a take-off at dawn the rocket would add its velocity, for a take-off at dusk it would subtract it. We may refer to these two cases as the "dawn rocket" and the "dusk rocket."

What would happen is shown by Figure 10-15. The dawn rocket, being "too fast" for the earth's orbit, will drift outward in the solar system, in the direction of the orbit of Mars. But in drifting outward, the rocket climbs "up" in the sun's gravitational field which gradually slows it up.

The dusk rocket, having subtracted its own velocity from that of the earth [Figure 10-16], would slide inward in the solar system. For the dusk rocket take-off point would be aphelion, with perihelion somewhere between the orbits of earth and Venus. This example shows the principle on which a trip to a neighboring planet is based. If you want to go to a planet nearer the sun you have to subtract from earth's orbital velocity. If you want to go to one farther from the sun you have to add to it.

It is a question of timing to arrive at a given point of the orbit of Mars when the planet is also at that point.

If the timing is important the dosing is even more so.

If the spaceship added too much speed to the orbital speed of the earth, it might acquire the tendency to drift across the orbit of Mars instead of just to the orbit. In such a case its own orbit and that of Mars would cross. If it had only enough speed to drift to the orbit of Mars, the two orbits would only touch.

That is the difference between economical and uneconomical orbits. If the orbits of ship and planet *touch*, both move around the sun in precisely the same direction, although not

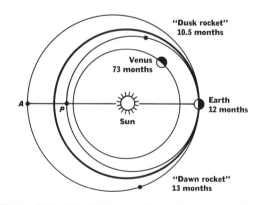

Figure 10-15. The "dusk rocket" and "dawn rocket." If two rockets left earth at escape velocity, one at dusk, the other at dawn, they would describe the two orbits shown and, after a few revolutions around the sun, would crash on earth again. P marks the perihelion point of the "dusk rocket," which has its aphelion at the position of the earth. Conversely, the position of the earth marks the perihelion of the "dawn rocket," and A marks its aphelion.

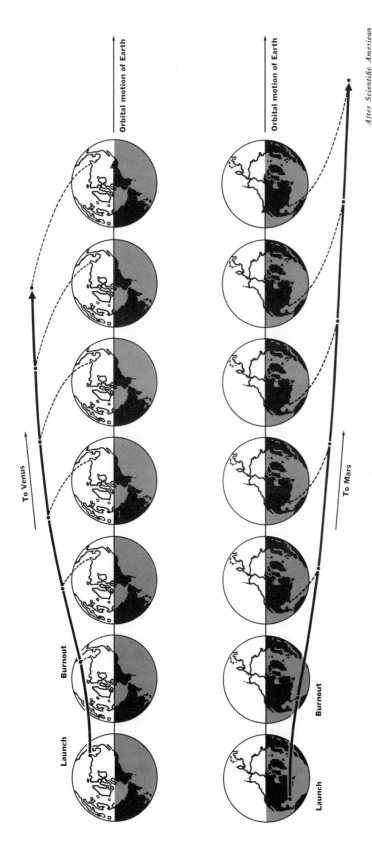

Figure 10-16. Escape trajectory of a space vehicle leaving earth is depicted to show the positions of the vehicle and the earth at intervals of about eight minutes. In relation to earth, the vehicle takes off along a hyperbolic path (black lines). For a flight to Venus (top) the vehicle is aimed backward along the orbit of the earth so that it moves more slowly than the earth, as suggested by the lengths of the black lines that plot the trajectories of the earth and the vehicle as seen from space. As a result, the sun's gravitation pulls the vehicle inward toward Venus. For a flight to Mars (bottom), the vehicle is fired in the direction that the earth is moving. Since it is now traveling more rapidly than earth, it moves outward toward the orbit of Mars.

After Scientific American

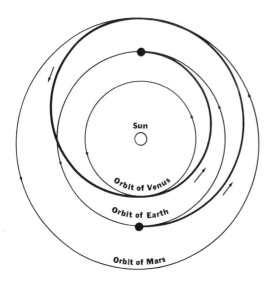

Figure 10-17. The so-called Hohmann round trip.

quite with the same speed. But if the orbits of ship and planet *cross*, the ship not only has to change direction but also has to eliminate a greater difference in velocities than in the case of touching orbits. Naturally a much larger amount of fuel would have to be expended in the case of crossing orbits and, since this fuel had to be lifted from earth first, it does mean *much* more fuel at the beginning of the trip.

The first man to work out the fuel require-ments for a number of inter-planetary trips was Dr. Walter Hohmann. The procedure of the trip to Venus as outlined by Hohmann, would be to ascend from the earth vertically in an arbitrary direction, until the ship is 500,000 miles from the surface. At this distance the gravitational field of the earth can be neglected. The ship is now independent of the earth, but still has the same orbital velocity as the earth. Now change the orbital velocity of the ship, a change of less than 2 miles per second. The ship is now on its way, drifting inward in the solar system (Figure 10-17).

Since we know so much from theoretical reasoning, the general reader is fully justified in asking what is standing between us and travel to the moon and other planets. It will be easier to answer this question, however, if it is phrased more specifically: Is there any specific unsolved problem standing between us and space travel, or is it just a question of improving the "state of the art" generally? The answer is that the problem is essentially one of improving rocket technology, and all associated technology, as a whole. While there are a few unsolved specific problems, they are of such a nature that they will be solved in the course of the general advance.

SCIENCE AND SURVIVAL THROUGH SPACE
by Bruce T. Lundin (1961)

In all of man's history, no venture has offered a wider range of challenges and opportunities as rapidly and as clearly as space exploration. In the short span of three and a half years, the exploration of space has become a major national program of two great powers, involving an annual expenditure of several billions of dollars and absorbing the energies and talents of thousands of scientific and technically trained people. These programs have, so far, produced the launchings of 49 American and 16 Soviet satellites and space probes, the journeys of four astronauts into the space environment, the delivery of a man-made object to the surface of the moon, a considerable reorientation of large segments of industry, and a remarkable impact on our educational processes.

The motivations for this rapid expansion in the scope of human effort are not difficult to find. Space exploration offers in one great swoop unparalleled opportunities for tangible expressions of man's questing and adventurous spirit, for unlocking vast realms of new knowledge, for applications of importance to our day-to-day affairs on earth, for visible demonstrations pertinent to national prestige, and for important advancements in our military strength.

One of the factors that gives significance to our efforts in space is thus the urge of man to discover and explore, and the thrust of his curiosity to go where no one has gone before. Beyond this, however, is the even more basic and universal urge of man towards a greater understanding of the world around him and his desire to master it intellectually as well as physically. At the entrance to the library of Carleton College are the words of the Norwegian explorer, Fridtjof Nansen, "The history of the human race is a continuous struggle from darkness toward light. It is, therefore, of no purpose to discuss the use of knowledge—man wants to know and when he ceases to do so, he is no longer man."

The psychological factor of space exploration, of course, is strongly related to our national prestige and our position in the world in the eyes of its people. Whether we like it or not, we are living in a technological age—an age in which the society and culture that makes the greatest advancement in science will be doing the things that matter and which command the greatest respect of people everywhere. While space research is only one of the many areas of scientific, economic, and political rivalry between great nations, it is the most exciting, difficult, and glamorous of all. For decades, the world at large has regarded this country—our own country—as pre-eminent in most scientific, technological, and industrial fields. But now, the Soviets have managed to convince many in both the relatively sophisticated western nations, and certainly in the less industrialized nations, that Russian accomplishments in space are the true measure of technological advancement, and thus the proof of the strength and vitality of their culture and form of government. If, therefore, we do not make it our business to keep America in the forefront of science and technology, it is likely we will lose the cold war with Russia and never really know just when or how it happened.

A summary statement of a recent study prepared by the Rand Corporation for our Con-gress is noteworthy. This study concludes, in part, with the following: "In reading Soviet scientific literature, one cannot help but be impressed by the boldness, the scope, and the dedication of the Soviet effort toward the ultimate conquest of the cosmos; i.e., manned interplanetary travel. There seems to be no question in the Soviet mind that the Communist Party's authoritarian directive to realize man's most cherished dream will be fulfilled in and by the Soviet Union."

Much has been said, in the public press and elsewhere, of the importance of various military applications in space. While it is a little early in the game to be planning military operations from lunar bases or developing space platforms from which to drop bombs, there are several important and foreseeable military uses for space vehicles. These applications lie principally in the fields of communications, meteorology, reconnaissance, and surveillance. The recent success of the Tiros cloud-cover satellite has certainly focused attention on the surveillance and reconnaissance possibilities of satellites. While this satellite is only an initial experiment related to weather forecasting, others of much higher observational quality will follow. For example, by providing a satellite that is orbiting at a height of, say, 200 miles with a 12-inch telescope, a resolution of some two or three feet at the surface of the earth is possible. And even the cover of darkness provides little seclusion. This same type of satellite would also have little difficulty in detecting the presence of a 60-watt light bulb on the surface of the earth. When coupled with advanced data handling and information selection techniques, these capabilities would provide the satellite's possessor with such information as the movement of ships at sea, the progress of major construction, the location of missile-launching sites, and troop movements. No secrets of an important military nature could be kept for long from a potential enemy. In both this sense, and as a reconnaissance device, the satellite seems a particularly powerful partner to the ICBM.

These are only two examples of presently foreseen military applications. The lessons of history remind us sharply of the limits of our vision and certainly other applications, presently unforeseen, will develop as our science and technology of space advance.

Beyond these immediate and near-future military and psychological factors, a profound and long-range objective of our explorations in space is, as already indicated, the expansion of scientific knowledge of the earth, our solar system, and the universe. Let us take a closer look at some of them. It is instructive to note here that up to the present time the sum total of our knowledge of our environment and all of its physical and biological processes is based upon observations made from the surface of our planet—from, indeed, one small speck of cosmic dust. Our view of the universe is certainly much like that of an inhabitant of a desert isle who is trying to perceive the nature of the earth by climbing a tree and looking over the horizon.

Now, for the first time in human history, we have the means to extend our observations beyond the earth and its protective, but obscuring, layer of atmosphere. But even more important than this vast extension of opportunities for observation, is the fact that man can now conduct experiments in the space environment. The distinction is important; to conduct controlled experiments leads to deduction while the mere taking of observations permits only the drawing of inferences. Just what good this expansion of scientific knowledge will be in an economic and materialistic sense is, for the most part, impossible to say. We are standing today, with respect to astronautics, about where the science of aviation was when the Wright Brothers flew their first airplane a distance of 120 feet. But the history of science has shown that scientific research has a remarkable way of paying off, and one interesting characteristic of really important discoveries is their unexpectedness.

It is convenient to consider that satellites can do essentially three different things. By orbiting about our earth many times each day, at various heights, in various orbital planes, and with varying degrees of eccentricity, they can look down upon our earth

from a vantage point of space, they can sense the environment in which they are traveling, and they can look out into our universe with great clarity. Similarly with space probes, it is possible to obtain direct measurements of the environment of space throughout our solar system—and it does appear to be a very busy and interesting place—probe the atmospheres of the planets and, later, explore their surface characteristics, structure, and chemical and biological constituents.

One of the most significant results so far obtained in the scientific program was the discovery of the great radiation belts surrounding the earth. These belts, first reported on May 1, 1958 by Dr. James Van Allen, extend from a few hundred to several thousands of miles above the earth's surface and consist of charged particles that are trapped and guided by the earth's magnetic field [Figure 10-18]. Although the existence of such belts of charged particles was postulated by Stoermer many years ago, his concepts necessarily remained little more than an interesting idea until verified by direct experiment.

Despite such predictions, the measurements obtained with Sputnik II and Explorers I, III, and IV which proved the existence of the inner belt of radiation came as a considerable surprise. The paths of these satellites were, however, confined to the relatively near-earth environment. Further surprises were therefore obtained from the deep space probes Pioneer III and IV when the second belt was discovered. With each experiment incorporating more refined instrumentation, knowledge rapidly accumulated until it can now be stated with confidence that the inner belt arises from beta decay of cosmic ray neutrons. The structure and composition of the outer belt is less clear. Solar disturbances are known to play a role. Plasma clouds from the sun, bearing electrons and protons, reach the earth and interact with its magnetic field. This interaction releases particles from the outer zone into the atmosphere and produces an increase in the number of electrons in the outer belt. Although the nature of this energy transfer is still uncertain, what is known is of fundamental significance. In the first place, a major

Figure 10-18. Structure of radiation belts as revealed by contours of radiation intensity (curved lines) is shown schematically by shading (left); dots (right) suggest distribution of particles in the two belts. Contour numbers give counts per second; horizontal scale shows distance in earth radii (about 4,000 miles) from the center of the earth. Particles in the inner belt may originate in the upper atmosphere by radioactive decay of neutrons liberated in the upper atmosphere by cosmic rays; those in the outer belt probably originate in the sun.

After James A. Van Allen

feature of our near space has been discovered and, in the second place, these belts suggest the possibility and offer the opportunity for the development of an integrated concept of a number of other geophysical phenomena and processes.

A second significant achievement made possible by satellites relates to the shape of the earth. Studies of the orbits of the first small Vanguard satellite by O'Keefe and his co-workers resulted in the postulation of a "pear-shaped" earth. Although the variations in shape from previous theoretical results were small—a difference of about 15 miles between equatorial and polar radii—they are of large importance in terms of the earth's structure and surface loading. Subsequent checks on surface distortions may have a profound effect on theories of isostasy and of the earth's internal mass distribution.

But these are only two examples among many. The list of tasks our scientists are eagerly awaiting to perform in space is nearly endless. The atmospheres and ionospheres program relates to the pressure, temperature, density, and composition of the atmospheres surrounding our earth and other planets and determination of the type of charged particles, their source, and radio propagation characteristics in the ionospheres that exist immediately beyond the atmosphere. The energetic-particles research program includes, in addition to the radiation belts already mentioned, investigations of the origins and nature of cosmic rays and auroral particles and their effects on both materials and living organisms.

We know, of course, that the earth and the sun have magnetic fields; whether similar fields exist around Mars, Venus, and our moon is not known. Definite information on these points would tell us much about the origin of our solar system. Another experiment of possibly far-reaching consequences is to put a very accurate atomic clock aboard a high-altitude satellite and compare its time, while traveling in a reduced gravitational field, with that of a similar clock near the surface of the earth. Measurement of the difference in time between these two clocks will provide an important experimental check on the general theory of relativity.

Of the total spectrum of light that strikes the earth's surface, much is, of course, absorbed by our atmosphere and what does come through is considerably distorted. With an astronomical telescope mounted in a satellite, our astronomers will be able to emerge from the fog of our atmosphere into the clear light of night and have, for the first time, a really clear view of our universe. In the field of geodesy, we have already been able to correct some rather significant errors in the locations of various islands in the Pacific and improved upon previous measurements of intercontinental distances.

In addition to these experiments in the physical sciences, the possibly great significance of space experiments in the field of life-sciences should be underscored. While it is difficult to be certain which direction this research may take, it seems obvious that the ability to study the emotional and physical behavior of humans in the silent, isolated, weightless, and strange environment of space will tell us much about ourselves. Here is a chance for the doctors to do some really new research that can't help but be of great benefit. It seems quite possible that the whole science of biology—what life is and how it works—is getting ready for some unifying theories such as occurred in the physical sciences some three to four hundred years ago. And here research in space and on other planets may be of fundamental significance. After all, life as we know it—from the living cell through the evolutionary process that has led to man's present physical structure and emotional makeup—has occurred on the surface of our earth, with its particular type of atmosphere, radiation from the sun, gravitational field, and chemical composition. Would the ecological and physiological principles of, say, plant succession, photosynthesis, and natural selection apply in the different conditions of another planet? The question is certainly an open one.

The benefits of this scientific program to the physical comfort and well-being of man are, of course, several years ahead of us.

There are, however, two areas in which the use of satellites offer near-future improvements in some important elements of our daily lives. These relate to the weather and to communications. The recent success of Tiros, the preliminary cloud-cover experiment, may lead some to believe that this is the only requirement for weather forecasting and that we may soon be able to place greater confidence in the weatherman's prognostications. There is, however, much more to weather forecasting than just knowing where the clouds are and it will be at least two or three years before the necessary operational system is established.

Although it is not generally appreciated, the amount of energy our earth receives from the sun is almost exactly balanced by the energy it radiates back into space. Otherwise the earth would gradually heat up or cool off. But more energy is received than is lost in the tropic regions and in the polar regions the process is reversed. It is this energy distribution that makes our weather. In addition to the heat budget and the cloud-cover, the temperatures at various layers in the atmosphere, the constituents present, and the location and movements of thunderstorms and hurricanes are also pertinent. At the present time, a knowledge of these factors is confined to observations that cover about 10 percent of the earth's surface. Meteorological satellites in polar orbits can, however, cover essentially the entire earth. It has been estimated by our weather department that the improved forecasting provided by such meteorological satellites may be worth 4 or 5 billion dollars a year to the United States alone—two or three times the cost of all of our present space activities.

In the area of communications, it has become increasingly evident that our present networks are reaching saturation. Overseas telephone messages will, for example, increase from 3 million this year to 21 million by 1970. The present trans-Atlantic telephone cable, which was installed in 1956, is now reaching its capacity, and even the new transistorized cable now under development will be saturated in 1965. Communication satel-lites provide an inherently global coverage that may solve this problem. Such satellites will probably take three forms. The first to be used will be passive reflection devices, such as a large mylar balloon. Later satellites will actively receive and retransmit messages by onboard electronic equipment. In such satellites information storage prior to transmission back to earth will obviously extend the coverage obtained. And finally will come a truly global coverage by either transmission from satellite-to-satellite in different orbits or satellites sufficiently far from the earth so that three or four of them may cover the entire globe. The prodigious communication capacity possible is revealed in the estimates of some experts that a 2,000-pound satellite could handle all of the messages now carried by all of the world's cables, telegraphs, and radio systems.

The potentials of space flight for both these scientific explorations and practical applications are indeed profound. It is also abundantly clear that man, himself, must, and will, play a basic role in the exploration and uses of space. A vigorous program of manned space flight has accordingly been in progress since America's first organized efforts in space. The first step in this long-range project has been Project Mercury—a project designed to place manned capsules into a 100-mile orbit, let them circle the earth three times, and bring them back safely to earth. . . .*

The next outstanding stride in this direction is the goal of achieving a manned landing on the moon within this decade. Such a venture—project Apollo—will require technological advancements far in excess of those needed for project Mercury. It will require the development of a launch vehicle that is 30 to 50 times as powerful as the Atlas booster and of new and highly reliable propulsion systems for the lunar landing and take-off. The spacecraft must be capable of being guided and steered toward the moon, of landing gently on the moon, of being launched from the moon, and of being guided back to a safe reentry and recovery on earth. Provi-

* See "A Chronology of Space Exploration," p. 398. Ed.

sions must also be made for protecting the three-man crew from radiation, thermal, and meteoroid hazards of space during the seven- or eight-day voyage to the moon and return. Equipment must be designed and developed to enable men to live and function effectively on the lunar surface, where a man will weigh 30 pounds, where there is no atmosphere, and where the temperature varies from 250° F during the lunar day to 250° below zero during the lunar night.

It is anticipated that the landing will be made at a site that has previously been surveyed by unmanned spacecraft. A precise knowledge of the surface environment, its hardness, and its composition is needed before even a landing gear can be designed. The preparations for take-off from the moon will require especially large advancements over today's operational procedures. When it is realized that a launching from Cape Canaveral involves hundreds of people in blockhouses and control centers and thousands more at checkout and tracking facilities, it is clear that a successful lunar take-off by three men in pressure suits will be a difficult task indeed.

Because of the large advancement in the state of the art required for this mission, the Apollo project has been divided into several intermediate steps. The first is to fly the spacecraft in an earth orbit where its many components and systems will be tested and evaluated in the space environment. This phase will also provide an orbiting laboratory for scientific measurements and observations in space. The craft will then be flown in successively larger orbits until circumlunar flight is achieved. In such circumlunar flight, the crew will perform many of the guidance and control tasks needed later for the landing mission. These preliminary flights in earth orbit and around the moon then lead logically to the final Apollo objective—a manned landing on the moon.

A most critical element of a space capacity for both manned space flight and instrumented payloads, and one without which nothing else is possible, is that of propulsion. It is also the area in which, at least in size of rocket engines, the Soviets clearly excel. As is

now well known, the Soviets concentrated on the development of the rocket-powered ballistic missile as their principal strategic weapon some five or six years before we did. Further, at the time they made this decision, nuclear warheads were considerably heavier than they were when we started our ICBM program. As a result, they now have available for use as basement booster stages rocket systems of between 600,000 and 800,000 pounds thrust—roughly twice that of our Atlas and Titan systems. And we may be certain that they are continuing to both refine their present units and to develop even more powerful launch vehicle systems.

To get our space program off to a rapid start, the majority of our launchings have employed the 150,000-pound-thrust Thor and Jupiter rockets. The full capability of even this thrust level was, furthermore, unavailable to us because of the lack of suitable upper stages that are required for space missions. It was necessary, therefore, to resort to pretty much a makeshift operation, making use of what was at hand. This procedure also precluded the repeated use of a few types of vehicles that is necessary to develop a good reliability. To correct this situation, urgent efforts are being made to develop a family of launching vehicles of greatly increased payload capacity. By keeping this family of vehicles small in number, they also should, through repeated usage, become very reliable.

The smallest of the family is Scout, an economical, four-stage solid rocket vehicle that will be capable of launching a 150-pound payload into orbit or carrying out a variety of atmospheric-probe missions. Next is Thor Agena B, a three-stage vehicle comprised of a Thor IRBM basement stage, the 15,000-pound-thrust Agena stage and a small solid-rocket third stage. This Agena stage also matches up fairly well with the Atlas booster, so for larger payloads there is also under development the Atlas Agena vehicle. Both of these vehicles will see initial use in mid-1962.*

Both the Thor and Atlas vehicles make use of conventional rocket engine propellants such

---

* The Atlas-Agena was used in the successful launch on Aug. 27, 1962, of the Mariner R, Venus fly-by spacecraft. Ed.

as liquid oxygen and kerosene. To achieve greater payload capabilities, the final versions of all future vehicles will use liquid hydrogen as the fuel in all but the basement stage. The first application will be in Centaur, a 30,000-pound thrust hydrogen-oxygen fuelled engine that will be used as a second stage atop an Atlas booster.

But much larger vehicles are needed for the important jobs ahead. The development of the Saturn vehicle—a cluster of eight ICBM engines, uprated to provide a total first-stage thrust of 1½ million pounds, is therefore proceeding with high priority. Looking farther down the road, there is also under development a single thrust chamber that will be capable of delivering 1½ million pounds thrust—10 times that of our present ICBM engines. And it is expected to cluster several of these giants together to form the Nova

vehicle—a vehicle that will tower over 250 feet high, be about 50 feet across at the base and have a total thrust of several million pounds [Figure 10-19].

A convenient way of specifying the payload capabilities of these vehicles is the weight that they can place in a 300-mile orbit about the earth. Many of the large vehicles will also be used for more ambitious missions with, of course, considerably reduced payloads. For example, a 60,000-pound orbital payload would also correspond to a soft landing on the moon of around 10,000 pounds. Starting with an almost insignificant weight in 1959, a payload of about 1,600 pounds will be possible with the Thor-Agena vehicle in 1962. Maximum payloads in 1961 and 1962 are both based on the use of the Atlas booster, with a growth from 5,000 pounds in 1961 to 8,500 pounds in 1962, reflecting the advan-

	Vanguard	Jupiter-C	Juno II	Thor-Discoverer	Thor-Delta	Scout	Atlas (Mercury)	Atlas-Vega	Atlas-Centaur	Titan	Saturn	Nova
umber of stages	3	4	4	2	3	4	1½	3½	3½	2	5	5
e-off thrust (lbs)	27,000	83,000	150,000	150,000	150,000	120,000	365,000	390,000	390,000	300,000	1,500,000	6,000,000

After Lee Dubridge

Figure 10-19. Evolution of rocket systems.

tage of hydrogen fuel in the Centaur vehicle as compared to conventional fuels in the Atlas-Agena. From here onward through the 60's, maximum payload capacities are obtained by the Saturn vehicle, growing from around 20,000 pounds in 1963 to nearly 80,000 pounds in 1967, as larger and more powerful upper stages become available. The Nova vehicle, although not yet definitely configured, will be aimed at an orbital payload of around 350,000 pounds. Now 350,000 pounds in orbit may seem like a large payload, and it is. More significantly, however, this payload is also equivalent to sending to the moon and returning to earth a weight of around 12,000 pounds—enough for three men to travel to the moon and back.

While these numbers may still seem like pretty good payloads, they become marginally small when one studies the future requirements of sustained lunar operations and manned interplanetary flights. A most attractive and necessary advancement for such missions is offered by the nuclear rocket. A nuclear rocket operates according to principles very similar to those of a chemical rocket except that the gases are heated by a nuclear reactor instead of by the combustion of a fuel and an oxident. Only a single propellant is required—hydrogen is the propellant of choice because of its low molecular weight and hence the high jet velocity that can be obtained from a given energy input. This propellant is pumped to a high pressure by a turbopump system and, after cooling the exhaust nozzle, reflector, and reactor shell, is heated by passing it over the hot, fissioning uranium in the reactor. Expansion of the hot hydrogen gas through an exhaust nozzle produces the propulsive thrust. To translate the great potential of the nuclear rocket into actual hardware, a joint AEC-NASA program has been established in which the AEC is responsible for the development of the reactor and the NASA for the non-nuclear components and the integration of the reactor into a complete propulsion system.

To obtain a general idea of what may be accomplished by a nuclear rocket system, let us consider a mission to the planet Mars.

Such a voyage would require on the order of 450 days, necessitating a crew of at least six or eight men and a payload, including radiation shielding, of possibly 200,000 pounds. To launch such a payload to Mars with chemical rocket engines would require a vehicle of nearly 10,000,000 pounds in orbit about the earth. And to get this vehicle into orbit with an all-chemical booster of the NOVA type would require the launch of some 300,000,000 pounds from the surface of the earth. Possible, but a rather large undertaking. The use of a nuclear powered spacecraft, however, can reduce these vehicle weight requirements in orbit some seven or eight fold. And, if we use a nuclear upper stage in the vehicle that delivers this equipment into orbit from the earth, we can do the job with only five or six vehicles in the 3,000,000-pound-thrust class. The nuclear rocket therefore offers the possibility of realizing one of the ultimate achievements of space exploration—that of a manned voyage to the nearby planets and return.

Taken altogether, the conduct of these explorations in space and their supporting research and development will lead, as many have pointed out, to an expanded technological capability in many areas—a capability that will become of increasing benefit to us in many of our day-to-day affairs and which is essential to our national strength and prestige. But the real challenge and the greatest significance of space flight goes much deeper. Demanding, as it does, the best in human creativity, enterprise, and devotion to common purpose, it offers the ultimate rewards of knowledge, understanding, and a greater consciousness of the grandeur of the universe around us. As have all great human adventures before, it will, by raising man's vision and expanding the scope of his intellectual activity, stimulate and release his creative energy in all aspects of human endeavor. It is no mere accident that the sixteenth century age of global exploration was also the age in which Harvey discovered the circulation of blood, Napier invented logarithms, and Shakespeare wrote his sonnets. As the anthropologist J. D. Unwin has observed, "In all human records there is no trace of any display of productive energy which has not been preceded by a display of expansive energy." And here, indeed, in the exploration of our universe, is an activity that will strain and extend the reach of all facets of our existence —our science, our culture, and our spirit.

Viewed in such a perspective, it seems clear that the society or culture that makes the greatest advancements in space will also be doing some of those things that matter most— that satisfy our curiosity, bestow comprehension, provide objects of intellectual contemplation, and release creative energies. Such is the total challenge and total opportunity of space flight. An opportunity provided by the technological capabilities of our times and a challenge given substance by the thrust of a totalitarian society not only into space but, indeed, into all aspects of our lives. Viewed in these terms, our task is clear—that wherever man will go, whatever knowledge he accumulates, and whatever values he creates, free men must play the leading role.

THE NATIONAL RESPONSE

SELECTIONS FROM THE REPORT OF THE SELECT COMMITTEE ON ASTRONAUTICS AND SPACE EXPLORATION
House Report No. 2710, 85th Congress, 2nd Session (1959)

III. A Space Program for America

National space policy in the United States, to be effective, will inevitably require the greatest partnership in the history of civilization and government. Industry, business, government, invention, and law, charged with spiritual motivations and enriched by the Nation's educational resources, must join in this project because mankind has never before been confronted with possibilities so hopeful and so awe-inspiring.

All civilization is encompassed by the unpredictable and the predictable mysteries that rest in outer space.

It cannot be overemphasized that the survival of the free world—indeed, all the world —is caught up in the stakes. Outer space is fast becoming the heart and soul of advanced military science. It constitutes at once the threat and the defense of man's existence on earth. Only a bold and dynamic program employing the total talents and the greatest strength of the United States and its friends is competent to meet a challenge so overwhelming.

The efforts of this committee have reflected an amity and a unanimity of purpose which extend to the Administration as well as to party points of view. In fact, all the work of the committee, in both the tone and substance of its reports, has been done with an eye single to the national interest and to international aims of peace and order. . . .

The circumstances under which this committee was created relate to events which have recently changed the course of world history and the development of civilization for all time to come.

The creative forces of modern science and technology, through which man is beginning to realize some of his finest powers of reason and constructive ability, are now moving like the breakup of an Arctic river in the spring.

What might be called the "intellectual freezeup" of our objective understanding of the universe, together with our relative inability to use its forces, has been showing tentative cracks and shifts for some time. Now the changes have accelerated, so that today we seem about to witness a major loosening of the ice jam of our intellectual past. We may, in fact, be ready to move swiftly into a scientific world as different from our early technical endeavors as a warm summer is from the frigid season which precedes it.

This is not a change which can be forestalled, for the growth of these forces is more powerful than any political government on earth.

The loud report of the first nuclear explosion at Alamogordo, N. Mex., in 1945 merely signaled an attainment which had become inevitable with the calculations of Leibnitz, Planck, and Einstein.

The appearance of manmade satellites in the skies, traveling millions of miles at speeds which would bring incandescence in the atmosphere, has been an even more vivid sign that a new age is dawning. If we are unprepared, we may be swept away. At best, our situation is dangerous. It finds us vulnerable not only to the threat of nuclear, chemical, and biological war, with space employed as a medium of attack, but to the more subtle and equally threatening danger which lies in moral, psychological, and political fields.

It is possible, with foresight and skill, to master these tremendous changes. But nothing short of a national effort by all those armed with power, ability, and devotion can guarantee safe navigation of the swift currents of change which are now coming into view. Success is almost certain to mean unparalleled progress for tomorrow. Failure, as the history of the complacent, wealthy, and unresponsive nations of the past attests, very probably points to a new Dark Age.

Philosophic observations such as these are doubtless unusual in a formal report to the Congress. Nevertheless, the members of this committee have been so impressed by the nature of their work that they feel it necessary to abandon the prosaic approach in order to convey some sense of the enormity of the problems to be faced.

As this report and its supporting staff studies will show, every phase of modern life is somehow bound up with the new space technology. This fact poses two questions:

(1) Will the United States move steadily to marshal the resources of the free world and insure that no threat of force from space will be able to control or destroy us?

(2) Will the United States provide the leadership to unite the world in dedicating its space capabilities to peaceful purposes?

Both the threat and the high potential of the peaceful use of space have emerged in unmistakable outline from the studies of the select committee during the past year. We can think of no other report to the Congress of equal gravity in its implications for our future. . . .

C. Policy Implications for the Space Program

1. *Inexorable changes in society and political power will follow the development of space capabilities; failure to take account of them would virtually be to choose the path of national extinction.* Space developments already have changed the course of world history as inevitably as the discovery of America changed the history of Europe. The space challenge must be met by the adaptability, the energy, and the vision of the American people. Informed citizens, progressive business managements, and the organs of Government, including the Congress, must understand these facts, create public awareness, and act decisively in their respective fields to put this scientific knowledge and space capability to practical use. This must be done with sound and understanding cooperation—particularly, in the field of Government, between the legislative and executive branches.

2. *What program the United States could achieve and what it will in fact achieve may be two very different things. . . .* We must warn that a policy of drift or neglect, or the frequent changing of goals would inevitably lead to our falling far short of the benefits and the capabilities that can be achieved in the next decade.

3. *Budget pressures in the short run should not be the primary basis for decisions on space programs which are inherently long range, and which involve the very survival of the Nation.* Budget problems of the Nation are very real. The budget represents an attempt to assign national resources with the greatest efficiency for the meeting of overall national goals. Stability of prices and the lowest practical level of taxes and Federal debt are worthy objectives in the interest of economic growth and flexibility. However, it is inevitable that certain expenditures on space must be made within the foreseeable future, and that delay will raise costs.

4. *This Nation should not make inadequate*

short-run expenditures on its space program at substantial risk to its survival a few years later. The American people prefer economic and fiscal stability and soundness, but must view them in long-run terms.

5. *The best advice obtainable by the committee supports the view that within a decade peaceful applications of space development to weather prediction and long-range communication alone will more than pay back to the economy all the funds previously required to achieve these capabilities.* Six satellites could handle the entire overseas mail volume of the World, as the Atlas satellite has already demonstrated in rudimentary form. Better weather predictions are expected to save the United States economy about $4 billion a year.

6. *The greatest benefits of space development and exploration in all probability cannot even be predicted today.* This has been true of countless past discoveries. The search which discovered America was intended to find a direct route to the Orient; the prize which was found was much more important. More recently, the byproducts of nuclear reactors seemed at first an unwanted nuisance. But already the economic benefits of radioactive isotopes bring a return great enough to pay the capital charges on our entire peaceful and military investment in the atomic field. What may come in resources, in understanding of the forces of nature, in solving many of the present mysteries of life may be beyond all immediate human understanding. This is not the kind of challenge man can safely ignore.

7. *Although engineering secrets related to national defense deserve the utmost protection, the greater part of the space program will progress more rapidly without the shackles of an undue security control.* No country has a monopoly on scientific knowledge, and history has shown that inventions and discoveries are frequently made independently at much the same time in different countries of the world. Because the space effort is so complex, almost every branch of human study has made some contribution to its success. Compartmentalization of research findings, within a narrow, need-to-know

framework, whether done in the name of national security or to protect proprietary interests, can only slow up our progress. Free exchange of information among scientists and engineers is particularly important for a country which is making a late start in developing its space capabilities.

8. *Full scientific and technical cooperation among the nations of the free world is essential to their joint survival and to the fastest growth of the American space program.* The recent report on international cooperation issued by this committee traced in detail the compelling reasons for international cooperation in space. Partly they are psychological. Partly they arise from the need for worldwide tracking and control facilities. Partly they are necessary in order to tap a rich pool of scientific talent in other countries which now is underused and not marshaled. Finally, the space program will soon reach such size that it will require the combined effort of many nations. It is our hope that the exploration of space will in time absorb the friendly common efforts of all nations. In the meantime the free world cannot afford to delay its own space development on a united plan while waiting for improved relations with the Communist bloc.

9. *Scientific education in the United States stands in need of critical review.* No phase of the soul-searching produced by the launching of the sputniks excited a more sympathetic response from an alarmed people or from educators and legislators than the realization that American education had failed to measure up to the needs of the hour. Public education fell under intense scrutiny, from teachers' salaries to the neglect of mathematics and science studies in the secondary schools and the institutions of higher learning. The performance of the Soviet schools in some of these respects presented a challenging contrast.

The Soviet Union appears to put a greater total emphasis on education. The difference would be hard to measure, even in terms of money and manpower, partly because the term "education" in Soviet use includes some activities which are not regarded by Americans as education at all. There is also good evidence that schooling is generally more intense in the Soviet Union than in the United States. In addition, the Soviet curriculum includes more study of mathematics and the physical sciences.

While the Soviet schools are also believed to have many shortcomings, such as rote learning and excessively strict "discipline," it behooves the United States to recognize those aspects of Soviet education which are better suited than its own to the demands of the future. At the same time, any changes which are made must be consistent with American objectives, ideals, and conditions. It is the view of this committee that prudent and imaginative steps must still be taken to give to mathematics and science the needed emphasis in school curricula. These steps should be designed not only to meet Soviet educational competition, but should, irrespective of Soviet standards, raise American standards to cope with the Space Age. The committee intends its use of the word "prudent" to imply an emphasis that does not neglect the humanities in favor of mathematics or related subjects.

Epilogue

As this committee concluded the meeting at which this report was adopted, the news of the Soviet lunar probe* became public. This committee has been consistent during the year of its life in believing that the Soviet Union has a distinct lead in astronautics over the United States, although it also believes that with time and toil the United States can surpass the Soviet achievements. Many prominent Americans, however, have minimized the Soviet advantage at various times during the year. The latest Soviet achievement proves the soundness of the view of this committee that our scientific race, not alone in space but in the broader realm of science, is serious and urgent and demands the utmost effort by this Nation.

* See Lunik II, "A Chronology of Space Exploration," p. 394. Ed.

SELECTION FROM THE STATEMENT OF THE PRESIDENT'S SCIENCE ADVISORY COMMITTEE
(May 24, 1959)

The Place of Science and Technology

Science, engineering and technology have obviously been responsible for a host of conspicuous changes at all levels of our modern civilization. There is much reason to expect that such changes will continue, and will indeed accelerate. There is no way to turn back the clock or to turn off scientific advance. There will be no international moratorium on science or technology. The people of the United States, on the most practical grounds, must accept and support these propositions. By ignoring them, or by fostering them only with reserve, they would doom their nation to unnecessary weakness and backwardness in a world where other nations are not so foolish. Alfred North Whitehead said in 1916:

In the conditions of modern life the rule is absolute: The race which does not value trained intelligence is doomed. Not all your heroism, not all your social charm, not all your wit, not all your victories on land or at sea, can move back the finger of fate. Today we maintain ourselves. Tomorrow science will have moved forward yet one more step, and there will be no appeal from the judgment which will then be pronounced on the uneducated.

This is even more forcibly apparent in 1959 than it was in 1916. It follows that we must educate more, and especially we must educate better, scientists and engineers. But this is not enough. We must have trained specialists in many fields. Even then we would not be successful if, having such specialists, the American people were merely to applaud and reward them for their contributions while still thinking of them as useful strangers, dimly understood and more feared than admired. Hence, we must also cultivate a widespread dedication to and respect for learning in all fields, and a deep understanding between the public and the experts.

Growth of Science

The story of man has from the very beginning involved his progress in the conquest of nature, and, less successfully, his effort to understand himself and to live amicably with his fellow men. Here we are concerned with the accelerating conquest of nature which began in prehistory and proceeded in spite of superstitions, of magic, and of taboos. Yet modern science had its beginnings only 300 years ago, and since then our ability to understand nature has grown by leaps and bounds and at an ever-accelerating rate. Twentieth-century advances in the techniques of research in applied science, replacing the simpler process of invention, have aided the explosive growth of modern industrial societies.

Science affects the life of every contemporary man every day. It conditions decisions that need to be made by his government on many matters, including national defense, foreign policy and public health. It affects the decisions made by individuals on business problems, on selecting a community in which to live, on choosing an automobile, a record player, or perhaps even a dentifrice. If an individual is ignorant of science he must guess what to do or else believe what he is told. Even if he is told what to do by an expert, he has no way to check on this advice or even to understand it. This unhappy predicament is precisely that of most citizens of the United States today. Their fate in important matters and in trivial matters alike may thus be decided without their participation. And it will not be otherwise so long as they remain illiterate about science and technology.

The march of science and technology is of growing importance to every American as a citizen. Congress regularly appropriates huge sums for scientific research and even larger ones for engineering and development; yet a majority of the voters have little grasp of what this is all about. Do we, for example, seek to make shots at the moon, or send vehicles to Mars, in order to extend scientific knowledge alone—and, if so, how much is that effort worth? Is our primary purpose to launch such vehicles before the Russians do for the sake of impressing the rest of the world? Then how much are such achievements worth? To what extent do these space ventures attain primarily a strengthening of our military capabilities? And are they indeed the best way to gain military strength? If our space ventures essay all of these purposes simultaneously, we must still have judgment on the weight to be given to each purpose. To be able to think beyond the press releases and publicity statements, to understand the background of national debate requires a greater comprehension of space problems than that provided by science fiction or the comic strip.

Yet the field of space research is only one important field of modern technology which is of concern to the average citizen. There are other fields involving communication, transportation, and human health. But are there still others which we do not recognize at all? Is it because no comparable Sputnik has awakened us? The shocks provided by achievement elsewhere may not be an adequate guide to our progress or our efforts. A national effort is required to strengthen our scientific and technological efforts in all fields, aimed at the advance of knowledge and the enhancement of the general welfare. In a democracy such an effort can succeed only if it has widespread public understanding and support.

Other Values

The educational values in the study of science go far beyond the practical matters of a cold technological war or even those of the wise use of science in the service of society. The student of science quickly learns that all scholars seek the truth and that they must be critical and honest with each other. The study of science may offer to the young student his first and possibly his best early opportunity for learning how easy it is to make mistakes and how hard it is to advance knowledge. It may also provide the simplest early experience of the supreme virtue of intellectual honesty.

Then, too, we must be aware of the humanizing aspects of science. The beauty and order of nature which science reveals are as moving in their way as great paintings or fine drama. The vast reaches of the universe now being examined by the modern astronomer are as inspiring as great music. The fact that the laws of science span all national and ideological boundaries makes science the universal language, a link between nations, and a real potential force for peace.

Americans diminish their capacity as citizens, give up an early strengthening intellectual experience, and forego great pleasure, excitement and adventure when they neglect to study science.

The study of science thus enhances the education of *every* citizen, in addition to providing the necessary basis for the education of the future professional scientist, engineer and technologist. For all these reasons we believe it is appropriate and necessary that the American educational system give due recognition to instruction in mathematics, science and technology.

Does this mean that every high school student should become a scientist? Of course not.

But he should have the opportunity to gain insight into the methods and concepts of science so that he can understand the world of science in which he lives. He should not undergo a regimen which stifles his childish curiosity about the world of nature.

Unfortunately, many children are thus stifled. Many schools do not have either the teachers or the facilities to provide good science instruction. Some children are frightened away from science by the mathematics it uses. Others find the traditional discussions of pulleys and levers, or a wearisome listing of species and genera, too dull to excite their curiosity to learn more. Still others are advised by parents or friends, or even teachers, to avoid difficult subjects like mathematics and science, in spite of the fact that many students find these the easiest, because the most exciting, subjects of all.

We emphasize that we are not urging that other fields of intellectual importance be reduced or diminished, but only that a proper balance be maintained in our educational offerings. We fear that in the past there has been inadequate emphasis on mathematics and science.

ASTRONOMY AND THE STATE*
by A. C. B. Lovell (1959)

The Soviet Union scored a major triumph by the successful launching of Sputnik One on 4 October, 1957, followed a few weeks later by the even greater accomplishment of orbiting Sputnik Two, weighing over a ton and packed with scientific instruments. Now, the avowed purpose of earth satellites is for geophysical and astronomical observations, and only those of a conservative outlook would deny the enormous advantages of astronomical investigations made above the absorbing and disturbing regions of the terrestrial atmosphere. However, the cost of such enterprises is, by any standards, very great, and it

is now well known that the launching rockets of the satellites, which represent the main cost, are military weapons of most devastating potential.

It seems unlikely that without the practical and military urge behind these developments the scientists of Russia and America would today be in a position to use these new astronomical tools. . . .

In these new fields of work we are dealing with an expenditure on an unprecedented scale, in which an experimental test of only a few minutes may cost more than the largest telescope yet built.

Those concerned with the astronomical sciences are therefore faced with an entirely new situation. It is understandable that some as-

* From *The Individual and the Universe* by A. C. B. Lovell. Copyright © 1958, 1959, by A. C. B. Lovell. Reprinted by permission of Harper & Row, Publishers, New York, and Oxford University Press, Fair Lawn, N.J.

tronomers, brought up in the tradition of the peaceful isolation of the observatory dome under the starlit sky, do not receive with enthusiasm these new developments, in which their instruments are launched from the rocket range under the glare of publicity. Others are happy to join in the initiation of this new era of observation which would be impossible but for the political and military divisions of the world which have forced the governments to an expenditure which would never be borne as a budget for fundamental scientific work alone.

The brilliant successes of the U.S.S.R. in this work contrasted sharply with the initial difficulties of the U.S.A., and it is a question of much importance to determine why the role of these nations both pursuing the same ends were so unexpectedly reversed. In this connexion one is struck most forcibly by the relative positions of the scientists and engineers in the U.S.S.R. and the West. During the vital years of the development of these projects American science was under the shadow of a Secretary of Defence who could see little value in research which had no immediate foreseeable economic or commercial value.

The relevant branches of American science were understaffed, uncorrelated, and without the necessary finance to such an extent that General James Gavin and others resigned in protest. By contrast, the power of the Academy of Sciences in Russia is very great. The essential factor appears to be that the initiation of scientific projects is determined by the desire of the scientists of the Academy and that the financial restrictions which place such grave handicaps on the Western scientists do not exist. The single-minded purpose behind such developments, which are carried through with human welfare taking second place, is a feature which has no parallel in Western life. The direct and continuous communication between the Council of Ministers and the senior Academicians determines that no human frailties or vacillations shall interfere with this unity of purpose. As a result, we see today a scientific and technological nation in the early stages of development which already has great

ability and power. In all events of the past year I find few things more symbolic than the ease with which the U.S.S.R. launched Sputnik One, weeks ahead of schedule.

It is ironical that the precedence which Russia established in this way appeared to be the one factor required to transform the American situation. At last money became of secondary importance, the divisions were at least partially healed in a fanatic drive to establish parity, and the recent creation of the National Aeronautics and Space Administration with an actual budget this year of three hundred million dollars, and a projected budget of a thousand million dollars in two years' time, gives a new and refreshing sense of well-being and unity to the American astronomical space projects. The deplorable nature of the competition which has led to this transformation has hastened the development of space research beyond anything which was conceivable a few years ago. . . .

The expenditure of large sums of money by the State on fundamental scientific research, although inevitable, is full of long-term dangers. In my second lecture I gave an example of the restriction of free astronomical inquiry in Russia today. In Great Britain the dangers are enhanced by the difficult and peculiar situation which exists in the Universities. The great scientists of the past were able to achieve their tremendous successes with so little expense that the University organizations have grown up without difficulty on the basis of reasonable equality of expenditure as between arts and science. The problem of absorbing the vast new instruments of science in conventional University departments is exceedingly difficult, and in fact the desirability of doing so is in question because of the fear of destroying the traditional balance of activities. It seems to me that those charged with the administration of the Universities in Great Britain are today faced with a delicate and perilous situation which is without precedent. A failure to absorb these great new scientific projects into a framework where the traditional University freedom of inquiry can flourish will be fraught with grave dangers to scholarship and scientific education.

In America the dangers at present are of a different kind. The financing of the radio astronomical projects is already heavily biased by the investments of the armed services, and early in the next decade when the 600-foot telescope is available it seems likely that these investments by the military authorities will dominate the American radio astronomical scene. At present the demands of the services for specialized work from these groups of scientists is small. There is, indeed, no reason for it to be otherwise, since the lines of work likely to be pursued with these telescopes by the free volition of the scientists is of great fundamental interest to the services. However, this may not always be so. I am unable to discover any safeguards which would enable this vast fabric of fundamental astronomical research to survive a change of emphasis or opinion in the armed services concerned. It is indeed fortunate that so far in Great Britain these new developments have been contained within a University framework where freedom is a prized and jealously guarded possession.

The main concern of the astronomer is with highly abstract and remote topics. Some of this work can still be pursued by the astronomers working in isolation from the daily turmoil of existence. But we are moving into a new epoch in which even the study of the remote parts of the universe demands a close partnership between the astronomer and the State. The instruments which are destined to solve the problems of the origin of the universe may well rise from the rocket range. The pursuit of the good and the evil are now linked in astronomy as in almost all science.

In so far as Great Britain is concerned I have tried to show that the recovery of our heritage in the astronomical sciences is in acute danger, and that the peril lies deep in our national well-being. The pessimists say that we cannot compete and that within the next decade the scientific and technological superiority of the U.S.S.R. over the West will be complete. I do not believe that this will necessarily be the case, because I think that the restraints on freedom which I discussed earlier may reduce the effectiveness of Russian science, and may counteract to some extent their enormous superiority in scientific manpower and finance. On the other hand, one thing seems beyond contention. Fundamental research in astronomy or any other subject is an essential component in the welfare of modern civilization. Unless the West overcomes its present parsimonious attitude to science and technology, then the relative quality of our civilization will decline, and our influence will pass to other peoples. I have referred to the great sums now being spent, particularly in the U.S.A., but in so far as they support research, these represent a quite negligible proportion of the national budget. Neither in Great Britain nor the U.S.A. have we yet provided the facilities to saturate our existing scientific manpower. Therein lie my grounds for personal pessimism. Moreover, our danger rests, not in our limited potential, but in those amongst us who think of science and astronomy in terms of the sacrifice of a television set or motor car today so that our grandchildren can get to the moon. Alas, the issues at stake are of a different order of gravity. The fate of human civilization will depend on whether the rockets of the future carry the astronomer's telescope or a hydrogen bomb.

SELECTION FROM PRESIDENT EISENHOWER'S FAREWELL ADDRESS TO THE NATION
(January 17, 1961)

In the councils of Government, we must guard against the acquisition of unwarranted influence, whether sought or unsought, by the military-industrial complex. The potential for the disastrous rise of misplaced power exists and will persist. We must never let the weight of this combination endanger our liberties or democratic processes. We should take nothing for granted. Only an alert and knowledgeable citizenry can compel the proper meshing of the huge industrial and military machinery of defense with our peaceful methods and goals, so that security and liberty may prosper together.

Akin to, and largely responsible for the sweeping changes in our industrial-military posture, has been the technological revolution during recent decades. In this revolution, research has become central; it also becomes more formalized, complex, and costly. A steadily increasing share is conducted for, by, or at the direction of the Federal Government. Today, the solitary inventor, tinkering in his shop, has been overshadowed by task forces of scientists in laboratories and testing fields. In the same fashion, the free university, historically the fountainhead of free ideas and scientific discovery, has experienced a revolution in the conduct of research.

Partly because of the huge costs involved, a Government contract becomes virtually a substitute for intellectual curiosity. For every old blackboard there are now hundreds of new electronic computers.

The prospect of domination of the nation's scholars by Federal employment, project allocations, and the power of money is ever present—and it is gravely to be regarded.

Yet, in holding scientific research and discovery in respect, as we should, we must also be alert to the equal and opposite danger that public policy could itself become the captive of a scientific-technological elite.

It is the task of statesmanship to mold, to balance and to integrate these and other forces, new and old, within the principles of our democratic system—ever aiming toward the supreme goals of our free society.

SOME COSMONAUTICAL QUESTIONS*
Editorial, Life Magazine (April 21, 1961)

Yuri Gagarin's space flight was not only a magnificent achievement of modern science, but a geo-political victory for the Soviets which poses some very urgent problems for the U.S. As President Kennedy said to the space experts with whom he discussed what to do next, "There's nothing more important." If this is a race, do we want to catch up? What's wrong with Mercury and our other lagging programs? Should we change our established priorities in favor of some great leapfrog effort? At what cost? Must we really (as one scientist testified last week) get up $25-$40 billion to speed an American to the moon? What is our national space objective: survival, knowledge, or prestige? The answers to these and similar questions are indeed urgent. Kennedy has some very complex command decisions to make in the next few months.

But even after they are all answered, an older question will remain. It is a question that has haunted the Western world at least since the first successful atomic test at Alamogordo, N. Mex.; indeed it goes back to Edison, to Descartes and to Newton. It is the question of the role of science in the organized life of mankind.

For the Soviets, this question does not exist. They answered it long ago by making science their god. Despite the wholly unscientific character of their political dogmas, they look to science as the chief tool and ultimate vindication of their system. It is a science-oriented system. Thus there is an eerie element of truth in Khrushchev's wild boast that Gagarin's flight "contains a new triumph of Lenin's ideas, a confirmation of the correctness of Marxist-Leninist teaching." Gagarin, too, gave the credit to "our own Communist party," the vanguard on the "great road to penetrating the secrets of nature."

Science is no nation's private property. It

* Reprinted by permission.

has been very kind to America, and vice versa. Americans will always delight in the marvels of science and respect its usefulness in the quest for truth. But our technological supremacy, which the Russians have now outstripped in space, has been a by-product of our free society, never its god or goal. The only test used in a scientific society—does it work?—has not been the sole test of our national endeavors, though they have met this test. In our current discomfiture, and our haste to meet the Soviet challenge, we should not let this fundamental question of science's role go by default.

The space adventure is of such huge proportions and its effects can be so pervasive, that technocracy (a broader word for what the Soviets live under) could overtake us while we overtake them. There are ways to live in a scientific age, and to maintain science as the servant of human freedom, without worshiping it or letting it organize our whole lives. But the way will not be found by pretending that the technocratic challenge, and the Orwellian danger, are not real. What role do Americans really want science to play in their lives? A greater role than now? A central role? What?

SELECTION FROM PRESIDENT KENNEDY'S ADDRESS TO CONGRESS
(May 25, 1961)

If we are to win the battle for men's minds, the dramatic achievements in space which occurred in recent weeks should have made clear to us all the impact of this new frontier of human adventure. Since early in my term, our efforts in space have been under review.

With the advice of the Vice President we have examined where we are strong and where we are not, where we may succeed and where we may not. Now it is time to take longer strides—time for a great new American enterprise—time for this nation to take a clearly leading role in space achievement.

I believe we possess all the resources and all the talents necessary. But the facts of the matter are that we have never made the national decisions or marshaled the national resources required for such leadership. We have never specified long-range goals on an urgent time schedule, or managed our resources and our time so as to insure their fulfilment.

Recognizing the head start obtained by the Soviets with their large rocket engines, which gives them many months of lead time, and recognizing the likelihood that they will exploit this lead for some time to come in still more impressive successes, we nevertheless are required to make new efforts.

For while we cannot guarantee that we shall one day be first, we can guarantee that any failure to share this effort will make us last. We take an additional risk by making it in full view of the world—but as shown by the feat of Astronaut Shepard, this very risk enhances our stature when we are successful.

But this is not merely a race. Space is open to us now; and our eagerness to share its meaning is not governed by the efforts of others. We go into space because whatever mankind must undertake, free man must fully share.

I therefore ask the Congress—above and beyond the increases I have earlier requested for space activities—to provide the funds which are needed to meet the following national goals:

First, I believe that this nation should commit itself to achieving the goal, before this decade is out, of landing a man on the moon and returning him safely to earth. No single space project in this period will be more exciting, or more impressive, or more important for the long-range exploration of space; and none will be so difficult or expensive to accomplish.

Including necessary supporting research, this objective will require an additional 531 million dollars this year and still higher sums in the future. We propose to develop alternate liquid and solid fuel boosters much larger than any now being developed, until certain which is superior.

We propose additional funds for other engine development and for unmanned explorations—explorations which are particularly important for one purpose which this nation will never overlook—the survival of the man who first makes this daring flight. But in a very real sense, it will not be one man going to the moon—it will be an entire nation. For all of us must work to put him there.

Second, an additional 23 million dollars, together with 7 million dollars already available, to accelerate development of the Rover nuclear rocket.

This is a technological enterprise in which we are well on the way to striking progress, and which gives promise of some day providing a means for even more exciting and ambitious exploration of space—perhaps beyond the moon, perhaps to the very ends of the solar system itself.

Third, an additional 50 million dollars to make the most of our present leadership by accelerating the use of space satellites for world-wide communications. When we have put into space a system that will enable people in remote areas of the earth to exchange messages, hold conversations, and eventually see television programs, we will have achieved a success as beneficial as it will be striking.

Fourth, an additional 75 million dollars—of which 53 million is for the weather bureau—to give us at the earliest possible time a satellite system for world-wide weather observation. Such a system will be of inestimable commercial and scientific value; and the information it provides will be made freely available to all the nations of the world.

Let it be clear—and this is a judgment which the members of the Congress must finally make—let it be clear that I am asking the Congress and the country to accept a firm commitment to a new course of action—a course which will last for many years and carry very heavy costs, 531 million dollars in the fiscal year 1962 and an estimated 7 to 9 billion dollars additional over the next five years.

If we are to go only halfway, or reduce our sights in the face of difficulty, in my judgment it would be better not to go at all.

This is a choice which this country must make, and I am confident that under the leadership of the space committees of the Congress and the appropriations committees you will consider the matter carefully. It is a most important decision that we make as a nation; but all of you have lived thru the last four years and have seen the significance of space and the adventures in space, and no one can predict with certainty what the ultimate meaning will be of the mastery of space.

I believe we should go to the moon. But I think every citizen of this country as well as the members of Congress should consider the matter carefully in making their judgment to which we have given attention over many weeks and months, as it is a heavy burden; and there is no sense in agreeing, or desiring, that the United States take an affirmative position in outer space unless we are prepared to do the work and bear the burdens to make it successful. If we are not, we should decide today.

Let me stress also that more money alone will not do the job. This decision demands a major national commitment of scientific and technical manpower, material and facilities, and the possibility of their diversion from other important activities where they are already thinly spread.

It means a degree of dedication, organization, and discipline which have not always characterized our research and development efforts. It means we cannot afford undue work stoppages, inflated costs of material or talent, wasteful interagency rivalries, or a high turnover of key personnel.

New objectives and new money cannot solve these problems. They could, in fact, aggravate them further—unless every scientist, every engineer, every service man, every technician, contractor, and civil servant involved gives his personal pledge that this nation will move forward, with the full speed of freedom, in the exciting adventure of space.

A LETTER*

TO THE EDITOR OF THE NEW YORK TIMES:

The President has asked us to make enormous efforts in a space race with the Russians to put a man on the moon in this decade. He estimates that this will cost $7 to $9 billion in the next five years, and The New York Times of May 25 indicated that the total cost might be $20 to $40 billion.

Thus we would accept the challenge to a race in which the Russians have chosen the ground, and in which they already have a lead. Moreover it would require a major diversion of our intellectual and financial resources from objects that are more important to us than the moon, and that are more in keeping with our aims in the world.

Why is it important to put a man on the moon? Not for military reasons, when we can already shoot rockets wherever we wish, or observe the world from unmanned satellites. Not for scientific reasons either, surely a more balanced program of scientific research would produce better and more significant scientific results.

Technological Task
The project to put a man on the moon is a gigantic technological task involving many true scientific problems, but it is essentially technological rather than scientific. . . .

Then perhaps we must put a man on the moon for political reasons—to impress the

*Reprinted by permission.

peoples of the world. This makes it a kind of propaganda project, but do we really want to spend $20 to $40 billion for propaganda, and if so, is this the best way?

I agree with the President that Americans must make sacrifices, accept high taxes, and make stronger efforts to combat world communism. But I do not believe that the way to do it is to put a man on the moon.

Rather let us make a balanced scientific effort, including space research, but informing the world that we are more interested in other things than racing to the moon. Let us improve our medical research and make it available to the world. Let us put more effort into social, economic and political research, to be used to ameliorate and improve the human condition at home and abroad.

Let us encourage cultural development—literature, the arts, music—at home and abroad, as evidence that we do not subscribe to the Communist idea that man is essentially an economic automaton. Let us improve our foreign aid. Let us keep up our defenses. Let us improve our educational system for all citizens.

Let us strive harder to realize our ideals of human rights and equality under democracy.

These are the things on which we could well spend $20 to $40 billion instead of shooting it to the moon.

Herbert S. Bailey, Jr.
Princeton, N.J., May 25, 1961

SPACE EXPLORATION IN THE SERVICE OF SCIENCE†
by Eugene Rabinowitch (1961)

As at the time of the first Sputnik in 1957, public acclaim for a spectacular technical achievement, now enhanced by admiration for the bravery of the lonely rider in the space capsule, has been tinged by alarm at the demonstration, for all the world to see, of Soviet leadership—and American backwardness—in the art of space navigation.

† From *Bulletin of the Atomic Scientists*, May–June, 1961. Copyright 1961 by the Educational Foundation for Nuclear Studies, Inc., Chicago. Reprinted by permission.

Space exploration began in close association with the arms race—a concomitant to the development of long distance delivery systems for nuclear weapons. The Soviet success in building booster systems far superior to those at the disposal of American rocketmen was a great achievement in this arms race and justly remains a source of American alarm. It would be, however, quite misleading to look for military implication in all deeds of space exploration made possible by the power of Soviet rocket boosters—the Moon hit, the circumnavigation of the Moon, the Venus rocket, the manned space flight. The talk of "dominating Earth by dominating space," of military Moon bases, of the strategic importance of Mars or Venus, not to speak of the colonization of other planets, . . . has little or no relation to the realities of the military balance of power in the foreseeable future. Nobody can preempt cosmic space by getting there "fustest with the mostest." The Soviet spaceships, as well as the great variety of miniaturized American satellites should be looked upon entirely as feats of scientific exploration whose only nonscientific implications lie in accretions to national prestige resulting from spectacular technological successes. Observation satellites are the only type of space vehicles apt to produce radical changes in the strategic balance between the East and the West by reducing the advantages of secrecy now favoring the Soviet Union.

The question has been asked by many, including such prominent scientists as Max Born in Germany, or the late Louis Ridenour in the United States: Is the scientific information made possible by penetrating into space worth the immense investments now being made in programs for space exploration?

If there is a field of science in which mankind as a whole is facing the universe and in which the division of mankind into different political and ideological units becomes a minor irrelevancy, it is the exploration of the Earth as a whole and of the cosmic space around it. A clear understanding of the disproportion between the narrow ambitions of the various fragments of humanity and man's confrontation with the immensity of the universe could become an important step toward the realization of the common origin, common fate and common aspirations of all mankind. Some statements attributed to the returning Soviet astronaut and some proclamations of the Soviet leaders praising his feat, while referring to it as a common achievement of mankind, did their best to present it, above all, as a heroic service to the Communist party and a demonstration of the superiority of the Communist society. This attitude is regrettable, but we have little right to criticize such statements as long as so many in America tend to look at the "space race" primarily as a competition between two political systems!

Sooner or later—and the sooner the better—competitive space exploration will have to yield to a cooperative effort. There are tasks such as interplanetary flights for which the resources of any country, however wealthy, may be not enough, and worldwide pooling of efforts will be needed for effective progress. . . .

This worldwide cooperation is not only desirable but ultimately inevitable.

PREMIER KHRUSHCHEV'S CONGRATULATORY LETTER TO PRESIDENT KENNEDY
On Successful Glenn Flight* (February 22, 1962)

Esteemed Mr. President:

On behalf of the people of the Soviet Union and myself personally, I congratulate you and the American people on the successful launching of a spaceship with a man on board.

Another step has been made in the exploration of space, and the family of the cosmonauts has this time been joined by a citizen of America, Lieut. Col. John Glenn.

Successful launchings of spaceships, mark-

ing the reaching of new heights in science and technology, make us justly proud of the unlimited potentialities of human genius to serve the welfare of man.

I should like to hope that the genius of man, who penetrated the depth of the universe, will be able to find a road to an enduring peace and to ensure prosperity to all peoples on our planet earth, which, in the space age, though it does not seem to be so large, is still dear to all its inhabitants.

If our countries pooled their efforts—scien-

* Furnished by United Press International, reprinted from *The New York Times*, February 22, 1962.

tific, technical and material—to explore outer space, this would be very beneficial to the advance of science and would be acclaimed by all peoples who would like to see scientific achievements benefit man and not to be used for "cold war" purposes and the arms race.

Please convey hearty congratulations and best wishes to astronaut John Glenn.

N. Khrushchev

PRESIDENT KENNEDY'S REPLY*

Dear Mr. Chairman:

I thank you warmly for your message of congratulations on Colonel Glenn's successful space flight, and I welcome your statement that our countries should cooperate in the exploration of space. I have long held this same belief and indeed put it forward strongly in my first State of the Union message.

We of course believe also in strong support of the work of the United Nations in this field and we are cooperating directly with many other countries individually. But obviously special opportunities and responsibilities fall to our own two countries.

I am instructing the appropriate officers of this Government to prepare new and concrete proposals for immediate projects of common action, and I hope that at a very early date our representatives may meet to discuss our ideas and yours in a spirit of practical cooperation.

J. F. Kennedy

* Furnished by Associated Press, reprinted from *The New York Times*, February 22, 1962.

Growth is achieved when an individual or a minority or a whole society replies to a challenge by a response which not only answers that challenge but also exposes the respondent to a fresh challenge which demands a further response on his part. . . .

We find that "virgin soil" produces more vigorous responses than land which has already been broken in and thus rendered "easier" by previous occupants. Thus, if we take each of the affiliated civilizations, we find that it has produced its most striking early manifestations in places outside the area occupied by the parent civilization. The superiority of the response evoked by new ground is most strikingly illustrated when the new ground has to be reached by a sea passage. . . . These overseas migrations have in common one and the same simple fact: in transmarine migration the social apparatus of the migrants has to be packed on board ship before it can leave the shores of the old country, and then be unpacked again at the end of the voyage. All kinds of apparatus—persons and property, techniques and institutions and ideas—are subject to this law. Anything that cannot stand the sea voyage at all has to be left behind, and many things—not only material objects—which the migrants do take with them, have to be taken to pieces, never perhaps to be reassembled in their original form. When unpacked, they are found to have suffered "a sea change into something rich and strange."

Arnold Toynbee
A Study of History (1946)

A CHRONOLOGY OF SPACE EXPLORATION
October 4, 1957 to October 3, 1962

Since the first artificial satellite was placed into orbit by the Soviet Union on October 4, 1957, ninety-six satellites have been put into orbit by the United States and twenty-four by the U.S.S.R., as far as known. Of these, fifty-three are still in orbit, and the others have decayed and dropped back into the earth's atmosphere and burned up or, in the case of manned spacecraft or some military satellites, have been brought back to earth.

Scientific Satellites: Earth Orbit

A total of thirty-one scientific satellites, not counting satellites that have a primary purpose exclusive of collecting data, such as manned craft, communications, navigation, etc., have been placed into orbit around the earth. Sixteen were orbited by the United States. The U.S.S.R. orbited fourteen. One satellite was cosponsored by the United States and Great Britain.

Scientific satellites are used to collect data on radiation, atmospheric density, micrometeorites, cosmic rays, temperature measurements, gravity measurements, and the like. With this information, scientists are better able to understand the environment of space and thus design spacecraft for manned flight, build equipment that can function in space, and better understand the phenomena of the universe.

Milestone Satellites

Weight, pounds	Country	Satellite	Launched	Status	Special significance
184	U.S.S.R.	Sputnik I	Oct. 4, 1957	Decayed Jan., 1958	First artificial satellite
1,120	U.S.S.R.	Sputnik II	Nov. 3, 1957	Decayed Apr., 1958	First satellite to carry animals in space with dog Laika
18	U.S.	Explorer I	Jan. 31, 1958	Still in orbit	First U.S. satellite in orbit; discovered Van Allen radiation belt
3.2	U.S.	Vanguard I	May 17, 1958	Still in orbit	Revealed earth to be pear-shaped
142	U.S.	Explorer VI	Aug. 7, 1959	Decayed Jul., 1961	First complete televised cloud-cover picture obtained; detected large ring of electrical current circling earth
80	U.S.	Explorer IX	Feb. 16, 1961	Still in orbit	First satellite to be launched with solid-fueled booster Scout and first to be launched from Wallops Island, Va.
132	U.S. and U.K.	Ariel	Apr. 26, 1962	Still in orbit	First international satellite, cosponsored by U.S. and U.K.
440	U.S.	OSO (Orbiting Solar Observatory)	May 7, 1962	Still in orbit	First of space observatory series, conducting thirteen different experiments

Scientific Satellites: Deep Space Probes

A total of nine scientific satellites have been sent on deep space missions. The United States launched five and the U.S.S.R. four. Deep space probes are those scientific satellites which are sent thousands of miles from the earth. Primarily, they are sent toward the Moon, Sun, or Venus. Their instruments gather data similar to the earth-orbiting scientific satellites, but in the farther reaches of space.

Milestone Satellites

Weight, pounds	Country	Satellite	Launched	Status	Special significance
84.4	U.S.	Pioneer I	Oct. 11, 1958	Decayed Oct. 12, 1958	First deep space probe, reaching altitude of 70,700 statute miles; first measurements of interplanetary magnetic field
12.9	U.S.	Pioneer III	Dec. 6, 1958	Decayed Dec. 7, 1958	Reached only 63,580 statute miles, but discovered second radiation belt around earth
800	U.S.S.R.	Lunik I (Mechta)	Jan. 2, 1959	Still in orbit	First satellite to be placed into orbit around sun
13.4	U.S.	Pioneer IV	Mar. 3, 1959	Still in orbit	First U.S. satellite to orbit sun
858.4	U.S.S.R.	Lunik II	Sept. 12, 1959	Decayed Sept. 13, 1959	First satellite to hit moon; contained instruments and Soviet coat of arms
959	U.S.S.R.	Lunik III	Oct. 4, 1959	Decayed Mar., 1960	Photographed and transmitted back to earth first pictures of dark side of moon
94.8	U.S.	Pioneer V	Mar. 11, 1960	Still in orbit	Established record in long-range communications; transmitted 22.5 million miles from earth; now in sun orbit
1,419	U.S.S.R.	Sputnik VIII	Feb. 12, 1961	Decayed Feb. 25, 1961	First demonstration of parking orbit technique, in which one satellite is launched from another already in earth orbit; attempt to send probe near Venus failed, but launching technique successful
727	U.S.	Ranger III	Jan. 26, 1962	Still in orbit	Attempt to impact moon and send back television pictures; mission failed owing to excessive injection velocity on departure from parking orbit; satellite missed moon by 22,862 miles and went on to orbit sun

Weight, pounds	Country	Satellite	Launehed	Status	Special significance
730	U.S.	Ranger IV	Apr. 23, 1962	Decayed Apr. 26, 1962	First time U.S. hit moon; parking orbit technique used

Communications Satellites

Four communications satellites have been placed into orbit around the earth by the United States, none by the U.S.S.R. Two basic approaches to satellite communications are being tested by the United States: active and passive. The passive approach relies on placing a large balloon into orbit with signals bounced off its reflecting surface between two ground stations, much like bouncing signals off the moon's surface. The active approach requires that the satellite be instrumented to actually receive a signal from a ground station and then transmit it on command to another ground station. These satellites can transmit voice conversations, television, data, and facsimile pictures.

Weight, pounds	Country	Satellite*	Launched	Status	Description
150	U.S.	Score	Dec. 18, 1958	Decayed Dec. 31, 1958	Active communications satellite; first time human voice beamed from outer space; message from Gen. Eisenhower received and transmitted back to earth
132	U.S.	Echo I	Aug. 12, 1960	Still in orbit	First passive satellite; voice transmissions successfully transmitted; first television transmission from space; 100-ft-diameter balloon inflated in space
300	U.S.	Courier I-B	Oct. 4, 1960	Still in orbit	More advanced than Score satellite; active communications satellite of "delayed repeater" type; able to simultaneously transmit, receive, and store about 68,000 coded words per minute; no longer functioning
125	U.S. (Owned by AT&T)	Telstar	Jul. 10, 1962	Still in orbit	First privately owned satellite to be orbited; demonstrated first international television transmissions as well as telephone calls, data transmissions, color television and facsimile

* Satellites Score and Courier were aimed primarily at the development of a military communications satellite system and Echo and Telstar at a commercial system. Technical data are freely exchanged among all projects, however.

Navigation Satellites

Five satellites aimed at perfecting an all-weather global navigational system primarily for ships and submarines, but eventually possibly for use by aircraft, have been launched by the United States, none by the U.S.S.R. The responsibility for developing the system, designated Project Transit, rests with the United States Navy. Although it is primarily for use by the Navy, merchant ships of all nationalities will be able to use it.

Weight, pounds	Country	Satellite	Launched	Status	Special significance
265	U.S.	Transit I-B	Apr. 13, 1960	Still in orbit	First navigation satellite
265	U.S.	Transit II-A	Jun. 22, 1960	Still in orbit	First launching of two satellites with one booster, termed "piggyback"; the two satellites were separated in space with each orbiting and transmitting separately
307	U.S.	Transit III-B and LOFTI	Feb. 21, 1961	Decayed Mar. 30, 1961	Third in series, carried two satellites; satellites failed to separate
370	U.S.	Transit IV-A	Jun. 29, 1961	Still in orbit	First satellite to use nuclear power in space; carried three satellites into orbit, but second and third failed to separate
400	U.S.	Transit IV-B	Nov. 15, 1961	Still in orbit	Two satellites placed into orbit; second satellite to use nuclear power

Meteorological Satellites

Five satellites under the Tiros program have been put into orbit by the United States to develop a global meteorological satellite system, none by the U.S.S.R. The satellites have provided thousands of pictures of cloud coverage and aided in hurricane warnings. One Tiros satellite is now kept in orbit at all times although the system is still in its developmental stage.

Weight, pounds	Country	Satellite	Launched	Status*	Special significance
270	U.S.	Tiros I	Apr. 1, 1960	Still in orbit	First Tiros satellite

Meteorological Satellites (continued)

Weight, pound	Country	Satellite	Launched	Status*	Special significance
280	U.S.	Tiros II	Nov. 23, 1960	Still in orbit	Second Tiros satellite
285	U.S.	Tiros III	Jul. 12, 1961	Still in orbit	Third Tiros satellite
285	U.S.	Tiros IV	Feb. 8, 1962	Still in orbit	Fourth Tiros satellite
286	U.S.	Tiros V	Jun. 19, 1962	Still in orbit	Fifth Tiros satellite

* Although all Tiros satellites are still in orbit, only IV and V are providing meteorological data, owing to dead batteries or other reasons.

Other Military Satellites

The United States has four or five military satellite systems other than the Transit navigation series under development, but details on the satellites are classified. Basically, the systems are aimed at collecting intelligence, providing early warning of missile launchings, satellite interception, and possibly other uses. The basic system, Discoverer, is designed to perfect techniques and test equipment. Project Samos is designed to collect intelligence; Project Midas to provide early warning; and Project Saint for satellite inspection and interception. At one time, the military furnished information on the satellites as they were launched. Now, however, no information is made public, and satellites are no longer identified by name.

The last satellite identified in the Discoverer series was the thirty-eighth; however, since that time there have been numerous launchings of military satellites without identity.

Manned Space Flights

Name, weight, and thrust	Date and flight time	Altitude, miles	Distance, miles	Top speed mph	Time of weightlessness
Gagarin in Vostok I; weight 10,460 lb, 800,000 lb thrust	Apr. 12, 1961; 108 min, 1 orbit	187.75	25,000	17,400	89.1 min
Shepard in Freedom 7, weight 4,040 lb, 78,000 lb thrust	May 5, 1961; 15 min, suborbital	116.5	302	5,100	5 min
Grissom in Liberty Bell, weight 4,040 lb, 78,000 lb thrust	Jul. 21, 1961; 16 min, suborbital	118	303	5,280	5 min

Name, weight, and thrust	Date and flight time	Altitude, miles	Distance, miles	Top speed, mph	Time of weight-lessness
Titov in Vostok II, weight 10,430 lb, 800,000 lb thrust	Aug. 6, 1961; 24 hr, 17 orbits	111–160		17,750	24 hr
Glenn in Friendship 7, weight 4,265 lb at launch, 360,000 lb thrust	Feb. 20, 1962; 4 hr 56 min, 3 orbits	100–162	83,450	17,545	4 hr 40 min
Carpenter in Aurora 7, weight 4,244 lb at launch, 360,000 lb thrust	May 24, 1962; 4 hr 56 min, 3 orbits	100–167	76,025	17,546	4 hr 40 min
Nikolayev in Vostok III, weight and thrust not given	Aug. 11, 1962; 94 hr 25 min, 64 orbits	110–141	1,625,000	18,000	About 94 hr
Popovich in Vostok IV, weight and thrust not given	Aug. 12, 1962; 71 hr 3 min, 48 orbits	110–146	1,242,500	18,000	About 70 hr 30 min
Shirra in Sigma 7, weight 3,000 lb, 363,050 lb thrust	Oct. 3, 1962; 9 hr 13 min, 6 orbits	100–176	160,000	17,560	About 9 hr 6 min

QUESTIONS TO CONSIDER

How will the exploration of space contribute to the solution of some of the problems we have been discussing? For example:

How was the universe created?

Does the earth move?

Is there other life in the universe?

Is there an order in nature that man can understand?

What are some of the other scientific questions that may be answered by the exploration of space?

What new knowledge might be gained by an expedition to the moon? Do you think we should try to send a man there before 1970? Is it worth the price?

Do you agree with Rabinowitch that ". . . man's confrontation with the immensity of the universe could become an important step toward the realization of the common aspirations of all mankind"?

SUGGESTIONS FOR FURTHER READING

Berkner, L. V., and Hugh Odishow (eds.): *Science in Space,* McGraw-Hill Book Company, Inc., New York, 1961. Provides a thorough review of the areas and opportunities for important research using space vehicles and suggests what appear to be major areas of emphasis for the national space effort.

Bloomfield, Lincoln P. (ed.): *Outer Space: Prospects for Man and Society,* Prentice-Hall, Inc., Englewood Cliffs, N.J., 1962.

Bulletin of the Atomic Scientists. The special May-June, 1961, issue, "Space Exploration," contains a very interesting series of articles on the scientific knowledge that may result from the exploration of space.

Dubridge, Lee A.: *Introduction to Space,* Columbia University Press, New York, 1960. This short collection of lectures makes pleasant easy reading.

* Hanrahan, James S., and David Bushnell: *Space Biology: The Human Factors in Space Flight,* Basic Books, Inc., Publishers, New York, 1962. This book is a good choice for those who would like to know more about the biological factors that are not included in these readings.

Ley, Willy: *Rockets, Missiles and Space Travel,* The Viking Press, Inc., New York, 1957. A fine general book on the science and technology of space.

* Paperback edition.

Does science create "a gigantic robot driving toward material success," or does it create and foster the very values that we hold most dear? Now, having seen scientists at work and having watched the evolution of some important scientific ideas, we are in a position to evaluate these opposing points of view.

Sullivan

Huxley

INTRODUCTION

"What hopes and fears does the scientific method imply for mankind? I do not think that this is the right way to put that question. Whatever this tool in the hand of man will produce depends entirely on the nature of the goals alive in this mankind. Once these goals exist, the scientific method furnishes means to realize them. Yet it cannot furnish the very goals. The scientific method itself would not have led anywhere, it would not even have been born without a passionate striving for clear understanding." These words from *Out of My Later Years* by Albert Einstein were written in 1950 and are even more pertinent today as the need becomes more urgent for a decision about the role that science should play in our society.

In the last ten parts we have been following the story of man's striving for understanding of the universe. We have seen how some of the great scientists worked out their contributions, have watched ideas grow and change, and have seen how new techniques led through greater accuracy to a new level of understanding. This has been a story of the power of reason, of man's rational approach to his environment. It has been brilliantly successful. But today men are beginning to wonder whether, like most success stories, it will have a happy ending. Many voices are being raised, decrying the effect that science has had on our way of life. They point to the emphasis on materialistic values, to the vast power that science has placed in the hands of people who may misuse it, to the amoral and pragmatic assumption that success is the only criterion. While others insist that these evils derive from a distortion of the aims and the spirit of science, that ". . . we are trying to employ the body of science without its spirit."* They say that the rational approach, which is embodied in scientific method, has fostered and encouraged the very values that we consider most important in Western civilization: independence of thought, freedom of speech, respect for truth, cooperation, justice, and human dignity.

One of the areas in which there is the most striking disagreement is the interpretation of the nature of scientific truth and the role it plays in fostering a regard for truth in society. The pragmatic philosophy, which took its inspiration from science, defines truth as utility. This idea was suggested by the way in which scientific theories change and are replaced by new ideas. In choosing between two scientific theories, the one that works is right. From this concept it is only a short step in thinking to say that whatever can be made to work, by force if necessary, is also right; and with enough power, man can

* Bronowski, p. 433.

even make truth. This thought, Russell points out, lends support to the Marxist view that ". . . what is important is not to understand the world but to change it."

Sharply contrasted with this interpretation is Bronowski's contention that an almost fanatical regard for truth is the motivating force and necessary condition for the practice of science. Although scientific truth is always provisional and changes from time to time, it changes in response to new and more accurate knowledge. Thus it represents a closer and closer approximation to a true understanding of the universe.

The opposition between these different attitudes is a central one in deciding whether science is suited to our democratic goals or whether it leads inevitably to a mechanistic and inhuman type of society. Having watched the evolution of some of the great scientific ideas and studied the role of facts and the nature of scientific truth, we are now in a better position to evaluate these opposing views and to take a backward look at the scientific process as a whole in order to appreciate its strengths and recognize its limitations. Einstein says that science is a tool and to use any tool properly we must understand what it cannot do as well as what it can do. A tool that is excellent for one purpose may be crude and destructive when used for another. Scientific understanding has given us increasing power over nature. Now it is becoming more and more important that we understand science itself so that we may use it effectively to achieve the goals that we desire. Otherwise might it not become ". . . a gigantic robot driving toward material success?"*

There is no doubt that the discoveries of science have greatly increased our material well-being. Some people fear that they may also have increased our emphasis on material things. But materialism as a philosophical concept, like determinism, is a concept that derives its inspiration from a scientific theory and is subject to the same type of evolution as theories themselves. These values, Sullivan points out, are even today undergoing a change in the light of the discoveries of modern physics. Matter and motion are no longer considered the sole realities, and matter itself has become dematerialized. What effect will this new outlook have on our social philosophy? There are, however, other values which derive directly from the scientific method itself, which have remained relatively constant over the years, and which have had a cumulative influence on our ideas and modes of thought. It is these values, as Whitehead expresses it, that have molded "the very springs of action of mankind."

* Margenau, p. 422.

THE LIMITATIONS OF SCIENCE*
by J. W. N. Sullivan (1933)

Scientific method, as we see from the work of its founders, Copernicus, Kepler, Galileo, began by quite consciously and deliberately selecting and abstracting from the total elements of our experience. From the total wealth of impressions received from nature these men fastened upon some only as being suitable for scientific formulation. These were those elements that possess *quantitative* aspects. Between these elements mathematical relations exist, and these men were convinced that mathematics is the key to the universe. It is interesting, in view of its immense importance, to know how they came by this belief, for it was by no means a general persuasion. It was not part of the dominant Aristotelianism of their time. It seems to have been in part due to an innate prejudice, very proper to born mathematicians, and in part to the neo-Platonic philosophy that was prevalent, at that time, in South Europe. This philosophy contained important Pythagorean elements, and gave to the mathematical aspects of the universe a much more exalted position than they occupied in the current Aristotelian outlook. Copernicus became acquainted with this philosophy during his stay in Italy, and also with the fact that some of the ancient Greek philosophers had put forward the hypothesis that the earth was in motion. Being led, in this way, to take the sun as his centre of reference, Copernicus found, as we have already said, that a great harmony was bestowed on the motions of the heavenly bodies. With the incorrect ideas of dynamics prevalent at the time, Copernicus's theory was open to grave objections. As a physical explanation of phenomena it was certainly no better than the Ptolemaic theory. Nevertheless, Copernicus was confident that its superior aesthetic charm would be sufficient to commend it to mathematicians.

This expectation was justified . . . Kepler . . . shows how greatly the aesthetic charm of the new theory appealed to him. To the mind of Kepler, however, the claims of the theory were greatly reinforced by the dignified position it gave to the sun, for Kepler, in a vague and mystical fashion, was a sun-worshipper. . . .

Kepler had a preconceived idea as to the sort of thing the universe is. He did not approach the facts with the docility and lack of prejudice that is proper to the ideal scientific investigator. His deepest conviction was that nature is essentially mathematical, and all his scientific life was an endeavour to discover nature's hidden mathematical harmonies. Galileo, also, had no doubt that mathematics is the one true key to natural phenomena. It was this persuasion that gave these men their criterion for selection amongst the total elements of their experience. They confined their attention to those elements amongst which mathematical relations exist. Bodies, for instance, have for their measurable aspects size, shape, weight, motion. Such other characteristics as they possess were regarded as belonging to a lower order of reality. The real world is the world of mathematical characteristics. In fact, our minds are so constructed, Kepler said, that they can know nothing perfectly except quantities.

With Galileo this separation of the mathematical from the other qualities became a perfectly clear and definite doctrine. Kepler had supposed that the non-mathematical qualities actually did belong to bodies, but that they were somehow less real. Galileo went further than this, and stated that the non-mathematical properties are all entirely subjective. They have no existence at all apart from our senses. Thus colours, sounds, odours and so on exist, as such, wholly in our minds. They are, in reality, motions of some kind or another in the external world, and these motions, impinging on our senses, give rise to these sensations of colour, sound, and so on. It is the mind that peoples the world with the songs of birds, the colours of the sunset, etc. In the absence of mind the universe would be a collection of masses of various sizes, shapes, and weights, drifting, without colour, sound, or odour, through space and time. . . .

We are not here concerned to discuss the validity of this division into primary and secondary qualities, but merely to show the role it played in the formation of the scientific outlook. We may mention, however, that it has been attacked, philosophically, in two ways. It has been denied, on the one hand, that the primary qualities are any less "subjective" than the secondary qualities. Both sets of qualities, it has been argued, depend on the mind, and cannot be conceived as existing apart from the mind. On the other hand, it has been denied that the secondary qualities are any less "objective" than the primary qualities. Each of these arguments denies that primary qualities are any more "real" that secondary qualities, although it may be true that only the primary qualities are susceptible of mathematical treatment. But the Galilean doctrine, which became part of the general scientific outlook, maintains that the primary qualities alone are real— the others are in some sense illusory.

With this reduction of the real world to colourless, soundless, odourless bodies in motion, the notions of space and time underwent a profound change. To the medieval philosophers the temporal process was the transformation of potentiality into actuality. The purpose of everything was to reach a higher state of being, culminating in union with God. The whole of the past, up to the present moment, was the ground already won, as it were. As the process continues, the ground won increases; the future is being drawn into the present. This process goes on until the final culmination is reached, when time stands still. We see how different is this notion of time from the mathematical time, introduced by Galileo. Time, as it appears in science, may be likened to an ever-moving mathematical point. The present moment, which has no finite duration, is merely a boundary point between a vanished past and a non-existent future. Time, conceived in this way, can be represented very simply mathematically as a straight line, successive points on the line representing successive instants of

time. This conception has hitherto proved quite adequate for the needs of science, and has therefore been generally adopted. Philosophically, however, it has brought in its train a host of unsolved puzzles, and there can be little doubt that a new conception of time will have to be formulated. Even science itself is now giving hints that this may be necessary.

With this change in the notion of time comes a corresponding change in the notion of cause. When all things were regarded as moving towards union with God, then union with God was regarded as the final cause of all change. This cause of a process was to be found in the end towards which it tended. The reason why things happened was to be found in the purpose the happening served. With the new notion of time the future, being non-existent, had no influence on present happenings. The cause of anything happening now was to be found in its immediate past. Further, all that really happens are motions— motions of the constituent particles of the bodies forming the real world. And these motions are themselves the products of preceding motions. Galileo also believed that there are "forces," which are revealed by motions, but as to the nature of force he refrained from speculating.

We see that the scientific outlook, as presented by Galileo, constitutes a really amazing revolution in thought. The vivid world of the medievalist, a world shot through with beauty and instinct with purpose, a world having an intimate relation to his own destiny and an intelligible reason for existing in the light of that destiny, is dismissed as an illusion. It has no objective existence. The real world, as revealed by science, is a world of material particles moving, in accordance with mathematical laws, through space and time.

The early creators of science did not assume that this real world was also purposeless. Although God was no longer invoked as the final cause of phenomena, He was still given an important role as the initiator of the whole process. But, having made matter with its properties, He then left the world to develop according to the laws of mathematical necessity. In course of time it came to be considered unnecessary to invoke God even for this purpose, and the way was clear for thorough-going materialism. That this doctrine was made plausible by scientific researches is the greatest possible testimonial to the "humanistic" importance of science. We have seen what the medieval outlook was in essentials. The essentials of the materialistic outlook may be given in the words of Bertrand Russell:

The man is the product of causes which had no prevision of the end they were achieving; that his origin, his growth, his hopes and fears, his loves and beliefs, are but the outcome of accidental collocations of atoms; that no fire, no heroism, no intensity of thought and feeling, can preserve an individual life beyond the grave; that all the labours of the ages, all the devotion, all the inspiration, all the noon-day brightness of human genius, are destined to extinction in the vast death of the solar system, and that the whole temple of Man's achievement must inevitably be buried beneath the debris of a universe in ruins—all these things, if not quite beyond dispute, are yet so nearly certain, that no philosophy which rejects them can hope to stand.

This astonishing change in outlook has been brought about by assuming that, of all the elements of our total experience, only those elements which acquaint us with the quantitative aspects of material phenomena are concerned with the real world. They alone refer to an objective world. None of the other elements of our experience, our perceptions of colour, etc., our response to beauty, our sense of mystic communion with God, has an objective counterpart. All these things, which are ultimately products of the motions of little particles, are illusory in the sense that they do not acquaint us with the nature of objective reality. Our knowledge of the little particles, itself, of course, a product of their motions, is the only result of their activities which is not illusory in this sense. But the materialistic doctrine had not reached this baffling stage of development in the early days of science. Secondary qualities had been classed as subjective, but men continued to argue as if God and His purposes were still part of reality. . . .

We have seen that, so far, the developing scientific outlook owed its main features to the predilections of the mathematician. And the main assumption of the philosophy accompanying this scientific achievement is that the real may be identified with the quantitative. Compared with the fully developed modern scientific outlook, we see that these early men of science were too prone to legislate for the universe on the basis of certain *a priori* assumptions—assumptions which were really expressions of their dominating mathematical predilections. The modern outlook differs from theirs by the more tentative character of its assumptions. Although mathematics has hitherto proved itself by far the most powerful tool for the scientific investigation of nature, it is no longer an article of belief that nature is necessarily mathematical. We now realize that mathematical deductions, however rigorous, must always be checked by experiment. Even Galileo, who strikes us as the most modern of all these early workers, tells us that often he did not consider experimental checks on his mathematical reasoning to be necessary, and undertook the experiments solely in order to convince his opponents. The first perfect fusion of the mathematical with the empirical outlook was accomplished by Isaac Newton.

Newton was not the first, of course, to realize the need of experiment. All his predecessors had realized this to some extent, and such men as Gilbert, Harvey, Boyle, were complete empiricists. But Newton was the first who ideally combined, in his own method, the two ways of approach. This combination was so unusual that none of his contemporaries understood it. It is still unusual in practice, although recognized as the ideal scientific method in theory. Mathematicians are still prone to have what the experimentalists consider an excessive confidence in their mathematical deductions, and the experimentalist sometimes seems to the mathematician to display an unnecessary degree of caution. Newton not only combined the attitude of both types; he also combined their powers. He was not only a supreme mathematician; he was also a great experimentalist.

Newton starts with no *a priori* ideas about the constitution of the world. He does not regard the world as necessarily mathematical, although the successes achieved by his predecessors show that mathematics is a very hopeful tool to employ. He tells us, in the *Principia,* that he has adopted the mathematical method of approach, and that it has led him to certain principles. But, unlike his great predecessors, he does not assume that mathematics is the one key to reality. He says: "I hope the principles here laid down will afford some light either to that or some truer method of philosophy." Having decided, in view of its proved efficacy, to employ the mathematical method, he employs it with certain safeguards. He says: "All the difficulty of philosophy seems to consist in this—from the phenomena of motions to investigate the forces of nature, and then from these forces to demonstrate the other phenomena." Newton's method sounds to us nowadays perfectly obvious. He starts by investigating experimentally a simple group of phenomena and disentangling from them their quantitative relations. He then deduces the mathematical consequences of these relations. These deductions, if correct, will cover the behaviour of phenomena over a wider field. Newton accordingly brings these phenomena to the experimental test, to see if his deductions are confirmed. He has no *a priori* standpoint from which he legislates for nature. Experiment is the final test. . . .

Although Newton did not share the mathematical *a priorism* of his predecessors, he shared their other assumptions. Like them, he dispensed with final causes, and found the cause of a phenomenon in its immediately preceding physical conditions. Also, he proceeded as if science formed a self-enclosed system, that is to say, as if a complete account of phenomena could be given in the terms mass, velocity, force, etc., which science had isolated, and without bringing in such concepts as beauty, purpose, etc., which did not form part of the scientific outlook. It is not possible to say that Newton held these opinions dogmatically, since he himself said that science, in the mathematical form it had assumed, was an adventure, which might have to be replaced by a truer method. But for practical working purposes he certainly made these assumptions, and his immense success caused these assumptions to be unquestioningly accepted by the whole scientific world. Newton also accepted the doctrine of the subjectivity of secondary qualities. He says:

If at any time I speak of light and rays as coloured or endued with colours, I would be understood to speak not philosophically and properly, but grossly, and according to such conceptions as vulgar people in seeing all these experiments would be apt to frame. For the rays to speak properly are not coloured. In them there is nothing else than a certain power and disposition to stir up a sensation of this or that colour. For as sound in a bell or musical string or other sounding body, is nothing but a trembling motion, and in air nothing but that motion propagated from the object, and in the sensorium 'tis a sense of that motion under the form of sound; so colours in the object are nothing but a disposition to reflect this or that sort of rays more copiously than the rest; in the rays they are nothing but their dispositions to propagate this or that motion into the sensorium, and in the sensorium they are sensations of those motions under the forms of colours.

Newton also accepted the idea that the mind is located somewhere in the brain—the sensorium. But he did not, as some of his followers did, regard man as a sort of irrelevant and accidental product of the vast objective mathematical machine that is external nature. Newton believed that nature was designed by God, and he thought that there were countless evidences to prove it. Further, he thought that God every now and then made adjustments to the mathematical machine, in order to keep it going. These theological ideas of Newton's are of no great interest to us, for they did not long survive. Men came to see that it was not logically necessary to postulate a "First Cause," nor did they find it necessary to suppose that the universe must keep going forever. Even if it be true, as Newton supposed, that the universe cannot keep going without divine intervention, we have only to accept the alternative, which scientific men are quite willing to do, that the universe will not keep going.

All this part of Newton's thinking dropped away. What remained was his method, and his fundamental concepts, mass, force, etc. These concepts, as he defined them, came to be regarded as ultimate and exhaustive. It was believed that every phenomenon would prove to be explicable in terms of these concepts. This was, in essentials, the outlook of science for nearly two hundred years, and this assumption still profoundly colours scientific thinking.

What is called the modern "revolution" in science consists in the fact that the Newtonian outlook, which dominated the scientific world for nearly two hundred years, has been found insufficient. It is in process of being replaced by a different outlook, and, although the reconstruction is by no means complete, it is already apparent that the philosophical implications of the new outlook are very different from those of the old one.

Science has become self-conscious and comparatively humble. We are no longer taught that the scientific method of approach is the only valid method of acquiring knowledge about reality. Eminent men of science are insisting, with what seems a strange enthusiasm, on the fact that science gives us but a partial knowledge of reality, and we are no longer required to regard as illusory everything that science finds itself able to ignore. But the enthusiasm with which some men of science preach that science has limitations is not really surprising. For the universe of science, if accepted as the final reality, made of man an entirely accidental by-product of a huge, mindless, purposeless, mathematical machine. And there are men of science sufficiently human to find such a conclusion disconcerting. Even the sturdy Victorians who preached the doctrine betray at times a despairing wish that things were not so. We need not be surprised, therefore, to find that the discovery that science no longer

compels us to believe in our own essential futility is greeted with acclamation, even by some scientific men.

This change in the scientific outlook seems to have taken place suddenly. It is not yet sixty years since Tyndall, in his Belfast Address, claimed that science alone was competent to deal with all man's major problems, and it is not yet twenty years since Bertrand Russell, contemplating the scientific answers, said that "only on the firm foundation of unyielding despair can the soul's habitation henceforth be safely built." But, in truth, so far as these remarks sprang from the conviction that the sole reality is "matter and motion," their foundations had already been undermined. The attempt to represent nature in terms of matter and motion was already breaking down. That attempt was at its most triumphant by the end of the eighteenth century, when Laplace was emboldened to affirm that a sufficiently great mathematician, given the distribution of the particles in the primitive nebula, could predict the whole future history of the world. The fundamental concepts isolated by Newton had proved themselves so adequate in the applications that had been made of them that they were regarded as the key to—everything.

The first indication that the Newtonian concepts were not all-sufficient came when men tried to fashion a mechanical theory of light. This endeavour led to the creation of the ether, the most unsatisfactory and wasteful product of human ingenuity that science has to show. For generations this monster was elaborated. Miracles of mathematical ingenuity were performed in the attempt to account for the properties of light in terms of the Newtonian concepts. The difficulties became ever more heartbreaking until, after the publication of Maxwell's demonstration that light is an electromagnetic phenomenon, they seemed to become insuperable. But the ether, by this time, had become too complicated to be credible. It was not only complicated; it was ugly, and ugliness in scientific theories is a thing no scientific man will tolerate if he can possibly help it. Copernicus was a true judge of the scientific temperament when he showed himself confident that the aesthetic charm of his theory would suffice to enable it to make its way against the insufferably complicated theory of Ptolemy. The construction of ethers became a decaying industry, and largely because there was so little demand for the product. For it had dawned on men of science that there was, after all, nothing sacrosanct about the Newtonian entities. It might be that his list of ultimates, mass, force, and so on, was not exhaustive. Instead of reducing electricity to these terms, it might be better to add it to the list. This was done. After a certain amount of hesitation, and a few last desperate efforts to make electricity mechanical, electricity was added to the list of irreducible elements.

This may seem to have been a simple and obvious step to take, but it was, in reality, of profound significance. For the Newtonian concepts were all of a kind that one seemed to understand intimately. Thus the mass of a body was the quantity of matter in it. Inertia was that familiar property of matter which makes it offer resistance to a push. Force was a notion derived from our experience of muscular effort. Of course, all these concepts, in order to be of use to science, had to be given quantitative expression. They entered our calculations as mathematical symbols. Nevertheless, we supposed that we knew the nature of what we were talking about but in the case of electricity its nature is precisely what we did not know. Attempts to represent it in familiar terms—as a condition of strain in the ether, or what not—had been given up. All that we knew about electricity was the way it affected our measuring instruments. The precise description of this behaviour gave us the mathematical specification of electricity and this, in truth, was all we knew about it.

It is only now, in retrospect, that we can see how very significant a step this was. An entity had been admitted into physics of which we knew nothing but its mathematical structure. Since then other entities have been admitted on the same terms, and it is found that they play precisely the same role in the formation of scientific theories as do the old entities. It has become evident that, so far as the science of physics is concerned, we do not require to know the nature of the entities we discuss, but only their mathematical structure. And, in truth, that is all we do know. It is now realized that this is all the scientific knowledge we have even of the familiar Newtonian entities. Our persuasion that we knew them in some exceptionally intimate manner was an illusion. So far as the science of physics is concerned, the old entities and the new are on the same footing—the only aspects of them with which we are concerned are their mathematical aspects.

With this realization it is no long step to Eddington's position that a knowledge of mathematical structure is the only knowledge that the science of physics can give us. Of all the philosophical speculations which have been hung on to the new physics, this seems to be the most illuminating and the best-founded. It seems to be true that "exact" science is a knowledge of what Eddington calls "pointer-reading"—the readings on an instrument of some kind. We assume, of course, that these readings refer to various qualities of the external world, but all we actually know about these qualities, for the purposes of exact science, is the way they affect our measuring instruments. As Eddington[1] says:

Leaving out all aesthetic, ethical, or spiritual aspects of our environment, we are faced with qualities such as massiveness, substantiality, extension, duration, which are supposed to belong to the domain of physics. In a sense they do belong; but physics is not in a position to handle them directly. The essence of their nature is inscrutable; we may use mental pictures to aid calculations, but no image in the mind can be a replica of that which is not in the mind. And so in its actual procedure physics studies not these inscrutable qualities, but pointer-readings which we can observe. The readings, it is true, reflect the fluctuations of the world-qualities; but our exact knowledge is of the readings, not of the qualities. The former have as much resemblance to the latter as a telephone number has to a subscriber.

[1] "The Domain of Physical Science," essay in *Science, Religion and Reality*.

. . . Science . . . would be confined to re-marking, of the Big Four at Versailles, that they numbered four, to use one of Eddington's illustrations.

The fact that science is confined to a knowledge of structure is obviously of great "humanistic" importance. For it means that the problem of the nature of reality is not pre-judged. We are no longer required to believe that our response to beauty, or the mystic's sense of communion with God, have no objective counterpart. It is perfectly possible that they are, what they have so often been taken to be, clues to the nature of reality. Thus our various experiences are put on a more equal footing, as it were. Our religious aspirations, our perceptions of beauty, may not be the essentially illusory phenomena they were supposed to be. In this new scientific universe even mystics have a right to exist.

The outlook just described may fairly be said to be a result of the new scientific self-consciousness. It is more than a mere speculation. . . .

The humanistic importance of this outlook, in the minds of its authors, seems to be that it leaves us more free to attach the traditional significance to our aesthetic, religious or, compendiously, mystic experiences. It does not actively reinforce any particular religious interpretation of the universe, but it cuts the ground from under those arguments which were held to prove that any such interpretation is necessarily illusory. This it does by showing that science deals with but a partial aspect of reality, and that there is no faintest reason for supposing that everything science ignores is less real than what it accepts. The question as to why science can afford to ignore these other elements has also been answered by Eddington. Why is it that science forms a closed system? Why is it that the elements of reality it ignores never come in to disturb it? The reason is that all the terms of physics are defined in terms of one another. The abstractions with which physics begins are all it ever has to do with. By starting with "point-events," for instance, we can, mathematically, grind out one expres-sion after another until we come to the mathematical specification of "matter." From this specification we can continue until we arrive back at our starting point.

We are doing what the dictionary compiler did when he defined a violin as a small violoncello, and a violoncello as a large violin. But what we have left out of this description is the process by which the mind of the scientist makes contact with one of the entities, namely, matter, which appears in this mathematical chain. It is in virtue of his recognition of this entity that the cycle of definitions has a meaning for him, and gives him genuine information. Similarly, to one who has seen either a violin or a violoncello, the dictionary definition gives information. But as long as the abstractions of physics form a closed cycle it is obviously immune from all disturbance from factors it has neglected.

It is not quite clear that this immunity will endure. The above analysis applies only to "field" physics which, as we have mentioned, covers a very large part of physics. But it does not cover the whole of physics, and the hope that it could be made to do so grows steadily less. In atomic and subatomic phenomena we seem to be faced by a state of affairs that lies right outside the cyclic scheme. The most disconcerting characteristic of this region is that strict causality, a cardinal assumption in science, does not seem to apply. In the motions of individual atoms and electrons there seems to be an element of free-will. Determinism has broken down, and the principle of indeterminacy has taken its place. There is great difference of opinion at present as to whether this is a genuine discovery, or as to whether it is a merely temporary technical device. Einstein, Max Planck, and others, think that strict causality will ultimately be restored in physics, while such men as Eddington and Schrödinger think that determinism must be definitely abandoned.

If the principle of indeterminacy comes to be definitely established, it will obviously have important philosophic consequences. It will make it easier to believe that our intuition of free-will is not an illusion. Moreover, instead of regarding the course of nature as the mere unrolling of a vast machine where every product is predetermined, we shall be freer to attribute to nature a genuine creative advance. And the distinction between the natural and the supernatural, as Eddington has pointed out, would be appreciably diminished. Indeed, if this principle be definitely admitted it will lead to the greatest revolution in scientific thought, and in the philosophy based on it, that has yet occurred.

So far we have dealt with the limitations of science as a method of acquiring knowledge about reality. We have seen that the new self-consciousness of science has resulted in the recognition that its claims were greatly exaggerated. The philosophy based on science had made "matter and motion" the sole reality. In doing so it had dismissed other elements of our experience, those that seemed to us to have the greatest significance and which, finally, made life worth living, as illusory. Science, in spite of all its practical benefits, had seemed to many thoughtful men, perhaps to the majority, to have darkened life. That the new attitude of science, as explained by such men as Eddington and Jeans, has obtained such widespread attention is not, therefore, surprising. It was the metaphysical doctrines that accompanied science that were found so depressing.

This is a striking testimonial to the fact that man is, after all, a philosophizing animal, for the purely practical aspects of science met with almost universal acclamation. And the wonderful vistas opened up by science seem to have been sufficient, in themselves, to inspire many men with optimism and a sense of freedom. Professor Millikan, an eminent man of science, has eloquently expressed this outlook. He points out that our civilization is the first one in history that has not been based on slave labour. This is unquestionably a great gain. Also the amenities of life are now more numerous and more widely distributed than they have ever been before. And we may have every confidence that this advancement will continue. . . .

Our religious impulses cannot be satisfied with anything less than a belief that life has a transcendental significance. And it is precisely this belief that the old philosophy of science made impossible. We conclude, therefore, that the truly significant change in modern science is not to be found in its increased powers to aid man's progress, but in the change in its metaphysical foundations.

The Values of Science

Science is one of those human activities which have undergone a change of purpose or, at least, have come to serve different purposes, in the course of their development. The full wealth of values served by the major human activities are not apparent from the beginning. The cave drawings of primitive man, for example, are justly looked upon as the beginnings of pictorial art in the world. But it is very unlikely that primitive man conceived and executed them for purely artistic motives. They had, it is probable, a religious or magic significance. These representations of animals pierced with arrows were probably designed to secure a good kill on the morrow. And the early essays in science, as we have seen, were undertaken for purely practical reasons. Astronomy originated in the desire to construct a calendar for the benefit of an agricultural community, and the official reason given today for its support by civilized governments is that it aids navigation at sea.

Astronomy later developed into astrology, which had as its purpose the extremely practical one of foretelling human destiny. Biology began as medicine. Chemistry was for a long time alchemy, which was pursued chiefly because it was thought to hold the key to the discovery of the philosophers' stone and the elixir of life. Even mathematics was not always pursued for "its own sake." Certain mathematical relations were sought out for their supposed magical potencies, and others were valued for their usefulness in interpreting cabbalistic writings.

We have seen, however, that the sciences gradually lost their purely practical orientation and came to be pursued for the part they played in meeting man's curiosity about the external world. The "search for truth" became the dominant motive in the prosecution of science. In the development of science it was often found, of course, that answers to questions of purely theoretic interest were also of great practical importance. But these practical applications were, very often, mere by-products of the scientific movement. Thus Maxwell's discovery of the electromagnetic theory of light was not prompted by the desire to provide every home with a wireless set.

Disinterested curiosity has been the great motive power of scientific research. Of the great "values" that condition our activities and make our lives worth living, Goodness, Beauty, Truth, science has been chiefly concerned with truth. But "truth" does not seem to be a simple and unambiguous concept. We hear of "higher truths" and "deeper truths." We may ask then, What sort of truth is science after? In what sense is a true scientific statement true? . . .

It is evident, even from this brief survey of scientific ideas, that a true scientific theory merely means a successful working hypothesis. It is highly probable that all scientific theories are wrong. Those that we accept are verifiable within our present limits of observation. Truth, then, in science, is a pragmatic affair. A good scientific theory accounts for known facts and enables us to predict new ones which are then verified by observation. Thus Newton's theory of gravitation accounted, within the then limits of observation, for the heavenly motions. Subsequently, in the hands of Adams and Leverrier, it enabled the existence of a hitherto unknown planet, Neptune, to be predicted. It did, in fact, lead a very successful career, and is as good an example of a scientific theory as can be found. But sufficiently precise observation showed that it did not perfectly account for the motion of the planet Mercury, and it was then seen that its account of the motions of the other planets only seemed complete because, in those cases, departures from the predicted motions were below the limits of observation.

The way in which scientific men attempted to remedy the defects in Newton's theory is instructive. Their method was to tinker with the details. They tried the effect of making the law of attraction just a little different from the exact inverse square law. They tried the effect of giving gravitation a finite velocity of propagation. But no advance was made in this way. The difficulties could not be met by any extension of the theory. It was not until Einstein introduced an entirely new theory, based on entirely new concepts, that the difficulties were cleared up. We now know that the apparatus of ideas with which Newton started, however deftly used, cannot be made to perform the task for which it was invented. It would probably be impossible to find another instance of a change as fundamental as this in the history of the sciences. Here we have no step by step modification of a theory, but the complete sweeping away of the very foundations of a scientific outlook. The one feature of the Newtonian outlook that is left is the insistence on a mathematical formulation of nature. . . .

The science of physics is concerned only with those aspects of the world which can be treated quantitatively. This imposes an immense restriction on the elements we select from the total elements of our experience. If we go further, and assume that only the elements of which physics treats are real, all the others being in some way illusory, then we are led to some such apparently fantastic conclusion as that "point-events" are the only objective realities. But we may leave the philosophical issue involved here to the philosophers. Science itself does not assume that it alone is concerned with the real. The statements of science are true within the limited region it claims for itself—the region of mathematical structure. If you are curious about the mathematical structure of the material universe, then science can give you information on that point.

In pursuit of its aim science has shown itself to be accommodating and flexible. The science of physics has shown itself willing, at different times, to adopt quite different principles and concepts provided they promised to be helpful in its one great aim of giving a mathematical description of nature. Where principles and concepts have persisted past their time of usefulness, this has been due to the inertia of mental habit. No scientific principles are sacrosanct; no scientific theory is held with religious conviction. Nevertheless, most scientific men believe that there is a final scientific truth about the universe to which succcessive scientific theories ever more closely approximate. But this is an article of faith. Science is still an adventure, and all its "truths" are provisional.

This atmosphere of provisional hypothesis and practically verifiable statements constitutes what has been called the "homely air" of science, and is one of its great charms. Science has adopted the pragmatic criterion of truth, namely, success, and as a result science has been successful. Indeed, it would not be too much to say that, judged by the criterion of general assent and practical efficacy, it is the most successful activity that man has yet hit upon. As Professor Levy[2] says:

Any such criterion of truth may not be one that commends itself to the professional philosopher. It may be that science ignores subtleties that appear vital to academic philosophy, that it skims easily over the surface of reality. The very principle that scientists must leave no differences behind may narrow the range to superficial agreement, and restrict the nature and number of the isolates it may form. Whether or not this be so, science can at any rate look upon itself as a united movement that has left in its wake a body of tested knowledge, while philosophy is still broken up into disunited schools of thought.

The criticism has, indeed, been made that science pays for its success by its superficiality. All the deepest problems of mankind, it has been pointed out, lie outside science. If neither philosophy nor religion can present any such "body of tested knowledge," it is because they have not been content with such cheap victories. There is doubtless some truth in this criticism, and it is probably true that the problems with which science deals are intrinsically inferior in human interest to those dealt with by either philosophy or religion.

[2] *The Universe of Science.*

Nevertheless, the actual atmosphere of science, the manner in which it goes about its work, is quite exceptionally agreeable. It is in the scientific attitude, as much as in the scientific results, that the true value of science is to be found. If the man of science has not aimed high, according to the philosopher, he has at least aimed with a single heart, with a docility in face of the facts, with an impersonal purpose to serve which is not always found amongst our prophets and philosophers, and which it is almost impossible to find elsewhere.

There is probably no other period in history, since modern science began, when the particular values it incorporates were so rarely to be encountered in other human activities. The human tendencies to prize certitude and fear knowledge, to indulge emotion at the expense of reason, were probably always as strong as they are today, but the circumstances of the time did not show them up in so pitiless a light. The mass of men were probably always as impatient of that careful, honest verification that is the very essence of science as they are today, but there was no huge popular press to bear daily witness to the fact.

If we are to judge from what seems the overwhelming evidence provided by such activities as politics, business, finance, we must conclude that the attention and respect accorded to science is directed wholly to its results, and that its spirit is the most unpopular thing in the modern world. Yet it could very reasonably be claimed that it is in its spirit that the chief value of science resides. This can be asserted without abating anything of our claim for the values of its results. Knowledge for the sake of knowledge, as the history of science proves, is an aim with an irresistible fascination for mankind, and which needs no defence. The mere fact that science does, to a great extent, gratify our intellectual curiosity, is a sufficient reason for its existence.

But it must be pointed out that this value is inextricably interwined with another value —the aesthetic value of science. If scientific knowledge consisted of a mere inventory of facts, it might still be interesting and even useful, but it would not be one of the major activities of the mind. It would not be pursued with passion. It could, at best, only exert a somewhat more intensified form of the attraction we feel for a time-table. Indeed, the greatest single testimonial to the fact-gathering power of science, resting, as it does, on centuries of labour and ingenuity, is probably the *Nautical Almanac*—useful, but not entrancing, reading.

For science to have inspired such ardour and devotion in men it is obvious that it must meet one of the deepest needs of human nature. This need manifests itself as the desire for beauty. It is in its aesthetic aspect that the chief charm of science resides. This is true, be it noted, for scientific men themselves. To the majority of laymen, science is valuable chiefly for its practical application. But to all the greatest men of science practical applications have emerged incidentally, as a sort of by-product. This is, perhaps, most obviously true of the men who have created the mathematical sciences. In the work of mathematicians, in particular, the aesthetic motive is very apparent. Many mathematicians have written about their work in a sort of prose poetry, and the satisfactions they get from it seem indistinguishable from those of an artist. The language of aesthetics is never far to seek in the writings of mathematicians. In their frequent references to the "elegance," "beauty," and so on of mathematical theorems they evidently imagine themselves to be appealing to sensibilities that all mathematicians share. Nearly all mathematicians show themselves uneasy in presence of a proof which is inelegant, however convincing—one which "merely commands assent," as Lord Rayleigh said—and, sooner, or later, endeavour to replace it by one which approaches closer to their aesthetic ideal. Some of them, as the late Henri Poincaré, have gone so far as to remark that the actual solution of a problem interests them much less than the beauty of the methods by which they found that solution.

There can be little doubt that it is the aesthetic element in mathematics that has been chiefly responsible for the attention it has received. If mathematics is to be ranked as a science, then it is, of all the sciences, the one most akin to the arts. The history of its development bears out this assertion, for this development, in the main, has been a formal development. Certain branches of mathematics, it is true, have been created to deal with some actual physical problem but for the most part, mathematics has been a remarkably autonomous activity. In this respect it greatly resembles the art of music, whose development also has been so largely conditioned by considerations springing from its own ground, and owing nothing, or almost nothing, to the external world.

But if the aesthetic element is most prominent in mathematics, it is certainly not lacking in the physical sciences. The search for universal laws and comprehensive theories is indubitably a manifestation of the aesthetic impulse. It is sometimes said that scientific men, in their choice of one of two theories that equally well cover the facts, always choose the simpler. But simplicity is, at bottom, an aesthetic criterion. Fresnel said: "Nature takes no account of analytical difficulties." If we interpret this to mean that there is no *a priori* reason to suppose that nature is simple, then the remark is doubtless true. But if nature was not simple, it is very doubtful if science would ever have been pursued. It would still be possible for science, of a kind, to exist. It is within the resources of mathematics to construct a formula for almost any sequence of changes, however arbitrary, but if this formula is of a kind from which no further deductions can be drawn, the whole investigation is regarded as being in a very unsatisfactory state. Where such formulae are used, as they often are in engineering, for example, it is solely for their immediate practical value. The exclusive construction of such empirical formulae is not an object that any scientific man would propose for himself.

It is because nature does seem to exhibit an order we can understand, because diverse phenomena can be grouped under general laws, that the pursuit of science is worth while. If nature did not possess a harmony that was beautiful to contemplate, said Poincaré, science would not be worth pursuing, and life would not be worth living. Life would not be worth living, that is to say, for Poincaré. But although most scientific men would doubtless find a scientifically unaesthetic universe quite worth living in, we may be confident that they would not devote themselves to science. "You are young, I am old," wrote Faraday to Tyndall, "but then our subjects are so glorious, that to work at them rejoices and encourages the feeblest; delights and enchants the strongest." And Einstein, writing on Max Planck, reveals himself when he says:

The longing to see this pre-established harmony is the source of the inexhaustible patience and persistence which we see in Planck's devotion to the most general problems of our science, undeflected by easier or more thankful tasks. I have often heard that colleagues sought to trace this characteristic to an extraordinary will-power; but I believe this to be wholly wrong. The emotional condition which renders possible such achievements is like that of the religious devotee or the lover; the daily striving is dictated by no principle or programme, but arises from an immediate personal need.

When we come to the sciences other than physics, we find the same spirit. Whether it be chemistry, biology, or what not, we find that all the great advances have come from the desire to uncover what Einstein calls "this pre-established harmony." Science can, of course, content many appetites. It enables many more millions of lives to exist than would be possible without it. Also it enables many more millions of lives to be destroyed than was possible without it. It can give us marvels to gape at: the distances of the stars, the minuteness of the atom. It can stun us with figures. It can even help the dividend-hunter in his absorbing quest. But to the great man of science, science is an art, and he himself is an artist. And his creation is not the less a work of art because it is but a faint and imperfect copy of another—of the supreme work of art which is nature itself.

The aesthetic appeal of science is due to the fact that it bestows comprehension. Under the phrase "aesthetic emotion," a number of elements are lumped together, and some only of them are present in any particular case. Our reaction to any great work of art is complex. But one of the most important of our reactions, in many cases, is that our desire for comprehension is gratified. To comprehend a thing is to see it in its relations, to see it in its place within a particular framework.

In the case of a work of literature this framework is provided by the artist's personal vision of life. This is, as it were, the unspoken context within which everything that the artist says acquires a meaning. And our lasting reaction to a work of art, the degree to which it works in us and modifies us when we have forgotten all its details, is dependent on the depth and comprehensiveness of this vision. This is the light which pervades the whole work, and bestows on it such harmony as it possesses, a harmony which lies much deeper than anything the artist may achieve by the technical dovetailing of the elements of his work. The chief function of art is to communicate this vision, and it is the mystery and miracle of art that it can do so.

The comprehension bestowed by a work of art is really the communication of the artist's personal vision. The comprehension bestowed by science is not so obviously personal. Indeed, it is generally supposed to be wholly impersonal. The framework of reference, or "vision," within which a scientific theory exists is the group of fundamental concepts and principles in terms of which that region of nature is to be described. These fundamental terms have often been regarded as necessary and unchangeable. We have seen that they are not. Theoretically they have alternatives, although their adoption at that particular time may seem to have been psychologically inevitable.

The Newtonian concepts, for instance, were the final formulation of ideas which, in a more or less vague state, had been "in the air" for many years. Similarly, the biological theory of evolution has a long history. The Darwinian form of it, in fact, was independently hit upon by two different men. It was, as people say, "bound to come." Nevertheless, even if the impetus of the whole scientific movement was towards the Newtonian concepts, we see now that those concepts were not theoretically necessary. Einstein's utterly dissimilar way of looking at the same group of phenomena was a theoretically possible alternative. Not that Einstein could have produced his theory if he had lived at Newton's time. In the absence of the necessary mathematical technique that would have been impossible. In Newton's time it is probable that Einstein would either have developed Newton's theory or else have been the impotent prey of intuitions that he could not formulate. But this would have been merely an accident of history. Theoretically, the Newtonian concepts had alternatives. They were chosen although, as a mere matter of psychology, it may be there was in fact no choice.

Einstein's theory is perhaps the clearest instance that can be given of our assertion that even a scientific theory may possess a personal element. Einstein's theory is so original that it is very difficult, even after the event, to provide it with an ancestry. It was not in the least a natural culmination of the ideas that preceded it. It was a bolt from the blue. The extraordinary lack of comprehension with which the scientific world at first greeted it was due not to its technical difficulties, but to the unfamiliarity of the outlook it assumed. It seemed to be the product of an alien mind.

We could say of this theory what Einstein said of some of the work of Gauss, that, if its author had not thought of it, there is no reason to suppose that it would ever have been thought of. Science provides few instances of theories as original as this—indeed, perhaps there is no other scientific theory so intensely original as Einstein's theory. But there are other scientific theories which have a strong element of originality. Maxwell's electromagnetic theory, for example, was a very lonely achievement.

And it is precisely this quality of originality which is the personal element in science. The majority of men of science, including

some of the greatest, impress us as journeying along the highroad. Newton, for instance, revealed nothing totally unsuspected by the best of his contemporaries. It is as if many converging lines of thought came to a focus in him. Newton's great quality was not a bewildering originality, but a bewildering and unequalled mastery of his material. Other men could see his problems; only Newton could solve them.

But the men who strike us as having branched away from the highroad, and having thereby given science an entirely new direction, have put to themselves entirely new problems. It is here, of course, that the personal element in the creation of a scientific theory is most clearly revealed. The history of science is not the history of some sort of automatic development. The actual course that science has pursued depends very largely on the types of mind which, as historical accident, happen to have risen to the level of genius at favourable instants.

It is often said that the essential distinction between science and art consists in the fact that science makes appeal to universal assent, whereas art does not. A scientific statement, we are told, is open to verification by anybody, whereas a work of art appeals only to people with certain sensibilities. A work of music means nothing to a man who is tonedeaf. Science deals with a "public" world, whereas art is concerned with a private world. A colour-blind man, for instance, would not appreciate painting, whereas a man born blind could master the whole theory of optics.

What are the primary judgments to which, according to this theory, science appeals? So far as the science of physics is concerned, they are judgments about the indications of measuring instruments. We have to say, for example, that a pointer coincides with a certain mark on a scale. We have to agree, also, about number judgments. We have to agree that an urn contains twelve balls, and not eleven or thirteen. These are the only judgments, we are told, that are involved in science, and about these we can secure unanimity. Two observers, with different colour perceptions, might disagree as to the colour of some particular bright line in the spectrum, but they would both agree as to its position on a numbered scale, that is, they would agree about its wave-length. And it is its wave-length, not its colour, that is dealt with by science. In any scientific statement where a colour is mentioned, the name of the colour could be deleted, and a figure for a wave-length substituted, without harming anything in the statement. The same is true about any scientific statement which seems to appeal to judgments about which men might differ. Two men might disagree as to whether one note was the octave of another, judging by sound only, but they would agree as to whether its rate of vibration, measured on a scale, was or was not double that of the other. And that, we are told, is all that is necessary for the purposes of science.

Now we may admit that universal agreement may be obtained about such things as the number of objects in a collection or coincidences in space without therefore concluding that science is potentially capable of securing universal assent. For science consists of a great deal more than such elementary judgments. The chief thing about science is its theories, and it is surely obvious that not all men are capable of assenting to its theories. A man may agree that a star crosses a wire in a transit telescope at the moment when the hands of a clock mark a certain time, but the theorem which enabled the astronomer to predict that occurrence may be for ever inaccessible to him. As a matter of fact, the upholders of this theory, which professes to be so realistic in the sense of dispensing with all "subjective" elements, are not realistic at all.

A man may be blind, deaf, dumb, and paralysed—that, they cheerfully maintain, does not matter at all. But he must be a very fine reasoner. If we adopt this criterion that the truth of science is to be decided by a unanimous vote, then we must point out this unanimity, when it comes to actual science, and is not confined to such questions as the number of matches in a match-box, cannot be obtained. A large section of mankind, perhaps the majority, are congenitally incapable

of understanding Einstein's theory, for example. If such people are to be ruled out as not affecting the unanimous vote, on what ground is the poet to be differentiated who rules out all those people who are insensitive to poetry? In both cases the claim could be made that if all people possessed the requisite sensibilities or faculties, the vote would be unanimous. And this is, in fact, the implied claim of those who preach the complete objectivity of science. For their criterion for objectivity is merely universal assent.

But even if we abandon the criterion of universal assent, and grant votes only to those capable of forming a judgment, we still do not get unanimity. It is notorious that theories that have been found convincing by some scientific men have been found unconvincing by others. Faraday, for instance, was opposed to the atomic theory at a time when, in the judgment of most of his contemporaries, it was well established.

At the present day we have an interesting example of the influence of purely "subjective" factors in the creation of scientific theories in the methods adopted by Einstein and Eddington respectively in their attempts to reduce the laws of electromagnetism to geometry. Judged by the scientific criterion of accounting for phenomena there seems nothing to choose between them. But Einstein has said that he dislikes Eddington's theory, although he is unable to disprove it, and Eddington has said of Einstein's theory that it is a matter of taste. Here we are in a region where the ordinary "objective" criteria fail us. Our attitude towards these theories seems to depend on considerations which are, at bottom, aesthetic.

Other instances could be given, particularly from present-day quantum theory, where a chain of reasoning which is found quite convincing by one authority is found unconvincing by another. And the different judgments seem to depend on considerations which the authorities concerned find too elusive for expression. This dilemma sometimes becomes so acute, Professor Levy tells us, that a scientific society, in view of the conflicting reports of its referees, cannot decide whether to publish a certain paper or not. And Poincaré has told us that even in pure mathematics, where reason, one would think, is most pure and undefiled, a proof which is quite satisfactory to one mathematician is often not at all satisfactory to another. Indeed, Poincaré was led to divide mathematicians into psychological types, and to point out that a kind of reasoning which would convince one type would never convince another. These differences, in his opinion, are fundamental, and play a great part in the actual construction of science.

In view of these facts it is obviously misleading to present science as differing fundamentally from the arts by its "impersonal" character. There is no absolute difference here, but only a difference of degree. Science is less personal than the arts, but it is a mistake to suppose that it is wholly impersonal. The reason for the difference lies in the fact that beauty and truth, in spite of Keats, are commonly distinguished. A work of art aims more consciously and deliberately at beauty than does a scientific theory. There are some works of art, indeed, where it is difficult to see that the criterion of truthfulness has any relevance at all. This is most obviously the case with some musical works. There are other works of art—e.g. in literature and painting—where truthfulness is relevant. And while it is probably true that no scientific theory has been constructed in complete independence of aesthetic considerations, it is nevertheless true that these alone are not sufficient.

Perhaps this is as far as the discussion can be carried on the common-sense level. A further analysis would have to distinguish between, for example, the "truth" of mathematics and the "truth" of physics. And we would have to question the complete independence of the quality called "beauty." We have already likened mathematics to music, and it could be objected that, since a mathematical development must be logical, any aesthetic charm it possesses must be incidental. But a musical development also obeys laws; it is not capricious. And although these laws are doubtless more various than those

of logic and have not yet been isolated and given names, they nevertheless exist.

And in neither case is the beauty of the development some kind of extraneous quality mysteriously added on. It is in virtue of the fact that the development does obey laws that it is beautiful. Here, at any rate, we see some sense in Keats' remark that Truth is Beauty. When we come to an activity, such as physics, or a great part of literature, which is concerned with matters of fact, the notion of truth becomes somewhat different. Here we have the criterion of correspondence with an external world which need not have been as it is. But here, again, the truth is beautiful. Everywhere we encounter what Einstein calls "pre-established harmonies," and since the discovery and revelation of such harmonies is the concern, in their different regions, of both the artist and the man of science, we see once again that there is no essential distinction between the sciences and the arts.

In discussing the aesthetic aspect of science we have been discussing, perhaps at too great length, an aspect which appeals to the layman hardly at all. The layman is impressed, naturally enough, by the magnificent panorama of nature that science spreads before him, but the beauty of scientific theories is perhaps a consideration that appeals only to the scientific man.

The matter is different, however, when we come to what may be called the *moral* values incorporated in science. These have always been held, theoretically, in the greatest respect, especially the chief of them, namely, disinterested passion for the truth. But, as we have said, if we are to judge by its comparative rarity in the other activities of mankind, it is the most unpopular of virtues. How does it come about, then, that it plays so dominant a role in science? The first, and most obvious, reason is that science is an activity where success is not possible on any other terms. A business man, by concealment and misrepresentation, may become rich, that is, he may, by his standards, achieve success. A politician who was impatient with misleading catchwords, who really tried to think things out, would probably find his "usefulness" destroyed, since he might become incapable even of simulating that degree of conviction and moral fervour which is necessary to sway large audiences. And an advocate whose speeches should reflect the purely scientific attitude, giving every fact its true weight, would not be likely to have a very successful career. Even those advocates who, we are told, never embrace a cause of whose justice they are not convinced, are hardly scientific, since they evidently have an extraordinary capacity for arriving at definite conclusions on matters which are obviously debatable.

Science is the activity where truthfulness is most obviously an essential condition for success. Its success, in fact, is measured by its truthfulness. Of hardly any other human activity can this be said. In nearly everything else truth is a means and not an end. And if it turns out to be an unsatisfactory means, it is quite natural that it should be replaced by something else. But a scientific man who should misrepresent his observations, or deliberately concoct arguments in order to reach false conclusions, would merely be stultifying himself as a scientific man. He would not be prosecuting science. An advertisement may tell lies, but then telling the truth is not its object. Its object is to sell the stuff, which is an entirely different object. This is not to say, of course, that scientific men invariably tell the truth, or try to, even about their science. They have been known to lie, but they did not lie in order to serve science but, usually, religious or anti-religious prejudices. They were aiming at a different form of "success."

Such cases are, as it happens, very rare. Perhaps the reason is to be found in the fact that the success thereby achieved is very short-lived. Always, the experiments are repeated, or the reasoning checked. The rigorous criticism, the complete lack of indulgence, that is shown by the scientific world, is one of its most agreeable characteristics. Its one simple but devastating criterion, "Is it true?" is perhaps the chief characteristic that makes it seem such an oasis for the spirit in the modern world.

One reason, then, for the embodiment of the disinterested passion for truth in science is that the activity is meaningless without it. But how did men come to pursue an object which can only be reached by what seems to be generally considered as a very painful discipline? The answer is that, owing to the nature of the subject-matter of science, the discipline was not felt to be painful. On all matters where their passions are strongly engaged, men prize certitude and fear knowledge. From certitude can come purpose and a feeling of strength. It breeds courage and action, and is a ready means of ensuring that most desired of all things, an increased sense of vitality. Only the man of strong convictions can be a popular leader of mankind. For most men in most matters, whether it be the justice of a war, the rightness of a political creed, the guilt of a criminal, the wholesomeness of apples, certitude, in the entire absence of adequate evidence, is easily arrived at and passionately welcomed.

The scientific insistence on evidence, and the scientific absence of generosity in drawing conclusions from evidence, are resented in these matters. The scientific attitude, it is felt, with its promise of a long and very probably inconclusive investigation, would merely dam up the emotions that are clamouring for an outlet. But the matters with which science has hitherto been chiefly concerned are comparatively indifferent to us. For that reason science has been so successful. When Galileo investigated the law governing the motion of falling bodies, we cannot imagine, that he cared in the least what the law would turn out to be. He could search for the truth with a single mind because none of his emotions could be outraged by the result. Similarly Newton's demonstration of the law of inverse squares roused no horror anywhere. Nobody had a strong emotional preference for the law of inverse cubes.

Towards most of the results of science we are indifferent. Their charm lies in the fact that they illustrate a harmony, but the results, in themselves, are matters of indifference. Any other results would do, provided they illustrated an equally beautiful harmony. The empirical fact that the velocity of light is nearer to 186,000 miles per second than it is to double that figure, excites no particular interest. But the fact that there must be an unsurpassable critical velocity in the sort of non-Euclidean universe we live in, is a matter of great interest.

Our reaction to most scientific facts is one of indifference, and our reaction to most scientific theories is one of purely aesthetic appreciation. But when a scientific theory has a philosophic, religious, or briefly, a "human" interest, we find at once that we are no longer content with our role of the disinterested seeker after truth. The opposition encountered by the Copernican theory and the Darwinian theory gives sufficient evidence of this. The splendid moral integrity manifested in scientific work, therefore, is due very largely to the nature of scientific material. It shows us the height to which man can rise, provided that a part only of his nature is involved. Science is truthful because it has practically no temptation to be anything else. In his work the scientific man is an artist, and his moral standard is superb, but the value of his example to the rest of mankind is limited by the fact that, in his work, the scientific man is not completely a man.

SCIENCE, LIBERTY AND PEACE*
by Aldous Huxley (1946)

"If the arrangement of society is bad (as ours is), and a small number of people have power over the majority and oppress it, every victory over Nature will inevitably serve only to increase that power and that oppression. This is what is actually happening."

It is nearly half a century since Tolstoy wrote these words, and what was happening then has gone on happening ever since. Science and technology have made notable advances in the intervening years—and so has the centralization of political and economic power, so have oligarchy and despotism. It need hardly be added that science is not the only causative factor involved in this process. No social evil can possibly have only one cause. Hence the difficulty, in any given case, of finding a complete cure. All that is being maintained here is that progressive science is one of the causative factors involved in the progressive decline of liberty and the progressive centralization of power, which have occurred during the twentieth century. . . .

* From Aldous Huxley, *Science, Liberty and Peace*. Copyright 1946 by Aldous Huxley. Reprinted by permission of Harper & Row, Publishers, New York, and Chatto & Windus, Ltd., London.

On many fronts nature had been conquered; but as Tolstoy foresaw, man and his liberties have sustained a succession of defeats. . . .

The continuous advance of science and technology has profoundly affected the prevailing mental climate. The basic postulates of thought have been changed, so that what to our fathers seemed obviously true and important strikes us as either false or negligible and beside the point. Let us consider a few of the more significant of these changes and their effects upon the social and political life of our times.

a) Unlike art, science is genuinely progressive. Achievement in the fields of research and technology is cumulative; each generation begins at the point where its predecessor left off. Furthermore, the results of disinterested research were from the first applied in such a way that the upper and middle classes of all industrialized societies found themselves becoming steadily richer and richer. It was, therefore, only to be expected that the professional thinkers who sprang from these classes, and who were familiar with the methods and achievements of science, should have based upon the facts of technological and economic progress a general theory of human life. The world, they affirmed, was becoming materially, intellectually and morally better and better, and this amelioration was in some way inevitable. The theory of progress—a theory that soon became a dogma, indeed an axiom of popular thought—was novel and, from an orthodox Christian point of view, heretical. For orthodoxy, man was a fallen being. Humanity if not actively deteriorating, was statically bad, with a badness which only grace in co-operation with the individual's free will could possibly mitigate. In illustration of this, let us consider how the thirteenth century was regarded by those who lived through it, and how it is regarded by modern historians. For the latter it seems one of the most glorious periods in European history; the former were unanimous (as Professor Coulton has shown) in regarding it as an age of peculiar wickedness and manifest degeneracy. Even in the age of Queen Elizabeth thoughtful men were still talking of humanity's decline. It was not until the late seventeenth century (the age of the rise of modern science) that the note of bumptious self-congratulation began to be sounded, not until the eighteenth and nineteenth centuries that the dogma of inevitable progress became an unquestioned article of popular faith.

The belief in all-round progress is based upon the wishful dream that one can get something for nothing. Its underlying assumption is that gains in one field do not have to be paid for by losses in other fields. For the ancient Greeks, *hubris*, or overweening insolence, whether directed against the gods, or one's fellow men, or nature, was sure to be followed, sooner or later, in one way or another, by avenging Nemesis. Unlike the Greeks, we of the twentieth century believe that we can be insolent with impunity.

So intense is our faith in the dogma of inevitable progress that it has survived two world wars and still remains flourishing in spite of totalitarianism and the revival of slavery, concentration camps and saturation bombing.

Faith in progress has affected contemporary political life by reviving and popularizing, in an up-to-date, pseudo-scientific and this-worldly form, the old Jewish and Christian apocalypticism. A glorious destiny awaits mankind, a coming Golden Age, in which more ingenious gadgets, more grandiose plans and more elaborate social institutions, will somehow have created a race of better and brighter human beings. Man's Final End is not in the eternal timeless Now, but in a not too distant utopian future. In order to secure the peace and happiness of their great-great-grandchildren, the masses ought to accept and their rulers need feel no qualms in imposing, any amount of war and slavery, of suffering and moral evil, in the present. It is a highly significant fact that all modern dictators, whether of the Right or of the Left, talk incessantly about the golden Future, and justify the most atrocious acts here and now, on the ground that they are means to that glorious end. But the one thing we all know about the future is that we are completely ignorant of what is going to happen, and that what does in fact happen is often very different from what we anticipated. Consequently any faith based upon hypothetical occurrences a long time hence must always, in the very nature of things, be hopelessly unrealistic. In practice, faith in the bigger and better future is one of the most potent enemies to present liberty; for rulers feel themselves justified in imposing the most monstrous tyrannies on their subjects for the sake of the wholly imaginary fruits which these tyrannies are expected (only an implicit faith in progress can say why) to bear some time, let us say, in the twenty-first or twenty-second century.

b) As theory, pure science is concerned with the reduction of diversity to identity. As a praxis, scientific research proceeds by simplification. These habits of scientific thought and action have, to a certain extent, been carried over into the theory and practice of contemporary politics. Where a centralized authority undertakes to make plans for an entire society, it is compelled by the bewildering complexity of the given facts to follow the example of the scientific experimenter, who arbitrarily simplifies his problem in order to make it manageable. In the laboratory this is a sound and entirely justifiable procedure. But when applied to the problems of human society, the process of simplification is a process, inevitably, of restraint and regimentation, of curtailment of liberty and denial of individual rights. This reduction of human diversity to a military and quasi-mechanical identity is achieved by propaganda, by legal enactments and, if necessary, by brute force—by the imprisonment, exile or liquidation of those persons, or those classes, who persist in their perverse desire to remain themselves and are obstinate in their reluctance to conform to the pattern which the political and economic bosses find it, at the moment, most convenient to impose. Philosophically, this ironing out of individual idiosyncrasies is held to be respectable because it is analogous to what is done by scientists, when they arbitrarily simplify an all too complex reality, so as to make nature comprehensible in terms of a few general laws. A highly organized and regimented society, whose members exhibit a minimum of personal peculiarities, and whose collective behavior is governed by a single master plan imposed from above, is felt by the planners and even (such is the power of propaganda) by the planees to be more "scientific," and therefore better, than a society of independent, freely co-operating and self-governing individuals.

c) The first step in this simplification of reality, without which (since human minds are finite and nature is infinite) scientific thought and action would be impossible, is a process of abstraction. Confronted by the data of experience, men of science begin by leaving out of account all those aspects of the facts which do not lend themselves to measurement and to explanation in terms of antecedent causes rather than of purpose, intention and values. Pragmatically they are justified in acting in this odd and extremely arbitrary way; for by concentrating exclusively on the measurable aspects of such elements of experience as can be explained in terms of a causal system they have been able to achieve a great and ever increasing control over the energies of nature. But power is not the same thing as insight and, as a representation of reality, the scientific picture of the world is inadequate, for the simple reason that science does not even profess to deal with experience as a whole, but only with certain aspects of it in certain contexts. All this is quite clearly understood by the more philosophically minded men of science. But unfortunately some scientists, many technicians and most consumers of gadgets have lacked the time and the inclination to examine the philosophical foundations and background of the sciences. Consequently they tend to accept the world picture implicit in the theories of science as a complete and exhaustive account of reality; they tend to regard those aspects of experience, which scientists leave out of account, because they are incompetent to deal with them, as being somehow less real than the aspects which science has arbitrarily chosen to abstract from out of the infinitely rich totality of given facts. Because of the prestige of science as a source of power, and because of the general neglect of philosophy, the popular *Weltanschauung* of our times contains a large element of what may be called "nothing-but" thinking. Human beings, it is more or less tacitly assumed, are nothing but bodies, animals, even machines; the only really real elements of reality are matter and energy in their measurable aspects; values are nothing but illusions that have somehow got themselves mixed up with our experience of the world; mental happenings are nothing but epiphenomena, produced by and entirely dependent upon physiology; spirituality is nothing but wish fulfillment and misdirected sex; and so on. The political consequences of this "nothing-but" philosophy are clearly apparent in that widespread indifference to the values of human personality and human life, which are so characteristic of the present age.

In Western Culture science is a pragmatic pursuit; it is the discovery of useful facts, whatever they may be. Its virtue lies in the honesty and accuracy with which these facts are gathered and in the completeness of the pattern that, as part of formulated knowledge, they finally compose. This factualness of science makes it blind to the differences between the trivial and the significant, the odious and the exquisite, the good and the bad; indeed the identification of science with the realm of discoverable fact has largely removed it from most basic human concerns and made it into a gigantic robot driving toward material progress.

Henry Margenau
Perspectives of Science (1959)*

* From Henry Margenau, "Perspectives of Science," *The Key Reporter*, Autumn, 1959, copyright United Chapters of Phi Beta Kappa, Washington, D.C. Reprinted by permission.

THE IMPACT OF SCIENCE ON SOCIETY†
by Bertrand Russell (1951)

Man has existed for about a million years. He has possessed writing for about 6,000 years, agriculture somewhat longer, but perhaps not much longer. Science, as a dominant factor in determining the beliefs of educated men, has existed for about 300 years; as a source of economic technique, for about 150 years. In this brief period it has proved itself an incredibly powerful revolutionary force. When we consider how recently it has risen to power, we find ourselves forced to believe that we are at the very beginning of its work in transforming human life. What its future effects will be is a matter of conjecture, but possibly a study of its effects hitherto may make the conjecture a little less hazardous.

The effects of science are of various very different kinds. There are direct intellectual effects: the dispelling of many traditional beliefs, and the adoption of others suggested by the success of scientific method. Then there are effects on technique in industry and war. Then, chiefly as a consequence of new techniques, there are profound changes in social organization which are gradually bringing about corresponding political changes. Finally, as a result of the new control over the environment which scientific knowledge has conferred, a new philosophy is growing

† From Bertrand Russell, *The Impact of Science on Society*. Copyright 1951 and 1952 by Bertrand Russell. Reprinted by permission of Simon and Schuster, Inc., New York.

up, involving a changed conception of man's place in the universe.

I shall deal successively with these aspects of the effects of science on human life. First I shall recount its purely intellectual effect as a solvent of unfounded traditional beliefs, such as witchcraft. Next, I shall consider scientific technique, especially since the industrial revolution. Last, I shall set forth the philosophy which is being suggested by the triumphs of science, and shall contend that this philosophy, if unchecked, may inspire a form of unwisdom from which disastrous consequences may result. . . .

It is hardly till the time of Lister and Pasteur that medicine can be said to have become scientific. The diminution of human suffering owing to the advances in medicine is beyond all calculation.

Out of the work of the great men of the seventeenth century a new outlook on the world was developed, and it was this outlook, not specific arguments, which brought about the decay of the belief in portents, witchcraft, demoniacal possession, and so forth. I think, there were three ingredients in the scientific outlook of the eighteenth century that were specially important:

(1) Statements of fact should be based on observation, not on unsupported authority.

(2) The inanimate world is a self-acting, self-perpetuating system, in which all changes conform to natural laws.

(3) The earth is not the center of the universe, and probably Man is not its purpose (if any); moreover, "purpose" is a concept which is scientifically useless.

These items make up what is called the "mechanistic outlook," which clergymen denounce. It led to the cessation of persecution and to a generally humane attitude. It is now less accepted than it was, and persecution has revived. To those who regard its effects as morally pernicious, I commend attention to these facts.

Something must be said about each of the above ingredients of the mechanistic outlook.

(1) *Observation versus Authority*. To modern educated people, it seems obvious that matters of fact are to be ascertained by observation, not by consulting ancient authorities. But this is an entirely modern conception, which hardly existed before the seventeenth century. Aristotle maintained that women have fewer teeth than men; although he was twice married, it never occurred to him to verify this statement by examining his wives' mouths. He said also that children will be healthier if conceived when the wind is in the north. One gathers that the two Mrs. Aristotles both had to run out and look at the weathercock every evening before going to bed. He states that a man bitten by a mad dog will not go mad, but any other animal will (*Hist. An.* 704a); that the bite of the shrewmouse is dangerous to horses, especially if the mouse is pregnant (ibid., 604b); that elephants suffering from insomnia can be cured by rubbing their shoulders with salt, olive oil, and warm water (ibid., 605a); and so on and so on. Nevertheless, classical dons, who have never observed any animal except the cat and the dog, continue to praise Aristotle for his fidelity to observation.

The conquest of the East by Alexander caused an immense influx of superstition into the Hellenistic world. This was particularly notable as regards astrology, which almost all later pagans believed in. The Church condemned it, not on scientific grounds, but because it implied subjection to Fate. There is, however, in St. Augustine, a scientific argument against astrology quoted from one of the rare pagan skeptics. The argument is that twins often have very different careers, which they ought not to have if astrology were true.

At the time of the Renaissance, belief in astrology became a mark of the free thinker: it must be true, he thought, because the Church condemned it. Free thinkers were not yet any more scientific than their opponents in the matter of appeal to observable facts.

Most of us still believe many things that in fact have no basis except in the assertions of the ancients. I was always told that ostriches eat nails, and, though I wondered how they found them in the Bush, it did not occur to me to doubt the story. At last I discovered that it comes from Pliny, and has no truth whatever. . . .

When Galileo's telescope revealed Jupiter's moons, the orthodox refused to look through it, because they knew there could not be such bodies, and therefore the telescope must be deceptive.

Respect for observation as opposed to tradition is difficult and (one might almost say) contrary to human nature. Science insists upon it, and this insistence was the source of the most desperate battles between science and authority. There are still a great many respects in which the lesson has not been learned. Few people can be convinced that an obnoxious habit—e.g. exhibitionism—cannot be cured by punishment. It is pleasant to punish those who shock us, and we do not like to admit that indulgence in this pleasure is not always socially desirable.

(2) *The Autonomy of the Physical World*. Perhaps the most powerful solvent of the prescientific outlook has been the first law of motion, which the world owes to Galileo, though to some extent he was anticipated by Leonardo da Vinci.

The first law of motion says that a body which is moving will go on moving in the same direction with the same velocity until something stops it. Before Galileo it had been thought that a lifeless body will not move of itself, and if it is in motion it will gradually come to rest. Only living beings, it was thought, could move without help of some external agency. Aristotle thought that the heavenly bodies were pushed by gods. Here on earth, animals can set themselves in motion and can cause motion in dead matter. There are, it was conceded, certain kinds of motion which are "natural" to dead matter: earth and water naturally move downwards, air and fire upwards; but beyond these simple "natural" motions everything depends upon impulsion from the souls of living beings.

So long as this view prevailed, physics as an independent science was impossible, since the physical world was thought to be not causally self-contained. But Galileo and Newton between them proved that all the movements of the planets, and of dead matter on the earth, proceed according to the laws of physics, and once started, will continue indefinitely. There is no need of mind in this process. Newton still thought that a Creator was necessary to get the process going, but that after that He left it to work according to its own laws.

Descartes held that not only dead matter, but the bodies of animals also, are wholly governed by the laws of physics. Probably only theology restrained him from saying the same of human bodies. In the eighteenth century French free thinkers took this further step. In their view, the relation of mind and matter was the antithesis of what Aristotle and the scholastics had supposed. For Aristotle, first causes were always mental, as when an engine driver starts a freight train moving and the impulsion communicates itself from truck to truck. Eighteenth-century materialists, on the contrary, considered all causes material, and thought of mental occurrences as inoperative by-products.

(3) *The Dethronement of "Purpose."* Aristotle maintained that causes are of four kinds; modern science admits only one of the four. Two of Aristotle's four need not concern us; the two that do concern us are the "efficient" and the "final" cause. The "efficient" cause is what we should call simply "the cause"; the "final" cause is the

purpose. In human affairs this distinction has validity. Suppose you found a restaurant at the top of a mountain. The "efficient" cause is the carrying up of the materials and the arranging of them in the pattern of a house. The "final" cause is to satisfy the hunger and thirst of tourists. In human affairs, the question "why?" is more naturally answered, as a rule, by assigning the final cause than by setting out the efficient cause. If you ask "why is there a restaurant here?" the natural answer is "because many hungry and thirsty people come this way." But the answer by final cause is only appropriate where human volitions are involved. If you ask "why do many people die of cancer?" you will get no clear answer, but the answer you want is one assigning the efficient cause.

This ambiguity in the word "why" led Aristotle to his distinction of efficient and final causes. He thought—and many people still think—that both kinds are to be found everywhere: whatever exists may be explained, on the one hand, by the antecedent events that have produced it, and, on the other hand, by the purpose that it serves. But although it is still open to the philosopher or theologian to hold that everything has a "purpose," it has been found that "purpose" is not a useful concept when we are in search of scientific laws. We are told in the Bible that the moon was made to give light by night. But men of science, however pious, do not regard this as a scientific explanation of the origin of the moon. Or, to revert to the question about cancer, a man of science may believe, in his private capacity, that cancer is sent as a punishment for our sins, but *qua* man of science he must ignore this point of view. We know of "purpose" in human affairs, and we may suppose that there are cosmic purposes, but in science it is the past that determines the future, not the future the past. "Final" causes, therefore, do not occur in the scientific account of the world. . . .

(4) *Man's Place in the Universe.* The effect of science upon our view of man's place in the universe has been of two opposite kinds; it has at once degraded and exalted him. It has degraded him from the standpoint

of contemplation, and exalted him from that of action. The latter effect has gradually come to outweigh the former, but both have been important. I will begin with the contemplative effect.

To get this effect with its full impact, you should read simultaneously Dante's *Divine Comedy* and Hubble on the *Realm of the Nebulae*—in each case with active imagination and with full receptiveness to the cosmos that they portray. In Dante, the earth is the center of the universe; there are ten concentric spheres, all revolving about the earth; the wicked, after death, are punished at the center of the earth; the comparatively virtuous are purged on the Mount of Purgatory at the antipodes of Jerusalem; the good, when purged, enjoy eternal bliss in one or other of the spheres, according to the degree of their merit. The universe is tidy and small: Dante visits all the spheres in the course of twenty-four hours. Everything is contrived in relation to man: to punish sin and reward virtue. There are no mysteries, no abysses, no secrets; the whole thing is like a child's doll's house, with people as the dolls. But although the people were dolls they were important because they interested the Owner of the doll's house.

The modern universe is a very different sort of place. Since the victory of the Copernican system we have known that the earth is not the center of the universe. For a time the sun replaced it, but then it turned out that the sun is by no means a monarch among stars, in fact, is scarcely even middle class. There is an incredible amount of empty space in the universe. The distance from the sun to the nearest star is about 4.2 light years, or 25×10^{12} miles. This is in spite of the fact that we live in an exceptionally crowded part of the universe, namely the Milky Way, which is an assemblage of about 300,000 million stars. This assemblage is one of an immense number of similar assemblages; about 30 million are known, but presumably better telescopes would show more.* The average distance from one assemblage to the next is

* Almost 1 billion as seen in the telescope at Mount Palomar Observatory. Ed.

about 2 million light years. But apparently they still feel they haven't elbow room, for they are all hurrying away from each other; some are moving away from us at the rate of 14,000 miles a second or more. . . . And as to mass: the sun weighs about 2×10^{27} tons, the Milky Way about 160,000 million times as much as the sun, and is one of a collection of galaxies of which about 30 million are known. It is not easy to maintain a belief in one's own cosmic importance in view of such overwhelming statistics.

So much for the contemplative aspect of man's place in a scientific cosmos. I come now to the practical aspect.

To the practical man, the nebulae are a matter of indifference. He can understand astronomers' thinking about them, because they are paid to, but there is no reason why *he* should worry about anything so unimportant. What matters to him about the world is what he can make of it. And scientific man can make vastly more of the world than unscientific man could.

In the pre-scientific world, power was God's. There was not much that man could do even in the most favorable circumstances, and the circumstances were liable to become unfavorable if men incurred the divine displeasure. This showed itself in earthquakes, pestilences, famines, and defeats in war. Since such events are frequent, it was obviously very easy to incur divine displeasure. Judging by the analogy of earthly monarchs, men decided that the thing most displeasing to the Deity is a lack of humility. If you wished to slip through life without disaster, you must be meek; you must be aware of your defenselessness, and constantly ready to confess it. But the God before whom you humbled yourself was conceived in the likeness of man, so that the universe seemed human and warm and cozy, like home if you are the youngest of a large family, painful at time, but never alien and incomprehensible.

In the scientific world, all this is different. It is not by prayer and humility that you cause things to go as you wish, but by acquiring a knowledge of natural laws. The power you acquire in this way is much greater and much more reliable than that formerly supposed to be acquired by prayer, because you never could tell whether your prayer would be favorably heard in heaven. The power of prayer, moreover, had recognized limits; it would have been impious to ask too much. But the power of science has no known limits. We were told that faith could remove mountains, but no one believed it; we are now told that the atomic bomb can remove mountains, and everyone believes it.

It is true that if we ever did stop to think about the cosmos we might find it uncomfortable. The sun may grow cold or blow up; the earth may lose its atmosphere and become uninhabitable. Life is a brief, small, and transitory phenomenon in an obscure corner, not at all the sort of thing that one would make a fuss about if one were not personally concerned. But it is monkish and futile—so scientific man will say—to dwell on such cold and unpractical thoughts. Let us get on with the job of fertilizing the desert, melting Arctic ice, and killing each other with perpetually improving technique. Some of our activities will do good, some harm, but all alike will show our power. And so, in this godless universe, we shall become gods. . . .

Science, ever since the time of the Arabs, has had two functions: (1) to enable us to *know* things, and (2) to enable us to *do* things. The Greeks, with the exception of Archimedes, were only interested in the first of these. They had much curiosity about the world, but, since civilized people lived comfortably on slave labor, they had no interest in technique. Interest in the practical uses of science came first through superstition and magic. The Arabs wished to discover the philosopher's stone, the elixir of life, and how to transmute base metals into gold. In pursuing investigations having these purposes, they discovered many facts in chemistry, but they did not arrive at any valid and important general laws, and their technique remained elementary. . . .

Science used to be valued as a means of getting to *know* the world; now, owing to the triumph of technique, it is conceived as showing how to *change* the world. The new point of view, which is adopted in practice throughout America and Russia, and in theory by many modern philosophers, was first proclaimed by Marx in 1845, in his *Theses on Feuerbach*. He says:

The question whether objective truth belongs to human thinking is not a question of theory, but a practical question. The truth, i.e. the reality and power, of thought must be demonstrated in practice. The contest as to the reality or nonreality of a thought which is isolated from practice, is a purely scholastic question. . . . Philosophers have only interpreted the world in various ways, but the real task is to alter it.

From the point of view of technical philosophy, this theory has been best developed by John Dewey, who is universally acknowledged as America's most eminent philosopher.

This philosophy has two aspects, one theoretical and the other ethical. On the theoretical side, it analyzes away the concept "truth," for which it substitutes "utility." It used to be thought that, if you believed Caesar crossed the Rubicon, you believed truly, because Caesar did cross the Rubicon. Not so, say the philosophers we are considering: to say that your belief is "true" is another way of saying that you will find it more profitable than the opposite belief. I might object that there have been cases of historical beliefs which, after being generally accepted for a long time, have in the end been admitted to be mistaken. In the case of such beliefs, every examinee would find the accepted falsehood of his time more profitable than the as yet unacknowledged truth. But this kind of objection is swept aside by the contention that a belief may be "true" at one time and "false" at another. In 1920 it was "true" that Trotsky had a great part in the Russian Revolution; in 1930 it was "false." The results of this view have been admirably worked out in George Orwell's "1984."

This philosophy derives its inspiration from science in several different ways. Take first its best aspect, as developed by Dewey. He points out that scientific theories change from time to time, and that what recommends a theory is that it "works." When new phenomena are discovered, for which it no longer "works," it is discarded. A theory—so Dewey concludes—is a tool like another; it enables us to manipulate raw material. Like any other tool, it is judged good or bad by its efficiency in this manipulation, and like any other tool, it is good at one time and bad at another. While it is good it may be called "true," but this word must not be allowed its usual connotations. Dewey prefers the phrase "warranted assertibility" to the word "truth."

The second source of the theory is technique. What do we want to know about electricity? Only how to make it work for us. To want to know more is to plunge into useless metaphysics. Science is to be admired because it gives us power over nature, and the power comes wholly from technique. Therefore an interpretation which reduces science to technique keeps all the useful part, and dismisses only a dead weight of medieval lumber. If technique is all that interests you, you are likely to find this argument very convincing.

The third attraction of pragmatism—which cannot be wholly separated from the second—is love of power. Most men's desires are of various kinds. There are the pleasures of sense; there are aesthetic pleasures and pleasures of contemplation; there are private affections; and there is power. In an individual, any one of these may acquire predominance over the others. If love of power dominates, you arrive at Marx's view that what is important is not to understand the world, but to change it. Traditional theories of knowledge were invented by men who loved contemplation—a monkish taste, according to modern devotees of mechanism. Mechanism augments human power to an enormous degree. It is therefore this aspect of science that attracts the lovers of power. And if power is all you want from science, the pragmatist theory gives you just what you want, without accretions that to you seem irrelevant. It gives you even more than you could have expected, for if you control the police it gives you the godlike power of *making truth*. You cannot make the sun cold, but you can confer pragmatic "truth" on the proposition "the sun is cold" if you can ensure that everyone who denies it is liquidated. I doubt whether Zeus could do more.

This engineer's philosophy, as it may be called, is distinguished from common sense and from most other philosophies by its rejection of "fact" as a fundamental concept in defining "truth." If you say, for example, "the South Pole is cold," you say something which, according to traditional views, is "true" in virtue of a "fact," namely that the South Pole is cold. And this is a fact, not because people believe it, or because it pays to believe it; it just *is* a fact. Facts, when they are not about human beings and their doings, represent the limitations of human power. We find ourselves in a universe of a certain sort, and we find out what sort of universe it is by observation, not by self-assertion. It is true that we can make changes on or near the surface of the earth, but not elsewhere. Practical men have no wish to make changes elsewhere, and can therefore accept a philosophy which treats the surface of the earth as if it were the whole universe. But even on the surface of the earth our power is limited. To forget that we are hemmed in by facts which are for the most part independent of our desires is a form of insane megalomania. This kind of insanity has grown up as a result of the triumph of scientific technique. Its latest manifestation is Stalin's refusal to believe that heredity can have the temerity to ignore Soviet decrees, which is like Xerxes whipping the Hellespont to teach Poseidon a lesson.

"The pragmatic theory of truth [I wrote in 1907] is inherently connected with the appeal to force. If there is a non-human truth, which one man may know while another does not, there is a standard outside the disputants, to which, we may urge, the dispute ought to be submitted; hence a pacific and judicial settlement of disputes is at least theoretically possible. If, on the contrary, the only way of discovering which of the disputants is in the right is to wait and see which of them is successful, there is no longer any principle except force by which the issue can be decided. . . . In international matters, owing to the fact that the disputants are often strong enough to be independent of outside control, these considerations become more important. The hopes of international peace, like the achievement of internal peace, depend upon the creation of an effective force of public opinion formed upon an estimate of the rights and wrongs of disputes. Thus it would be misleading to say that the dispute is decided by force, without adding that force is dependent upon justice. But the possibility of such a public opinion depends upon the possibility of a standard of justice which is a cause, not an effect, of the wishes of the community; and such a standard of justice seems incompatible with the pragmatist philosophy. This philosophy, therefore, although it begins with liberty and toleration, develops, by inherent necessity, into the appeal to force and the arbitrament of the big battalions. By this development it becomes equally adapted to democracy at home and to imperialism abroad. Thus here again it is more delicately adjusted to the requirements of the time than any other philosophy which has hitherto been invented.

"To sum up: Pragmatism appeals to the temper of mind which finds on the surface of this planet the whole of its imaginative material; which feels confident of progress, and unaware of non-human limitations to human power; which loves battle, with all the attendant risks, because it has no real doubt that it will achieve victory; which desires religion, as it desires railways and electric light, as a comfort and a help in the affairs of this world, not as providing non-human objects to satisfy the hunger for perfection. But for those who feel that life on this planet would be a life in prison if it were not for the windows into a greater world beyond; for those to whom a belief in man's omnipotence seems arrogant; who desire rather the stoic freedom that comes of mastery over the passions than the Napoleonic domination that sees the kingdoms of this world at its feet—in a word, to men who do not find man an adequate object of their worship, the pragmatist's world will seem narrow and petty, robbing life of all that gives it value, and making man himself smaller by depriving the universe which he contemplates of all its splendor."

SCIENCE AND HUMAN VALUES*
by J. Bronowski (1956)

1.

My theme is that the values which we accept today as permanent and often as self-evident have grown out of the Renaissance and the Scientific Revolution. The arts and the sciences have changed the values of the Middle Ages; and this change has been an enrichment, moving towards what makes us more deeply human. . . .

2.

The concepts of value are profound and difficult exactly because they do two things at once: they join men into societies, and yet they preserve for them a freedom which makes them single men. . . .

* From J. Bronowski, *Science and Human Values.* Copyright 1956 by J. Bronowski. Reprinted by permission of Julian Messner, Publishers, Inc., New York.

The society which I will examine is that formed by scientists themselves: it is the body of scientists.

It may seem strange to call this a society, and yet it is an obvious choice; for having said so much about the working of science, I should be shirking all our unspoken questions if I did not ask how scientists work together. The dizzy progress of science, theoretical and practical, has depended on the existence of a fellowship of scientists which is free, uninhibited and communicative. It is not an upstart society, for it derives its traditions, both of scholarship and of service, from roots which reach through the Renaissance into the monastic communities and the first universities. The men and women who practice the sciences make a company of scholars which has been more lasting than any modern state, yet which has changed and evolved as no church has. . . .

3.

The values of science derive neither from the virtues of its members, nor from the finger-wagging codes of conduct by which every profession reminds itself to be good. They have grown out of the practice of science, because they are the inescapable conditions for its practice.

Science is the creation of concepts and their exploration in the facts. It has no other test of the concept than its empirical truth to fact. Truth is the drive at the center of science; it must have the habit of truth, not as a dogma but as a process. Consider then, step by step, what kind of society scientists have been compelled to form in this single pursuit. If truth is to be found, not given, and if therefore it is to be tested in action, what other conditions (and with them, what other values) grow of themselves from this?

First, of course, comes independence, in observation and thence in thought. I once told an audience of school children that the world would never change if they did not contradict their elders. I was chagrined to find next morning that this axiom outraged their parents. Yet it is the basis of the scientific method. A man must see, do and think things for himself, in the face of those who are sure that they have already been over all that ground. In science, there is no substitute for independence.

It has been a by-product of this that, by degrees, men have come to give a value to the new and the bold in all their work. It was not always so. European thought and art before the Renaissance were happy in the faith that there is nothing new under the sun. John Dryden in the seventeenth century, and Jonathan Swift as it turned into the eighteenth, were still fighting Battles of the Books to prove that no modern work could hope to rival the classics. They were not overpowered by argument or example (not even by their own examples), but by the mounting scientific tradition among their friends in the new Royal Society. Today we find it as natural to prize originality in a child's drawing and an arrangement of flowers as in an invention. Science has bred the love of originality as a mark of independence.

Independence, originality, and therefore dissent: these words show the progress, they stamp the character of our civilization as once they did that of Athens in flower. From Luther in 1517 to Spinoza grinding lenses, from Huguenot weavers and Quaker ironmasters to the Puritans founding Harvard, and from Newton's heresies to the calculated universe of Eddington, the profound movements of history have been begun by unconforming men. Dissent is the native activity of the scientist, and it has got him into a good deal of trouble in the last years. But if that is cut off, what is left will not be a scientist. And I doubt whether it will be a man. For dissent is also native in any society which is still growing. Has there ever been a society which has died of dissent? Several have died of conformity in our lifetime.

Dissent is not iself an end; it is the surface mark of a deeper value. Dissent is the mark of freedom, as originality is the mark of independence of mind. And as originality and independence are private needs for the existence of a science, so dissent and freedom are its public needs. No one can be a scientist, even in private, if he does not have independence of observation and of thought. But if in addition science is to become effective as a public practice, it must go further; it must protect independence. The safeguards which it must offer are patent: free inquiry, free thought, free speech, tolerance. These values are so familiar to us, yawning our way through political perorations, that they seem self-evident. But they are self-evident, that is, they are logical needs, only where men are committed to explore the truth: in a scientific society. These freedoms of tolerance have never been notable in a dogmatic society, even when the dogma was Christian. They have been granted only when scientific thought flourished once before, in the youth of Greece.

4.

I have been developing an ethic for science which derives directly from its own activity. It might have seemed at the outset that this study could lead only to a set of technical rules: to elementary rules for using test tubes or sophisticated rules for inductive reasoning. But the inquiry turns out quite otherwise. There are, oddly, no technical rules for success in science. There are no rules even for using test tubes which the brilliant experimenter does not flout; and alas, there are no rules at all for making successful general inductions. This is not where the study of scientific practice leads us. Instead, the conditions for the practice of science are found to be of another and an unexpected kind. Independence and originality, dissent and freedom and tolerance: such are the first needs of science; and these are the values which, of itself, it demands and forms.

The society of scientists must be a democracy. It can keep alive and grow only by a constant tension between dissent and respect, between independence from the views of others and tolerance for them. The crux of the ethical problem is to fuse these, the private and the public needs. Tolerance alone is not enough; this is why the bland, kindly civilizations of the East, where to contradict is a personal affront, developed no strong science. And independence is not enough either: the sad history of genetics, still torn today by the quarrels of sixty years ago, shows that. Every scientist has to learn the hard lesson, to respect the views of the next man—even when the next man is tactless enough to express them.

Tolerance among scientists cannot be based on indifference, it must be based on respect. Respect as a personal value implies, in any society, the public acknowledgements of justice and of due honor. These are values which to the layman seem most remote from any abstract study. Justice, honor, the respect of man for man: What, he asks, have these human values to do with science? The question is a foolish survival of those nineteenth-century quarrels which always came back to equate ethics with the Book of Genesis. If critics in the past had ever looked practically to see how a science develops, they would not have asked such a question. Science confronts the work of one man with that of another and grafts each on each; and it cannot survive without justice and honor and respect between man and man. Only by these means can science pursue its steadfast object, to explore truth. If these values did not exist, then the society of scientists would have to invent them to make the practice of science possible. In societies where these values did not exist, science has had to create them.

Science is not a mechanism but a human progress. To the layman who is dominated by the fallacy of the comic strips, that science would all be done best by machines, all this is puzzling. But human search and research is a learning by steps of which none is final, and the mistakes of one generation are rungs in the ladder, no less than their correction by the next. This is why the values of science turn out to be recognizably the human values: because scientists must be men, must be fallible, and yet as men must be willing and as a society must be organized to correct their errors. William Blake said that "to be an Error & to be Cast out is a part of God's design." It is certainly part of the design of science.

There never was a great scientist who did not make bold guesses, and there never was a bold man whose guesses were not sometimes wild. Newton was wrong, in the setting of his time, to think that light is made up of particles. Faraday was foolish when he looked in his setting for a link between electromagnetism and gravitation. And such is the nature of science, their bad guesses may yet be brilliant by the work of our own day. We do not think any less of the profound concept of General Relativity in Einstein because the details of his formulation at this moment seem doubtful. For in science as in literature, the style of a great man is the stamp of his mind and makes even his mistakes a challenge which is part of the march of its subject. Science at last respects the scientist more than his theories, for by its nature, it must prize the search above the discovery and the thinking (and with it the thinker) above the thought. In the society of scientists each man, by the process of exploring for the truth, has earned a dignity more profound than his doctrine. A true society is sustained by the sense of human dignity.

I take this phrase from the life of the French naturalist Buffon who, like Galileo, was forced to recant his scientific findings. Yet he preserved always, says his biographer, something deeper than the fine manners of the court of Louis XV; he kept "le sentiment exquis de la dignité humaine." His biographer says that Buffon learned this during his stay in England where it was impressed on him by the scientists he met. Since Buffon seems to have spent at most three months in England, this claim has been thought extravagant. But is it? Is history really so inhuman in arithmetic? Buffon in the short winter of 1738–9 met the grave men of the Royal Society, heirs to Newton, the last of a great generation. He found them neither a court nor a rabble, but a community of scientists seeking the truth together with dignity and humanity. It was, it is, a discovery to form a man's life.

The sense of human dignity that Buffon showed in his bearing is the cement of a society of equal men, for it expresses their knowledge that respect for others must be founded in self-respect. Theory and experiment alike become meaningless unless the scientist brings to them, and his fellows can assume in him, the respect of a lucid honesty with himself. The mathematician and philosopher W. K. Clifford said this forcibly at the end of his short life, nearly a hundred years ago.

If I steal money from any person, there may be no harm done by the mere transfer of possession; he may not feel the loss, or it may even prevent him from using the money badly. But I cannot help doing this great wrong towards Man, that I make myself dishonest. What hurts society is not that it should lose its property, but that it should become a den of thieves; for then it must cease to be society. This is why we ought not to do evil that good may come; for at any rate this great evil has come, that we have done evil and are made wicked thereby.

This is the scientist's moral: that there is no distinction between ends and means. Clifford goes on to put this in terms of the scientist's practice.

In like manner, if I let myself believe anything on insufficient evidence, there may be no great harm done by the mere belief; it may be true after all, or I may never have occasion to exhibit it in outward acts. But I cannot help doing this great wrong towards Man, that I make myself credulous. The danger to society is not merely that it should believe wrong things, though that is great enough; but that it should become credulous.

And the passion in Clifford's tone shows that to him the word "credulous" had the same emotional force as a "den of thieves."

The fulcrum of Clifford's ethic here, and mine, is the phrase "it may be true after all." Others may allow this to justify their conduct; the practice of science wholly rejects it. It does not admit that the word true can have this meaning. The test of truth is the fact, and no glib expediency nor reason of state can justify the smallest self-deception in that. Our work is of a piece, in the large and in detail, so that if we silence one scruple about our means, we infect ourselves and our ends together.

The scientist derives this ethic from his method, and every creative worker reaches it for himself. This is how Blake reached it from his practice as a poet and a painter.

He who would do good to another must do it in Minute Particulars: General Good is the plea of the scoundrel, hypocrite & flatterer, For Art & Science cannnot exist but in minutely organized Particulars.

The Minute Particulars of art and the fine structure of science alike make the grain of conscience.

5.

Usually when scientists claim that their work has liberated men, they do so on more practical grounds. In these four hundred years, they say, we have mastered sea and sky, we have drawn information from the electron and power from the nucleus, we have doubled the span of life and halved the working day, and we have enriched the leisure we have created with universal education and high-fidelity recordings and electric lights and the lipstick. We have carried out the tasks which men set for us because they were most urgent. To a world population at least five times larger than in Kepler's day, there begins to be offered a life above the animal, a sense of personality, and a potential of human fulfilment, which make both the glory and the explosive problem of our age.

These claims are not confined to food and bodily comfort. Their larger force is that the physical benefits of science have opened a door and will give all men the chance to use mind and spirit. The technical man here neatly takes his model from evolution, in which the enlargement of the human brain followed the development of the hand.

I take a different view of science as a method; to me, it enters the human spirit more directly. Therefore I have studied quite another achievement: that of making a human society work. As a set of discoveries and devices, science has mastered nature; but it has been able to do so only because its values, which derive from its method, have formed those who practice it into a living, stable and incorruptible society. Here is a community where everyone has been free to enter, to speak his mind, to be heard and contradicted; and it has outlasted the empires of Louis XIV and the Kaiser. Napoleon was angry when the Institute he had founded awarded his first scientific prize to Humphry Davy, for this was in 1807, when France was at war with England. Science survived then and since because it is less brittle than the rage of tyrants.

This is a stability which no dogmatic society can have. There is today almost no scientific theory which was held when, say, the Industrial Revolution began about 1760. Most often today's theories flatly contradict those of 1760; many contradict those of 1900. In cosmology, in quantum mechanics, in genetics, in the social sciences, who now holds the beliefs that seemed firm fifty years ago? Yet the society of scientists has survived these changes without a revolution and honors the men whose beliefs it no longer shares. No one has been shot or exiled or convicted of perjury; no one has recanted abjectly at a trial before his colleagues. The whole structure of science has been changed, and no one has been either disgraced or deposed. Through all the changes of science, the society of scientists is flexible and single-minded together and evolves and rights itself. In the language of science, it is a stable society.

The society of scientists is simple because it has a directing purpose: to explore the truth. Nevertheless, it has to solve the problem of every society, which is to find a compromise between man and men. It must encourage the single scientist to be independent, and the body of scientists to be tolerant. From these basic conditions, which form the prime values, there follows step by step the spectrum of values: dissent, freedom of thought and speech, justice, honor, human dignity and self-respect.

Our values since the Renaissance have evolved by just such steps. There are of course casuists who, when they are not busy belittling these values, derive them from the Middle Ages. But that servile and bloody world upheld neither independence nor tolerance, and it is from these, as I have shown, that the human values are rationally derived. Those who crusade against the rational and receive their values by mystic inspiration have no claim to these values of the mind. I cannot put this better than in the words of Albert Schweitzer in which he, a religious man, protests that mysticism in religion is not enough.

Rationalism is more than a movement of thought which realized itself at the end of the eighteenth and the beginning of the nineteenth centuries. It is a necessary phenomenon in all normal spiritual life. All real progress in the world is in the last analysis produced by rationalism. The principle, which was then established, of basing our views of the universe on thought and thought alone is valid for all time.

So proud men have thought, in all walks of life, since Giordano Bruno was condemned to be burnt for his cosmology, about 1600. They have gone about their work simply enough. The scientists among them did not set out to be moralists or revolutionaries. William Harvey and Huygens, Euler and Avogadro, Darwin and Willard Gibbs and Marie Curie, Planck and Pavlov practiced their crafts modestly and steadfastly. Yet the values they seldom spoke of shone out of their work and entered their ages and slowly re-made the minds of men. Slavery ceased to be a matter of course. The princelings of Europe fled from the gaming table. The empires of the Bourbons and the Hapsburgs crumbled. Men asked for the rights of man and for government by consent. By the beginning of the nineteenth century, Napoleon did not find a scientist to elevate tyranny into a system; that was done by the philosopher Hegel. Hegel had written his university dissertation to prove philosophically that there could be no more than the seven planets he knew. It was unfortunate, and characteristic, that even as he wrote, on 1st January 1801, a working astronomer observed the eighth planet Ceres.

6.

. . . Has science fastened upon our society a monstrous gift of destruction which we can neither undo nor master, and which, like a clockwork automaton in a nightmare, is set to break our necks? Is science an automaton, and if so has it lamed our sense of values?

These questions are not answered by holding a Sunday symposium of moralists. They are not even answered by the painstaking neutralism of the textbooks on scientific method. We must indeed begin from a study of what scientists do, when they are neither posed for photographs on the steps of spaceships nor bumbling professorially in the cartoons. But we must get to the heart of what they do. We must lay bare the conditions which make it possible for them to work at all.

When we do so we find, leaf by leaf, the organic values which I have been unfolding. And we find that they are not at odds with the values by which alone mankind can survive. On the contrary, like the other creative activities which grew from the Renaissance,

science has humanized our values. Men have asked for freedom, justice and respect precisely as the scientific spirit has spread among them. The dilemma of today is not that the human values cannot control a mechanical science. It is the other way about: the scientific spirit is more human than the machinery of governments. We have not let either the tolerance or the empiricism of science enter the parochial rules by which we still try to prescribe the behavior of nations. Our conduct as states clings to a code of self-interest which science, like humanity, has long left behind.

The body of technical science burdens and threatens us because we are trying to employ the body without the spirit; we are trying to buy the corpse of science. We are hag-ridden by the power of nature which we should command because we think its command needs less devotion and understanding than its discovery. And because we know how gunpowder works, we sigh for the days before atomic bombs. But massacre is not prevented by sticking to gunpowder; the Thirty Years' War is proof of that. Massacre is prevented by the scientist's ethic, and the poet's, and every creator's: that the end for which we work exists and is judged only by the means which we use to reach it. This is the human sum of the values of science. It is the basis of a society which scrupulously seeks knowledge to match and govern its power. But it is not the scientist who can govern society; his duty is to teach it the implications and the values in his work. Sir Thomas More said this in 1516, that the single-minded man must not govern but teach; and went to the scaffold for neglecting his own counsel.

7.

I have analysed . . . only the activity of science. Yet I do not distinguish it from other imaginative activities; they are as much parts one of another as are the Renaissance and the Scientific Revolution. The sense of wonder in nature, of freedom within her boundaries, and of unity with her in knowledge, is shared by the painter, the poet and the mountaineer. Their values, I have no doubt, express concepts as profound as those of science and could serve as well to make a society—as they did in Florence, and in Elizabethan London and among the famous doctors of Edinburgh. Every cast of mind has its creative activity which explores the likenesses appropriate to it and derives the values by which it must live.

The exploration of the artist is no less truthful and strenuous than that of the scientist. If science seems to carry conviction and recognition more immediately, this is because here the critics are also those who work at the matter. There is not, as in the arts, a gap between the functions (and therefore between the fashions) of those who comment and those who do. Nevertheless, the great artist works as devotedly to uncover the implications of his vision as does the great scientist. They grow, they haunt his thought, and their most inspired flash is the end of a lifetime of silent exploration. . . .

Whether our work is art or science or the daily work of society, it is only the form in which we explore our experience which is different; the need to explore remains the same. This is why, at bottom, the society of scientists is more important than their discoveries. What science has to teach us here is not its techniques but its spirit: the irresistible need to explore. Perhaps the techniques of science may be practiced for a time without

its spirit, in secret establishments, as the Egyptians practiced their priestcraft. But the inspiration of science for four hundred years has been opposite to this. It has created the values of our intellectual life and, with the arts, has taught them to our civilization. Science has nothing to be ashamed of even in the ruins of Nagasaki. The shame is theirs who appeal to other values than the human imaginative values which science has evolved. The shame is ours, if we do not make science part of our world, intellectually as much as physically, so that we may at last hold these halves of the world together by the same values. For this is the lesson of science, that the concept is more profound than its laws and the act of judging more critical than the judgment. In a book that I wrote about poetry I said:

Poetry does not move us to be just or unjust, in itself. It moves us to thoughts in whose light justice and injustice are seen in fearful sharpness of outline.

What is true of poetry is true of all creative thought. And what I said then of one value is true of all human values. The values by which we are to survive are not rules for just and unjust conduct, but are those deeper illuminations in whose light justice and injustice, good and evil, means and ends are seen in fearful sharpness of outline.

[We have been following] a record of a great adventure in the region of thought. It was shared in by all the races of western Europe. It developed with the slowness of a mass movement. Half a century is its unit of time. The tale is the epic of an episode in the manifestation of reason. It tells how a particular direction of reason emerges in a race by the long preparation of antecedent epochs, how after its birth its subject-matter gradually unfolds itself, how it attains its triumphs, how its influence moulds the very springs of action of mankind, and finally how at its moment of supreme success its limitations disclose themselves and call for a renewed exercise of the creative imagination. The moral of the tale is the power of reason, its decisive influence on the life of humanity. The great conquerors, from Alexander to Caesar, and from Caesar to Napoleon, influenced profoundly the lives of subsequent generations. But the total effect of this influence shrinks to insignificance, if compared to the entire transformation of human habits and human mentality produced by the long line of men of thought from Thales to the present day, men individually powerless, but ultimately the rulers of the world.

Alfred North Whitehead
Science and the Modern World (1925)

QUESTIONS TO CONSIDER

What are the goals of science? Do you agree with Einstein that it is society and not science that must furnish the social goals?

Russell says, "Science used to be valued as a means of getting to know the world; now, owing to the triumph of technique, it is conceived as showing how to change the world." How did this change of goals come about? Does it represent a change in the aims of science itself?

Is truth in science that which succeeds? The pragmatic philosophy as described by Russell on page 426 rejects facts as the fundamental concept in defining truth. Do you think Kepler would have accepted this philosophy? Or do you agree with Sullivan that ". . . science is truthful because it has practically no temptation to be anything else"?

Huxley says that science leads through the method of simplification to conformity and regimentation. "This is held to be philosophically respectable because it is the same method that leads to success in science." Bronowski, on the other hand, says that the opposite traits of independence, originality, and dissent are necessary to a scientist and that conformity would cause the death of science. Which one seems to you to be right?

Both Sullivan and Bronowski suggest that the chief value of science lies in its spirit. How would you characterize the spirit of science?

SUGGESTIONS FOR FURTHER READING

*   Bronowski, J.: *The Common Sense of Science*, Vintage Books, Random House, Inc., New York, 1953. Readers who have enjoyed the Bronowski selection in this part will be interested in chaps. 8 and 9: "Truth and Value" and "Science, the Destroyer or Creator."

*   Conant, James: *Modern Science and Modern Man*, Anchor Books, Doubleday & Company, Inc., Garden City, N.Y., 1952. A collection of a series of

* Paperback edition.

lectures delivered in 1952, discussing the role of modern science and its relation to society.

Hutchings, Edward, Jr. (ed.): *Frontiers in Science*, Basic Books, Inc., Publishers, New York, 1958. The section entitled "Science and Society" contains a number of essays that are of particular interest in connection with this part.

* Huxley, Aldous, *Brave New World*, Bantam Books, Inc., New York, 1963.

* ———: *Brave New World Revisited*, Bantam Books, Inc., New York, 1960.

———: *Science, Liberty, and Peace*, Harper & Row, Publishers, New York, 1946.

These three books present in vivid terms the dangers of a technological society. Readers who would like to understand more thoroughly the point of view presented by Huxley in the selection in this part are urged to read all of his little book *Science, Liberty, and Peace*.

Oppenheimer, J. Robert: *The Open Mind*, Simon and Schuster, Inc., New York, 1955. A collection of lectures on atomic weapons and the significance of the atomic age. The last four lectures deal with the relationship between science as an intellectual activity and the wider culture of our times.

Russell, Bertrand: *The Impact of Science on Society*, Simon and Schuster, Inc., New York, 1953. A vivid penetrating analysis of the effect science has had on our society.

Snow, C. P.: *The Two Cultures and the Scientific Revolution*, Cambridge University Press, New York, 1959. This dynamic little book has focused public attention on the lack of communication and understanding between science and society. Well worth reading.

GLOSSARY*

The following is a glossary of terms which appear in the text and which may be unfamiliar to the reader. Definitions of these terms are included for easy reference, and in some cases supplementary information is also given. A few simple algebraic derivations have been included for the interest of those readers who prefer a mathematical explanation. Cross references in the glossary are indicated by italics in those cases in which the cross reference may throw additional light on the term being defined, for example, "metagalaxy: a system of *galaxies* or extragalactic nebulae. See page 326." The word "galaxies" is in italics to show that it is also defined in the glossary. The page number refers the reader to material in the body of the text that will provide additional help in understanding the term.

acceleration The rate of change of velocity with respect to time. $a = (v - v_0)/t$, where v_0 is the starting velocity and v the velocity at the time t. If the body starts from rest ($v_0 = 0$), then $a = v/t$. The average velocity $(v + v_0)/2$ will be $v/2$, and the distance traveled in time t will be $(v/2) t$. Therefore, by simple algebra, if

$$d = \frac{v \ (t)}{2}$$

and $\quad a = \dfrac{v}{t}$

$$v = at$$
$$d = \frac{at \ (t)}{2} = \frac{1}{2} at^2$$

In case of uniform acceleration, where a is constant, distance is proportional to t^2. See page 126 and Figure 4–18. Since velocity is a vector quantity having both magnitude and direction, in problems involving curvilinear motion it is necessary to consider the rate of change of the different components of the velocity. In the case of uniform circular motion, there is no change in the magnitude of the velocity, but there is a constant change in the direction and therefore a constant acceleration.

acceleration of gravity Acceleration of a body falling freely in a vacuum. This varies in different localities as a result of the rotation of the earth and the distance from the center of mass of the earth. The standard accepted value at sea level is 32.2 feet per second per second. See page 127.

accuracy In every form of physical measurement there is some inaccuracy, and the degree of this inaccuracy must be known if the measurement is to have any scientific value. There are three ways of specifying a measurement that is known to be reliable to about 1 in 1,000:

$$x = 1.234 \pm 0.001$$
$$x = 1.234 \pm 0.1 \text{ per cent}$$
$$x = 1.234$$

In the third form, the last digit, the number 4, is understood to be unreliable, but we have less information about just how unreliable it is than we have in the first two forms. See the editor's note on page 150.

aerobic Pertaining to organisms that can grow only where there is free oxygen available.

Agena A 15,000-pound-thrust second stage designed for use on both Atlas and Thor vehicles. The stage features the use of "storable" liquid propellants and restart capability in space. The Thor-Agena vehicle is used in the Discoverer program, and the Atlas-Agena launched the Samos and Midas payloads.

alpha particle ($\propto$ particle) Helium nucleus; i.e. a close combination of two *neutrons* and two *protons*, and therefore positively charged. Alpha particles are emitted from the nuclei of certain *radioactive* elements.

ammonia (NH$_3$) Pungent smelling gas, very soluble in water. Like methane it is a prime constituent of the atmospheres of the outer planets.

amplitude See *waves*.

anaerobic Pertaining to organisms that can grow in the absence of free oxygen.

angular momentum A vector quantity that is the product of angular velocity and moment of inertia. The law of *conservation* applies to angular as well as linear momentum. This law is one of the guide posts of the theoretical work on the origin of the solar system, for it tells us that the original angular momentum must still be present somewhere in the system. See page 310.

angular velocity Rate of motion through an angle about an axis, measured in degrees, radians, or revolutions per unit time.

apastron See *aphelion*.

aphelion The aphelion of an orbit is the point of farthest distance from the sun. This point is also an *apse*, being on the major axis of the ellipse. A similar term, used in connection with double stars, is *apastron*. See Figure 5–10.

approximation When we know that a number is

* We wish to acknowledge the kind permission granted to us by Penguin Books, Inc., to reprint from their *A Dictionary of Science*, by E. B. Uvarov and D. R. Chapman, the definitions in whole or in part for alpha particle, continuum, diffraction, electrons, galaxy, interference of wave motions, ion, meteor, parsec, proton, protoplasm, radioactivity, thermal neutrons, waves. We wish also to acknowledge our indebtedness to the *McGraw-Hill Encyclopedia of Science and Technology*, McGraw-Hill Book Company, Inc., New York, 1960, from which we adapted the definitions for carbon cycle, cepheid variables, conservation, cosmic rays, diffraction grating, logarithmic scale, Fitzgerald-Lorentz contraction, proton-proton chain, refraction, relativity, spectroscope, statistics, telescope.

only approximately correct, we can express this by writing it $x \approx 500$ or $x \cong 500$. Both these signs means "equals approximately." For still rougher estimates we use the sign $y \sim 1,000$. This sign expresses the order of magnitude and means that y is nearer 1,000 than 100 or 10,000. See also *accuracy* and the editor's note on page 150.

apse or apside The apse of an orbit is that point at which the distance of the body from the center of the attraction is either greatest or least. The line that joins the two apse points is called the line of the apse. In an elliptical orbit this line of the apse is the major axis of the ellipse, and the two points are the points of nearest (see *perihelion*) and farthest (see *aphelion*) distance.

asteroids See *planetoids*.

astronomical unit Unit of measurement in astronomy defined as the mean distance from the earth to the sun and taken as 92,897,000 miles.

Atlas Intercontinental ballistic missile (ICBM) having a maximum speed of over 15,000 miles per hour and a range of over 6,000 miles. It uses liquid propellant and is designed to carry nuclear warheads. It has also been used as the first stage of several space-launch vehicles such as Atlas-Able, Atlas-Agena, and Atlas-Mercury. The Atlas-Mercury placed about 2,400 pounds in orbit.

axiom A statement accepted as a self-evident truth but incapable of formal proof. See page 17.

beta particle (β particle) Term applied to a swiftly moving *electron*, β^-, positron, β^+, when emitted by a *radioactive* substance.

billion The American billion is a thousand million, or 10^9; the British billion is a million million, or 10^{12}.

binary system A binary system of stars is a pair of stars located sufficiently near each other to be connected by a mutual bond of gravitational attraction that compels them to describe an orbit around a common center of mass. See page 224 and Figure 9–15.

bise or bice A pale blue pigment prepared from blue carbonate of copper.

Boyle's law At a constant temperature the volume of a given quantity of any gas varies inversely as the pressure to which the gas is subjected; that is, for an ideal gas

$$P \times V = \text{constant}$$

where P = pressure
V = volume

Actually, the law is only approximately true, even for such gases as hydrogen and helium. Since a gas consists of a large number of small elastic particles in rapid motion and the pressure on the walls is simply the effect of bombardment, Boyle's law can be looked upon as a statistical or probability picture of the motion of the gas particles. We cannot, at any one time, give a history of any one particular particle, but we can say what the probability is that a certain number of these particles may be in some specific state of motion. See page 40.

brennschluss The German term for the instant at which the rocket fuel is shut off.

carbon cycle The carbon cycle, or, properly, the carbon-nitrogen-carbon cycle, is the name applied to a theoretically deduced chain of *thermonuclear* reactions that appears to be important as an energy-producing process in certain types of stars. The cycle has the property that C^{12} (carbon) nuclei act as *catalysts* for a chain of nuclear reactions that finally converts four *protons* into one He^4 (helium) nucleus with a release of much energy. The following series is in agreement with the experimental evidence:

$$C^{12} + H^1 \rightarrow N^{13} + \gamma$$
$$N^{13} \rightarrow C^{13} + {}_{+1}e + \nu$$
$$C^{13} + H^1 \rightarrow N^{14} + \gamma$$
$$N^{14} + H^1 \rightarrow O^{15} + \gamma$$
$$O^{15} \rightarrow N^{15} + {}_{+1}e + \nu$$
$$N^{15} + H^1 \rightarrow C^{12} + He^4$$

where ${}_{+1}e$ is a *positron*, ν is a *neutrino*, and γ is a *gamma ray*. With the production of He^4 and the release of energy, a new C^{12} catalyst nucleus is created, so that the reaction can continue. See page 316.

carbon dioxide (CO_2) A colorless gas with a faint smell. Formed by the oxidation of carbon and carbon compounds, it is present in our atmosphere and is used by plants. It seems to be present in the atmosphere of Venus in very large amounts. See page 333.

catalyst A substance which alters the rate at which a chemical reaction occurs but which is itself unchanged at the end of the reaction.

celestial equator If the equator of the earth were projected out until it cut the apparent sphere of the sky, it would mark a line known as the celestial equator. See Figure 3–4 and page 54.

Centaur See page 377.

Cepheid variables A class of variable stars. Variable stars are those which have detectable changes in their intensities, often accompanied by other physical changes. The changes in brightness of variable stars may be a few thousandths of a magnitude to 20 magnitudes or more. Cepheid variables are characterized by several important relations. They are among the most luminous stars known and thus can be seen at great distances. There is a definite correlation between period and luminosity; as a result of this relationship, they are used as measuring tapes for the universe. There are two types of Cepheids, based on the classification of stars as being in type I or type II *populations*. Classical Cepheids resemble the prototype and belong to type I; they are found in large numbers in the Milky Way. Having periods ranging from 1 to 50 days, but commonly about 5 days, about 500 are recognized in our galaxy. They are quite steady in periodicity and form of light curve. Type II Cepheids are grouped with type II population stars and are found more frequently in the globular clusters. They differ from classical Cepheids in the form of the light curve and the period-luminosity relationship as well as by spatial difference.

chain reaction A reaction in which one of the agents necessary to the reaction is itself produced by the reaction so as to cause like reactions. In the neutron-fission chain reaction, a *neutron* plus a fissionable atom causes a fission resulting in a number of neutrons that in turn cause other fissions. See also *carbon cycle*.

color The term usually refers to the visible part of the electromagnetic spectrum, each color being represented by different wavelengths or frequencies of light. One end of this visible color range is red and the other violet, the red having a longer wavelength or lower frequency. White light consists of a mixture of the wavelengths in the visible range. A surface that reflects all of these will appear white; some surfaces, however, have the property of absorbing some of the radiations they receive and reflecting the rest. Thus, a surface that absorbs all light radiations excepting those corresponding to green will appear green by reflecting only those radiations. In the case of color seen by transmitted light, as in colored glass, the glass absorbs all the radiations except those which are transmitted. See page 177 and Figure 6–1.

comets Objects which are moving in space under the influence of the sun's gravitational field and which occasionally come close enough to the earth to be observed. As they move in toward the sun, radiation pressure causes tails to form, sometimes millions of miles in length. After passing close to the sun, they may become permanent members of the sun's family. Comets are believed to have a very low mass—less than one hundred-thousandth of the mass of the earth.

concave mirror A concave mirror curves inwards; the center of the reflecting surface is lower, or thinner, than the mirror at the edges. The curvature of a concave mirror is called negative curvature. Remembering the rule that the angle of reflection of a beam of light is equal to the angle of incidence, it is a simple matter to calculate the point at which the reflected beams will be brought to a focus. If the mirror is spherical, as in the upper figure, the focal length is just one-half of the radius of curvature of the mirror. If the mirror is parabolic, as in the lower figure, rays of light from a source so distant that the rays are parallel are brought to a focus at one point (called the focal point of the mirror). Conversely, if a source of light is placed at the focus, the light will be reflected in a parallel beam. Parabolic mirrors are used in reflecting telescopes to collect light from distant stars and bring it to an accurate focus.

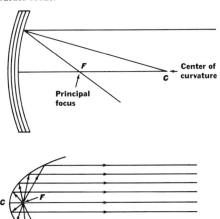

concept A broad term meaning, generally, an idea or notion but differing from perception by involving the process of abstraction. A scientific concept may be mathematical, for example, a formula; it may be

denominative or simply a name given to a class of objects, for example, metal; or it may be a property of something, for example, elasticity. The term *concept* is also sometimes used to designate theoretical systems such as Newton's gravitational theory. See page 61.

conic sections When a solid circular cone is cut by a plane in various directions, the line of intersection of plane and cone defines the various figures called conic sections. A cone cut "straight across" gives a circle. If the cut is slanted, the section is an *ellipse*. With greater slant, just "parallel to the cone's edge," the section is a *parabola*. With still more slant, the section is a *hyperbola*.

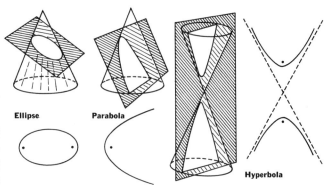

Ellipse   Parabola   Hyperbola

conservation laws It has been found experimentally that certain physical quantities are conserved in processes into which they enter, and that in spite of changes in form or distribution their sum total remains the same. The most commonly known of the conservation laws are those which have been generalized for *mass, energy,* and *momentum.*

    conservation of mass The total mass of a system remains constant.

    conservation of energy The total quantity of energy in a closed system remains constant. (This law is often called the first law of thermodynamics.) In view of the fact that energy and mass are mutually convertible, a conclusion of the special theory of relativity, the laws of conservation of mass and of energy are recognized as special cases of the conservation of mass-energy. See pages 239 and 291.

    conservation of momentum: In a perfectly elastic collision, the total momentum of two bodies before impact is equal to their total momentum after impact. When velocities comparable to the speed of light are under study, the variation of mass with velocity must be considered.

continuum A continuous series of component parts passing into one another; e.g. the three space dimensions and the time dimensions are considered to form a four-dimensional continuum. See page 240.

convex mirror A mirror that curves outwards, having a positive curvature. The center of curvature and the principal focus are both behind the mirror. After reflection, the rays of light leave the mirror as if they came from a point behind the mirror. This kind of image is called a virtual image.

Image

coordinates A set of numbers that locate a point in space. The most common are the cartesian or orthogonal coordinates in which mutually perpendicular axes are used. The values of x and y refer to distances along these axes measured from the origin O. Another commonly used system is that of polar coordinates. In general relativity the most used are gaussian coordinates, in which the surface is not a plane but of constant gaussian curvature. This gaussian curvature G is $G = 1/R_1R_2$, where R_1 and R_2 are radii of the principle curvature.

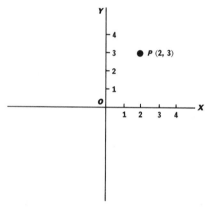

corona The outer part of the sun's atmosphere seen during an eclipse when the moon blocks out the sun's disk. See Figure 6–14. This corona extends beyond the sun's surface as much as thirty times the diameter of the sun and has a temperature of about $1000000°$K.

cosmic rays The nuclei of atoms, largely hydrogen, which impinge upon the earth from all directions of space with nearly the speed of light. These nuclei with relativistic speeds are often referred to as primary cosmic rays to distinguish them from the cascade of secondary particles generated by their impact against air nuclei at the top of the terrestrial atmosphere. The secondary particles shower down through the atmosphere and are found with decreasing intensity all the way to the ground and below. Cosmic rays are detected principally by the *ionization* they produce in the matter through which they are passing. The primary cosmic-ray particles coming into the top of the terrestrial atmosphere make inelastic collisions with nuclei in the atmosphere, splitting one or both particles into a number of smaller nuclear fragments, each of which carries away some of the primary particle's energy. Individual cosmic-ray nuclei have energies as low as a few hundred million electron volts (Mev), and occasionally energies as high as 10^9 Bev. The large individual energies indicate that cosmic rays are not confined just to the solar system but are a phenomenon of at least galactic scale.

cosmical constant This constant was introduced by Einstein into the field equations of *general relativity* to make possible a static solution of these equations. This term introduced a repulsive force that increased with distance to balance the attractive force of gravity. The static solution was abandoned by Einstein and most other physicists in 1929 when observations of the *red shift* showed that the universe is not static, as astronomers had previously thought. However, by assigning different values to the cosmical constant it is possible to construct other world models like, for instance, the one proposed by Lemaître that begins expanding, then goes through a static period, and finally expands again. See pages 276 to 279.

cosmogony The branch of astronomy that deals with the origin of the universe.

cosmology The branch of astronomy that deals with the general structure of the universe and the laws of space and time, as well as the study of the parts of the universe such as the origin of the solar system and the life history of the stars.

covariant When an equation transforms so that the equational relationship is undisturbed, we speak of the equation being covariant with respect to that *transformation*. Einstein in *Relativity: The Special and General Theory* gives the following example of covariance:

> Every general law of nature must be so constituted that it is transformed into a law of exactly the same form when, instead of the Space-Time variable x, y, z, t of the original co-ordinate system k, we introduce new Space-Time variables x', y', z', t' of a co-ordinate system k'. In this connection the relation between the ordinary and the accented magnitudes is given by the Lorentz transformation, or, in brief, General Laws of Nature are *covariant* with respect to Lorentz *transformations*. See page 235.

declination The measure of angular position of a heavenly body from the celestial equator. The measurement is in degrees, $0°$ at the equator and $90°$ at each pole. See page 149.

deductive reasoning The process of reasoning from a generalization that is assumed to be true to a set of specific conclusions about the system. These conclusions may then be checked by observation or experiment. See page 17.

deferent See *epicycle*.

degrees, minutes, and seconds of arc Each full circle contains $360°$. Each degree contains 60 minutes and each minute 60 seconds of arc. Therefore one full circle has 21,600 minutes or 1,296,000 seconds of arc. See footnote 1, page 149, and the editor's note, page 161.

density Mass per unit volume. When expressed in grams per cubic centimeter, it is numerically equal to specific gravity.

diffraction When a beam of light passes through an aperture or past the edge of an opaque obstacle and is allowed to fall upon a screen, patterns of light and dark bands (with monochromatic light) or colored bands (with white light) are observed near the edges of the beam, and extend into the geometrical shadow. This phenomenon, which is a particular case of interference, is due to the wave nature of light, and is known as diffraction. The phenomenon is common to all wave motions. See Figures 6–8 and 6–9.

diffraction grating An optical device consisting of an assembly of narrow slits or grooves, such as *A* or *B*, that by diffracting light produces a large number of beams that can interfere with one another in such a way as to produce spectra. Since the angles at which constructive interference patterns are produced by a grating depend on the lengths of the waves being diffracted, the waves of various lengths in a beam of light *W* striking the grating will be separated into a number of spectra, produced in various orders of interference on either side of the undiffracted central image *F*. By controlling the shape and size of the diffracting grooves when producing a grating and by illuminating the grating at suitable angles *i*, a beam of light can be thrown into a single spectrum whose purity and brightness may exceed that produced by a prism. Gratings can be made with much larger apertures than prisms and in such form that they waste less light and give higher intrinsic dispersion and resolving power. A single grating can be used over a much broader range of spectrum than can any single prism, and its dispersion will vary less rapidly with wavelength. Gratings are being used increasingly in large *spectrographs* and for precise spectroscopic work, as well as in monochromators and analytical spectrographs.

Doppler shift The amount of the effect upon the apparent frequency of a wave-train produced by

relative motion of the source and the observer. The direction of the shift tells in what direction the source is moving relative to the observer: in the case of light, if the shift is toward the red or longer wavelengths, the motion is away from the observer; if the shift is toward the blue or shorter wavelengths, the motion is toward the observer. See page 196 and Figure 6–15.

dwarf stars These are stars that have a low luminosity and very high density and are considered to be the end result of stellar evolution. See Figure 9–6 and page 318.

eccentric A circle not having the same center as another contained within it. In Ptolemaic astronomy, in order to account for the observed irregularities of the planets' motions, it was necessary to elaborate the theory of epicycles by having the center of the deferents move in an eccentric manner.

eclipse There are two types of eclipses commonly observed on earth: the solar and the lunar. The solar eclipse occurs when the moon passes between the earth and the sun so that the disk of the moon totally or partially covers the disk of the sun. The minimum speed at which the moon's shadow moves across the earth's surface is about 2,300 miles per hour and the maximum speed can be as high as 5,000 miles per hour. The maximum time that a total solar eclipse can last is $7\frac{1}{2}$ minutes. The lunar eclipse takes place when the earth passes between the sun and moon and the earth's shadow sweeps across the moon. A total lunar eclipse can last for 1 hour and 40 minutes.

VELOCITY	DISTANCE
KH	
125 miles per second	900,000 light years
1,400 miles per second	7,000,000 light years
3,400 miles per second	23,000,000 light years
9,600 miles per second	85,000,000 light years
14,300 miles per second	135,000,000 light years

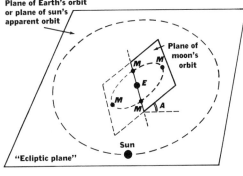

ecliptic The apparent annual path of the sun in the sky relative to the stars; or the great circle cut out on the celestial sphere by the plane containing the orbit of the earth. See page 55.

electron The electron is one of the fundamental particles of nature. It has a mass of 9.1×10^{-28}

grams and a negative charge of 4.8×10^{-10} electrostatic units. See page 197. See *positron*.

ellipse The locus of a point that moves so that the sum of its distance from two foci is a constant. See also *orbits* and *conic sections*. The equation of the ellipse in rectangular coordinates is $x^2/a^2 + y^2/b^2 = 1$.

empirical A term used to describe facts or truths established by observation or experiment rather than those deduced from axioms or theory. See page 20.

energy Capacity for doing work. There are many different forms of energy: potential, kinetic, electrical, heat, chemical, atomic, and radiant. Energy is particularly important because it is a conserved quantity (see *conservation*). It cannot be created or destroyed but it may be exchanged among various bodies or converted from one form to another. The most obvious form of energy is kinetic energy, the energy of a body in motion:

$$\text{Kinetic energy} = \frac{1}{2}\,mv^2$$

where m is the mass of the moving body and v is the velocity.

epicycle A small circle the center of which moves around the circumference of a larger circle called the deferent. This system of motions was used in Ptolemaic astronomy to account for the observed periodic irregularities in planetary motions. See Figures 3–34 and 3–35.

equinox See *precession of equinoxes*.

escape velocity The velocity that must be reached if an object is to escape from the attractive force of a gravitating body. This velocity for the earth is approximately 7 miles per second. A speed of approximately 25 miles per second would be needed to escape from the solar system, starting from the earth's surface.

ether A hypothetical medium that was postulated to act as a medium for the transmission of the wave characteristics of light through space. This medium was assumed to be transparent, undispersive, incompressible, continuous, and without viscosity. All experimental attempts to demonstrate the existence of this medium have failed. See pages 227 and 229 to 231.

exhaust velocity See *propellant*.

exponents Numbers indicating the power of a quantity. Thus the exponent of x in x^4 is 4. The laws of exponents are methods of handling these powers and are very useful in dealing with large numbers:

Law	*Example*
$\dfrac{1}{A^a} = A^{-a}$	$\dfrac{1}{10^3} = 10^{-3}$
$A^a \times A^b = A^{a+b}$	$10^3 \times 10^5 = 10^8$
$\dfrac{A^a}{A^b} = A^{a-b}$	$\dfrac{10^6}{10^3} = 10^3$
$(A^a)^b = A^{ab}$	$(10^2)^3 = 10^6$

extrapolation The method by which data of a restricted range may be projected to establish inferences about data lying outside that range. See page 18.

Fitzgerald-Lorentz The contraction of a moving body in the direction of its motion. In 1893, G. F. Fitzgerald and H. A. Lorentz proposed independently that the failure of the Michelson-Morley experiment to prove the existence of an ether and to detect an absolute motion of the earth in space arose from a physical contraction of the interferometer in the direction of the earth's motion. See page 227. According to this hypothesis, as formulated more exactly by Albert Einstein in the special theory of *relativity* (see page 237), a body in motion with speed v is contracted by a factor $\sqrt{1 - v^2/c^2}$ in the direction of motion, where c is the speed of light. For the earth traveling at 18.5 miles per second in its orbit, such a contraction is about one part in 2×10^8 or about 2.5 inches along the diameter of the earth. Such an amount accounts precisely for the Michelson-Morley result, because it allows for a shrinkage in distance between the light source and the mirror when the system is moving lengthwise. See also *transformation*.

force Any agent that causes a change of momentum in a body. It is measured by the time rate of change of that momentum. If the speeds are low compared with that of light, a force may be defined as the product of the mass m of a body and the acceleration a that is produced by the force. Thus $F = ma$. Force is a vector quantity, requiring both a magnitude and a direction for its complete specification. See page 217.

frequency See *waves*.

galaxy Enormous cluster of stars and other heavenly bodies of which the solar system forms a part— Milky Way. See page 259.

galaxies Gigantic star clusters separated by even vaster regions of space. See Figures 8–3 and 8–9.

gamma rays Electromagnetic waves of very short lengths, shorter than those of X rays.

geocentric A system of measurements of position in which the origin of the system (center point) is located at the center of the earth. The word is used in connection with the theory that the earth is the center of the stellar and planetary motions and that all revolve about the earth. This is called the geocentric theory. See Figure 3–23.

geodesic A curve representing the shortest distance between two fixed points. In three-dimensional Euclidian geometry, the geodesic is a straight line. If the path is constrained to the two-dimensional surface of a sphere, it is a segment of a great circle. In the non-Euclidian geometries appropriate to the general relativity theory, the geodesic is the path followed by a particle upon which no electromagnetic forces act. See Figure 7–6.

giant stars Stars that are abnormally large and very luminous. The material in these stars is extremely rarefied. The giant stars appear on the Russell diagram above the main sequence. See Figure 9–6 and page 318.

gravitation, law of The Newtonian law expressed by the equation

$$F = \frac{GMm}{R^2}$$

where M and m are the masses of two bodies, R is the distance between them, and G is the gravitational constant. See page 218.

H-H chain See *proton-proton chain*.

heliocentric A system of measurements of position in which the origin of the system (center point) is located at the center of the sun. Heliocentric is also used to denote the theory that requires the sun to be the center of the solar system and the earth to revolve around the sun. See Figure 3–23.

Hubble's constant The equation $v = R/T$ is the relation between the velocity v of a nebula and its distance R. The value $1/T$ is known as Hubble's constant. $T = 5 \times 10^9$ years is sometimes called the age of the universe, although there is no evidence that the name should be taken literally.

hypothesis A tentative theory that is employed to explain certain observed facts and to serve as a guide for the investigation of other facts. See page 17.

indeterminacy principle See *uncertainty principle*.

inductive reasoning The logical method by which a quantity of data may be employed as the basis of a generalization that will be assumed valid for the explanation of subsequent data of the same kind in the same system. See pages 13 and 16.

inertia The tendency of a body to preserve its state of rest or uniform motion in a straight line. This is the property that necessitates the exertion of force upon the body to give it acceleration. The law of inertia is Newton's first law of motion, which states that material bodies not subjected to the action of forces remain at rest or move in a straight line with constant speed. See page 126.

Interference of wave motions The addition or combination of waves; if the crest of one wave meets the trough of another of equal amplitude, the wave is destroyed at that point; conversely, the superposition of one crest upon another leads to an increased effect. The color effects of thin films are due to interference of light waves; beats produced by two notes of similar frequency are the result of the interference of sound waves. See also *Waves, Diffraction*, and Figure 6–10.

interpolation A method of inference by which previously unknown facts are obtained from known facts when the former lie within the range over which the known data are valid. See page 18.

invariant An expression involving the coefficients of an algebraic function that remain constant when a *transformation*, such as translation or rotation of coordinate axes, is made. Einstein and Infeld in *The Evolution of Physics* give the following example of invariance:

> Suppose we have, in our simplest case, two coordinate systems, that is two rigid rods; we draw one above the other and call them respectively the "upper" and "lower" coordinate system. We assume that the two coordinate systems move with a definite velocity relative to each other. . . .

> Take two fixed points on the upper rod and consider the distance between them. This distance is the difference in the coordinates of the two points. To find the positions of the two points relative to different coordinate systems, we have to use transformation laws. But in constructing the differences of the two positions the contributions due to the different coordinate systems cancel each other and disappear, as is evident from the drawing. We have to add and subtract the distance

between the origins of two coordinate systems. The distance of two points is, therefore, *invariant*, that is, independent of the choice of the *coordinate* system.

ion An electrically charged atom or group of atoms. Positively charged ions have fewer *electrons* than is necessary for the atom or group to be electrically neutral; negative ions have more. Gases can be ionized by the passage of charged particles, electric sparks, *X rays, gamma rays*, etc.

isostasy The theory of gravitational balance between relatively broad, contiguous areas of different average altitudes or topographical relief, applied particularly to the equilibrium of the major topographical features of the earth—continents and ocean basins. Thus the continents are assumed to "stand high," relative to the ocean basins, because they are lighter (or less dense) material. Whenever any large segment of the earth's crust is out of balance with its surroundings, adjustment is assumed to take place by means of solid flow in a deep subcrustal zone. Since the surfaces of the continents are constantly being worn down by erosion, if it were not for isostasy, early in the geologic history of the earth all land areas would have been reduced to ocean level.

Jupiter-C A four-stage research test vehicle comprised of the Redstone ballistic missile as the first stage and solid *propellant* upper stages. First stage thrust is 75,000 pounds. The Jupiter-C placed America's first satellite, Explorer I, in orbit on January 31, 1958.

Kepler Johannes Kepler, in the *Mysterium Cosmographicum* (1596), attempted to fit the orbits of the six known planets into the five regular solids as follows: (1) a cube inscribed within the orbit of Saturn would touch the outside of the orbit of Jupiter and contain it; (2) a tetrahedron (four sides) inscribed within the orbit of Jupiter would touch the outside of the orbit of Mars and contain it; (3) a dodecahedron (twelve sides) inscribed within the orbit of Mars would touch the outside of the orbit of earth and contain it; (4) an icosihedron (twenty sides) inscribed within the orbit of earth would touch the outside of the orbit of Venus and contain it; (5) an octahedron (eight sides) inscribed within the orbit of Venus would touch the outside of the orbit of Mercury and contain it. See Figure 1–3. That theory did not comprehend the elliptical shape of planetary orbits and was, therefore, superseded by the laws of motion twenty-two years later. Kepler's three laws of planetary motion are:

1. The orbit of every planet is an ellipse with the sun at one focus.

2. A line joining any planet to the sun sweeps over equal areas in equal times.

3. The squares of the periods of revolution of any two planets around the sun are in the same proportion as the cubes of their mean distances from the sun.

Looking more closely at these laws, we find that the second law tells us that the speed of a planet in its orbit is not constant:

Area A = Area B.

Time from A_1 to A_2 = Time from B_1 to B_2.

The planet covers more of the arc during the A^1 to A^2 passage.

Written as an algebraic statement the third, or, as it is known, the harmonic law, is as follows:

$$\frac{T_a{}^2}{T_b{}^2} = \frac{R_a{}^3}{R_b{}^3}$$

where T_a = period of planet A for one trip around the sun

T_b = period of planet B for one trip around the sun

R_a = mean distance of planet A from the sun

R_b = mean distance of planet B from the sun

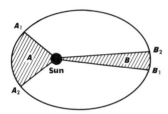

latitude The angular distance north or south from the equator of a point on the earth's surface, measured on the meridian of the point. The equator is 0 degrees latitude and each pole is 90 degrees north or south.

laws of motion See *Newton's laws of motion*.

laws of planetary motion See *Kepler*.

lichen Perennial plants that are in reality a combination of two plants growing together in an association so intimate that they appear as one. Such an association is called symbiosis. The components of a lichen are always an alga and a fungus. See page 342.

light This term properly refers to the range of electromagnetic radiation associated with vision or the wavelength range 4×10^{-5} to 7×10^{-5} centimeter approximately. See Figure 6–1. The velocity of light, which is approximately 3×10^{10} centimeters per second or 186,000 miles per second, is considered to be the top limiting velocity in the universe.

light-year The distance a photon of light travels in one year at the velocity of 186,000 miles per second—5.88 trillion miles or 5.88×10^{12} miles.

logarithmic scale A scale so divided that the distance from any point on the scale to the origin is in proportion to the logarithm of the number used to mark that distance. The scale is often used in graphical presentation. See Figures 9–1 and 9–18.

longitude Angular distance in the east and west direction on the face of the earth, the zero point being on the meridian passing through the Greenwich Observatory.

Lorentz-Fitzgerald contraction See *Fitzgerald-Lorentz contraction*.

main sequence of stars The vast majority of stars fit within a narrow band running from the upper left-hand corner to the lower right-hand corner of the

Russell diagram. This band of stars is known as the main sequence. See Figures 9–6 and 9–18.

mass There are two principal ways of describing and measuring mass. We will discuss each separately and then the relationship between them. Inertial mass is the constant m in the equation $F = ma$. It is the physical measure of the resistance of any body to a change of motion and can be measured by finding the acceleration produced by a known force acting on the body in question (if the speeds are small compared to the speed of light). Except at very high speeds, inertial mass is believed to be an unchangeable property of matter, having the same value anywhere in the universe. Gravitational mass is a measure of the amount of matter acted upon by a gravitational field and is proportional to the weight of the object in question. It should be borne in mind, however, that the weight (which is the *force* of attraction of the earth on a given mass) varies with location, depending on the position from the center of the earth, just as the acceleration of gravity, g, also varies in the same proportion. The relationship becomes clear if we substitute weight W for Force and g for acceleration in the equation $F = ma$, which then becomes $W = mg$. W and g both vary, depending on the position, but m remains constant. If the proper units are chosen, gravitational mass equals inertial mass and is assumed to remain constant everywhere in the universe except at speeds approaching the speed of light. See page 219.

metagalaxy A system of *galaxies* or extragalactic nebulae. See page 326.

meteor Solid body from outer space. A meteorite becomes incandescent ('shooting star') on entering the earth's atmosphere owing to frictional forces set up at its surface. Consists of various materials, often metallic iron. See page 365.

methane (CH₄) A colorless and odorless gas sometimes called marsh gas. The fact that this gas remains in a gaseous state at very low temperatures permits it to be the prime constituent of the atmosphere of the outer planets.

momentum The product of the mass and the velocity of a moving body; $p = mv$. It should be borne in mind that the velocity is a *vector* quantity. For speeds approaching that of light, the variation of mass with velocity must be taken into account, and the value of m appropriate to the velocity of the body must be used in the expression for the momentum. See also *conservation of momentum* and *angular momentum* and page 221.

neutrino A fundamental particle whose existence was postulated in order to preserve the laws of *conservation* of mass and energy and conservation of momentum in certain nuclear reactions. The neutrino has no charge and very small (possibly zero) rest mass.

neutron A particle possessing no electric charge and having a mass slightly greater than the *proton*. A constituent of all atomic nuclei except the normal hydrogen nucleus, which is a single proton. Owing to the absence of electric charge, the neutron can pass relatively easily through matter.

Newton's laws of motion There are three in number and form the basis of classical mechanics:

    1. Every body continues in its state of rest or uniform motion in a straight line except

insofar as it is compelled by external forces to change that state.

2. Rate of change of *momentum* is proportional to the applied force and takes place in the direction in which the force acts.
3. To every action there is always an equal and opposite reaction.

See pages 216 to 221.

nova and supernova A nova is a variable star that occasionally expands and becomes abnormally bright. It expands and contracts many times during its lifetime, each time losing part of its material. A supernova, on the other hand, explodes with great brilliance, destroying itself and scattering its material throughout space. Some supernova have been so bright that they were visible in daylight. Supernovae can be seen in other galaxies and give us one method of determining the distance of the galaxy. See page 320 and Figure 8–13.

nova rocket See Figure 10–19.

opposition A planet having its orbit outside that of the earth is in opposition when the earth is in a direct line between the sun and the planet.

orbits See *Kepler* for laws of planetary motion. The derivation of elliptical orbits from Newton's law of gravitation requires either calculus or rather cumbersome geometry, with the result that we will not give it here; but the reader with some mathematical background may be interested in seeing how Kepler's third law derives from the Newtonian theory. The following diagram and proof are from Eric Roger's *Physics for the Inquiring Mind:*

> To deduce Kepler's Third Law, Newton had merely to combine his *laws of motion* with his laws of universal *gravitation*. For elliptical orbits, calculus is needed to average the radius and to deal with the planet's varying speed, but the same law then follows:
> For circular orbits, suppose a planet of mass m moves with speed v in a circle of radius R around a Sun of mass M. This motion requires an inward resultant force on the planet, mv^2/R to produce its centripetal acceleration v^2/R (see page 218). Assume that gravitational attraction between sun and planet just provides this needed force. Then
>
> $$G \frac{Mm}{d^2} \text{ must} = \frac{mv^2}{R}$$
>
> and distance d between m and M = orbit-radius, R. But
>
> $$v = \frac{\text{circumference}}{\text{time of revolution}} = \frac{2\pi R}{T}$$
>
> where T is the time of one revolution.
>
> $$\therefore G \frac{Mm}{R^2} = \frac{m (2\pi R/T)^2}{R}$$
>
> $$\therefore G \frac{Mm}{R^2} = \frac{4\pi^2 mR^2}{T^2 R}$$
>
> To look for Kepler's Law III, collect all R's and T's on one side; move everything else to the other.
>
> $$\therefore \frac{R^3}{T^2} = \frac{GM}{4\pi^2}$$

Now change to another planet, with different orbit radius R' and time of revolution T' then the new value of $(R')^3/(T')^2$ will again be $GM/4\pi^2$; and this has the same value for all such planets since G is a universal constant and M is the mass of the sun, which is the same whatever the planet. Thus R^3/T^2 should be the same for all planets owned by the sun, in agreement with Kepler's Third Law. For another system, such as Jupiter's moons, M will be different (this time the mass of Jupiter) and R^3/T^2 will have a different value, the same for all the moons.

The planet's mass, m, cancels out. Several planets of different masses could all pursue the same orbit with the same motion. . . . Calculus predicts Law III for elliptical orbits too, where R is now the average of the planet's greatest and least distances from the sun. These relationships make it simple to calculate the speed with which satellites will circumnavigate the earth if the average distance (R) of the satellite from the center of the earth is known, by substituting the value for G and mass of the earth in the expression $\dfrac{GM}{4\pi^2}$. The relationship is independent of the mass of the satellite and for a given average radius there is only one speed that will result in a stable orbit.

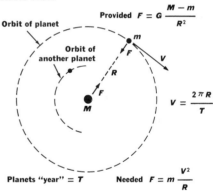

Orbit of planet

Orbit of another planet

$\text{Provided } F = G \dfrac{M - m}{R^2}$

M m F V R

$V = \dfrac{2\pi R}{T}$

Planets "year" = T $\text{Needed } F = m \dfrac{V^2}{R}$

ozone (O_3) A form of oxygen, containing three atoms instead of two in a molecule. It is produced when an electric spark is passed through air. It is very active chemically and a powerful oxidizing agent. See page 340.

parabola One of the families of conic sections and defined as the locus of a point that moves

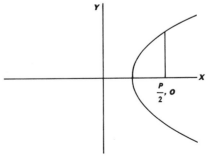

Y

X

$\dfrac{P}{2}, O$

so as to remain equidistant from a fixed point and a fixed line. The standard equation in cartesian coordinates is $y^2 = 2\ px$. See *conic sections*.

paradox A statement or proposition seemingly self-contradictory or absurd and yet explicable as expressing a truth. A famous example of a paradox is the one proposed by Zeno, concerning the race between Achilles and the tortoise. If Achilles, being a very fast runner, allows the tortoise to start first, then when Achilles starts at *A* the tortoise is at *B*. When Achilles reaches *B* the tortoise has moved on a small distance to *C* and when Achilles reaches *C*, the tortoise has progressed an even smaller distance to *D*. As this description can go on and on, apparently Achilles never catches the tortoise, but actually we know that he will.

parallax Difference in direction or shift in the apparent position of a body, due to a change in position of the observer. As the earth revolves around the sun, we see the nearby stars move against the so-called fixed stars much farther away. This periodic shift called the parallactic shift is very small in angular measure, the largest known parallactic shift being less than 1 second of arc. The amount of parallactic shift is inversely proportional to the distance of the object. See footnote, page 68.

parsec Astronomical unit of distance, corresponding to a parallax of one second of arc, 19×10^{12} miles, 3.3 *light-years*.

periastron See *perihelion*.

perigee See *perihelion*.

perihelion The perihelion point of a planetary orbit is defined as the point of closest approach to the sun, helios being the word for sun. This point is also an *apse* point on the major axis of the elliptical orbit. A similar term is used in connection with work in double stars but is called periastron. The point of the moon's closest approach to the earth is called perigee. See Figure 5–10.

photon A packet or *quantum* of electromagnetic energy. The energy of a photon is $h\nu$, where h is *Planck's constant* and ν is the *frequency* associated with the photon. See pages 196 to 202.

Planck's constant A very small constant that is denoted by the letter h and expressed in units of action ($h = 6.624 \times 10^{-27}$ erg sec). When multiplied by the frequency of radiation ν, it gives the quantity of energy ($= h\nu$) contained in one *quantum*. See page 197.

plane A flat surface mathematically defined as a surface containing all the straight lines passing through a fixed point and also intersecting a straight line in space.

planetary system, solar

	Mean distance from Sun, miles	Period of revolution		Period of rotation	
Mercury	36,000,000	88.0	days	88 days	
Venus	67,240,000	225.0	days	30 days (?)	
Earth	93,000,000	365.3	days	23 hr, 56 min	
Mars	141,000,000	687.0	days	24 hr, 37 min	
Jupiter	483,900,000	11.86	yr	9 hr, 50 min	
Saturn	887,200,000	29.46	yr	10 hr, 02 min	
Uranus	1,785,000,000	84.01	yr	10 hr, 45 min	
Neptune	2,797,000,000	164.8	yr	15 hr, 48 min	
Pluto	3,670,000,000	248.4	yr	Unknown	

	Maximum diameter, miles	Mass (Earth = 1)	Surface gravity (Earth = 1)	Velocity of escape, mph	Maximum temp. °F
Mercury	3,100	0.056	0.38	2.0	770
Venus	7,700	0.82	0.88	6.3	212 (?)
Earth	7,927	1.00	1.00	6.95	136
Mars	4,250	0.106	0.39	3.1	80
Jupiter	88,700	318.35	2.65	37.0	−215
Saturn	71,500	95.3	1.17	22.0	−245
Uranus	29,400	14.54	1.05	13.0	−305
Neptune	28,000	17.2	1.23	15.0	−325
Pluto	3,600	0.03 (?)	0.16 (?)	?	−350
Sun	865,000	332,100.0	28.00	392.0	10,300

	Mean distance from Earth, miles	Period of revolution	Diameter miles
Moon	238,857	27 days, 7 hr, 43 min	2,162

planetoids Known also as asteroids or minor planets, they occupy a region between Mars and Jupiter at 2.8 astronomical units from the sun. They vary in diameter from 500 miles to a fraction of a mile. They number in the tens of thousands, and it is believed that they may be fragments of a planet that disintegrated or one that never completely formed. See page 313.

population, stellar types I and II See pages 322 and 323.

positron The positive electron, an elementary particle having the same mass as the electron and a positive charge numerically equal to the negative charge of the electron.

postulate An idea assumed without proof as a basis for reasoning. See page 17.

precession of equinoxes The equinoxes are the points or nodes where the projection of the earth's orbit intersects the ecliptic, one point being called the vernal equinox and the other the autumnal equinox. Owing to a phenomena called precession (the same type of motion that a dying top exhibits) these two points do not remain fixed but move very slowly to the westward at such a rate that they will complete one revolution of the ecliptic in approximately 25,000 years. This westward motion of these points of intersection is called the precession of the equinoxes. See pages 52 and 109.

premise See *syllogism*.

pressure The force per unit area acting on a surface. For instance, the pressure of the earth's atmosphere at sea level is about 15 pounds per square inch. See page 33.

probability The likelihood that some particular form of event might occur. This likelihood is expressed in numerical form by the numbers between 0 and 1, a probability of 1 being certain that some event would occur and the probability 0 being certain that the event would not occur. The probability 0.5 means an equal likelihood that the event would or would not occur. This number is obtained by evaluating the ratio R/N, R being the number of elements in the set of events to take place and N being the total possibilities. For example, what is the probability of picking a spade from a deck of cards? The total possibilities are 52 of which 13 are spades, therefore the probability is 13/52 or 0.25.

propellant A liquid or solid substance burned in a rocket for the purpose of developing a thrust. The velocity (relative to the nozzle) of the gases that exhaust through the nozzle of a rocket engine is called the exhaust velocity.

proportion A statement of equality between two ratios as $a/b = c/d$. One variable may be said to be proportional to another variable if they both increase at the same rate as, for instance, a is twice as large as b, or $a = 2b$. This could also be written $a/b = 2/1$, giving it the same form as the ratio above. Sometimes the notation $a \propto b$ is used, meaning a is proportional to b.

protein Class of organic compounds of very high molecular weights that compose a large part of all living matter. Protein molecules invariably contain the elements carbon, hydrogen, oxygen, and nitrogen; often also sulphur and sometimes phosphorus.

proton Positively-charged particle, having a mass approximately 1840 times greater than that of the electron (i.e. 1.00757 atomic mass units) and charge numerically equal but opposite in sign to that of the electron. Constituent of all atomic nuclei.

proton-proton chain An energy-releasing nuclear reaction chain that is believed to be of major importance in energy production in hydrogen-rich stars. The net effect of the proton-proton, or H-H, chain is the conversion (fusion) of four protons into one He[4] (helium) nucleus with the release of about 26 Mev of energy.

protoplasm A highly complex substance containing *protein*-like materials; essential constituent of all living cells.

qualitative Dealing only with the nature, and not the amounts, of the substances under consideration. See page 38.

quantitative Dealing with quantities; measurements that relate the quantities of objects or phenomena under consideration.

quantum A discrete quantity of radiation (also called a *photon*). A quantum has a particle-like behavior, and an energy equal to $h\nu$, where h is Planck's constant and ν is the frequency of the radiation. See pages 196 to 202.

radar Pulses of radio waves of very short wavelength are transmitted from a unit, and this unit then listens for the echo that is reflected by an object intercepting the transmitted wave. The time lapse between transmission of a pulse and receipt of the echo indicates the range of the reflecting surface. This method is now being used to find the distances to planets and the sun.

radio telescope A device for receiving waves of radio frequencies emitted or reflected from astronomical sources. The wavelengths received are much longer than lightwaves, and this fact makes it difficult to design a radio telescope of high resolution. For instance, a 50-foot-diameter radio telescope for use with wavelengths around 20 centimeters has a resolving power of about 1°. See page 268, and Figure 8–12.

radioactivity The spontaneous disintegration of unstable atomic nuclei to give more stable product nuclei, usually accompanied by the emission of charged particles and electromagnetic energy, e.g. *alpha* or *beta particles* and *gamma rays*.

rainbow A bow or arc of prismatic colors that are caused by refraction and internal reflection of the sun's rays from small water droplets in the atmosphere. To see the rainbow the observer must have his back to the sun.

red shift See *Doppler shift*.

refraction Refraction of waves is the change in direction of propagation of any wave phenomenon that occurs when the wave velocity changes. The term is most frequently applied to visible light, but it is also applied to all other electromagnetic waves, as well as to sound and water waves. The physical nature of the effect can be visualized by considering orderly rows of automobiles driving in a column across a boundary between smooth concrete and heavy snow. If they drive perpendicular to the boundary, the rows are simply slowed up and crowded close to one another when they cross it to the snow; but if they drive at an angle, one end of each row is slowed down sooner than the opposite end, and the row swings around to a direction nearer to the perpendicular. A train of waves is affected in the same manner in passing from one medium to another. The simple mathematical relation governing refraction is known as Snell's law. Thus, if θ_1 is the angle of incidence and θ_2 the angle of refraction, Snell's law states that $\sin \theta_1 = n \sin \theta_2$, where n is the ratio of the indexes of refraction of the two mediums. (The index of refraction of a medium is the ratio of the speed of waves in a vacuum to their speed in the medium.) Refraction can and does occur in a single medium if its properties vary from one place to another because of changes in conditions through the portion of the medium traversed by the waves. The twinkling of stars is caused by variations in the atmosphere resulting from temperature differentials.

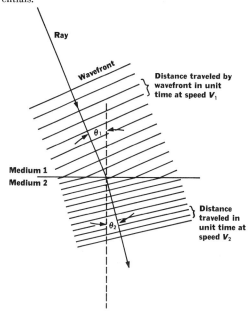

Ray

Wavefront

Distance traveled by wavefront in unit time at speed V_1

θ_1

Medium 1
Medium 2

Distance traveled in unit time at speed V_2

θ_2

relativity A theory of the physical meaning of space and time due largely to Albert Einstein. In its present form, the theory consists of two parts: (1) the special, or restricted, theory (1905), which explains why the laws of nature appear the same to all observers moving with constant velocity relative to one another; and (2) the general theory (1916), which is the relativistic theory of gravitation and an extension of the special theory. Einstein's ideas have been of the greatest significance in the clarification of the foundations of theoretical physics, in addition to their direct contribution to experimental physics.

    special theory The special theory was based on the hypothesis that the velocity of light is constant when measured by one of a set of observers moving with constant relative velocity (see *transformation*). It resulted in two important modifications of the concepts of space and time that arose from Newton's laws. These modifications lead to the conclusion (1) that clocks in rapidly moving systems slow down and (2) that a rapidly moving body contracts in the direction of motion (see page 237 and

Fitzgerald-Lorentz *contraction*). A third important consequence of this theory is indicated in the equation $E = mc^2$, which says that energy and mass are directly related to each other in proportion to the square of the speed of light.

    general theory The general theory of relativity rests on the so-called principle of equivalence, which asserts the equivalence of gravitational forces with inertial forces, that is, the forces experienced by accelerated observers, such as persons in a rolling ship or in an automobile coming to a sudden stop. In addition, one postulates a generalized relativity principle, that the equations of mechanics have the same form for all observers, whether accelerated or not. Capitalizing on the principle of equivalence, the general theory modifies further the space and time concepts of special relativity and arrives at the notion of the curved space-time continuum.

retrogressions of the planets As the earth moves faster in its orbit than the outer planets, the earth "catches up" to these planets, and as it passes them they appear to move backward. This apparent backward motion is called the retrograde motion of the planets. See Figure 8–4.

right ascension The astronomical measurement of position measured westward from the vernal equinox. The value is given in hours, minutes, seconds, which of course can be translated to degrees and may be likened to the measure of longitude on the earth. See *degrees, minutes, and seconds of arc*.

Saturn rocket See Figure 10–19.

spectrograph An instrument by which spectra may be photographed; also, a photograph taken by such an instrument.

spectroscope An optical instrument that separates composite light into its components, thus producing a spectrum for visual observation to determine what wavelengths are present. Its essential elements are a slit S, a collimating lens C, for making the light from the split parallel before entering the prism, one or more dispersing prisms P, and a telescope T, for forming images of the slit in the various wavelengths and so providing a method for viewing or photographing the spectrum. Modern spectroscopes employ the *diffraction grating* instead of the prism; the name spectroscope is also commonly applied to instruments that can separate other electromagnetic radiation than visible light into its component wavelengths.

stations of the planets These stations or stationary points are the points at which a planet appears to be motionless when viewed from the earth, owing to the combined motions of the earth and the planet around the sun. See Figure 8–4.

stroboscopic Stroboscopic methods are used for viewing moving objects in such a way that they appear stationary, by using flashes of illumination of very short duration. The object being observed moves a negligible distance while the light is on and thus appears sharply defined. See Figures 4–17 and 4–19.

sun spots Huge vortexlike storms on the sun. They show very strong magnetic fields and appear dark when seen in a photograph because they are much cooler than the other areas of the sun's surface. See page 269.

supernova See *nova*.

syllogism The species of reasoning in which two statements are taken as true, making a third statement inevitably valid. The first two statements are termed premises. The third statement is called the conclusion. In the most common type of syllogism, the first premise (major) usually asserts something of a class or category, for example, "All men are mortal." The second premise (minor) proposes a certain relationship between the class and a particular entity, for example, "Socrates is a man." The conclusion asserts that "Therefore, Socrates is mortal." See pages 13 and 17.

telemeter Apparatus for recording physical events at a distance by radioing instrument readings from a rocket to a recording machine on the ground.

telescope An optical instrument that increases the visibility of distant objects. The simplest type of telescope consists of an objective lens, O, which forms a real image of the object, and an ocular or eyepiece E for magnifying and viewing this image. A telescope having 'an objective lens is called a refracting telescope. The objective lens can be replaced by a mirror or by a system containing refracting and reflecting elements, such as a concave parabolic mirror; such a telescope is a reflective telescope. The telescope used by Galileo was a refracting telescope. A converging or convex lens O, the objective lens, forms at its principal focus a real inverted image R of a distant object. Before reaching the focal plane of the objective, the converging rays are intercepted by a diverging or concave lens E. If the eye is placed behind E, an enlarged virtual image of the object is observed. Telescope builders of the seventeenth and eighteenth centuries were unable to obtain glass disks of sufficient clearness and homogeneity for the construction of large object lenses, and turned to the reflecting type of telescope. The largest reflecting telescope ever built is the 200-inch Hale Telescope at Mount Palomar, California, while the telescope at Yerkes Observatory—with a 40-inch objective lens—is the largest refractive telescope ever built.

thermal neutrons *Neutrons* of very slow speed and consequently of low energy. Their energy is of the same order as the thermal energy of the atoms or molecules of the substance through which they are passing. Thermal neutrons are responsible for numerous types of nuclear reactions, including nuclear fission.

thermodynamics First law: see *conservation laws*. Second law: Heat energy cannot of itself pass from a body of low temperature to one of high. In an isolated system containing energy in concentrated form the transformations that occur always involve the passage to a less concentrated or more disorganized form. From this law very broad inferences have been drawn. It is contended that if this process of disorganization proceeds without hindrance it will result in a stage of uniform distribution of energy in the universe and all energy interchange will cease. See page 249.

thermonuclear A nuclear reaction that takes place only at very high temperatures.

Thor A single-stage intermediate-range ballistic missile of 150,000-pound thrust. Also used as the first stage of a series of launch vehicles for space missions such as the Thor-Able, Thor-Agena, and Thor-Delta series. Among the space vehicles launched by the Thor series are Transit, Tiros, Echo, Explorers VI and X, and the Discoverer series.

Titan Intercontinental ballistic missile (ICBM) having a maximum speed of over 15,000 miles per hour and a range over 6,000 miles. It uses liquid-propellant rockets in two stages (two 150,000-pound thrust engines in the first stage and one 80,000-pound thrust engine in the second stage).

trajectory The curve that a body describes in space when acted upon by two or more forces, as the path of a planet or a projectile. See Figure 4–18 and page 128.

transformation A change of variables in an algebraic expression, as in changing from one *coordinate* system to another. Suppose that we have two coordinate systems K and K' as indicated in the figure below. K' has a velocity of v to the right relative to K. Any event can be measured in space with respect to K by the three coordinates x, y, z and with regard to time by t. Relative to K', the same event would be measured by the corresponding values x', y', z', t', which, of course, are not identical to x, y, z, t. If the magnitudes x, y, z, t of an event are known, how can the magnitude of x', y', z', t' for the same event with respect to K' be found? Transformation equations establish the relationships for the solution of this problem. If the origins of the two frames are coincident at $t = 0$ and $t' = 0$, then, using the principle of the addition of velocities, the Galilei transformation sets up the relationships in the following manner:

$$x' = x - vt$$
$$y' = y$$
$$z' = z$$
$$t' = t$$

If, on the other hand, we use Einstein's condition that the speed of light in vacuo must be contant (c) as measured in both coordinate systems, the relationships below are found to apply:

$$x' = \frac{x - vt}{\sqrt{1 - v^2/c^2}}$$
$$y' = y$$
$$z' = z$$
$$t' = \frac{t - xv/c^2}{\sqrt{1 - v^2/c^2}}$$

This system of equations is known as the Lorentz transformation. These equations reduce to the Galilei transformation above when $v/c \to 0$. The Lorentz transformation equations form the basis of Einstein's special theory of relativity. See page 237. For a simple algebraic derivation of the Lorentz transformations see Einstein's *Relativity: The Special and General Theory*, Appendix I.

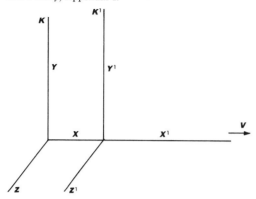

uncertainty principle Sometimes called *indeterminacy principle*. This principle, first stated by Heisenberg, has the mathematical formulation.

$$\Delta p \cdot \Delta q \geqq h$$

where Δq is the range of values that might be found for the coordinate q of a particle, and Δp is the range in the simultaneous determination of the corresponding component of its momentum p. The product of these uncertainties will always be greater than or equal to h, which is *Planck's constant*, owing to the fact that every observation is an interaction between the system and the measuring device, which will itself alter the state. See page 201.

V-2 Also called A-4. A liquid-oxygen–alcohol–fuelled single-stage ballistic missile developed by the Germans at Peenemünde during World War II as a long-range artillery device. The finished missile was 47 feet long, 5½ feet in diameter, and had a gross weight at take-off of 14 tons. The motor developed 56,000 pounds of thrust and carried a 1-ton warhead 150 miles. The United States captured some 70 of these missiles, which were used for upper atmosphere research. See Fig. 10–19.

vacuum A perfect vacuum would be a space entirely without matter of any sort. To our knowledge there does not exist a perfect vacuum anywhere in nature. Even the space between the stars is occupied by some matter, very thin to be sure, but still not empty. The term "vacuum" is generally taken to mean a space containing air or other gas at very low pressure. See page 30.

variable A symbol to which any number of values in a given set may be assigned. See page 38.

vector Any physical quantity that requires a statement of direction as well as magnitude for its complete definition, for example, *velocity*. A vector is often indicated graphically by means of an arrow. The length of the arrow is proportional to the scalar magnitude of the vector, and the direction in which the arrow points is the direction of the vector.

velocity Velocity is the rate of change of distance with respect to time. Average velocity can be found by dividing the distance covered by the time interval: d/t. Velocity is a vector quantity having both magnitude and direction in which the motion takes place. See page 128.

Viking A liquid-fuelled high-altitude sounding rocket developed in 1949. The original series of vehicles was 48.6 feet long and 32 inches in diameter. It weighed 10,700 pounds and developed 20,000 pounds of thrust. Rockets of this series carried 500 pounds to an altitude of 136 miles.

violet shift See *Doppler shift*.

virus An infective agent smaller than the common microorganisms and requiring living cells for multiplication. See page 314.

Wac Corporal A liquid-propellant sounding rocket developed by the Army Ordnance Department capable of launching a 25-pound pay load to an altitude of 19 miles. The missile was 16 feet long, and the engine delivered about 1,500 pounds of thrust for 45 seconds. It was first flight-tested in 1945.

waves The propagation of a periodic disturbance carrying energy. At any point along the path of a wave motion, a periodic displacement or vibration about a mean position takes place. This may take the form of a displacement of air molecules (e.g. sound waves in air), of water molecules (waves on water), a displacement of elements of a string or wire, displacement of electric and magnetic vectors, etc. The locus of these displacements at any instant is called the wave. Wavelength is the distance in convenient units from crest to crest or from any one place on a wave to the same place on the next wave. The amplitude is the maximum departure from the equilibrium value. Waves in which the vibration or displacement takes place in the direction of propagation of the waves are called longitudinal waves. Sound is an example of longitudinal wave motion. Waves in which the vibration or displacement takes place in a plane at right angles to the direction of propagation are called transverse waves, e.g. electromagnetic waves. See page 187.

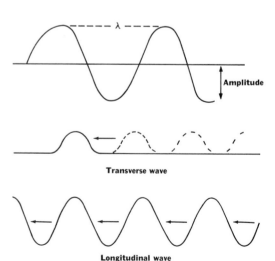

Transverse wave

Longitudinal wave

weight The *force* of attraction of the earth on a given mass is the weight of that mass. See also *mass* and page 219.

weightlessness Strictly speaking, the absence of any force of gravity acting on a given body. However the term is generally used in a broader sense to mean the absence of sensations of resistance to gravity. The human body does not actually feel gravity. It feels the resistance to gravity—the pressure of the feet on the floor or pavement that prevents the body from following the pull of gravity. The feeling of weightlessness, or zero-G as it is sometimes called, can occur in several different types of situations: (1) in cases in which there is actually no resultant force of gravity acting on the body, as, for example, when the body is so far from the earth that the earth's gravitational field is just balanced by the sun's field and (2) in cases in which the body is being accelerated by the force of gravity but in which, because everything around it is also being accelerated at the same rate, there is no sensation of resistance to the attraction of gravity. This second type is the situation encountered in satellites as well as in free fall. See also the discussion by Willy Ley on pages 362 and 364.

X rays Electromagnetic radiation extending from the extreme ultraviolet into the gamma-ray region, that is, from 10^{-7} to 10^{-9} centimeter wavelength.

zero-G See *weightlessness* and page 364.

zodiac As the earth moves around the sun, the sun appears to move through the background stars during the period of one year. The twelve different constellations through which the sun apparently moves in the course of one year are called the zodiac and indicate the position of the sun for each month of the year. It must be understood that this apparent motion of the sun is really the reflected motion of the earth in its orbit around the sun. The zodiacal constellations are Capricornus, Aquarius, Pisces, Aries, Taurus, Gemini, Cancer, Leo, Virgo, Libra, Scorpius, Sagittarius. See page 55 and Figure 3–10.

zodiacal light A faint glow extending along the zodiac, probably due to sunlight reflected from a great number of tiny particles in or near the plane of the ecliptic. This glow extends around the entire *zodiac*, but it shows most prominently in the neighborhood of the sun. It can best be observed in the western sky in the spring just after the sunset twilight has completely disappeared, or in the eastern sky in the fall just before the morning twilight appears. See page 310.

Index